Mayberry

My Hometown

Mayberry
My Hometown

The Ultimate Guidebook
to America's Favorite
TV Small Town

by

Stephen J. Spignesi

Pierian Press
1987

ISBN 0-87650-211-7
LC 86-60552

Published by The Pierian Press Inc., P.O. Box 1808, Ann Arbor, Michigan 48106

This book is dedicated to Pam,
who had to live alone
while I was working in Mayberry...

and also to my mother, the amazing Lee;
and the memory of my father Dominic.

"To Steve...
Thank you.
Good luck with your book.
I hope everybody enjoys
the good people
who lived in Mayberry.
They were very real to me."

Andy Griffith

"Dear Steve...
The five years I spent
working with Andy Griffith
were the most enjoyable
and exciting of my career.
And that's a fact!
Mayberry *was* my home."

Don Knotts

Contents

========================= PART I =========================
The Mayberry Pocket Almanac:
A Handy Guide to
Mayberry People, Places & Things

========================= PART II =========================
The Mayberry Encyclopedia:
From "A1A" to "Zone Detection System"

The Encyclopedia

========================= PART III =========================
Going Home to Mayberry:
A Look at the "Return"

List of Illustrations

1. **FRONTISPIECE.** Sheriff Andy Taylor, the wisest, kindest man ever to enter our lives through television. Andy Taylor was the embodiment of the Mayberry experience, creating out of whole cloth (and a little tip of the hat to his own hometown, Mt. Airy, North Carolina) the most fully realized vision of the ultimate American hometown. Andy Griffith/Taylor *was* Mayberry, North Carolina and we are all the better for his achievement. (Photo from author's collection.)

2. **PAGE XIV.** Mayberry's First Family. Aunt Bee Taylor, Opie Taylor, Helen Crump Taylor, and Sheriff Andy Taylor. This casual shot of the four was probably taken on a quiet Saturday afternoon. Opie was out playing, Bee was getting ready to go shopping, and Andy and Helen were probably going to give her a ride into town. (Photo courtesy Aneta Corsaut.)

3. **PAGE XV.** A rare, exclusive shot of the Mayberry wedding of the decade. The groom, Sheriff Andy Taylor; the bride, nee Helen Crump; aunt of the groom, Miss Beatrice Taylor; and son of the groom, Master Opie Taylor. (Photo courtesy Aneta Corsaut; photographer: John Engstead.)

4. **PAGE XVI.** This picture was taken in the last few minutes of the best "Andy" episode ever, "Opie the Birdman" (101F/96B). Opie had just released Wynken, Blynken, and Nod, and Andy had spoken his most memorable line: "But don't the trees seem nice and full." In the final edited version of the episode as broadcast, however, Andy does not appear with his hands on his hips as he does in this photo. It's likely that this picture was taken during the filming but, for the final broadcast print of the episode, was edited out, leaving instead the head shots of Andy and Opie as they dealt with the separation anxiety. (Photo courtesy Rance Howard.)

5. **PAGE XX.** Four of Mayberry's best friends—Andy and Helen, Barney and Thelma Lou—friends who walked through their Mayberry years together and ended up, finally, back in Mayberry as two of the town's happily married couples. (Photo courtesy Aneta Corsaut.)

6. **PAGE XXIII.** A very early shot of Andy Griffith, likely taken in the fifties. At this point in his life, Andy was attempting to establish a career as an actor. He had already written and recorded "What It Was Was Football," and he was being represented by the William Morris Agency. Richard O. Linke—Andy's friend, manager, and partner for over thirty years now—heard the football piece and approached Andy about doing television. Andy's appearance on "The Danny Thomas Show"—in the episode "Danny Meets Andy Griffith"—was the pilot for "The Andy Griffith Show." The rest is history. (Photo from author's collection.)

7. **PAGE 4.** What a face!! This early photo of Don Knotts, likely taken sometime in the fifties, gives us a close look at the face that would eventually define Barney Fife. (Photo from author's collection.)

8. **PAGE 8.** Aunt Bee Taylor. The perfect everything! Mother, friend, cook, aunt . . . she was the ultimate Mayberry matriarch. She made Andy and Opie's home a haven from the pressures of the world and gave them a sense of balance and security. And—except for her pickles and marmalade—her meals were a gustatory delight. (Photo courtesy Viacom.)

9. **PAGE 10.** Howard "Floyd Lawson" McNear. One of the nicest guys ever to walk the streets of Mayberry, North Carolina. Everyone's friend, Floyd was never too busy to sit and talk in front of his shop. Howard McNear came to Mayberry after a busy career in drama and radio, most notably playing the role of Doc in the radio version of "Gunsmoke." But his greatest achievement had to be the bringing to life of one of the most well-defined and brilliantly portrayed characters ever to hit TV: Mayberry's own Floyd Lawson. (Photo courtesy AP/Wide World Photos.)

10. **PAGE 16.** You can almost hear Otis chanting "Barney's in jail! Barney's in jail!" This scene, from the episode "The Big House," shows that no matter how well-intentioned and diligent our Deputy Fife was, he very often spent more time on the wrong side of the cell doors than imaginable! But, as always, Andy was there to straighten things out, and Barney could go back to keeping the lid on Mayberry. Because, after all, let your guard down even a little (sound familiar?) and before you know it, Mayberry'll end up "a regular sin town!" (Photo courtesy Viacom.)

11. **PAGE 17.** Jack "Howard Sprague" Dodson. In a letter from Jack, he told me: "[This] is what I look like now with some color in my hair, which is actually quite gray—but this is what I look like in the film we are about to make called 'Return to Mayberry.' Best wishes for the success of your book." Jack spent five years—not counting his return to Mayberry—creating one of the most unique characters ever to appear on network television. Howard was a sensitive, prissy kind of guy who also happened to be amazingly intelligent, as well as a true and loyal friend. Howard Sprague was probably one of the most dependable guys you would ever want to meet. Two of Jack's most notable recent projects included "You Can't Take It With You" (shown on cable's Showtime network) with Jason Robards, and one of my personal favorites, "Something Wicked This Way Comes." Interestingly, Jack's first appearance on "The Andy Griffith Show" was not as Howard Sprague, but rather as Ed Jenkins, the insurance agent, in "Lost and Found" (178F/B). (Photo courtesy Jack Dodson.)

12. **PAGE 22.** Don Knotts with his third Emmy for his work on "The Andy Griffith Show." This picture was taken Sunday, May 26, 1963, immediately following the Emmy telecast in Hollywood. This Emmy was for the 1962-1963 season and Don won in the category "Outstanding Performance in a Supporting Role by an Actor." He beat out Tim Conway, Paul Ford, Hurd Hatfield, and Robert Redford. The 1962-1963 "Andy Griffith" season included such Barney classics as "Lawman Barney" (73F/70B), "Barney and the Governor" (76F/78B), and "Barney's First Car" (90F/B). This season was the first in which the National Academy of Television Arts and Sciences did not categorize an actor's performance as either comedy or drama, but rather created a

general category to judge all supporting roles. This put Don up against some stiff competition (Paul Ford and Robert Redford!!)—but our deputy still won! Don would go on to win two more Emmys for his work as Barney Fife, both of them for guest appearances on "The Andy Griffith Show." (See "Andy & the Emmys" in this book.) (Photo courtesy AP/Wide World Photos.)

13. **PAGE 24.** George "Goober" Lindsey as he appears today. George continued to live in Mayberry after "The Andy Griffith Show" by remaining a regular on "Mayberry, R.F.D." for the run of that series. When that show went off the air, he went on to become a regular on the syndicated "Hee Haw." George has kept busy, that's for sure. He's appeared in everything from "M*A*S*H" and "Twilight Zone" to the films "Ensign Pulver" and "Cannonball Run II" (with his good friend, Jim Nabors). George has gotten raves for his work on Broadway, and he's been very effective as the spokesperson for a jeans company. But with all these credits, Mayberry fans will always know and love him best as our own Goober Pyle (of the Mayberry Pyles, that is). George recently returned to Mayberry with the rest of the gang. (Photo courtesy George Lindsey.)

14. **PAGE 26.** Denver "Briscoe Darling" Pyle. Mayberry's mountain man, the sage patriarch of the Darling clan. Pyle has appeared in everything from "The Roy Rogers Show" to his own series, "The Dukes of Hazzard," as Uncle Jessie. For Mayberry followers, though, his most notable achievement would have to be the bringing to life of the amazing Briscoe Darling, both in the original "Andy Griffith" series and in the recent TV-movie, "Return to Mayberry." (Photo courtesy Lew Sherrell Agency, Ltd.)

15. **PAGE 28.** Ken "Sam Jones" Berry. Ken first appeared on "The Andy Griffith Show" in the episode "Sam for Town Council" (247F/246B). Sam was typical Mayberry: respectful, quiet, and permanently laid-back. In the final broadcast episode of the series, "Mayberry, R.F.D.," Ken Berry did an admirable job of continuing the Mayberry tradition, but after three years "Mayberry, R.F.D." was cancelled, a victim of TV's "rural slaughter" of the early seventies. (Photo courtesy Richard O. Linke Associates, Inc.)

16. **PAGE 30.** Andy, Helen, and Thelma Lou. Think Barney got jealous seeing this shot? No way. Ange could hug Thelma Lou anytime he liked. Barney trusted Andy with anything—including his girl! (Photo courtesy Aneta Corsaut.)

17. **PAGE 33.** Andy and Barney not only had to worry about jaywalkers and speeders, they also had to contend with intoxicated citizens—such as the lovable "Hot Rod" Otis (Hal Smith) Campbell—riding farm animals down Main Street. Life was lively in Mayberry when Otis was around, that's for sure! (Photo courtesy Viacom.)

18. **PAGE 37.** Wonder what Andy's reading in the "Mayberry Gazette" that's so funny? Maybe "Little Orphan Annie"? Or it could even be a not-so-cleverly disguised rumor about a fellow Mayberrian in the "Mayberry After Midnight" column. In any case, Aunt Bee seems to be wanting to get some point across to Andy, but Andy just smiles and reads his paper. (Photo courtesy Viacom.)

19. **PAGE 40.** One of the greatest moments in the history of Mayberry. Opie accepts Aunt Bee into the Taylor household and a long, loving relationship begins. And we're all the better for this moment, even if it involved Opie running out to the truck in his pajamas to call Aunt Bee back! (Photo courtesy Viacom.)

20. **PAGE 71.** Andy and Helen in a quiet moment. (Photo courtesy Aneta Corsaut.)

21. **PAGE 76.** Yet another clever Barney Fife undercover disguise. Here Barney attempts to snare "The Shoplifters." "The Shoplifters" ended up being one old lady with a big coat. (And she was caught by Andy, anyway.) (Photo courtesy Viacom.)

22. **PAGE 80.** Opie Taylor, young man about Mayberry. His father's pride and his Aunt Bee's delight, Opie always walked the straight and narrow, even when he got into that evil rock-and-roll! (Complete with turtleneck and cool-looking potato chips!) Nonetheless, Opie grew up to be the editor of the Mayberry paper, and even though, at this writing, he and his wife have moved away from Mayberry to live in New York, we're all sure that—as Andy put it—"someday they'll be coming back." (Photo courtesy Viacom.)

23. **PAGE 95.** The beginning of Sgt. Carter's high blood pressure: the arrival of Gomer Pyle at Camp Henderson. The bumbling gas jockey became the bumbling Marine shortly after this shot was taken. (Photo courtesy Viacom.)

24. **PAGE 102.** Here's our favorite sheriff, home from work, taking a break with "The Mayberry Gazette," while Aunt Bee prepares supper. Maybe he's reading Red Akins' "Mayberry After Midnight" column? That column would sure add some "spice" to Aunt Bee's chicken fricasee, wouldn't it? (Photo courtesy Viacom.)

25. **PAGE 107.** Wonder what Thelma Lou said when she saw this shot? Here's Daphne, one of the Mt. Pilot "fun girls," trying to involve Barney in a little fun. Barney was always ready for fun when he wore his salt-and-pepper suit, and this picture is evidence that when he was out of uniform he was ready to swing! (Photo courtesy Viacom.)

26. **PAGE 109.** This shot was taken approximately eight minutes into the episode "Howard and Millie" (233F/231B). However, in the actual episode, Opie never appeared. The scene from which this shot was drawn took place in the Taylor living room. Present are Andy—sitting on either the edge of the fireplace or a hassock—Helen, sitting on the couch, and Howard and Millie, sitting huddled together in the middle of the couch. Howard and Millie have come to ask Andy and Helen to be their best man and maid of honor. In the photo Andy is wearing a shirt, but in the episode he was wearing a blue sportscoat. To further confuse things, in the original collection of stills from the show, the series of still pictures from this episode show Andy wearing the coat and just a shirt. The same stills also show Opie standing over Andy's shoulder as in the picture above. So, two possibilities regarding the picture exist: either it was taken during a rehearsal or it was taken during filming and never used. In any case, the presence of Opie was edited out before broadcast. All stills were shot January 10, 1967. Since "Howard and Millie" was broadcast on November 27, 1967, we can see the long lead-time between actual filming and broadcast. (Photo courtesy Viacom.)

27. **PAGE 130.** Another of our deputy's ingenious undercover disguises. If you were in Mayberry on the day this shot was taken, you wouldn't be able to tell this was Barney Fife, now would you? (Photo courtesy Viacom.)

28. **PAGE 143.** Maybe Goober got good news? Perhaps in the form of a date with Flora from the Diner? (Photo courtesy Viacom.)

29. **PAGE 148.** Andy and Opie enjoying a tune under the trees on a sunny afternoon. Andy might be singing "Dan Tucker" or even "The Fishin' Hole!" (Photo courtesy Viacom.)

30. **PAGE 159.** Andy Taylor, sheriff of Mayberry. Barney's best friend, the love of Helen Crump's life, the role model of Opie Taylor, and the best thing to ever happen to the town of Mayberry, North Carolina. The soul of Mayberry, Andy gave new meaning to the word "integrity." Andy was a gentleman and, as Betty Lynn put it, a "gentle man." (Photo courtesy Viacom.)

31. **PAGE 168.** "Barney's Bloodhound," Blue, tries to pick up the scent of the escaped crook, Ralph Neal. (Photo courtesy Viacom.)

32. **PAGE 170.** This is an extremely rare shot of Sheriff Andy Taylor and his son Opie. What's so special about this picture? The "Sheriff without a gun" has his sidearm strapped on! Guess he wasn't kidding about the sign. (Photo courtesy Viacom.)

33. **PAGE 176.** Opie first discovers the abandoned Garland baby. And when "Opie Finds a Baby," he does the only logical thing: he goes around town asking people if they'd like to have it! Andy straightened things out, though, and the baby went back to his parents. (Photo courtesy Viacom.)

34. **PAGE 178.** Sheriff Taylor and his best girl Helen relaxing during a stroll out by Myer's Lake. This picture is one of Aneta Corsaut's favorites. (Photo courtesy Aneta Corsaut.)

35. **PAGE 182.** A young Ron "Opie Taylor" Howard. Even at the early age of seven or eight, Ron was a baseball nut. And so it makes sense that his favorite "Andy" episode is "The Ball Game." (See the interview with Ron Howard in this book.) This picture doesn't seem to be from any episode and was probably a publicity shot taken in the first or second season of the show. Special thanks to Rance Howard for allowing use of this—and other—special photos from his own collection. (Photo courtesy Rance Howard.)

36. **PAGE 184.** Andy Griffith as he is today. After leaving his own show, Andy established a second career playing "heavies" in films and on TV. Then the role of the murdered girl's father in "Fatal Vision" came up. The role was such a success for him that NBC gave him a movie—"Diary of a Perfect Murder"—based on the character and, in the fall of 1986, he was given his own series—"Matlock"—also based on the character. (Photo courtesy Richard O. Linke Associates, Inc.)

37. **PAGE 194.** Don Knotts as he is today. Since leaving "The Andy Griffith Show," Don has had numerous film and TV roles, the most well-known of which is probably that of Mr. Furley, the outrageous landlord on "Three's Company." His most recent role of note for "Andy" fans, of course, was his return to Mayberry as our favorite deputy, Barney Fife. (Photo courtesy Bash-Cleary Management.)

38. **PAGE 196.** Jim Nabors now spends a good portion of his time overseeing operations of his macadamia nut farm on Maui in Hawaii. He also appears in movies with his close friend Burt Reynolds, and does the occasional nightclub appearance. The last week of May 1986, Jim appeared at Harrah's in Reno. Most notable for Mayberry fans, though, was Jim's return to Mayberry as one of our favorite gas jockey's, Gomer Pyle. (See the interview with Jim Nabors in this book.) (Photo courtesy Naborly Productions.)

39. **PAGE 198.** Jim Nabors as Gomer Pyle, U.S. Marine. Wonder what Gomer's smiling about? Maybe he smiling because he's thinking about how Andy convinced Sgt. Carter that Gomer was the son of Major General Lucius Pyle? In any case, Camp Henderson was never the same after Gomer's arrival. (Photo courtesy Viacom.)

40. **PAGE 200.** Aneta "Helen Crump" Corsaut as she looks today. An excellent actress, Aneta appeared in the 1958 horror film "The Blob" (with Steve McQueen), and then in the sitcom "Mrs. G. Goes To College"/"The Gertrude Berg Show" before taking on the role of, first, Andy Taylor's girlfriend and, later, Mrs. Andy Taylor. In the early seventies, she guest-starred on a "Nanny & The Professor" episode with Pat Morita called "My Son the Sitter." (Pat later went on to work for many years with Ron Howard on "Happy Days.") Her longest-running role—other than that of Helen Crump—was that of Head Nurse Bradley on the sitcom "House Calls," which featured Wayne Rodgers, Lynn Redgrave, and Sharon Gless. But Aneta's most important recent role was that of none other than our favorite schoolteacher, Helen Crump, in the NBC movie "Return to Mayberry." (See the interview with Aneta Corsaut in this book.) (Photo courtesy The Dietrich Agency.)

41. **PAGE 203.** The ever-so-lovely Helen Crump. With a face like this—look at those eyes, as beautiful today as they were in this shot—it's no wonder that Andy fell under Helen's spell. (Photo coutesy Aneta Corsaut.)

42. **PAGE 206.** Two of the lovliest Mayberryites ever to grace Main Street—Helen Crump and Thelma Lou. It looks as though this shot was taken just as they were leaving the courthouse. They probably stopped in to show Andy and Barney what they bought during their downtown visit. (See the interview with Betty Lynn in this book.) (Photo courtesy Aneta Corsaut.)

43. **PAGE 212.** Elinor "Ellie Walker" Donahue. Andy Taylor's first girlfriend and one of the brightest Mayberryites ever. Ellie was Mayberry's first feminist and professional woman. Her accomplishments included graduating as a registered pharmacist (when most Mayberry women were more concerned with baking pies!) and running for—and winning—the town council election. Her work after "The Andy Griffith Show" was varied and eclectic, but her most famous role would have to be that of Felix Unger's girlfriend, Miriam Welby, on "The Odd Couple." Lately, Elinor Donahue has appeared as a wicked nurse on "Days of Our Lives." (See the interview with Elinor Donahue in this book.) (Photo courtesy Fred Amsel & Associates.)

44. **PAGE 214.** Ron and Clint's father. Rance Howard has been an actor and a writer all his life. He has appeared in everything from "The Andy Griffith Show" and "Gentle Ben" (with his son Clint) to "Cocoon," "Splash," and "Gung Ho" (all directed by his other son Ron). Rance is a kind, considerate gentleman who, with his wife Jean—the concensus goes—did a textbook job of raising both his boys in probably one of the most difficult atmospheres in which to raise children: Hollywood, California. (See the interview

with Rance Howard in this book.) (Photo courtesy Rance Howard.)

45. **PAGE 219.** From left to right: Clint Howard, Rance Howard, and Ron Howard. This shot was taken during the filming of "A Black Day for Mayberry" (102F/B), in which all three Howards participated. Rance played and FBI agent, Clint played Leon and, of course, Ronny played Opie. Interestingly, Rance's character was played by himself *and* another actor. At the beginning of the episode, Rance and another agent enter the courthouse and tell Barney they'll wait for the sheriff. Barney huffs and puffs because they won't talk to him, but finally accepts it. The next scene has Opie entering the courthouse, also looking for his father. In this scene, Rance is not present, his character now being played by another actor who is wearing a hat. In the next scene—beginning when Andy enters the courthouse—the agent is back to being played by Rance. Apparently, the Opie scene was shot out of sequence, Rance wasn't available, and they pasted the three scenes together later. Again, special thanks to Rance Howard for allowing the use of this and other special photos from his personal collection. (See the Rance, Ron, and Clint Howard interviews in this book.) (Photo courtesy Rance Howard.)

46. **PAGE 220.** Clint "Leon" Howard. Ron's brother, Rance's son, and a Mayberry resident who was never in public without a cowboy outfit and a peanut butter-and-jelly sandwich. Clint—like Ron—has worked all his life in show business, from his early days on "The Andy Griffith Show" up through his starring role in TV's "Gentle Ben," to his recent film appearances, the most memorable of which include "Rock & Roll High School" and "Cocoon." Clint recently finished filming "The Wraith" with Randy Quaid, and is participating in the television adaptation of his brother's "Gung Ho." Clint is hoping to reprise his role as Leon if the talked-about TV-movie "Christmas in Mayberry" becomes a reality. (See the interview with Clint Howard in this book.) (Photo courtesy Clint Howard.)

47. **PAGE 226.** Ron "Opie Taylor" Howard. As I'm writing this, Ron's film "Bitter Harvest" is playing on cable's Showtime network. As Ned DeVries, a farmer threatened with the loss of his herd and his dairy farm, Ron gave a performance that ranked among his best. At the age of thirty-two, Ron has achieved artistic milestones some actors strive all their lives to even approach, let alone accomplish. Recently, Ron and Brian Grazer formed Imagine Films Entertainment, a company devoted to developing film and TV projects and which is open to the public. With all this going on, Ron still found time to work "Return to Mayberry" into his schedule. The real-life Ron Howard is a living example of the nature of Mayberry and of Mayberry people. (See the interview with Ron Howard in this book.) (Photo courtesy Ron Howard.)

48. **PAGE 229.** This is a very early shot of Ronny Howard as Opie Taylor. He looks six or seven years old, which would place this picture in the first season of the show. This is likely a publicity shot since it doesn't seem to be from an episode. Again, special thanks to Rance Howard for allowing the use of this and other rare photos from his personal collection. (See the Rance, Ron, and Clint Howard interviews in this book.) (Photo courtesy Rance Howard.)

49. **PAGE 232.** Another rare shot from Andy and Helen's wedding. From left to right: Emmett Clark, Opie Taylor,

Andy Taylor, Helen Crump, Howard Sprague, best man Barney Fife, and Goober Pyle. Shortly after this picture was taken, Andy and Helen went off on their honeymoon and then moved to Ohio, where they spent the next twenty years before returning to Mayberry in 1986. (Photo courtesy Aneta Corsaut; photographer, Jack Engstead.)

50. **PAGE 234.** As evidenced by this candid shot of the future Mr. and Mrs. Fife, Thelma Lou was sure crazy for Barney. And Barney felt the same way—he even took off his salt-and-pepper jacket! (Photo courtesy Viacom.)

51. **PAGE 237.** This little puppy was only the beginning. Shortly after this picture was taken, this little pooch invited a few of his friends to the courthouse, where Andy and Barney had to contend with "Dogs, Dogs, Dogs!" (Photo courtesy Viacom.)

52. **PAGE 238.** I guess from Opie's blackboard valentine, Andy had a little competition for Helen's attentions! But as Opie once said, he didn't care if Helen was his wife or his mother, as long as she was in the family. (Photo courtesy Viacom.)

53. **PAGE 242.** Andy and Barney never knew what problems they'd have to contend with: here they try to figure out a way to get Jimmy, "The Loaded Goat," safely out of town without blowing a nice big hole in the Mayberry firmament. (Photo courtesy Viacom.)

54. **PAGE 249 (Left).** From left to right: My friend Jim Clark, Presiding Goober of "The Andy Griffith Show" Rerun Watchers Club and author of *The Andy Griffith Show Book*; Andy Taylor; Goober Pyle; and Ken Beck (Jim Clark's co-author). This picture was taken in February 1986 in Los Olivos, California. Jim and Ken went to the filming of "Return to Mayberry" and the next issue of the Club's newsletter, "The Bullet" (dated April 13, 1986 to commemorate the TV-movie's air-date), was devoted to their experiences meeting the crew and watching the filming. (See the interview with Jim Clark.) (Photo courtesy Jim Clark.)

55. **PAGE 249 (Right).** Well, lookee here! It's Ernest T. Bass hisself! This recent shot of the inimitable Howard "ETB" Morris was taken in Nashville during "Ernest T. Bass Day," an event hosted by Jim Clark's "Andy Chapter" of "The Andy Griffith Show" Rerun Watchers Club. Morris, who reprised his Ernest T. role in the 1986 TV-movie "Return to Mayberry," is also a consummate director who has helmed everything from "The Andy Griffith Show" and "Get Smart" to almost 1,000 TV commercials. He is an amazingly deft comic actor and, in addition to his TV work, he has also worked for none other than Ron Howard in Ron's smash fish tale, "Splash." Special thanks to Robert W. Shockley, Jr. for taking this photo before Ernest T. broke the window in the Diner, and to my pal Jim Clark for sending it to me. (Photo courtesy Robert W. Shockley, Jr.)

56. **PAGE 250.** Helen Crump and her soon-to-be stepson Opie enjoying a quiet "between innings stretch." Close at hand—naturally—is Opie's Louisville Slugger. (Photo courtesy Aneta Corsaut.)

57. **PAGE 252.** Who's Barney talking to? Not Juanita, that's for sure. It was probably a call from the state police informing Barney about a dangerous escaped criminal heading towards Mayberry. After he hung up, Barney probably took out his bullet and loaded up. "Fearless Fife"—ready for action! (Photo courtesy Viacom.)

Preface

Mayberry, My Hometown was a two-year labor of love, and I have tried to be as complete and accurate as possible.

However, since my research material was the original episodes themselves, and since I had to rely on the broadcasts of those episodes for my notes, I was literally at the mercy of the programmers for the various stations in my area that carried "The Andy Griffith Show."

Like Rodney Dangerfield, syndicated sitcoms seem to get no respect.

Without mentioning specific stations, suffice it to say that in many instances what was finally broadcast in syndication bore little or no resemblance to the original script as initially shown, with its commercials at scene breaks, its openings and tags, etc.

One station regularly omitted the opening scenes for many episodes, thereby preventing me from getting one or another piece of data about the show. And another station routinely omitted both the closing tags and the credits for more than an entire season of episodes.

This, of course, drove me nuts. But I was fortunate to live in an area that had three stations showing "The Andy Griffith Show," so what one station cut from its broadcast, in most cases I was able to get from another station.

However, there will be a few unintentional omissions and for those I apologize.

I would suggest that anyone who objects to the butchery practiced by syndicated stations should write letters to these stations expressing the desire to enjoy their "Andy" uncut and shown as close to the original broadcast as possible.

After all, is the money received for another sixty-second hemmorhoid commercial worth losing some of our precious time in Mayberry? I think not.

Write the stations in your area. And then you can also write each of the fine clubs dedicated to the show and to its preservation and continuing broadcast. They are:

"The Andy Griffith Show" Rerun Watchers Club
27 Music Square East
Suite 146
Nashville, TN 37203

and

"The Andy Griffith Show" Appreciation Society
P.O. Box 330
Clemmons, NC 27012

I hope you all enjoy *Mayberry, My Hometown*. Long live Mayberry!

Introduction

"THE MAGIC OF MAYBERRY"

"A Glossary, so long as it does not seek,
and is not permitted,
to replace the original universe it describes,
has value
in that it can clarify
deep-hidden historical obscurities
and draw together facts
whose relation is easily overlooked,
thus aiding the wanderer in that universe
in his quest for its particular
Truth."

Robert Foster
"A Guide To Middle Earth"

Why Mayberry?
Because of "The Magic."

The magic of Mayberry was present in certain scenes and moments that evoked the best of what Mayberry was all about: the tranquil, almost transcendent peace, the calm detachment from the outside world, and the comfort and ease that came from knowing you were safe in your one, true home.

Mayberry was—and is—the quintessential small hometown. It was a self-contained world that existed for and unto itself. The striving, the pressure, the disenchanted malaise that marks the search for today's American dream was nowhere to be found in Mayberry. Of course, there were goals to be met and dreams to fulfill, but their achievement was accomplished with integrity, dignity, and—above all—fairness and respect.

The few times that greediness or deceit appeared, the perpetrator always ended up learning a lesson and realizing that the right thing to do had been known to them all along—deep in their heart. The episode that comes to mind as the most glaring example of this is "The Horse Trader." In this episode, Andy Taylor, the most honest, just man we've ever met, tried to sell a beat-up old cannon to an antique dealer by telling him a fabricated story about the cannon being Teddy Roosevelt's. (See entry THE CANNON.) Andy Taylor *lied*. The only possible justification—and this is not an absolution—is that he did it for the good of the town. Nonetheless, he lied, and his friends and family simply refused to believe it. Barney was so upset that he even went so far as to sit at the bar and pour down four drinks in fifteen minutes. OK, it was the drugstore bar and the drinks were root beer floats, but the incident still shows just how distraught he was over his cousin's fall from grace. But Andy learned his lesson when his son—his heart and soul—tried to pull off the same deceitful deed with one of his friends. Perhaps instead of focusing on the magic of Mayberry, we should emphasize the morality of Mayberry?

I have always loved the town, the people, and the Mayberry World.

And the magic helped the town seduce me.

There was more to the town of Mayberry than a few thousand people, some ordinary businesses, and the day-to-day trivialities that comprise most people's lives. Don Knotts personally told me the following: "The five years I spent working with Andy Griffith were the most enjoyable and exciting of my career. And that's a fact! Mayberry *was* my home." Imagine! Admitting—and actually being proud—that a TV town was his real home. Mayberry was special. Very, very special.

Such heartfelt involvement and love for a fictional creation is typical of everyone who was even remotely involved with the series. Elinor Donahue's conception of what it would be like to return to Mayberry and see her old friend Andy again is another example of what this town has done to the people who lived there. (See the interview with Elinor Donahue in this volume.)

Andy Griffith, in the epigraph to *Mayberry, My Hometown*, made a point of emphasizing that the people in Mayberry were "very real" to him.

I think a very important point to keep in mind when considering the Mayberry experience is that there is nothing trivial about Mayberry trivia. I hesitate to even use the word "trivia" in the same sentence with the word Mayberry. What is trivial to one person is vitally important to another. The people of Mayberry had pasts that were very dear to them. Sure, it's trivial that Vicki Harmes used to bite off the bottom of Barney's *raspberry* sno-cone and suck out all the juice. The writers could have just written "sno-cone." But Vicki was one of Barney's first loves, and so he remembered every little detail about their encounters. It was important to him to remember those details. And recognizing the importance of those details made "The Andy Griffith Show" all it was for those eight short years: the best-written, acted, and produced half-hour of American televison to ever hit our screens. The people of Mayberry had pasts, they talked about them, and they cherished them. It's almost a privilege to be allowed a glimpse into their world.

The first appearance of the magic took place in, appropriately, the very first episode "The New Housekeeper." At the end of the episode, Aunt Bee was preparing to leave. She was convinced that Opie would never accept or love her, and Andy reluctantly agreed. As Andy helped her into the truck, Opie came running down from his bedroom, still in his pajamas, hollering for Aunt Bee not to leave. You can't leave, he told her. She couldn't do anything important, like fish or play baseball, so she'd never survive in the "real world," he explained. She needs me, he told his Paw. This was a touching scene and it started the long, loving relationship between Opie and Aunt Bee.

Another of my favorite moments is at the beginning of "Prisoner of Love." This scene fills me with everything the best of "The Andy Griffith Show" is capable of evoking. It's dusk. Andy and Barney are sitting outside the courthouse. They've taken two of the chairs from opposite Andy's desk and brought them outside. They sit on the right wall of the courthouse, rather than the left, where there's already a bench. It's very quiet and there's hardly any activity on the street. The shopkeepers have closed and gone home, and you know that in their comfortable homes, people are sitting down to their evening meal and then a night of peace and quiet. But not Andy and Barney. They're still at their real home, the courthouse. They sit there and look over the town center, of which the courthouse is the focal point. It's truly tranquil. And then Barney starts: He's going to "go home, change, drop by Thelma Lou's, watch that George Raft movie on the TV." In case Andy didn't get it initially, he repeats it for him. More than once. Andy good naturedly goes along with Barney until they get the call regarding the prisoner, and then the episode really starts. This opening scene, however, was the heart of that show.

Another favorite is the last scene of "Class Reunion." A very simple scene, actually. Andy and Barney are cleaning up after the reunion. They start to sing, in perfect harmony, the "Mayberry Union High Theme Song." At the very end of the song, they look at each other and Andy asks, "Do the tears on your pillow bespeak the pain that is in your heart?" And Barney simply replies, "Yeah." Andy then smiles and says "Me, too." That quote was what Ramona Wiley had written in Barney's yearbook, so many years ago. A lovely moment.

At the end of "Howard's New Life," Howard has returned from the Caribbean after realizing that his true home was Mayberry. He didn't need to start a new life: he had it all here. Howard, Andy, Goober, and Emmett are hanging around outside the filling station, sharing bottles of pop, and listening to the night. Again, the contentment is tangible on all of their faces, but none more so than Howard's. You can almost hear the crickets.

In "The Return of Barney Fife," Barney summarizes the entire Mayberry experience into one perfect sentence. He and Andy are standing on the sidewalk outside the courthouse. Barney has returned to town for a reunion. It's obvious he's missed Mayberry. He says to Andy "You know, you people that live in the small towns, you really got it made." Andy just looks at him and then says, "Yeah, I guess." Andy then takes Barney inside and the former deputy walks around almost in awe, saying, "Same old courthouse, same old desk, same chair." People change, but Mayberry remains the same.

But the single most poignant, beautiful moment in the entire run of the show took place at the end of the single best episode of all, "Opie the Birdman." In this episode, Opie killed a mother songbird and then adopted her three babies, naming them Wynken, Blynken, and Nod. Throughout the episode, Opie takes care of them, feeding them, taking over as their mother. The theme here is that of the motherless child, paralleling Opie's experience with the death of his own mother. As the birds grow and begin to outgrow their cage, Barney and Andy realize that they should be set free. Here we have the theme of the empty nest, paralleling Andy's future release of Opie as he outgrows his childhood life. Andy talks to Opie and Opie agrees to free the birds. As he sets them aflight one by one, watching every wing flap with joy, he experiences the joy and sadness that comes with parenting. At the very end of the show, Opie looks at the cage and says to Andy, "Cage sure looks awful empty, don't it, Paw?" Andy agrees and then speaks the best line of the entire series: "But don't the trees seem nice and full?" The camera then pulls back and up as though the three songbirds were watching Andy and Opie. A beautiful, touching moment and episode. Opie—and we—learned that in sadness can be found joy.

Kudos to writer Harvey Bullock and director Dick Crenna for creating a classic moment in American television. This episode, without question, should have won an Emmy. And that it didn't is an outrageous oversight. (It was beat out in three categories—Best Comedy, Best Actor, and Best Director—by "The Dick Van Dyke Show." Granted, "The Dick Van Dyke Show" was an excellent sitcom, but I think the Academy made an error in judgement that year.)

"The Andy Griffith Show" was a superb example of what can happen when the best people get together for the purpose of creating television art. The writers and directors were the best around, and the cast was good beyond belief. Just having *one* actor of the caliber of a Howard McNear or a Don Knotts in a show today would likely guarantee its success and ensure it a long, healthy run. The cast of "The Andy Griffith Show" were all the best: they were pros who had learned their craft and practiced it with diligence. The screenplays reflected the type of writing seldom found today. The laughs came from knowing and anticipating how Opie or Otis or Barney would act in a given situation, rather than from one-liners or double-entendres. And the slapstick physical comedy involved more than just pratfalls and props. Hal "Otis" Smith acted with his whole body. Don/Barney's body radiated high-strung hilarity, and Andy Griffith/Taylor's body language exuded ease and comfort, contentment and peace.

Mayberry, My Hometown is for all of you who have always loved Mayberry and, up until now, have had no ultimate guidebook to the town. If you've been touched by the magic of Mayberry, too, please drop me a line care of my publisher. I'd like to hear how your life has been affected and changed by being a Mayberryite, and whether the values of Mayberry have in any way influenced your own. Feel free to drop me a line.

Long live Mayberry!!

ACKNOWLEDGEMENTS

Mayberry, My Hometown was essentially a solo project, but throughout the two years it took me to research and write it I was assisted by many people in ways both material and immaterial. For those acts of kindness I will be ever grateful. The following people are the ones I made a point to remember, either by jotting down a note or by constant, almost weekly revision of this page. However, I know that there are people who helped me along the way whom I have unintentionally omitted. Sorry. But let it be known that anyone who in any way helped with this book shall forever be in the Mayberry section of my heart. Thanks, all.

Special Thanks To...
my editor Tom Schultheiss, for his enthusiasm from Day One, and for his invaluable advice and guidance; my agent John White, for his immediate, professional, and continuing support; my friend Jay Halpern, for his never-ending tutelage; Andy Griffith and Don Knotts, for their participation, and for being Andy and Barney; Jack Dodson, for the photo and his encouragement; George Lindsey, Richard O. Linke, Randy Bash, and Judy Murata for their help; Jody Rein, Clayton Smudsky, and Ted Miller, for their consideration and kindness; Dr. Angelyn Spignesi, for her psychic support; Ted Turner, for never failing to show the episodes; Rich Hodgkins and Dave Wrenn, for their computer expertise; Ben, for letting me write; Cindy Adams, for one special column; Pete DeBrino, Frank Mandato, Janet Spignesi, David and Maureen Spignesi, Antoinette Capelli, Joe Parcella, Doug Altmannsberger, Dante and Marie Fasano, Dan Fasano and Laurie Mordecai, Laura Spignesi, Cathy and Clem Esposito, Ralph Savo, Bernadette DeSerio, Edith and Frank Cupo, and my buddy Joe Badamo—for all their encouragement; Carolyn Wyman, for her interest and much appreciated help; Lynn Fasano, for her help; very special thanks to Steve and Marge Rapuano, for being two true believers from the start; Robbie Keefer, for being more help than she probably realizes; Dolores Fantarella, for everything; Tony, Sheryl, and Linda Fantarella, for always believing; Paul Spignesi, for teaching me about "The Mail"; Peg Quintin, for her kindness and much appreciated generosity; my friend Sonya Monty; John Griffin at Wideworld for his prompt assistance; Joann LaVerde-Curcio at A.C. Neilsen for her help and accommodation; John Meroney for all he's done to keep the best show ever produced on the air; Jim Clark for his unending belief in the greatness of our hometown and for all his help and kindness; and finally Richard Kelly for his book, his essay, and his commitment and devotion to "The Andy Griffith Show" and the spirit of Mayberry.

And a Very Special Thanks To...
Elinor Donahue, for her encouragement, participation, generosity, and overwhelming kindness in the early days of this project;

Jim Nabors, for his friendliness and sincerity, and for being a quintessential gentleman to a caller from the other side of the world;

Aneta Corsaut, for her vibrancy, for her unbelievable generosity with her personal photos, for introducing me to Betty Lynn, and for being great fun;

Rance Howard, for his enthusiasm, willingness to help and his characteristic generosity;

Betty Lynn, for her quiet grace, her honesty, and her engaging charm;

Clint Howard, for his immediate offer of assistance and for being "a fun-loving guy";

and Ron Howard, for his involvement, for being Opie...and for being his father's son.

How To
Use This Book

Browse through it.

Look up something while watching the show.

Read it cover to cover and learn the entire history of our favorite hometown.

The main section of this work is similar to a traditional glossary of terms.

The "terms" or subjects dealt with in the glossary are arranged alphabetically, word-by-word.

Entries pertaining to characters can be found under the character's last name, assuming it was mentioned in the series, otherwise in the alphabet for their first name if that's all they were known by. First names preceded by such designations as "Aunt" or "Uncle" are placed in the alphabet for the first name, except for "Aunt Bee," who I couldn't bring myself to refer to as just "Bee" most of the time (although I did slip up on a few occasions, so look under "Bee" as well!). As every resident of Mayberry knows, our Aunt Bee's name is "Aunt Bee," and she belongs under "A." When was the last time you were so disrespectful as to refer to your Aunt Myrtle as "Myrtle"?

Names of things beginning with the same word as the name of a character are located following the latter (e.g., TUCKER ENTERPRISES, the name of a company, follows the list of characters with the last name TUCKER).

Numbers are filed as if spelled out (e.g., 24 Elm Street can be found under "Twenty-four . . . ").

Initial articles (A, An, The) do not figure in the alphabetical sequence, and are ignored.

Simple abbreviations (Mr., Mrs., Dr.) are filed as if spelled out. Such abbreviations when used in conjunction with a character's last name (e.g., Mr. MacGruder) take the place of first names, but when used as part of an appellation (e.g., "Mr. Big Wheels") become the basis for alphabetizing ("*Mister* Big Wheels" is filed in the "Mi" sequence, not in under "Wheels"). More complex abbreviations are treated as if they were words, and are not spelled out.

Acronyms and initialisms are treated as single letter words and are placed at the start of each letter sequence.

Names beginning with "Mc" (e.g., Sharon McCall) are filed as if spelled "Mac."

For the most part, isolated monetary amounts have been spelled out as words; on the other hand, prices and amounts which appeared in particular episodes as numerals on signs or posters have been left in numerical form, even when they begin a sentence. Episode numbers have likewise been left in numerical form following the titles of episodes.

Occasional cross-references have been made from alternative forms to the preferred form (for the purpose of this book) of an entry whenever deemed appropriate.

For the most part, subjects appear in bold face type at the beginning of each entry (titles of episodes appear in bold italics, titles of books appear in medium italics). This is followed by a series of numbers in parentheses. These numbers refer to the exact episode(s) from which the entry was derived, and are keyed to the section of this book preceding the main glossary called "The Seasons," which lists episodes in the order in which they were filmed/broadcast, by season, giving the original broadcast dates.

As an example, the entry "Mrs. Beggs" is followed by the numbers (112F/111B). These numbers refer to the episode called "Barney's Sidecar" which was the 112th episode filmed but was the 111th episode broadcast.

By using both of these sections, the reader can quickly find any character or episode.

Special Note: Virtually every character that ever appeared or was even mentioned in "The Andy Griffith Show" appears in *Mayberry, My Hometown*, cross-referenced to the specific episode in which they either made their appearance or were mentioned.

However, there were ten main characters who were so ubiquitous throughout the run of the series that to list every episode in which they appeared would involve columns and columns of meaningless episode numbers. These ten characters were:

> Andy Taylor
> Barney Fife
> Bee Taylor
> Opie Taylor
> Helen Crump
> Thelma Lou
> Floyd Lawson
> Gomer Pyle
> Goober Pyle
> Howard Sprague

For each of these friends of ours, I have instead created a single background entry. In these general overviews, I was more concerned with expressing the spirit of these people, rather than specific details about them. However, since they were such important participants in the happenings of Mayberry, you will find extensive details about their activities in countless other encyclopedia entries.

I sincerely tried to be as faithful to the original broadcast scripts as possible. This prohibited assumptions and conjecture about details for which there was no corresponding support in an episode. This sometimes resulted in multiple listings for characters with the same name. For instance, there are three "Sams" listed in the encyclopedia. The episode reference numbers are 12F/10B, 48F/B, and 174F/173B. In all these episodes, there was a character named Sam. Each is listed here independently because nowhere in the three scripts was it indicated that they were the same man. When there was a question regarding such characters, I always made the judgement that if a character wasn't specifically identified in detail, it should be listed separately. Also, I made no assumptions regarding familial connections if such information was not specifically spelled out in the script. Therefore, you will find characters with the same family name who are represented here as unrelated individuals.

I hope this attention to detail enhances your visit to Mayberry, my hometown.

"I'd sit on his lap
In that big old Buick
As we drove through town.
He'd tousle my hair and say
'Son, take a good look around,
This is your hometown'."

Bruce Springsteen
"My Hometown"

"Well I was born in a small town
And I live in a small town
Prob'ly die in a small town
And that's prob'ly where they'll bury me."

John Cougar Mellencamp
"Small Town"

Mayberry
My Hometown

Part I
The Mayberry Pocket Almanac:
A Handy Guide to
Mayberry People, Places & Things

"You people are living in another world!"

Malcolm Tucker
"Man In A Hurry"

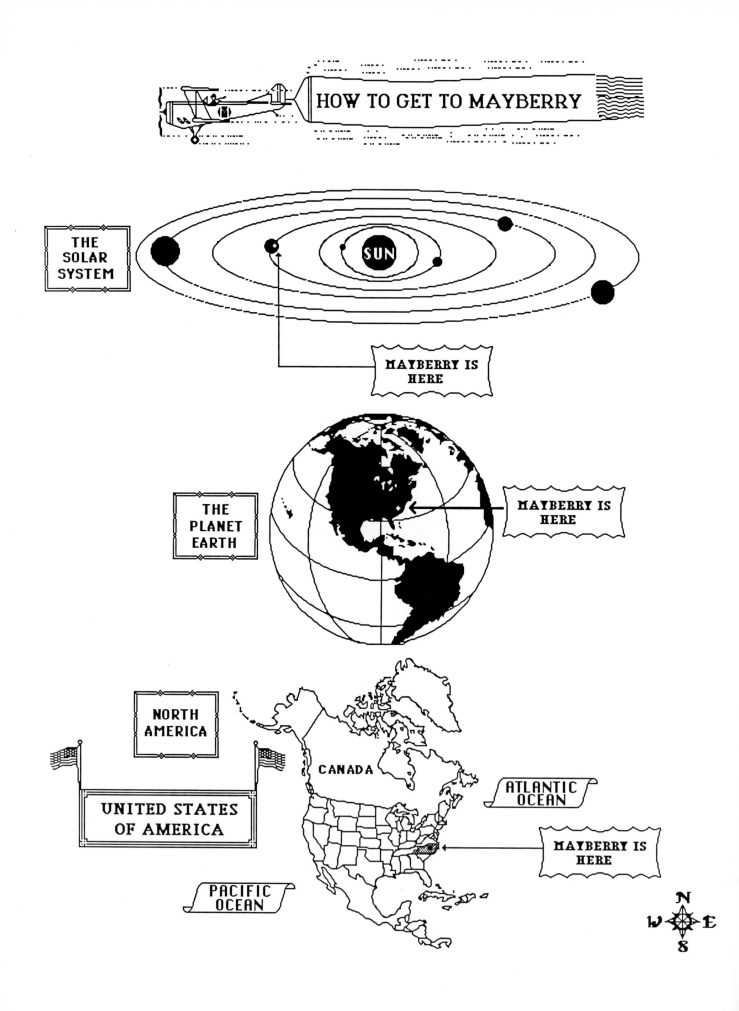

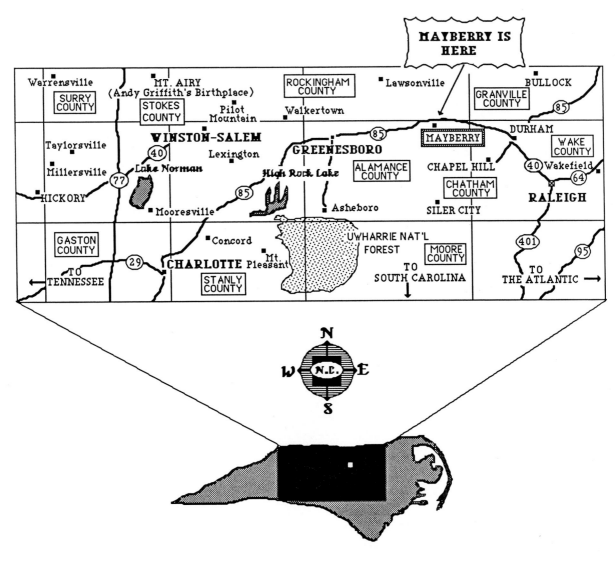

MAYBERRY IS HERE

NORTH CAROLINA

MAYBERRY, NORTH CAROLINA

LEGEND FOR "MAYBERRY CENTER"

With this map, I attempt to give the reader a detailed look at the ever-changing face of Mayberry. As with the floor plans, I had to make some judgements as to what episodes to use for my source material. I went with the episodes that had what I thought were the broadest, easiest-to-read scenes of the four streets that bounded Mayberry's town center and the other locales mentioned. These were:

"Ellie Comes To Town" (6F/4B)
"Stranger in Town" (10F/12B)
"Mayberry Goes Hollywood" (13F/B)
"The Merchant of Mayberry" (54F/B)
"The Mayberry Band" (72F/71B)
"The Sermon for Today" (100F/99B)
"The Return of Barney Fife" (176F/B)
"Wyatt Earp" (179F/B)
"Opie Finds A Baby" (202F/199B)
"Only A Rose" (203F/201B)
"Floyd's Barbershop" (210F/211B)
"Howard's Main Event" (222F/225B)

Additional episodes used as sources are mentioned in the following legend. The end result is a bird's-eye view of the center of Mayberry as it might have looked at any given moment during the run of the series. I hope that this representative rendering of the town's center adds to your visit to Mayberry, my hometown.

1. **THE MAYBERRY COURTHOUSE** Our first view of Mayberry's courthouse came in the first few seconds of the first episode of the series, "The New Housekeeper" (1F/B). We saw the courthouse in just about every episode of the series from that point on. The soul of Mayberry, this was where it all started. (See #26 below)

2. **FLOYD'S BARBERSHOP & EM-METT'S FIX-IT SHOP** From episode 10F/12B, "Stranger in Town," up through 219F/B, "Goober's Contest," Floyd's Barbershop occupied the building right next to the courthouse. From 221F/235B, "Goober the Executive," through the end of the series, the building was occupied by Emmett Clark, owner of Emmett's Fix-It Shop. The building was originally owned "for twenty or thirty years" by the Robinson family of Mayberry. When they moved to California, they decided to sell the building (in 210F/211B, "Floyd's Barbershop"). Howard Sprague bought the building and it is assumed he continued on as Emmett's landlord when Floyd closed up and retired. Floyd's and Emmett's were two of the favorite gathering spots for the men of the town. It was a place to sit, talk, play checkers, read the paper, or just doze. Opie described the activities of the men quite accurately in 210F/211B: the guys would "play checkers, talk, grunt." (See #34 below)

3. **ORVILLE MONROE'S TV REPAIR/FUNERAL PARLOR** This was part of the same building that housed Floyd's Barbershop, although after the first season or so, Orville's role was just about eliminated. The TV repair sign was still on the front window of this building right through the end of the series, however. It appeared that when Emmett took over Floyd's, he took the rest of the building as well, although his work area was confined to the original area of Floyd's. Emmett probably used the room next door for storage.

4. **CROWLEY'S/FOLEY'S/DOAKES' MARKET** The Mayberry grocery store. From approximately 45F/B, "The Farmer Takes A Wife," through 61F/B, "Andy on Trial," the market was owned and operated by Art Crowley. From approximately 120F/119B, "Bargain Day," through 202F/199B, "Opie Finds A Baby," the market was owned and operated by Charlie Foley, although in 161F/160B, "Opie's Job," the market was called Doakes' Market and it was owned and operated by Mr. Doakes. Mr. Foley probably decided to sell the store to Mr. Doakes and then either Foley or Doakes decided to back out of the deal, but not before Mr. Doakes had had a brief turn at running the store. (See #25 and #27 below)

5. **MAYBERRY HOTEL** Mayberry's only hotel, although the Blue View Motel was also available to those seeking lodging in town. (The motel also had a banquet room.) At the hotel, a single room with a bath ran $2.50 a night, a single room without a bath, $1.75. Room 27 was the room furthest in the back. Wilbur Hennesey once got drunk and fell out the window of room 209, and in 10F/12B, "Stranger in Town," room 216 had just been freshly painted green. (See #28 below)

6. **THE MAYBERRY/GRAND THEATER** Mayberry's only theater. They showed—among other films—Greer Garson, Gregory Peck, and Rock Hudson movies. In 239F/238B, "Opie's Drugstore Job," it was mentioned that the theater had at one time been owned by Old Man MacKnight, and that Andy's very first job as a boy was running the popcorn machine at the theater. (See #35 below)

7. **OSCAR SKINNER'S FEED AND GRAIN STORE** Oscar owned this store—which was behind the courthouse at the end of Central Avenue—for just about the entire run of the series. The store was established in 1890, probably by one of Oscar's kin, and in 62F/B Otis Campbell said that he might have a job working for Oscar at the store. It wasn't said whether Otis got the job.

8. This brick building appeared to be an apartment building from the number of floors and windows. There was one main entrance on Central Avenue.

9. **BOYSINGER'S BAKERY** This was where Millie Hutchins worked, and where Howard, Andy, Goober, and many of the other townsfolk often bought their cakes, pies, and cream buns. The bakery had a striped awning. (See #33 below)

10. Any structure with a "10" in it was an unattributed private home. One of the houses on Maple Road on Andy's side of the street belonged to Fred Hartley.

11. **THE TAYLOR HOUSE** This is the house in which Andy, Aunt Bee, and Opie Taylor lived for the entire run of the series. Andy originally bought the house from Old Man Parmalee. It had four bedrooms and one-and-a-half baths. At the time of 143F/B, "Barney Fife the Realtor," the Taylor house was worth $24,000. The house had noisy plumbing, a crack in the kitchen ceiling,

and a leaky roof. The backyard was where Aunt Bee raised her prizewinning "Deep Pink Ecstasy" rose. (It was also where Opie and Billy broke the rose.) Opie had his clubhouse in the backyard (202F/199B), and the Taylors also had a garage. The clubhouse was where Opie brought the abandoned Garland baby (202F/199B), and the garage was where Opie practiced with his band, "The Sound Committee" (229F/228B) and where he brought Dolly, the horse, when Dolly wouldn't eat for him (214F/B). Unbelievably, at the end of the series (and the beginning of the spin-off, "Mayberry, R.F.D.") Andy Taylor and his new wife, Helen (the former Helen Crump of Kansas, then of Mayberry), moved away from Mayberry. (See #30 below)

12. PURCELL BRANCH'S HOUSE Purcell would sit on his front porch and stare at Andy and Helen as they sat on the front porch of the Taylor house (160F/163B). (See #31 below)

13. MAPLE ROAD At various times throughout the run of the series, this street was called Maple Street (201F/204B), Maple Road (87F/B) and, mistakenly, Elm Street (50F/B). (See #30 below and the entry ANDY'S ADDRESS)

14. ELM STREET Elm Street was around the corner from Andy's house, and it was where the Mayberry Band paraded for Mayor Stoner in order to convince him they were good enough to go to Raleigh for the band festival (72F/71B). (Little did Stoner know they had Freddy Fleet and his Band with a Beat "sitting in" with them.) The band started at the courthouse, went down Central, took a right onto Elm, and then another right onto the unnamed street that had the old oak tree in the middle of it. Elm was also where the Franklyn Pharmacy was located. There was a bus stop in front of the pharmacy. (See #29 and #36 below)

15. MAIN STREET The heart of the town of Mayberry. Everybody went to Main Street for just about anything and everything. Grocery shopping, getting a haircut, going to the movies, picking up a birthday cake, stopping by the courthouse to pay a traffic ticket or just to say hello to Andy and Barney. Main Street was where it happened in our hometown.

16. ALL SOULS CHURCH The Mayberry house of worship, presided over by the Reverend Hobart Tucker. There seemed to be only one other church in town, although it was never seen. In 240F/B, "Barney Hosts A Summit Meeting," Barney mentioned the Moravian Church basement. It wasn't said where the Moravian Church was located. All Souls Church had an old broken-down organ that was replaced—thanks to Andy's persistence and Clara's rendering of "Some Enchanted Evening"—in 174F/173B, "The Church Organ."

17. BIGG'S NEW AND USED FUR-NITURE One of a few places in Mayberry that sold furniture. (A couple of others were Weaver's Department Store and the furniture factory.) In 179F/B, "Wyatt Earp," townsfolk ran into Biggs' when it appeared that Andy and Clarence Earp were going to have shoot-out on Main Street.

18. WEAVER'S DEPARTMENT STORE Mayberry's largest and most diverse department store. Weaver's carried everything from furniture (28F/B) to a beer can opener with an umbrella on it (117F/116B). (See #32 below)

19. WALKER'S DRUGSTORE Store owned and operated by the Walker family in the early years of the show. Ellie Walker came to Walker's fresh out of pharmacy school to work with her Uncle Fred. Walker's let the Mayberry residents run up tabs and the store also had an old-fashioned soda fountain. It wasn't specifically said what the Walkers did with the business, but it's likely that they sold it to either Mr. Crawford, who owned and operated it towards the end of the series (specifically, 239F/238B), or Mrs. Mason, who had a drugstore called Mason's Drugstore (85F/B.) (See #21 below)

20. THE MAYBERRY/BLUEBIRD DINER One of the most popular eateries in Mayberry. At various times throughout the run of the series it was called both The Mayberry Diner and The Bluebird Diner. Everyone—and I mean everyone—at one time or another, ate at the Diner. In 13F/B, "Mayberry Goes Hollywood," the Diner was briefly changed to "The Cinemascope Cafe."

21. FRANKLYN'S PHARMACY Another drugstore in Mayberry. In 62F/B, "Cousin Virgil," Barney's cousin Virgil got off his bus at the stop in front of Franklyn's. (See #36 below)

22. This appeared to be a brick apartment building.

23. THE OLD OAK TREE This tree was considered the center of the town of Mayberry. Andy remembered climbing up the tree when he was a young 'un and, in 13F/B, "Mayberry Goes Hollywood," some of the townsfolk foolishly wanted to cut down the tree—which they called an "eyesore"—when the Hollywood movie was to be made in town.

24. CENTRAL AVENUE One of the four main roads that bounded Mayberry center. Andy usually drove down Maple, onto Central, and then onto Main when he went to work. The area at the end of Central in front of the Feed & Grain Store (which opened onto the backyard of the courthouse) was often used by Andy and Barney for outdoor chores and jobs. The most notable use of that area was in 100F/99B, "The Sermon for Today," when Barney and Gomer used it to try and repair the old bandstand.

25. This vacant lot was part of the market's property. In 54F/B, when it was owned by Art Crowley, Andy and Barney used it to set up a little temporary market for Bert Mille, the peddler. In that same episode, Opie set up a lemonade stand on the same lot. Also, in 179F/B, "Wyatt Earp," Opie and Johnny Paul had a fight on what appeared to be the same lot.

26. The front of the courthouse. On the left side, facing the front door, there was a park bench.

27. The sidewalk in front of the market. In 84F/B, "Opie and the Spoiled Kid," Arnold Winkler knocked over Mrs. Rosenbach and spilled her groceries all over the sidewalk.

28. The porch of the hotel. In 91F/B, "The Rivals," this is where Opie would wait for—at first—Karen Burgess, and then later (to Barney's chagrin) Thelma Lou.

29. This is where Mayor Stoner sat and watched the "enhanced" version of the Mayberry Band parade before him. (See #14 and #36 below)

30. The street in front of Andy's house. In 180F/B, "Aunt Bee Learns to Drive," Aunt Bee moved her car without a driver sitting next to her and wrecked the right rear fender.

31. The front of Purcell Branch's house. Purcell would sit on his porch and stare at Andy and Helen.

32. The sidewalk in front of Weaver's Department Store. In 117F/116B, "The Shoplifters," Andy weighed the shoplifter with a scale from Weaver's to prove that she was "weighed down" with merchandise. She weighed 163 pounds.

33. The front of Boysinger's. In 222F/225B, "Howard's Main Event," Howard watched Millie enter the store from his post across the street. He then decided he had a sudden urge for a cream bun.

34. The sidewalk in front of Floyd's Barbershop. Floyd had a couple of chairs out there and folks would often stop and sit a spell. In 203F/201B, Floyd had his pansies out there, soaking up "the rays."

35. The front of the theater. Barney would often stop there and watch them change the marquee.

36. The bus stop in front of Franklyn's Pharmacy.

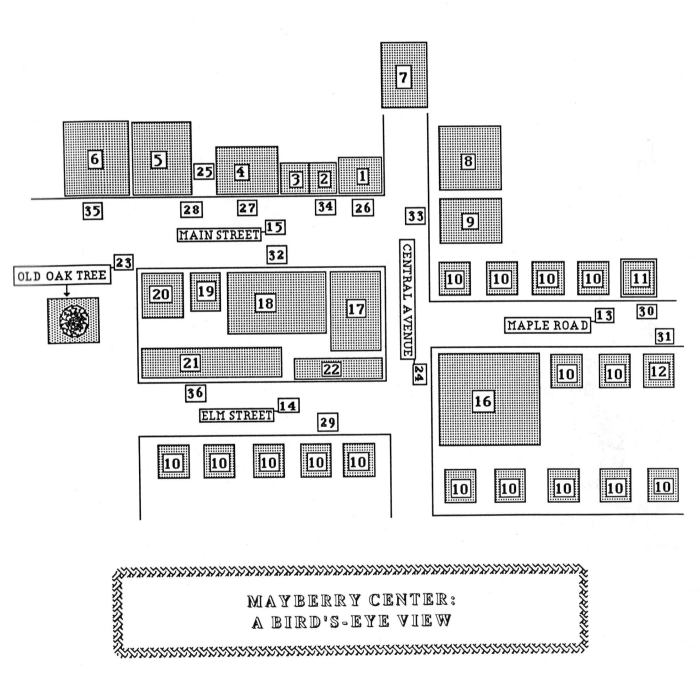

MAYBERRY CENTER:
A BIRD'S-EYE VIEW

FLOOR PLAN
INTRODUCTION

The following section consists of floor plans for some of my favorite places in Mayberry.

I've included these to give visitors to my hometown a better sense of place and a clearer picture of Mayberry, North Carolina.

I chose the places in town that were used most often by the residents, necessarily eliminating some sets and locales that were seen a few random times during the run of the series. (For instance, I didn't think that a floor plan of The Darlings' cabin would be of much interest to anyone except Briscoe Darling and his boys.) So, I stuck with those places where we spent the majority of our time during the eight years Mayberry was in our homes.

I've tried to be as specific as possible regarding details such as placement of lamps, tables, pictures, etc., but the changing face of Mayberry necessitated creating—in many instances—a composite view of a certain set.

Floyd's Barbershop, for example, changed quite a

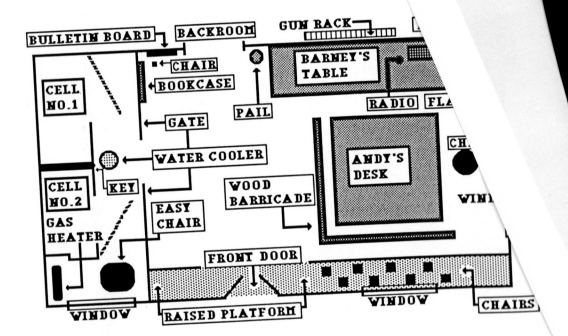

THE MAYBERRY COURTHOUSE

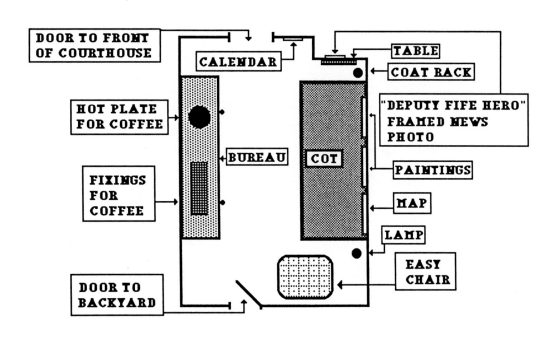

DOOR TO FRONT OF COURTHOUSE

CALENDAR

TABLE

COAT RACK

HOT PLATE FOR COFFEE

BUREAU

COT

"DEPUTY FIFE HERO" FRAMED NEWS PHOTO

PAINTINGS

FIXINGS FOR COFFEE

MAP

LAMP

EASY CHAIR

DOOR TO BACKYARD

BACKROOM AT THE
MAYBERRY COURTHOUSE

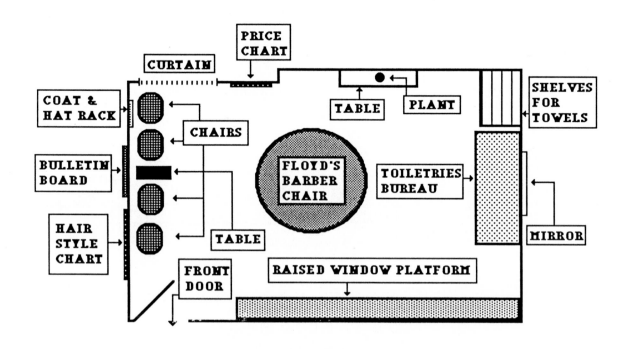

PRICE CHART

CURTAIN

COAT & HAT RACK

CHAIRS

TABLE

PLANT

SHELVES FOR TOWELS

BULLETIN BOARD

FLOYD'S BARBER CHAIR

TOILETRIES BUREAU

MIRROR

HAIR STYLE CHART

TABLE

FRONT DOOR

RAISED WINDOW PLATFORM

FLOYD'S BARBERSHOP

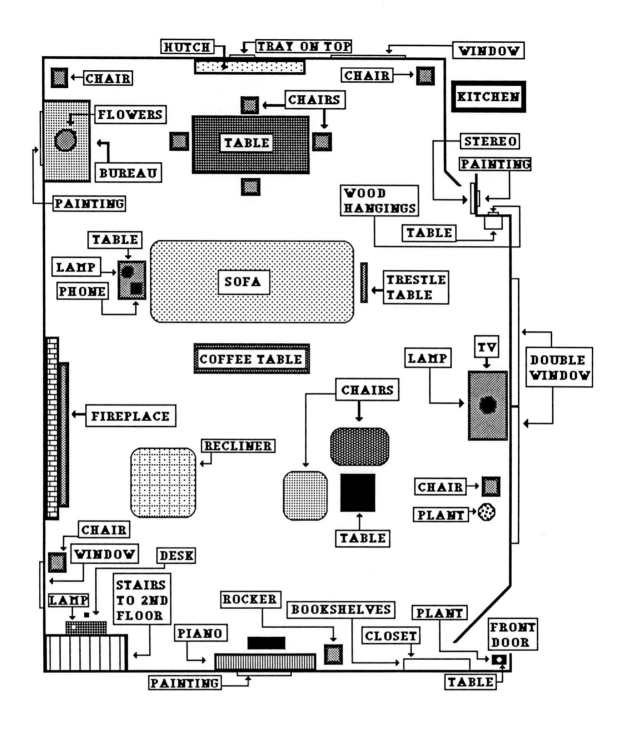

HUTCH TRAY ON TOP WINDOW

CHAIR

CHAIRS

CHAIR

KITCHEN

FLOWERS

STEREO

PAINTING

BUREAU

TABLE

PAINTING

WOOD HANGINGS

TABLE

TABLE

LAMP

SOFA

TRESTLE TABLE

PHONE

COFFEE TABLE

TV

LAMP

DOUBLE WINDOW

FIREPLACE

CHAIRS

RECLINER

CHAIR

PLANT

TABLE

CHAIR

WINDOW DESK

LAMP

STAIRS TO 2ND FLOOR

ROCKER

BOOKSHELVES

PLANT

PIANO

CLOSET

FRONT DOOR

PAINTING

TABLE

THE TAYLOR HOUSE
LIVING ROOM & DINING AREA

12

31. The front of Purcell Branch's house. Purcell would sit on his porch and stare at Andy and Helen.

32. The sidewalk in front of Weaver's Department Store. In 117F/116B, "The Shoplifters," Andy weighed the shoplifter with a scale from Weaver's to prove that she was "weighed down" with merchandise. She weighed 163 pounds.

33. The front of Boysinger's. In 222F/225B, "Howard's Main Event," Howard watched Millie enter the store from his post across the street. He then decided he had a sudden urge for a cream bun.

34. The sidewalk in front of Floyd's Barbershop. Floyd had a couple of chairs out there and folks would often stop and sit a spell. In 203F/201B, Floyd had his pansies out there, soaking up "the rays."

35. The front of the theater. Barney would often stop there and watch them change the marquee.

36. The bus stop in front of Franklyn's Pharmacy.

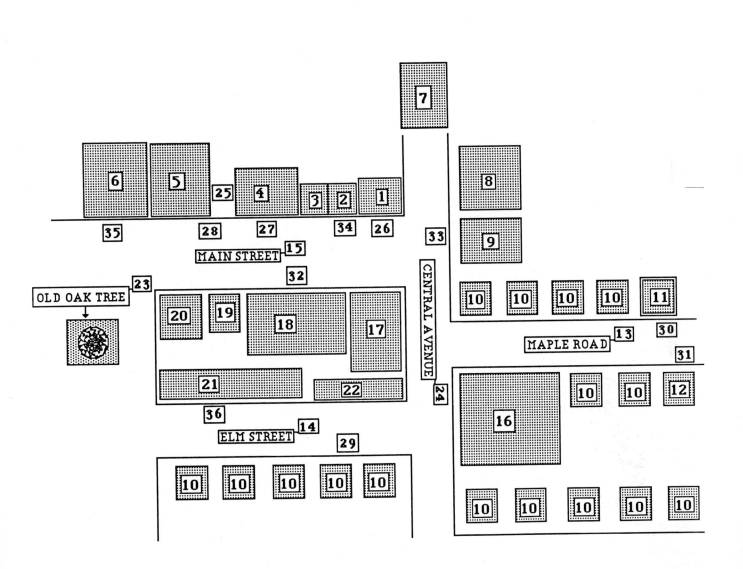

MAYBERRY CENTER:
A BIRD'S-EYE VIEW

FLOOR PLAN INTRODUCTION

The following section consists of floor plans for some of my favorite places in Mayberry.

I've included these to give visitors to my hometown a better sense of place and a clearer picture of Mayberry, North Carolina.

I chose the places in town that were used most often by the residents, necessarily eliminating some sets and locales that were seen a few random times during the run of the series. (For instance, I didn't think that a floor plan of The Darlings' cabin would be of much interest to anyone except Briscoe Darling and his boys.) So, I stuck with those places where we spent the majority of our time during the eight years Mayberry was in our homes.

I've tried to be as specific as possible regarding details such as placement of lamps, tables, pictures, etc., but the changing face of Mayberry necessitated creating—in many instances—a composite view of a certain set.

Floyd's Barbershop, for example, changed quite a bit during the run of the series. So did Opie's bedroom and—most dramatically—The Bluebird Diner. So, what I did with many of these chameleon locales was to start with a generalized picture of these sets and then add details from a few representative episodes to come up with a floor plan which, while not exactly accurate for every episode, does show what the place might have looked like at a given moment, if you happened to stop by for a visit.

There were, however, certain considerations that influenced my selection of which episodes to use as my reference episodes for these plans. Opie's bedroom came directly from "The New Housekeeper" (1F/B). I felt it only right to use the first view of his room as the definitive one. Andy's bedroom came from "Suppose Andy Gets Sick" (232F/233B), the episode which had the best scenes of his room. For the same reasons, I used "A Baby in the House" (184F/B) for Aunt Bee's Bedroom, and "Up in Barney's Room," (104F/105B) for Barney's Room in Mrs. Mendlebright's boarding house.

Browse through these plans and if you think you might like to set a spell in one of them, go right ahead. After all, Mayberry is our hometown, and you're welcome to come back and visit any old time you like.

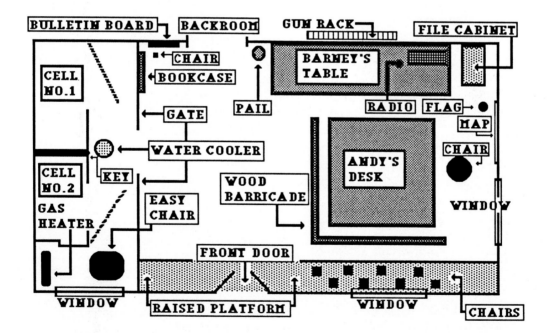

THE MAYBERRY COURTHOUSE

9

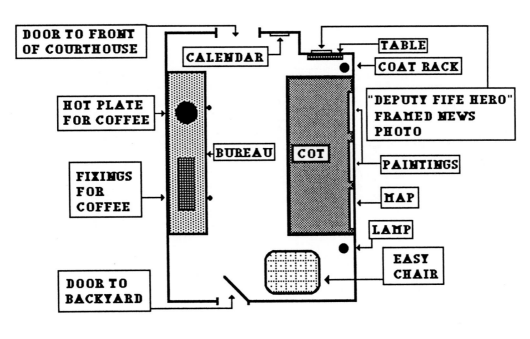

DOOR TO FRONT OF COURTHOUSE

CALENDAR

TABLE

COAT RACK

HOT PLATE FOR COFFEE

"DEPUTY FIFE HERO" FRAMED NEWS PHOTO

BUREAU

COT

FIXINGS FOR COFFEE

PAINTINGS

MAP

LAMP

EASY CHAIR

DOOR TO BACKYARD

BACKROOM AT THE
MAYBERRY COURTHOUSE

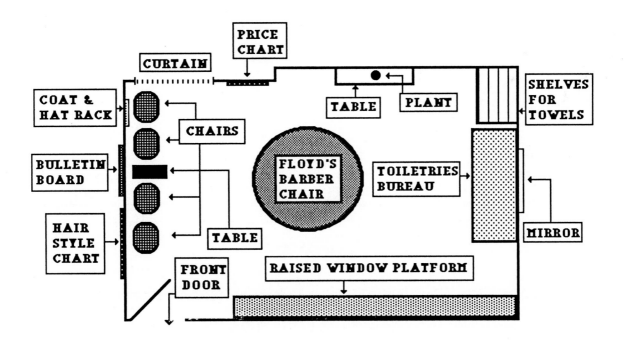

PRICE CHART

CURTAIN

COAT & HAT RACK

CHAIRS

TABLE

PLANT

SHELVES FOR TOWELS

BULLETIN BOARD

FLOYD'S BARBER CHAIR

TOILETRIES BUREAU

HAIR STYLE CHART

TABLE

MIRROR

FRONT DOOR

RAISED WINDOW PLATFORM

FLOYD'S BARBERSHOP

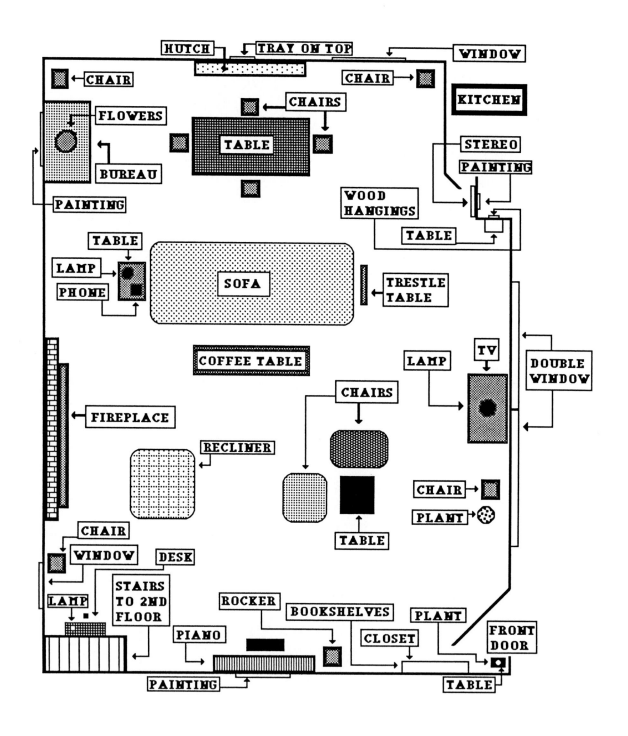

HUTCH   TRAY ON TOP   WINDOW

CHAIR ←

CHAIR ← ☐

KITCHEN

→ CHAIRS

FLOWERS

STEREO

PAINTING

TABLE

BUREAU

WOOD
HANGINGS

PAINTING

TABLE

TABLE

LAMP

SOFA

PHONE

TRESTLE
TABLE

COFFEE TABLE

LAMP   TV

DOUBLE
WINDOW

FIREPLACE

RECLINER

CHAIRS

CHAIR → ☐

PLANT → ⚬

TABLE

CHAIR

WINDOW   DESK

STAIRS
TO 2ND
FLOOR

ROCKER   BOOKSHELVES

PLANT

LAMP

PIANO

CLOSET

FRONT
DOOR

PAINTING

TABLE

THE TAYLOR HOUSE
LIVING ROOM & DINING AREA

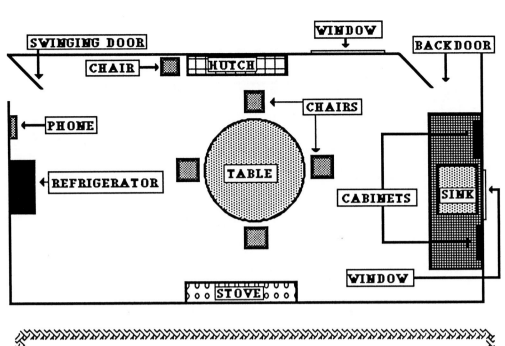

AUNT BEE'S KITCHEN

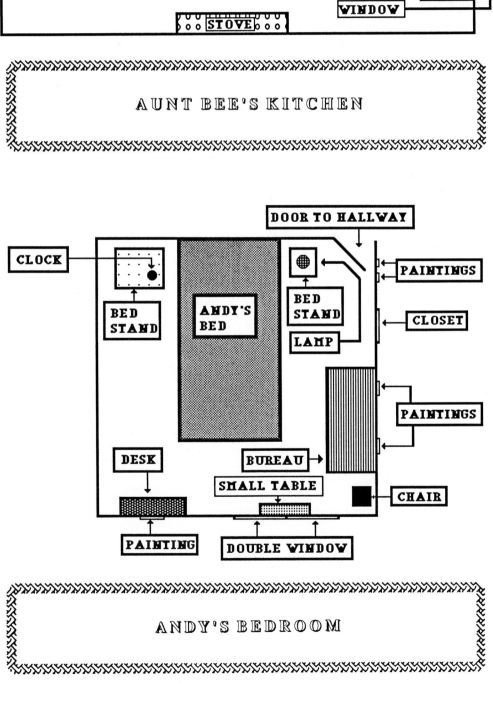

ANDY'S BEDROOM

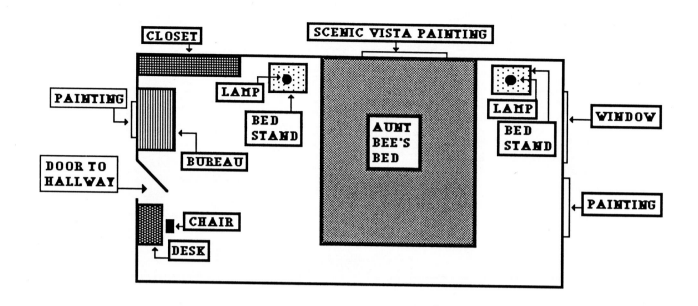

CLOSET

SCENIC VISTA PAINTING

PAINTING

LAMP

BED STAND

AUNT BEE'S BED

LAMP

BED STAND

WINDOW

DOOR TO HALLWAY

BUREAU

PAINTING

CHAIR

DESK

AUNT BEE'S BEDROOM

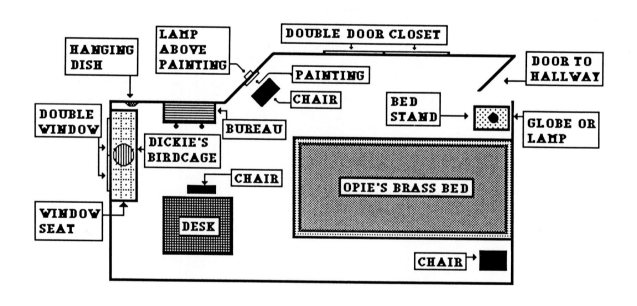

HANGING DISH

LAMP ABOVE PAINTING

DOUBLE DOOR CLOSET

DOOR TO HALLWAY

PAINTING

CHAIR

BED STAND

GLOBE OR LAMP

DOUBLE WINDOW

DICKIE'S BIRDCAGE

BUREAU

OPIE'S BRASS BED

CHAIR

WINDOW SEAT

DESK

CHAIR

OPIE'S BEDROOM

14

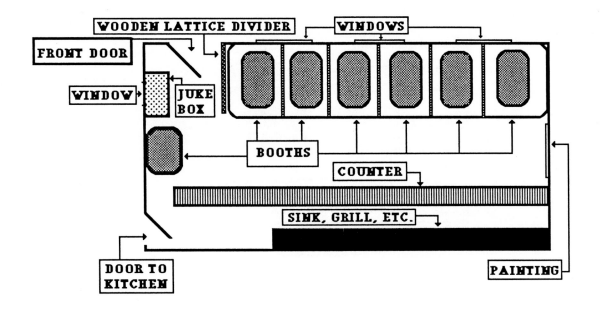

WOODEN LATTICE DIVIDER

WINDOWS

FRONT DOOR

WINDOW

JUKE BOX

BOOTHS

COUNTER

SINK, GRILL, ETC.

DOOR TO KITCHEN

PAINTING

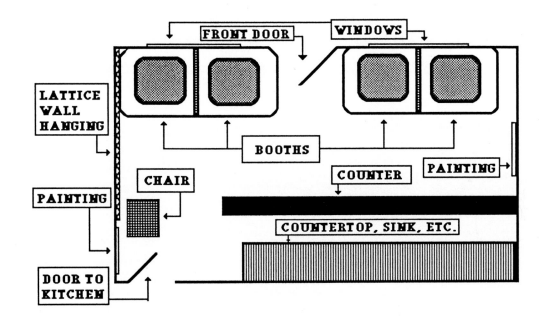

FRONT DOOR

WINDOWS

LATTICE WALL HANGING

BOOTHS

COUNTER

PAINTING

PAINTING

CHAIR

COUNTERTOP, SINK, ETC.

DOOR TO KITCHEN

THE MAYBERRY/BLUEBIRD DINER
(TWO VERSIONS)

15

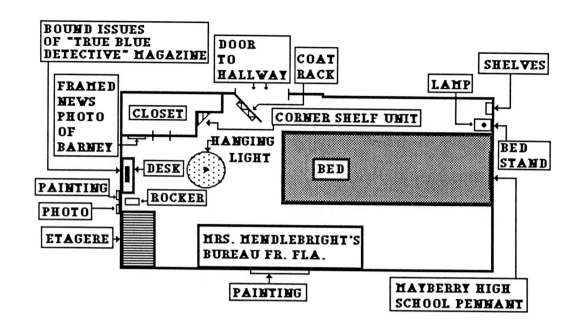

BOUND ISSUES OF "TRUE BLUE DETECTIVE" MAGAZINE

DOOR TO HALLWAY

COAT RACK

SHELVES

FRAMED NEWS PHOTO OF BARNEY

CLOSET

LAMP

CORNER SHELF UNIT

HANGING LIGHT

BED

BED STAND

DESK

PAINTING

ROCKER

PHOTO

ETAGERE

MRS. MENDLEBRIGHT'S BUREAU FR. FLA.

PAINTING

MAYBERRY HIGH SCHOOL PENNANT

BARNEY'S ROOM AT
MRS. MENDLEBRIGHT'S BOARDING HOUSE

THE SEASONS

FIRST SEASON

Filmed	Broadcast	Title	Broadcast Date
1	1	The New Housekeeper	Oct. 3, 1960
2	2	The Manhunt	Oct. 10, 1960
3	3	Guitar Player	Oct. 17, 1960
4	6	Runaway Kid	Nov. 7, 1960
5	8	Opie's Charity	Nov. 28, 1960
6	4	Ellie Comes To Town	Oct. 24, 1960
7	5	Irresistible Andy	Oct. 31, 1960
8	9	A Feud Is A Feud	Dec. 5, 1960
9	7	Andy the Matchmaker	Nov. 14, 1960
10	12	Stranger In Town	Dec. 26, 1960
11	11	Christmas Story	Dec. 19, 1960
12	10	Ellie for Council	Dec. 12, 1960
13	13	Mayberry Goes Hollywood	Jan. 2, 1961
14	14	The Horse Trader	Jan. 9, 1961
15	15	Those Gossipin' Men	Jan. 16, 1961
16	20	Andy Saves Barney's Morale	Feb. 20, 1961
17	17	Alcohol and Old Lace	Jan. 30, 1961
18	18	Andy the Marriage Counselor	Feb. 6, 1961
19	19	Mayberry on Record	Feb. 13, 1961
20	16	The Beauty Contest	Jan. 23, 1961
21	21	Andy and the Gentleman Crook	Feb. 27, 1961
22	22	Cyrano Andy	Mar. 6, 1961
23	23	Andy and Opie, Housekeepers	Mar. 13, 1961
24	24	The New Doctor	Mar. 27, 1961
25	25	A Plaque for Mayberry	Apr. 3, 1961
26	26	The Inspector	Apr. 10, 1961
27	27	Ellie Saves A Female	Apr. 17, 1961
28	28	Andy Forecloses	Apr. 24, 1961
29	29	Quiet Sam	May 1, 1961
30	30	Barney Gets His Man	May 8, 1961
31	31	The Guitar Player Returns	May 15, 1961
32	32	Bringing Up Opie	May 22, 1961

SECOND SEASON

Filmed	Broadcast	Title	Broadcast Date
33	34	Barney's Replacement	Oct. 9, 1961
34	33	Opie and the Bully	Oct. 2, 1961
35	35	Andy and the Woman Speeder	Oct. 16, 1961
36	37	Barney on the Rebound	Oct. 30, 1961
37	40	The Perfect Female	Nov. 27, 1961
38	41	Aunt Bee's Brief Encounter	Dec. 4, 1961
39	36	Mayberry Goes Bankrupt	Oct. 23, 1961
40	38	Opie's Hobo Friend	Nov. 13, 1961
41	39	Crime-free Mayberry	Nov. 20, 1961
42	42	The Clubmen	Dec. 11, 1961
43	43	The Pickle Story	Dec. 18, 1961
44	44	Sheriff Barney	Dec. 25, 1961
45	45	The Farmer Takes A Wife	Jan. 1, 1962
46	46	The Keeper of the Flame	Jan. 8, 1962
47	47	Bailey's Bad Boy	Jan. 15, 1962
48	48	The Manicurist	Jan. 22, 1962
49	49	The Jinx	Jan. 29, 1962
50	50	Jailbreak	Feb. 5, 1962
51	51	A Medal for Opie	Feb. 12, 1962
52	52	Barney and the Choir	Feb. 19, 1962
53	53	Guest of Honor	Feb. 26, 1962
54	54	The Merchant of Mayberry	Mar. 5, 1962
55	55	Aunt Bee the Warden	Mar. 12, 1962
56	56	The County Nurse	Mar. 19, 1962
57	57	Andy and Barney in the Big City	Mar. 26, 1962
58	58	Wedding Bells for Aunt Bee	Apr. 2, 1962
59	59	Three's A Crowd	Apr. 9, 1962
60	60	The Bookie Barber	Apr. 16, 1962
61	61	Andy on Trial	Apr. 23, 1962
62	62	Cousin Virgil	Apr. 30, 1962
63	63	Deputy Otis	May 7, 1962

THIRD SEASON

Filmed	Broadcast	Title	Broadcast Date
64	73	Opie's Rival	Dec. 3, 1962
65	67	Andy and Opie—Bachelors	Oct..22, 1962
66	64	Mr. McBeevee	Oct. 1, 1962
67	65	Andy's Rich Girlfriend	Oct. 8, 1962
68	69	Barney Mends A Broken Heart	Nov. 5, 1962
69	66	Andy and the New Mayor	Oct. 15, 1962
70	68	The Cow Thief	Oct. 29, 1962
71	72	Floyd, the Gay Deceiver	Nov. 26, 1962
72	71	The Mayberry Band	Nov. 19, 1962
73	70	Lawman Barney	Nov. 12, 1962
74	74	Convicts at Large	Dec. 10, 1962
75	75	The Bed Jacket	Dec. 17, 1962
76	78	Barney and the Governor	Jan. 7, 1963
77	79	Man In A Hurry	Jan. 14, 1963
78	76	The Bank Job	Dec. 24, 1962
79	77	One-Punch Opie	Dec. 31, 1962
80	80	High Noon in Mayberry	Jan. 21, 1963
81	81	The Loaded Goat	Jan 28, 1963
82	82	Class Reunion	Feb. 4, 1963
83	83	Rafe Hollister Sings	Feb. 11, 1963
84	84	Opie and the Spoiled Kid	Feb. 18, 1963
85	85	The Great Filling Station Robbery	Feb. 25, 1963
86	86	Andy Discovers America	Mar. 4, 1963
87	87	Aunt Bee's Medicine Man	Mar. 11, 1963
88	88	The Darlings are Coming	Mar. 18, 1963
89	89	Andy's English Valet	Mar. 25, 1963
90	90	Barney's First Car	Apr. 1, 1963
91	91	The Rivals	Apr. 8, 1963
92	92	A Wife for Andy	Apr. 15, 1963
93	93	Dogs, Dogs, Dogs	Apr. 22, 1963
94	94	Mountain Wedding	Apr. 29, 1963
95	95	The Big House	May 6, 1963

FOURTH SEASON

Filmed	Broadcast	Title	Broadcast Date
96	100	Briscoe Declares for Aunt Bee	Oct. 28, 1963
97	101	Gomer the House Guest	Nov. 4, 1963
98	97	The Haunted House	Oct. 7, 1963
99	98	Ernest T. Bass Joins the Army	Oct 14, 1963
100	99	The Sermon for Today	Oct. 21, 1963
101	96	Opie the Birdman	Sept. 30, 1963
102	102	A Black Day for Mayberry	Nov. 11, 1963
103	103	Opie's Ill-gotten Gain	Nov. 18, 1963
104	105	Up in Barney's Room	Dec. 2, 1963
105	104	A Date for Gomer	Nov. 25, 1963
106	106	Citizen's Arrest	Dec. 16, 1963
107	127	Gomer Pyle, U.S.M.C.	May 19, 1964
108	107	Opie and His Merry Men	Dec. 30, 1963
109	108	Barney and the Cave Rescue	Jan. 6, 1964
110	109	Andy and Opie's Pal	Jan. 13, 1964
111	110	Aunt Bee the Crusader	Jan. 20, 1964
112	111	Barney's Sidecar	Jan. 27, 1964
113	112	My Fair Ernest T. Bass	Feb. 3, 1964
114	113	Prisoner of Love	Feb. 10, 1964
115	114	Hot Rod Otis	Feb. 17, 1964
116	115	The Song Festers	Feb. 24, 1964
117	116	The Shoplifters	Mar. 2, 1964
118	117	Andy's Vacation	Mar. 9, 1964
119	118	Andy Saves Gomer	Mar. 16, 1964
120	119	Bargain Day	Mar. 23, 1964
121	120	Divorce, Mountain Style	Mar. 30, 1964
122	121	A Deal is a Deal	Apr. 6, 1964
123	122	Fun Girls	Apr. 13, 1964
124	123	The Return of Malcolm Merriweather	Apr. 20, 1964
125	124	The Rumor	Apr. 27, 1964
126	125	Barney and Thelma Lou, Phfftt	May 4, 1964
127	126	Back to Nature	May 11, 1964

THE SEASONS

FIFTH SEASON

Filmed	Broadcast	Title	Broadcast Date
128	133	Barney's Bloodhound	Oct. 26, 1964
129	130	Family Visit	Oct. 5, 1964
130	132	Aunt Bee's Romance	Oct. 19, 1964
131	129	Barney's Physical	Sept. 28, 1964
132	128	Opie Loves Helen	Sept. 21, 1964
133	131	The Education of Ernest T. Bass	Oct. 12, 1964
134	134	Man in the Middle	Nov. 2, 1964
135	135	Barney's Uniform	Nov. 9, 1964
136	136	Opie's Fortune	Nov. 16, 1964
137	137	Goodbye, Sheriff Taylor	Nov. 23, 1964
138	138	The Pageant	Nov. 30, 1964
139	139	The Darling Baby	Dec. 7, 1964
140	140	Andy and Helen Have Their Day	Dec. 14, 1964
141	142	Otis Sues the County	Dec. 28, 1964
142	141	Three Wishes for Opie	Dec. 21, 1964
143	143	Barney Fife, Realtor	Jan. 4, 1965
144	144	Goober Takes A Car Apart	Jan. 11, 1965
145	145	The Rehabilitation of Otis	Jan. 18, 1965
146	146	The Lucky Letter	Jan. 25, 1965
147	147	Goober and the Art of Love	Feb. 1, 1965
148	148	Barney Runs for Sheriff	Feb. 8, 1965
149	149	If I Had A Quarter-Million	Feb. 15, 1965
150	150	TV or not TV	Mar. 1, 1965
151	151	Guest in the House	Mar. 8, 1965
152	152	The Case of the Punch in the Nose	Mar. 15, 1965
153	153	Opie's Newspaper	Mar. 22, 1965
154	154	Aunt Bee's Invisible Beau	Mar. 29, 1965
155	155	The Arrest of the Fun Girls	Apr. 5, 1965
156	156	The Luck of Newton Monroe	Apr. 12, 1965
157	157	Opie Flunks Arithmetic	Apr. 19, 1965
158	158	Opie and the Carnival	Apr. 26, 1965
159	159	Banjo-Playing Deputy	May 3, 1965

SIXTH SEASON

Filmed	Broadcast	Title	Broadcast Date
160	163	Aunt Bee, the Swinger	Oct. 4, 1965
161	160	Opie's Job	Sept. 13, 1965
162	164	The Bazaar	Oct. 11, 1965
163	161	Andy's Rival	Sept. 20, 1965
164	162	Malcolm at the Crossroads	Sept. 27, 1965
165	169	Aunt Bee on TV	Nov. 15., 1965
166	166	Off to Hollywood	Oct. 25, 1965
167	167	Taylors in Hollywood	Nov. 1, 1965
168	168	The Hollywood Party	Nov. 8, 1965
169	165	A Warning from Warren	Oct. 15, 1965
170	171	A Man's Best Friend	Nov. 29, 1965
171	172	Aunt Bee Takes a Job	Dec. 6, 1965
172	170	The Cannon	Nov. 22, 1965
173	174	Girl-Shy	Dec. 20, 1965
174	173	The Church Organ	Dec. 13, 1965
175	175	Otis, the Artist	Jan. 3, 1966
176	176	The Return of Barney Fife	Jan. 10, 1966
177	177	The Legend of Barney Fife	Jan. 17, 1966
178	178	Lost and Found	Jan. 24, 1966
179	179	Wyatt Earp	Jan. 31, 1966
180	180	Aunt Bee Learns to Drive	Feb. 7, 1966
181	181	Look Paw, I'm Dancing	Feb. 14, 1966
182	183	Eat Your Heart Out	Feb. 28,1966
183	182	The Gypsies	Feb. 21, 1966
184	184	A Baby in the House	Mar. 7, 1966
185	185	The County Clerk	Mar. 14, 1966
186	187	Goober's Replacement	Mar. 28, 1966
187	186	The Foster Lady	Mar. 21, 1966
188	188	The Battle of Mayberry	Apr. 4, 1966
189	189	A Singer in Town	Apr. 11, 1966

SEVENTH SEASON

Filmed	Broadcast	Title	Broadcast Date
190	190	Opie's Girlfriend	Sept. 12, 1966
191	192	The Barbershop Quartet	Sept. 26, 1966
192	191	The Lodge	Sept. 19, 1966
193	195	The Darling Fortune	Oct. 17, 1966
194	194	Aunt Bee's Crowning Glory	Oct. 10, 1966
195	193	The Ball Game	Oct. 3, 1966
196	203	Goober Makes History	Dec. 19, 1966
197	198	The Senior Play	Nov. 14, 1966
198	200	Big Fish in a Small Town	Nov. 28, 1966
199	196	Mind Over Matter	Oct. 31, 1966
200	197	Politics Begin at Home	Nov. 7, 1966
201	204	A New Doctor in Town	Dec. 26, 1966
202	199	Opie Finds a Baby	Nov. 21, 1966
203	201	Only a Rose	Dec. 5, 1966
204	202	Otis the Deputy	Dec. 12, 1966
205	205	Don't Miss a Good Bet	Jan. 2, 1967
206	206	Dinner at Eight	Jan. 9, 1967
207	209	Andy's Old Girlfriend	Jan. 30, 1967
208	212	The Statue	Feb. 20, 1967
209	210	Aunt Bee's Restaurant	Feb. 6, 1967
210	211	Floyd's Barbershop	Feb. 13, 1967
211	207	A Visit to Barney Fife	Jan. 16, 1967
212	208	Barney Comes to Mayberry	Jan. 23, 1967
213	213	Helen, the Authoress	Feb. 27, 1967
214	214	Goodbye Dolly	Mar. 6, 1967
215	215	Opie's Piano Lesson	Mar. 13, 1967
216	216	Howard, the Comedian	Mar. 20, 1967
217	217	Big Brothers	Mar. 27, 1967
218	218	Opie's Most Unforgettable Character	Apr. 3, 1967
219	219	Goober's Contest	Apr. 10, 1967

EIGHTH SEASON

Filmed	Broadcast	Title	Broadcast Date
220	220	Opie's First Love	Sept. 11, 1967
221	235	Goober the Executive	Dec. 25, 1967
222	225	Howard's Main Event	Oct. 16, 1967
223	226	Aunt Bee the Juror	Oct. 23, 1967
224	221	Howard the Bowler	Sept. 18, 1967
225	224	Opie Steps Up in Class	Oct. 9, 1967
226	223	Andy's Trip to Raleigh	Oct. 2, 1967
227	222	A Trip to Mexico	Sept. 25, 1967
228	227	Tape Recorder	Oct. 30, 1967
229	228	Opie's Group	Nov. 6, 1967
230	229	Aunt Bee and the Lecturer	Nov. 13, 1967
231	230	Andy's Investment	Nov. 20, 1967
232	233	Suppose Andy Gets Sick	Dec. 11, 1967
233	231	Howard and Millie	Nov. 27, 1967
234	232	Aunt Bee's Cousin	Dec. 4, 1967
235	234	Howard's New Life	Dec. 18, 1967
236	237	Emmett's Brother-In-Law	Jan. 8, 1968
237	236	The Mayberry Chef	Jan. 1, 1968
238	239	The Church Benefactors	Jan. 22, 1968
239	238	Opie's Drugstore Job	Jan. 15, 1968
240	240	Barney Hosts a Summit Meeting	Jan. 29, 1968
241	249	Mayberry, R.F.D.	Apr. 1, 1968
242	241	Goober Goes to an Auto Show	Feb. 5, 1968
243	242	Aunt Bee's Big Moment	Feb. 12, 1968
244	243	Helen's Past	Feb. 19, 1968
245	244	Emmett's Anniversary	Feb. 26, 1968
246	245	The Wedding	Mar. 4, 1968
247	246	Sam for Town Council	Mar. 11, 1968
248	247	Opie and Mike	Mar. 18, 1968
249	248	A Girl for Goober	Mar. 25, 1968

"THE ANDY GRIFFITH SHOW" TIME SLOT CHART

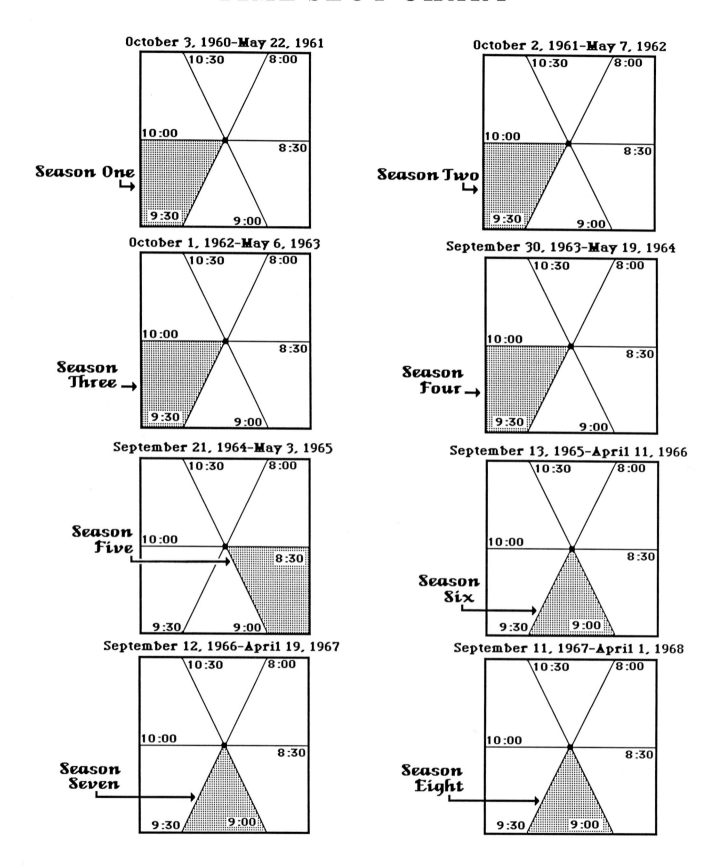

October 3, 1960-May 22, 1961

October 2, 1961-May 7, 1962

October 1, 1962-May 6, 1963

September 30, 1963-May 19, 1964

September 21, 1964-May 3, 1965

September 13, 1965-April 11, 1966

September 12, 1966-April 19, 1967

September 11, 1967-April 1, 1968

Season One
Season Two
Season Three
Season Four
Season Five
Season Six
Season Seven
Season Eight

A.C. NIELSEN RANKINGS
FOR "ANDY GRIFFITH" RELATED SHOWS
BROKEN DOWN BY YEAR, RANK & SEASON

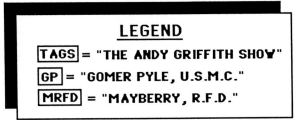

LEGEND

TAGS = "THE ANDY GRIFFITH SHOW"

GP = "GOMER PYLE, U.S.M.C."

MRFD = "MAYBERRY, R.F.D."

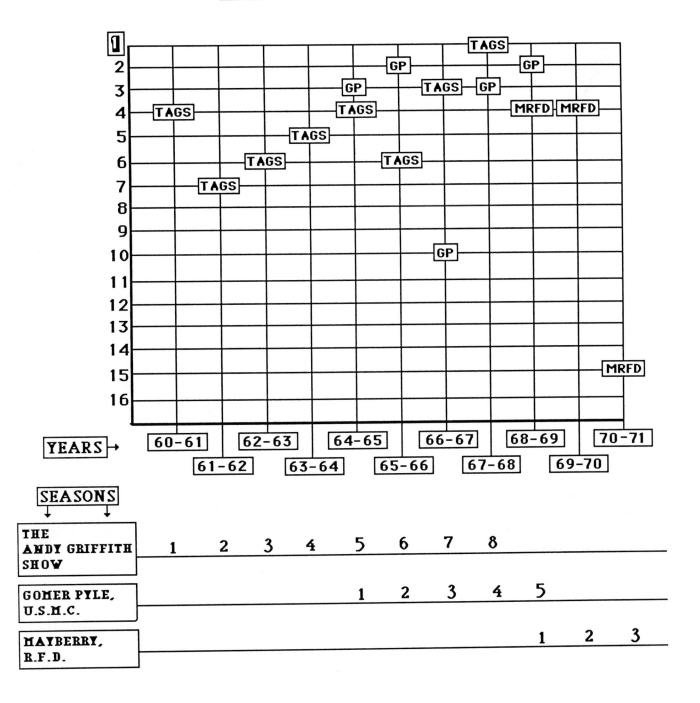

ANDY & THE EMMYS

"The Andy Griffith Show"
Emmy Awards & Nominations

1960-1961 Season

NOMINATIONS

"THE ANDY GRIFFITH SHOW"
Outstanding Program Achievement in the Field of Humor

DON KNOTTS
Outstanding Performance in a Supporting Role
by an Actor or Actress in a Series

WINS

DON KNOTTS
Outstanding Performance in a Supporting Role
by an Actor or Actress in a Series

———

1961-1962 Season

NOMINATIONS

"THE ANDY GRIFFITH SHOW"
Outstanding Program Achievement in the Field of Humor

DON KNOTTS
Outstanding Performance in a Supporting Role by an Actor

WINS

DON KNOTTS
Outstanding Performance in a Supporting Role by an Actor

———

1962-1963 Season

NOMINATIONS

DON KNOTTS
Outstanding Performance in a Supporting Role by an Actor

WINS

DON KNOTTS
Outstanding Performance in a Supporting Role by an Actor

1965-1966 Season

NOMINATIONS

DON KNOTTS in "The Return of Barney Fife"
Outstanding Performance by an Actor in a Supporting Role
in a Comedy

WINS

DON KNOTTS in "The Return of Barney Fife"
Outstanding Performance by an Actor in a Supporting Role
in a Comedy

———

1966-1967 Season

NOMINATIONS

"THE ANDY GRIFFITH SHOW"
Outstanding Comedy Series

DON KNOTTS in "Barney Comes to Mayberry"
Outstanding Performance by an Actor in a Supporting
Role in a Comedy

FRANCES BAVIER
Outstanding Performance by an Actress in a Supporting
Role in a Comedy

WINS

DON KNOTTS in "Barney Comes to Mayberry"
Outstanding Performance by an Actor in a Supporting
Role in a Comedy

FRANCES BAVIER
Outstanding Performance by an Actress in a Supporting
Role in a Comedy

WHAT A BUNCH OF CHARACTERS!

This section lists almost six hundred of the characters that walked the streets of Mayberry, along with the names of the actors or actresses that played them. This "census" should enable you to find just about any character that appeared in the show and also learn who the lucky thespian was that got to visit Mayberry.

The Actress—June Vincent
The Airport Clerk—Eddie Carroll
Al—Ross Elliot
Nettie Albright—Alberta Nelson
Alvin—Hollis Morrison
Ramona Anchram—Jackie Joseph
Teena Andrews—Diahn Williams
The Announcer—Jack Bannon
The Announcer—Steve Dunne
Arnie—Kenneth Butts
Arnold—Sheldon Golomb
Asa—Charles Thompson
Arnold Bailey—Sheldon Golomb Collins
Ronald Bailey—Bill Bixby
Detective Bardolli—Allan Melvin
Mrs. Barton—Mary Lou Taylor
Asa Bascomb—Charles Thompson
Ernest T. Bass—Howard Morris
Sam Becker—William Schallert
Miss Bedloe—Hope Summers
Tom Bedlowe—Sam Edwards
Ben Beecham—Dub Taylor
The Bellhop—Eddie Quillan
Bryan Bender—Gavin McCleod
Dr. Bennett—George Selk
Henry Bennett—John Qualen
Dr. Robert Benson—George Nader
Sam Benson—Burt Mustin
Myles Bentley—Jerome Guardino
Attorney Neil Bentley—Jay Novello
Bernice—Janet Stewart
Bernie the Furrier—Ronnie Schell
Betsy—Joy Ellison
Betty Ann—Betsy Hale
Clint Biggers—Roy Barcroft
Bill—Bob McQuain
Billy—John Bangert
Billy—John Reilly
Billy—Don Wyndham
Erma Bishop—Lillian Bronson
Eddie Blake—Herbie Faye
Pat Blake—Barbara Stuart
Miss Blanchard—Connie Sawyer
Mr. Bluett—Jason Johnson
Fred Boone—Jesse White
Jennie Boone—Claudia Bryar
Jean Boswell—Ruta Lee
Harry Bosworth—Byron Foulger

Trey Bowden—David A. Bailey
Boy #3—Chuck Campbell
Mr. Brady—Willis Bouchey
Emma Brand—Cheerio Meredith
Mr. Breckinridge—Ivan Bonar
Asa Breeny—Charles P. Thompson
Mrs. Briggs—Diane Deininger
Mr. Bronson—Larry Thor
Ellen Brown—Barbara Eden
David Browne—Buddy Ebsen
Bruce—Kenneth Butts
Roger Bryant—Keith Andes
Karen Burgess—Ronda Jeter
Burt/Jud—Burt Mustin
Burt the Crewman—Burt Taylor
Gentleman Dan Caldwell—Dan Tobin
Mr. Calvin—Dick Johnstone
Otis Campbell—Hal Smith
Ralph Campbell—Stanley Adams
Rita Campbell—Dorothy Neumann
Verline Campbell—Dorothy Neumann
John Canfield—Charles Ruggles
Ella Carson—Ruth Thom
Harold Carson—Chet Stratton
Hannah Carter—Tammy Windsor
Mr. Carter—Willis Bouchey
Sgt. Vince Carter—Frank Sutton
Ralph Case—Tod Andrews
Charlie—Billy Halop
Frank Chase—Vaughn Taylor
The Chauffeur—Thom Carney
The Checker Player—William Chalee
Emmett Clark—Paul Hartman
Martha Clark—Mary Lansing
Miss Clark—Luana Anders
Mr. Clark—Herbie Faye
The Clerk—Peter Madsen
Clete—Ralph Rose
Clifford—Jim Kidwell
Mr. Clifford—Michael Higgins
Mr. Coefield—James O'Rear
Floyd Colby—Howard McNear
The Conductor—Roy Engel
Naomi Connors—Jane Dulo
Flip Conroy—Rockne Tarrington
A.J. Considine—Hayden Rourke
Corlis—Pam Ferdin
The Counterboy—Don Sturdy
The Counterman—Charles Smith
Cousin Virgil—Michael J. Pollard
Mrs. Crane—Monty Magretts
Judge Cranston—Rhys Williams
Mr. Crawford—Robert F. Simon
Tracy Crawford—Jack Mann
Lydia Crosswaithe—Josie Lloyd
Elizabeth Crowley—Jean Hagen
Mr. Crowley—Burt Mustin
Helen Crump—Aneta Corsaut
The Customer—Carol Veazie
Cynthia—Mary Ann Durkin
Daphne—Jean Carson
Briscoe Darling—Denver Pyle

Charlene Darling—Margaret Ann (Maggie)
   Peterson
The Darling Boys—The Dillards
Darryl—Jim Connell
Sheldon Davis—Jay Novello
Mrs. Dennis—Ohola Nesmith
Captain Dewhurst—Richard X. Slattery
The District Attorney—Tom Palmer
Mr. Doakes—Norris Goff
Doris—Maggie Peterson
Dorothy—Mary Lansing
Attorney Lee Drake—Whitney Blake
The Driver—Tol Avery
The Driver—Douglas McCairn
Duane—James Brewer
Clarence Earp—Richard Jury
Edna—Christine Burke
Uncle Edward—Emory Parnell
Bertha Edwards—Hope Summers
Clara Edwards—Hope Summers
Ella—Ann Morgan Guilbert
Ella—Ruth Thom
Elmo—Vince Barnett
Estelle—Cynthia Hull
Ethel—Ronda Jeter
Irene Fairchild—Nina Shipman
Mrs. Farley—Penny Kunard
Warren Ferguson—Jack Burns
Mr. Fields—Pat O'Malley
Barney Fife—Don Knotts
Mrs. Fife—Lillian Culver
Arnold Finch—James Milhollin
Wilbur Finch—Jack Finch
First Character—Tom Steele
First Trooper—James Seay
Bobby Fleet—Henry Slate
Fletch—Willis Bouchey
Jud Fletcher—Burt Mustin
Mrs. Fletcher—Almira Sessions
Floss—Barbara Perry
Flossie—Sylvia Lewis
George Foley—Pat Rosson
Mr. Foley—Frank Ferguson
Karen Folker—Ronda Jeter
Jubell Foster—Everett Sloane
Mrs. Foster—Irene Tedrow
Willard Foster—Robert Emhardt
Frank—George Spence
Frankie—Robert Carricart
Mr. Franklin—Tod Andrews
Fred—Sam Edwards
Fred—Joe Turkell
Mr. Frisby—Charles Lane
Mr. Garland—Jack Nicholson
Mrs. Garland—Jamie Kelly
The Gateman—Herb Vigran
George—Bob Becker
George—Bo Hopkins
George the TV Repairman—Howard Morris
Gerald—Ted Jordan
Dr. Edith Gibson—Nancy Malone
Fred Gibson—Pat Hingle

Mr. Giddings—Richard Collier
Mr. Gilbert the Prosecutor—Henry Beckman
The Girl—Terri Garr
The Girl—Yvonne Shubert
The Girl—Sue Taylor
Mr. Glendon—Ward Ramsey
Gloria—Jan Shutan
Fred Goss—Fred Sherman
Mary Grace Gossage—Mary Grace Canfield
Mr. Granger—Richard Chambers
Madeline Grayson—Doris Dowling
Harold Grigsby—Kelly Thordsen
Sue Grigsby—Vici Raaf
Grover—Don Keefer
Mr. Hammond—Owen Bush
Mr. Hampton—Leon Ames
Governor George C. Handley—J. Edward McKinley
Hank—Norm Alden
Aunt Hannah—Ida Mae MacKenzie
Roger Hanover—Wallace Ford
Harlan—Joe di Reda
Alice Harper—Joanna McNeil
Harriet—Christine Burke
Harry—Dave Ketchum
Harry—James McCallion
Harry—Don Sturdy
Harvey—Anthony Jochim
Allen Harvey—George Ives
Colonel Harvey—John Dehner
Keevy Hazleton—Jesse Pearson
Mr. Heathcote—William Christopher
Evan Hendricks—Bobby Diamond
Orville Hendricks—Woodrow Chamblis
Sid Hickox—Sid Hickox
Hilda Mae—Florence MacMichael
Warden Hix—Harry Holcomb
George Hollander—Sandy Kenyon
Laura Hollander—Joyce Van Patten
Bill Hollenback—Dick Curtis
Hollis—Michael Freeman
Mrs. Hollister—Isabel Randolph
Rafe Hollister—Jack Prince
Homer—Chuck Brummit
The Hotel Clerk—Natividad Vacio
Howard—Joey Scott
Millie Hutchins—Arlene Golonka
Mr. Hutchins—Steve Pendleton
Mrs. Hutchins—Elizabeth Harrower
Mr. Izamoto—Yuki Shimoda
Jack—Robert Carnes
Jack—Lloyd Kino
Brian Jackson—Dale McKennon
Mr. Jackson—Richard Bull
Mrs. Jackson—Janet Stewart
Sheriff Jackson—Wally Engelhardt
Gilbert Jamel—Gavin McCleod
Johnny Paul Jason—Richard Keith
Mr. Jason—Owen Bush
Mrs. Jeffreys—Kay Stewart
Jenkins—Charles Horvath
Jenkins—Hollis Morrison
Ed Jenkins—Jack Dodson

Marvin Jenkins—Jack Nicholson
Jesse—Gary Chase
Joe—Rob Reiner
Joey—Kirk Travis
John—Justin Smith
Johnny—Dennis Bradshaw
Clara Johnson—Hope Summers
Mr. Johnston—Vernon Rich
Jones—Don Gazzaniga
George Jones—Roger Perry
Mike Jones—Buddy Foster
Sam Jones—Ken Berry
Joy/Phoebe—Kay Ann Kemper
Jud—Burt Mustin
Judd—Burt Mustin
The Judge—Warren Parker
Juror—Alan Dexter
Juror—Frederic Downs
Juror—Emory Parnell
Jury Foreman—Tol Avery
Kelly—Harry Arnie
Mr. Keyes—Jim Begg
Tillie Kincaid—Maxine Semon
Ralph Kingsley—Milton Frome
Eva Kryger—Eva Kryger
La Farona—Argentina Brunetti
Mrs. Edna Larch—Maudie Prickett
Mrs. Larch—Carol Veazie
Larry—Charles Dierkop
Andrew Paul Lawson—Andy Griffith
Floyd Lawson—Howard McNear
Charlie Lee—Keye Luke
Mrs. LeGrande—Jesslyn Fax
Reverend Leighton—Ian Wolfe
Leon—Clint Howard
Myrt Lesh—Ellen Corby
Bill Lindsay—Richard Bull
Jim Lindsey—James Best
Mr. Lockridge—Peter Hobbs
Lou—Gil Lamb
Lou—James McCallion
Lowell—Raymond Kark
Luke—Frank Cady
Mac—John McLiam
Mac/Max—Bill McLean
Mr. McBeevee—Karl Swenson
Mr. McCabe—Paul Fix
Sharon McCall—Ronda Jeter
Peggy McMillan—Joanna Moore
The Maid—Monty Magretts
Flora Mallerby—Alberta Nelson
The Man—David Azar
The Man—Jim Begg
The Man—Sam Green
The Man—Edgar Hess
The Man—Tom Jacobs
The Man—Jason Johnson
The Man—Sir Lancelot
The Man—George Sawaya
Man #1—Stanley Farrar
Man #2—Johnny Coons
The Man on the Train—Ollie O'Toole

The Manager—Herbie Faye
The Manicurist—Patty Regan
Martha—Candace Howard
Martha—Mary Lansing
Martha—Janet Stewart
Jim Martin—Ronnie Schell
Reverend Martin—William Keene
Mary—Mary Lansing
Darlene Mason—Ruta Lee
Ralph Mason—Casey Adams
John Masters—Olan Soule
Mr. Maxwell—Hugh Marlowe
Peggy McMillan—Joanna Moore
Bill Medwin—Herb Vigran
Mr. Meldrim—Warren Parker
Mrs. Mendlebright—Enid Markey
Malcolm Merriweather—Bernard Fox
Fred Michaels—David Ketchum
Pat Michaels—Sid Melton
Bert Miller—Sterling Holloway
Jerry Miller—Jerry Van Dyke
Trooper Leroy Miller—Roy Jenson
Newton Monroe—Don Rickles
Karen Moore—Gail Davis
Jess Morgan—Roy Engel
The Morrison Sisters—Charity Grace & Gladys
    Hurlburt
Bess Muggins—Margaret Kerry
Jim Muggins—Sam Edwards
Mr. Mundt—Forrest Lewis
Murillos—Vito Scotti
Myra—Amzie Strickland
Myrtle—Ruth Thoms
Ralph Neal—Arthur Batanides
Mavis Neff—Elaine Joyce
Neil—Allan Melvin
Jeff Nelson—Hamilton Camp
Avery Noonan—Ted White
Nora—Maudie Prickett
Miss Oakley—Sari Price
The Old Geezer—Burt Mustin
Oldfield—Robert Ball
Ollie—James Westerfield
Charlie O'Malley—Willis Bouchey
Agnes Jean Parker—Margaret Teele
Betty Parker—Elizabeth MacRae
Henny Parker—Richard Chambers
Leroy Parker—Gene Rutherford
Ma Parker—Betty Kean
Tommy Parker—Scott Lane
The Pastor—William Keene
Mrs. Pendleton—Ruth McDevitt
Mr. Perkins—Roy Engel
Pete—Lewis Charles
Pete—Ronny Dapo
Maggie Peters—Ruth Thom
Peterson—Charles Horvath
Peterson—Peter Madsen
Peterson/Wormser—Colin Male
Dr. Thomas Peterson—William Christopher
Uncle Phil—Robert B. Williams
Carl Phillips—Don Keefer

The Photographer—Sam Reese
Josephine Pike—Josie Lloyd
Juanita Pike—Josie Lloyd
Mayor Pike—Dick Elliot
Wilbur Pine—Frank Ferguson
Clyde Plaunt—Allan Melvin
Fred Plummer—Allan Melvin
Alpha Porter—Ceil Cabot
Sharon Porter—Ronda Jeter
Eleanora Poultice—Reta Shaw
Miss Primrose—Mary Lansing
The Prisoner of Love—Susan Oliver
The Proprietor—Harry Dean Stanton
Howard Pruitt—Joey Scott
Howie Pruitt—Dennis Rush
Jeff Pruitt—Alan Hale
Purvis—Arthur Malet
Gomer Pyle—Jim Nabors
Goober Pyle—George Lindsey
Luke Rainer—Jack Prince
The Relief Bus Driver—Robert Nichols
Renee—Patty Regan
Mrs. Rigsby—Mary Jackson
Parnell Rigsby—Jon Lormer
Doc Roberts—Charles Thompson
Mr. Roberts—Bartlett Robinson
Harlan Robinson—Woodrow Chamblis
Roger—Billy Booth
Bob Rogers—Mark Miller
Inspector Rogers—Ken Lynch
Rose—Mary Treen
Miss Rosemary—Amzie Strickland
Miss Roundtree—Mary Lansing
Rudy—Pitt Herbert
Mr. Ruskin—Alan Oppenheimer
Ruth—Claudia Bryar
Sabella—Francesca Bellini
Professor Hubert St. John—Edward Andrews
The Salesman—Jack Good
The Salesman—Alvy Moore
Sally—Jean Carson
Sam—Ray Lanier
Sam—Robert B. Williams
Bob Saunders—Marc London
Violet Rose Schumaker—Maggie Magennis
Helen Scoby—Margaret Kerry
Lester Scoby—Sam Edwards
Mary Scoby—Joy Ellison
Sebastian—Mark Brown
Second Character—Bill Catching
Second Trooper—Brad Trumbull
Sergeant—Mike Steen
Sharon—Ronda Jeter
Sheldon—Terry Dickinson
The Shopkeeper—Jose Gonzalez-Gonzalez
The Shoplifter—Lurene Tuttle
Annabelle Silby—Lurene Tuttle
Tom Silby—Stu Erwin
Lila Simms—Amzie Strickland
Mary Simpson—Julie Adams
Mary Simpson—Sue Ann Langdon
Walt Simpson—Tom Tully

Skip—Lee Van Cleef
Skippy—Joyce Jameson
Jim Slater—Bert Remsen
Frank Smith—Charles Aidman
Mr. Smith—Arthur Hansen
Mr. Somerset—Robert Cornthwaite
Howard Sprague—Jack Dodson
Mrs. Sprague—Mabel Albertson
The Stage Manager—Richard Poston
The State Trooper—Troy Melton
Stella—Sally Mansfield
Mr. Stevens—Jackie Coogan
The Stewardess—Yvonne Lime
Mayor Roy Stoner—Parley Baer
Tom Strongbow—Norm Alden
Roy Swanson—Noam Pitlik
Sylvio/Grecos—Jamie Farr
Cyrus Tankersley—George Cisar
Mrs. Tarbochs—Mary Lansing
Andy Taylor—Andy Griffith
Aunt Bee Taylor—Frances Bavier
Bradford J. Taylor—Jack Albertson
Opie Taylor—Ronny Howard
Rose Temple—Hallene Hill
Thelma Lou—Betty Lynn
Farley Thurston—Lyle Latell
Tillie—Maxine Semon
Tim—Johnny Jenson
Colonel Tim—Dick Haynes
Tommy—Michael Petit
Mr. Tracy—Peter Hobbs
The Truck Driver—Andrew Duncan
Reverend Hobart Tucker—William Keene
Malcolm Tucker—Robert Emhardt
Myra Tucker—Amzie Strickland
Maude Tyler—Reta Shaw
Farley Upchurch—Frank Cady
Farley Upchurch—Clinton Sundberg
Mr. Vasilievich—Ben Astar
Mario Vincente—Gabrielle Tinti
Papa Vincente—Bruno della Santina
Sophia Vincente—Letitia Roman
The Violinist—Manuel Martin
Miss Vogel—Mary Jackson
The Waiter—Richard Poston
The Waiter—Freddy Roberto
Ellie Walker—Elinor Donahue
Fred Walker—Harry Antrim
Gilly Walker—Larry Hovis
Wally—Blackie Hunt
Wally—Norman Leavitt
Wally—Cliff Norton
Wary Willy the Hobo—Douglas Fowley
Charlene Darling Wash—Maggie Peterson
Dudley J. Wash—Bob Denver
Mr. Watkins—Iggie Wolfington
Emma Watson—Cheerio Meredith
Deputy Joe Watson—Buck Young
Ben Weaver—Tol Avery
Ben Weaver—Jason Johnson
Ben Weaver—Will Wright
Wes—Sam Greene

Henry Wheeler—Edgar Buchanan
Whitey—Dennis Rush
The Wife/Ella—Ruth Thom
Mrs. Wiley—Doris Packer
Doris Williams—Barbara Perry
Howie Williams—Dennis Rush
Mr. Williams—Harlan Warde
Wilson—Joe Leitch
Sheriff Blake Wilson—Ken Mayer

Mr. Wilson—Dick Ryan
Arnold Winkler—Ronnie Dapo
Simon Winkler—Harlan Warde
The Woman—Jean Inness
Woman #1—Virginia Sale
Woman #2—Edna M. Holland
The Young Girl—Coleen O'Sullivan
The Young Man—Jim Begg

ACTORS WITHOUT A NAME

The following list of actors and actresses consists of those lucky people who got to visit Mayberry, but who were never given names. The rule in weekly TV usually went like this: if an actor or an actress had a speaking part—no matter how small—they were to be given an on-screen credit. However, in many cases the part was so small that the writers didn't bother naming the character. The following character actors played their part in contributing to the greatness of Mayberry by being, perhaps, a man Andy talked to on Main Street, or a woman with whom Aunt Bee would exchange pleasantries outside of Foley's Market. They have been, and always shall be, our friends.

Yvonne Adrian
Frank Albertson
Tom Allen
Elvia Allman
Rachel Ames
Richard Angarola
Harry Antrim
R.G. Armstrong
Phil Arnold
Alice Backes
Paul Bakanas
Walter Baldwin
Trevor Bardette
Alex Barringer
Leslie Barringer
Fred Beir
Rodney Bell
Mike Brent
Robert Brubaker
Jerry Brutsche
Joan Carey
Thom Carney
Phil Chambers
Lewis Charles
Al Checco
George Cisar

Pat Coghlan
Pat Colby
The Country Boys
Ronnie Dapo
Terry Dickinson
Molly Dodd
Ralph Dumke
George Dunn
Herb Ellis
Roy Engel
William Erwin
Adoree Evans
Stanley Farrar
Frank Ferguson
Byron Folger
Dan Frazer
Robert Gallagher
Noreen Gammill
Leo Gordon
Dabbs Greer
Barbara Griffith
Billy Halop
Joe Hamilton
Elizabeth Harrower
Kathryn Hart
Wayne Heffley

Tom Browne Henry
Jonathan Hole
Dennis Holmes
Rance Howard
Hoke Howell
Arthur Hunnicut
Chubby Johnson
Claude Johnson
Warner Jones
Richard Keith
Sherwood Keith
Ray Kellogg
Rita Kenaston
Arthur Kendall
George Kennedy
Helen Kleeb
Lee Krieger
Jack Lambert
Hal Landon
Ray Lanier
Mary Lansing
William Lanteau
Donald Lawton
Ralph Leabow
Norman Leavitt
Grace Lenard
Frank Levya
David Lewis
Forrest Lewis
David Lipp
Donald Losby
Gail Lucas
Karl Lukas
Ken Lynch
Scott McCartor
Peggy McCay
Bob McQuain
Laurie Main
Sally Mansfield
Edris March
Flip Mark
Allan Melvin
Sally Mills
Byron Morrow

Burt Mustin
Charles Myers
Tom Myers
Dorothy Neumann
William Newell
Frank Osborne
Ruth Packard
Hank Patterson
Barbara Perry
George Petrie
Narney Phillips
Isabel Randolph
Alan Reed, Jr.
Carl Benton Reid
Mark Rodney
Jewel Rose
Michael Ross
Bing Russell
Eddie Ryder
Virginia Sale
Sherman Sanders
James Seay
Sara Seegar
Jack Shea
Fred Sherman
Orville Sherman
Johnny Silver
Joseph Sirota
Paul Smith
Mike Steen
William Eben Stephens
Rory Stevens
Tim Stevenson
Janet Stewart
Dub Taylor
Charles P. Thompson
Mary Treen
Kim Tyler
Richard Vath
Carol Veazie
Janet Waldo
Frank Warren
Doodles Weaver
Marlene Willis

MAYBERRY
CHARACTER FREQUENCY CHART
COVERING ALL EPISODES

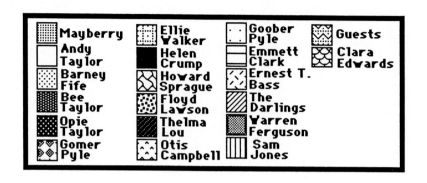

Legend:
- Mayberry
- Andy Taylor
- Barney Fife
- Bee Taylor
- Opie Taylor
- Gomer Pyle
- Ellie Walker
- Helen Crump
- Howard Sprague
- Floyd Lawson
- Thelma Lou
- Otis Campbell
- Goober Pyle
- Emmett Clark
- Ernest T. Bass
- The Darlings
- Warren Ferguson
- Sam Jones
- Guests
- Clara Edwards

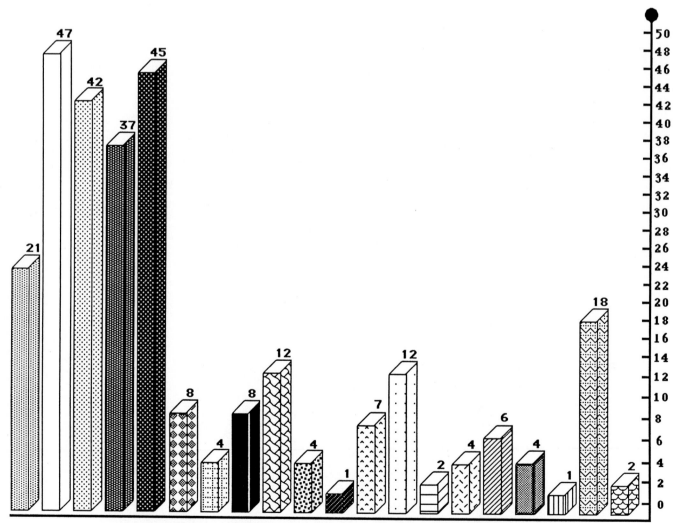

**COMPOSITE CHART OF ALL EIGHT SEASONS
BROKEN DOWN BY SUBJECT & NUMBER OF EPISODES**

CHARACTER FREQUENCIES
BROKEN DOWN BY SEASON

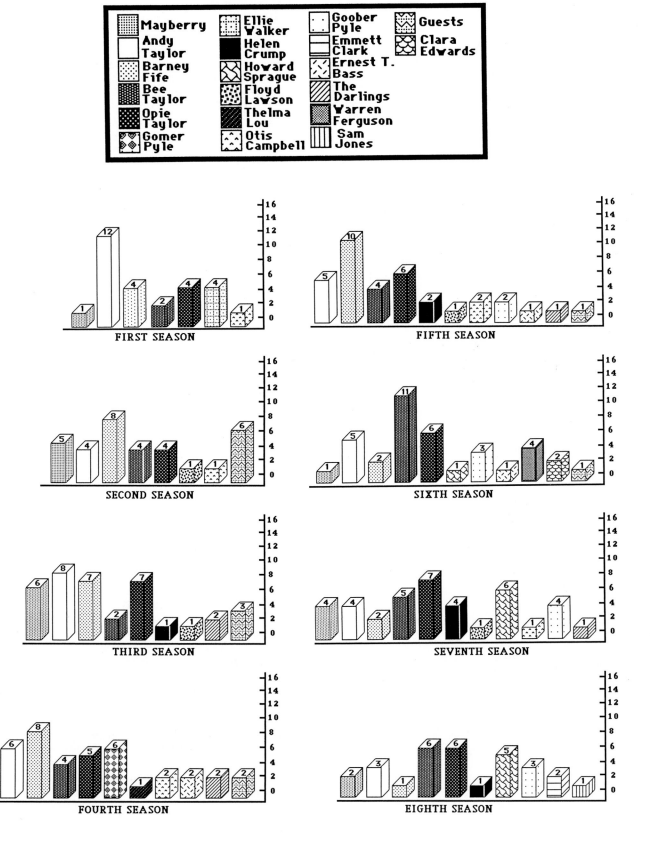

SAMPLE PRODUCTION CREDITS

Although each episode entry in the alphabetic section of *Mayberry, My Hometown* gives the credits for writers, directors, and actors involved, I felt it necessary to include at least a sampling of the complete production credits of "The Andy Griffith Show." No book that aspired to completeness can fail to recognize the talent and contributions of the individuals listed, many of whom remained with the show during its entire history. Rather than give the credits for each episode, or even for one episode per season, though, I decided that three key episodes would give an overall picture of who was involved on the production end of the series. The three episodes were not picked randomly, however. As representative sources for this information, I chose the following: the very first episode, "The New Housekeeper" (1F/B), to show who was working on the show in the early days; "The Rumor" (125F/124B), to show who was on the crew at exactly the midpoint of the series run; and, finally, "Mayberry, R.F.D." (241F/249B), the last episode broadcast, to let us see who was with the series in its final days. I hope this look at the "who's who" of the production end of the show will add to your visit to *Mayberry, My Hometown*. (Note: The order and layout of the credits is exactly as broadcast.)

The New Housekeeper   (1F/B)

Produced by Aaron Ruben
Music by Earle Hagen
Director of Photography. . . Sid Hickox, A.S.C.
Associate Producer. . . Richard O. Linke
Production Manager. . . Frank E. Myers
Supervising Editor. . . Joe Gluck, A.C.E.
Asst. to Producer. . . Ronald Jacobs
Assistant Director. . . Bruce Bilson
Production Supervisor. . .W. Argyle Nelson
Propmaster. . . Reggie Smith
Story Consultant: Aaron Ruben
Art Directors. . . Ralph Berger
                          Kenneth A. Reid
Set Decorator. . . Bob Priestley
Re-recording Editor. . . Robert Reeve
Wardrobe. . . Ann Helfgott
Makeup. . . Lee Greenway, S.M.A.
Sound Engineer. . . David Forrest
Recorded by. . . Glen Glenn Sound Co.
Executive Producer Sheldon Leonard in association with Danny Thomas
The Andy Griffith Show
A Mayberry Enterprises Production
Copyright 1960

The Rumor   (125F/124B)

Produced by Aaron Ruben
Associate Producer. . . Richard O. Linke
Music by Earle Hagen
Director of Photography. . . Sid Hickox, A.S.C.
Art Director. . . Kenneth A. Reid
Supervising Editor. . . Joe Gluck, A.C.E.
Set Decorator. . . Ken Swartz
Assistant Director. . . Robert Saunders
Assistant to Producer. . . Joel Swanson
Prop Master. . . Reggie Smith
Casting. . . Ruth Burch
ReRecording Editor. . . Richard LeGrand
Music Editor. . . Donn Cambern
Story Consultant. . . Aaron Ruben
Costumes. . . Robert Odell
Makeup. . . Lee Greenway, S.M.A.
Hair Stylist. . . Eva Kryger
Script Continuity. . . Dorothy Aldworth
Sound Engineer. . . David Forrest
Recorded by Glen Glenn Sound Co.
Automobiles Furnished by Ford Motor Co.
Executive Producer. . . Sheldon Leonard
In Association with Danny Thomas Enterprises
A Mayberry Enterprises Production
Copyright 1964

Mayberry, R.F.D.   (241F/249B)

Music by Earle Hagen
Editorial Supervisor. . . Jerry Jameson
Director of Photography. . . Sid Hickox, A.S.C.
Art Directors. . . Kenneth A. Reid
                          Howard Campbell
Film Editor. . . Tom Stevens
Set Decorator. . . Harry Gordon
Assistant Director. . . Robert Saunders
Prop Master. . . Reggie Smith
Casting. . . Fred Roos
Music Editor. . . Mark Southern
Sound Editor. . . Victor Guarnier
Costumes. . . Stan Kufel
Makeup. . . Lee Greenway, S.M.A.
Hair Stylist. . . Eva Kryger
Script Continuity. . . Rosemary Dorsey
Sound Engineer. . . E. Campbell
Recorded by. . . Glen Glenn Sound Co.
Automobiles Furnished by. . . Ford Motor Co.
Assistant to Producer. . . Joel Swanson
Construction Co-ordinator. . . Ideal Dottini
Executive Producer. . . Sheldon Leonard
In Association with Danny Thomas Enterprises
Production Supervisor. . . Ronald Jacobs
Production Manager. . . Edward M. Hillie
Filmed at Paramount Studios
The Andy Griffith Show
A Mayberry Enterprises Production
Copyright 1967

THE "COMMERCIAL ANDY"

In the fifities and sixties, it was common practice for corporate sponsors to be intimately involved with a television program. Unlike today, when sponsors buy commercial time by the minute and there are usually a great number of sponsors for each show, in the olden days of American television sponsors bought commercial time *by the show* and, in most situations, the stars of the show were contractually bound to appear in the commercials, hawking everything from automobiles to breakfast cereals.

"The Andy Griffith Show" was no different in this respect, and latter-day fans can only imagine what fun it must have been to see Andy, Barney, Opie, Aunt Bee, and everybody else in the cast selling shaving lotion and coffee while still in character as our favorite Mayberryites.

The following transcript is from a Post Toasties corn flakes commercial aired during the original run of the series. We don't know the actual broadcast date, but based on the appearance of the set and a stab at Opie's age, I estimate that the commercial probably aired in the second or third season. The commercial is in black and white, the phone in the kitchen is still the old fashioned "Sarah, get me the courthouse" type, and Opie looks around eight years old. Also, the back door of the house is still on the right hand wall of the kitchen, so the second or third season is probably a pretty good guess. The commercial starred Andy Griffith, Ronny Howard, and Frances Bavier, all in character as Andy, Opie, and Aunt Bee Taylor. It ran about forty seconds, and included a laugh track.

"The Andy Griffith Show" Post Toasties Corn Flakes Commercial

Scene: The Taylor kitchen, morning. Andy and Aunt Bee are sitting at the kitchen table, drinking coffee. Reading a book, Opie enters from the living room:
Andy Taylor: "Whatcha readin' Ope?"
Opie Taylor: "Magic from your bookcase, Paw."
Andy Taylor: "Oh?"
Opie Taylor: "Can you do any tricks?"
Andy Taylor: "Yeah, I'll show you. How would you like to have Post Toasties for breakfast?"
Opie Taylor: "Swell!"
Andy Taylor: "Cracklin' Fresh!" (Rips open an ear of corn that is filled with Post Toasties corn flakes. Opie is amazed.) "Post Toasties. Cracklin' with fresh corn flavor. So light they fairly float into the bowl."
Opie Taylor: (Excited.) "Did you see that, Aunt Bee?"
Aunt Bee: (Nodding and smiling.) "Uh, huh. A hundred times."
Opie Taylor: "How'd you do that, Paw?"
Andy Taylor: "Magic words!"
Opie Taylor: "Cracklin' Fresh!" (Rips open an ear of corn, but it's nothing but a plain old ear.) "Gee Whiz!" (Disappointed.)

Andy Taylor: (Pouring corn flakes into Opie's bowl.) "Guess you'll have to get yours out of the Post Toasties box, Ope." (Holding up the box of corn flakes.) "They're every bit as cracklin' fresh!"

More information about Mayberry, our hometown, from an unexpected source! From these forty seconds, we learn that Andy had at least one book on magic in his bookcase, that Aunt Bee had to sit through magic tricks at the breakfast table, and that Opie read at the breakfast table. We also learn that Aunt Bee didn't cook a hot breakfast every morning (there were only cereal dishes on the table) and that Opie loved corn flakes.

What a shame we can't see *all* the original commercials as they aired during the run of the series. What a goldmine of information about our hometown they must be!

THE FISHIN' HOLE

I

Well now, take down your fishin' pole
And meet me at the fishin' hole
We may not get a bite all day
But don't you rush away
What a great place to rest your bones
And mighty fine for skippin' stones
You'll feel fresh as lemonade
A settin' in the shade
Whether it's hot, whether it's cool
Oh what a spot
For whistlin' like a fool
What a fine day
To take a stroll
And wander by the Fishin' Hole
I can't think of a better way
To pass the time o' day

II

We'll have no need to call the roll
When we get to the Fishin' Hole
There'll be you, me and Old Dog Trey
To doodle time away
If we don't hook a perch or bass
We'll cool our toes in dewy grass
Or else pull up a weed to chaw
And maybe set and jaw
Hangin' around
Takin' our ease
Watchin' the hound
A-scratchin' at his fleas
Come on, take down your fishin' pole
And meet me at the Fishin' Hole
I can't think of a better way
To pass the time o' day

Mayberry
My Hometown

Part II
The Mayberry Encyclopedia:
From "A1A" to "Zone Detection System"

MY HOMETOWN

"My hometown
Is the greatest place I know.
Where the neighbors I find
Are gentle and kind
And the living is easy and slow.
My hometown
Is the only place to be.
Here the worries are small
And the kids grow tall and strong
And healthy and free...
It's my hometown,
My hometown,
Mayberry, Mayberry."

Bee Taylor & Clara Edwards
"A Singer In Town"

STAYING ALIVE
IN MAYBERRY

I will never forget the day I walked into a Waldenbooks in downtown New Haven and first saw Richard Kelly's book. Richard Kelly is the author of the book which is likely to stand for a long, long time as the definitive look at the making of "The Andy Griffith Show." Appropriately, the book is called *The Andy Griffith Show* and it was published by John F. Blair in 1981. A revised and expanded edition was issued in 1984. Richard Kelly is a professor of English at the University of Tennessee and is a prolific, literate writer. I asked Dr. Kelly to write something for *Mayberry, My Hometown* and the following essay is the result. "Staying Alive in Mayberry" examines the power that a fully realized fantasy landscape can have on the reader/viewer. As Richard says, "To visit Mayberry is, in a sense, to live forever." My sincere thanks and appreciation go to Richard Kelly for his willingness to participate in my ode to Mayberry. He and I are in agreement that the characters of the show—that is, the residents of Mayberry—are, as he says in "Staying Alive in Mayberry," "immortal." Thanks, Richard. You and I share the same hometown!—**Steve Spignesi**

As the ancient quotation says, art is long and life is brief. Growing old, moving steadily away from our childhood dreams, can be a disturbing process. Over the centuries people have tried every imaginable way—from embalming to plastic surgery—to slow down the ruthless tide of the sun, the inevitable decay of the flesh. Our awareness of death has lead to the creation of complex mythologies to give shape and meaning to our otherwise absurd lives. One of the most powerful and magical potions we have come up with to sustain us in this relentless march into darkness has been fantasy. Works as diverse as *The Adventures of Sherlock Holmes, Alice's Adventures in Wonderland, A Christmas Carol,* and "The Andy Griffith Show" all share—in varying degrees of complexity—a common thread out of which they weave a unique, imaginative, and unchanging world.

To visit Mayberry is, in a sense, to live forever. The people there are frozen in time: Floyd in his barbershop dreaming of opening a three-chair shop in Mount Pilot, Andy and Barney on a front porch relaxing after a satisfying dinner, and Ernest T. seeking the perfect woman to take back to his world of possums and goats. Stability lies at the heart of the fantasy here. The town and its people must stay the same. If they change, then we become aware of time and how we, too, are being swept down the same river.

One of the greatest stabilizing forces in Mayberry is the structure of the town itself. Despite Aunt Bee and Ellie Walker, Mayberry is a patriarchal village and wants to stay that way. There is never any doubt who is in charge: Sheriff Taylor. Whenever Aunt Bee ventures out of the kitchen, she gets clobbered (once by Howard Sprague in an election for city council and once when she attempts to open a Chinese restaurant and demonstrates her lack of a business sense). True, Ellie got elected as a councilwoman, but she only lasted on the show for a year. When Helen Crump came

along, Sheriff Taylor could relax, and so could a conservative town whose hierarchy was threatened by feminine independence.

Sheldon Leonard, Aaron Ruben, Andy Griffith, and others maintained this immaculate fantasy for eight years. Once the characters and the town were established, they remained the same, far removed from the real world. The real world at this time (1960-1968) included such goings on as the Vietnam War, race riots, militant student unrest, and the space program. As pure and isolated from its day as the paintings of Norman Rockwell, "The Andy Griffith Show" went far beyond the removal of current events from its scripts. In Mayberry, there is no sex, violence, serious disease, believable death, hatred, lust, or any of the other ills of most societies. And this is precisely the way a fantasy ought to operate. The genius of the writers, producers, and actors was that they were able to create and sustain for many years a complex fantasy that convinced people that this is the way the world once was. After all, most of us have aunts, know or know about sheriffs and deputies, children, town drunks, and all of the other features of small town life.

Through a wonderful process of selective forgetting, however, most of us manage to filter out the unpleasant realities of the past and construct for ourselves a dream version of days gone by. Currier and Ives engravings, old photograph albums, Norman Rockwell drawings are able to capture the same sort of idealized pasts for us. No show in the history of television, however, has so successfully mastered the art of nostalgia and created an imaginative role model of an ideal society as "The Andy Griffith Show." The adolescent attempt in the recent past to find a town in North Carolina willing to change its name to Mayberry shows a fundamental misunderstanding of the show's magical structure.

The episode in which Barney returns to Mayberry for a high school reunion and discovers that his old girlfriend, Thelma Lou, has gotten married also demonstrated a failure to work within the established fantasy structure. This segment is unique in that it seriously damaged the sense of stability the show built up over the years. If Barney can lose his girl, then, it seems, almost anything can happen—and the warm sense of Mayberry's security cools down. The "Return to Mayberry" TV special attempted to restore that lost harmony by allowing Barney to marry Thelma Lou. The death of Aunt Bee, however, brought a sad note of realism into the "Return."

In the pilot episode for the series, "Danny Thomas Meets Andy Griffith," the writer and producers faced the subject of death right off. About the size of a pumpkin, Opie comes running into the courthouse in tears. He explains to his father than his pet turtle got stepped on by a woman in the drugstore. When he demands that his turtle be brought back to life, Andy tries to explain the impossibility: "When your Ma died, I didn't get another Ma." Opie stops crying for a moment, looks puzzled, and asks, "Who stepped on Ma?" A wonderfully human and comic exchange, and one that allows us to see death from the simple perspective of a child who has not yet left fantasyland.

Years later, the episode "Opie the Birdman" again brought up the subject of death. Opie accidentally kills a mother bird with his slingshot. Instead of giving him a whipping, Andy opens the boy's bedroom window so that he can hear the baby birds "chirping for their mama that's not coming back." This segment was a risky one for a comedy series because it came dangerously close to reminding us of unpleasant realities. The magic of Mayberry, however, comes through as the boy takes on the responsibility of raising the three baby birds (named Wynken, Blynken, and Nod)—with some help from Barney, who claims to understand their language—and then releases them back to nature. There may have been a death, but the story is about resurrection of new life, and it is definitely upbeat.

The focus of Mayberry is always upon life in its simplest and most affable form. The town sparkles with energy, love, and eternal youth. Perhaps it is best to allow it to remain forever what it was in our first mind, in that far away world where all the complex shades of reality were reduced to black and white, a world built around a father, his son and aunt, his friends and neighbors, a world where getting a haircut or going on a picnic was a notable event. The safest return to Mayberry is through the old episodes, where Aunt Bee is still making her pickles, Floyd is still evening up someone's sideburns, and Andy and Barney are still drowsing on the Taylors' front porch. Those characters will never age: they are immortal, and whenever we join in their company we share, for a brief moment, their extraordinary longevity.

Richard Kelly
Knoxville, Tennessee
1986

A1A (76F/78B) The governor's license plate number.

ABLE, BAKER AND CHARLIE (68F/70B) Investigator Upchurch assumed three men stole Tate Fletcher's cow. He named them Able, Baker and Charlie.

"ACCIDENTAL INJURY OCCURRING ON COUNTY PROPERTY" (141F/142B) The form Barney made Otis fill out when Otis tripped and fell in the courthouse.

"ACE" (222F/225B) Nickname Clyde Plaunt gave to Howard Sprague.

ACME GASOLINE (102F/B) (119F/118B) (199F/196B) Brand sold at Wally's Service Station.

JOHNNY ADAMS (195F/193B) A member of the Mt. Pilot Comets softball team.

"ADVENTURE SLEEPING" (77F/79B) An ironing board between two chairs. Opie would have to "adventure sleep" if Malcolm Tucker stayed overnight in the Taylor house.

AFGHAN (123F/122B) Barney planned on crocheting Andy an afghan with the state colors and "Bless This House" across the front. He learned to crochet by watching his mother.

"AG" (211F/207B) The name Barney called Agnes Jean Parker.

"THE AGE OF MIRACLES" (120F/119B) Andy told Opie that's where they were living.

AGNES JEAN (216F/B) Baton twirler who preceded Howard Sprague on "Colonel Tim's Talent Time" amateur show.

REVEREND AIKEN (17F/B) Minister in earlier episodes, mentioned by Barney as a possible deputy for the still raid in "Alcohol and Old Lace."

AIR CONDITIONER, NEW STOVE, COLOR TV, STEREO PHONOGRAPH (39F/36B) The things Frank Meyers planned on ordering when he thought he was going to collect on his hundred-year-old Town of Mayberry bond.

AIR FRESHENER AND ANTACID TABLETS (176F/B) The two necessities Aunt Bee had to buy when she heard that Barney was coming back to Mayberry for a class reunion.

RED AKINS (136F/B) Sixteen-year-old writer of the "Mayberry After Midnight" column in the "Mayberry Gazette."

VIDA AKINS (130F/132B) Bee got a letter postmarked from Raleigh and guessed it was from Vida.

AKRON, OHIO (227F/222B) Emmett once went there for a radio company maintenance class. According to Emmett, Akron was "wide open."

AL (50F/B) State investigator Horton's partner.

AL (68F/69B) (123F/122B) Daphne's boyfriend. Andy had a fight with him in 68F/69B. In 123F/122B, Skippy called Al "a bum."

AL (74F/B) One of the "convicts at large" said Barney reminded her of "Al at the old Cascade Club" in Toledo because Barney had the "same dumb face, weak chin, round shoulders." All the cons—and Floyd—called Barney "Al" from then on.

AL (80F/B) Driver of Raleigh Bus #78. He noticed Luke Comstock getting off the bus carrying a shotgun case.

AL (112F/111B) One of the World War I vets in Mayberry.

AL'S POULTRY HEADQUARTERS (77F/79B) The site of chicken burglaries, all of which were perpetrated by Buzz Jenkins.

ALASKA (226F/223B) Goober told Lee Drake that Andy went to Alaska.

BEULAH ALBRIGHT (230F/229B) Lady friend of Bee and Clara. It wasn't said if she or her son, Harold, were related to Nettie.

HAROLD ALBRIGHT (230F/229B) Son of Beulah. He saw Bee and Professor St. John at Myer's Lake.

NETTIE ALBRIGHT (176F/B) Classmate of Barney's. She was always hooked on the deputy. She was a tall blonde, and she was able to take his mind off his misery after he heard that Thelma Lou had gotten married.

THE ALBRIGHTS (185F/B) Howard Sprague and his mother played bridge with them.

ALCOHOL AND OLD LACE 17th episode filmed and broadcast. Original broadcast date was January 30, 1961. It was written by Charles Stewart and Jack Elinson, and directed by Gene Reynolds. Regulars included Andy Griffith, Don Knotts, Howard McNear, and Hal Smith as Otis. Guests included Jack Prince, Thom Carney, and Gladys Hurlburt and Charity Grace as the Morrison sisters.

"ALICE" (138F/B) The part Bee played in a church play called "The Little Prince," many years ago.

ALL SOULS CHURCH (100F/99B) Andy's, Bee's, Barney's, Opie's, Clara's, and Goober's church, presided over by the Reverend Hobart M. Tucker, D.D.

SAM ALLEN (26F/B) State inspector and a friend of Andy's. Whenever the state scheduled an inspection of the Mayberry jail, Sam and Andy went fishing or hunting. On Otis's birthday, the state sent Ralph Case—a real "by-the-book" guy—instead of Sam.

AN "ALLIGATOR FARM IN FLORIDA" (115F/114B) The place Barney thought Otis might have gone with the money he saved from working his night job.

ALLSPICE (43F/B) Clara used it in her pickle brine.

ALMA (203F/201B) Lady friend of Bee and Clara, she served as entry clerk at the Mayberry Garden Club flower show.

ALMA SWARTHOUSE SUNSET PINK (203F/201B) Rose variety Bee cross-pollinated with a "Mrs. Pinckney Variegated Red" to create her "Deep Pink Ecstasy."

ALTOONA (3F/B) The town the one-man band came from. Andy recalled him: "Wadn't that the fella that got all mixed up and come durn near poppin' his eyes out and blowin' through the wrong end of a clarinet?"

ALUMINUM SIDING (35F/B) Rafe Peterson, the attorney, was now selling it.

ALVIN (71F/72B) Man Andy said "Hi" to while waiting for Floyd to open.

ALVIN (232F/233B) Goober hit him while driving the squad car.

AMALGAMATED MOTORS (242F/241B) The company for which Roy Swanson pretended to work. He said he was a Senior Vice President in Charge of Engineering.

AMALGAMATED OXIDATION & ALUMINUM CORPORATION OF AMERICA (80F/B) Barney's stock. He owned one-eighth of a share with Floyd, Wally, and some of the boys. In 80F/B, the company sent him a twenty-seven cent dividend.

AMANDA (92F/B) One of the potential "wives for Andy" that Barney sent over to Andy's house.

AMBER ALERT (99F/98B) A Number 2 Alert: either Andy or Barney awake at all times.

JEREMY AMBROSE (69F/66B) Infant son of Mrs. Ambrose. Barney sometimes baby-sat with him while his mother shopped.

MRS. AMBROSE (69F/66B) Woman who dropped off her infant son, Jeremy, at the courthouse so Barney could watch him while she shopped. This upset the then new Mayor Stoner.

AMERICAN HISTORY (196F/203B) The course Andy took with Helen, Howard, Goober and Floyd in an adult education class.

CINDY AMES (153F/B) Classmate of Opie's. Cindy didn't invite her best friend, Diana, to her birthday party.

AMMONIA (43F/B) Aunt Bee's marmalade tasted like it.

AMUSING TALES OF TINY TOTS (213F/B) Children's book written by Helen Crump. The book was published by Bryant Publishing Co. of Richmond, Virginia, with Roger Bryant as editor/publisher. Robling Flask was the cover designer, and Harold Mosley, the promotion director. The book was published under the pseudonym Helene Alexian Dubois.

RAMONA ANCHRAM (113F/112B) Young woman who seemed to be "under the wing" of Mrs. Wiley. She and Ernest T. Bass hit it off at one of Mrs. Wiley's singles dances. She was the granddaughter of Rotten Ray Anchram.

ROTTEN RAY ANCHRAM (113F/112B) Grandfather of Ramona. He came down from the hills in 1870 and burned down Mayberry.

ANCHRAM CHARCOAL COMPANY (113F/112B) Company founded by Rotten Ray Anchram (grandfather of Ramona) after he came down from the hills in 1870 and burned down Mayberry.

ANDELINA (139F/B) Daughter of Charlene Darling Wash and Dudley J. Wash. She was named for Andy. The Darlings brought her to Mayberry to betroth her to Opie. Her dowry was an eight-by-ten cottage on the back twenty (it only needed a roof and some fresh mud on the floor); the cottage came with a cow and two acres of side hill with good strong boulders.

"BIG JACK" ANDERSON (98F/97B) Moonshiner who, with Otis, ran a still in the Old Rimshaw Place.

DR. ANDERSON (190F/B) He told Bee to keep foreign objects out of the eye.

ANDRE KOSTALANEZ MARCHERS (72F/71B) The cymbals Barney bought to play in the Mayberry Band. They cost $18.50. He bought them at Cymbal City. The cheaper pair were $14.50 (with leatherette).

"ANDREW TAYLOR—SHERIFF OF MAYBERRY" (171F/172B) Bee had business cards printed for Andy. Printed in green ink, Andy noted. The counterfeiters Kingsley and Finch—for whom Aunt Bee worked—did them for her.

DOC ANDREWS (87F/B) Mayberry physician who aggravated Bee by insisting on reminding her that she was "no spring chicken."

TEENA ANDREWS (212F/208B) The former Irene Flogg of Mayberry. She made it big in Hollywood as a movie star. Barney used to date her, and Andy went to school with her and helped her with her homework. Teena said she was Mayberry's "ugly duckling." When Barney came back to Mayberry for a two-week vacation after he "cracked" (with Andy's help) the supermarket robberies in Raleigh, it turned out that Teena was back in town for the premiere of her new movie. Her publicity man, Harold Carson, saw an interesting angle and asked Barney to escort Teena to the gala. Barney, of course, conjured up hopes of undying romance and eternal love, but once again his balloon was burst when he discovered Teena was engaged.

ANDY AND BARNEY IN THE BIG CITY 57th episode filmed and broadcast. Original broadcast date was March 26, 1962. It was written by Harvey Bullock, and directed by Bob Sweeney. Regulars included Andy Griffith, Don Knotts, Ronny Howard, and Frances Bavier. Guests included Allan Melvin as Detective Bardolli.

ANDY AND HELEN HAVE THEIR DAY 140th episode filmed and broadcast. Original broadcast date was December 14, 1964. It was written by Bill Idelson and Sam Bobrick, and directed by Howard Morris. Regulars included Andy Griffith, Don Knotts, Aneta Corsaut, George Lindsey, and Frances Bavier. Guests included Howard Morris as George, and Colin Male as Peterson, although in the credits Male's character was listed as "Wormser."

ANDY AND HELEN'S BEDROOM (125F/124B) When Barney thought that Andy and Helen were getting married (exactly 125 episodes too soon), he, Bee, and Thelma Lou decided to get everybody to chip in and do over Andy's room because they assumed that that's where Andy and Helen would be staying. They painted, wallpapered, put up new curtains, and bought a bed with a canopy. Thelma Lou explained the bed by mentioning Errol Flynn and Olivia DeHaviland in "The Dashing Prince." Barney called it "a bed with a fringe on top." He said it was "kissy-looking."

ANDY AND OPIE—BACHELORS 65th episode filmed and 67th episode broadcast. Original broadcast date was October 8, 1962. It was written by Jim Fritzell and Everett Greenbaum, and directed by Bob Sweeney. Regulars included Andy Griffith, Frances Bavier,

Ronny Howard, and Howard McNear. Guests included Joanna Moore as Peggy McMillan, and Ray Lanier.

ANDY AND OPIE, HOUSEKEEPERS 23rd episode filmed and broadcast. Original broadcast date was March 13, 1961. It was written by David Adler, and directed by Bob Sweeney. Regulars included Andy Griffith, Frances Bavier, and Ronny Howard. Guests included Hope Summers as Bertha Edwards, and Rory Stevens.

ANDY AND OPIE'S PAL 110th episode filmed and 109th episode broadcast. Original broadcast date was January 13, 1964. It was written by Harvey Bullock, and directed by Dick Crenna. Regulars included Andy Griffith, Ronny Howard, Don Knotts, and Jim Nabors. Guests included Richard Keith, Dennis Rush, and David A. Bailey as Trey Bowden.

ANDY AND THE GENTLEMAN CROOK 21st episode filmed and broadcast. Original broadcast date was February 27, 1961. It was written by Ben Gershman and Leo Solomon, and directed by Bob Sweeney. Regulars included Andy Griffith, Ronny Howard, Frances Bavier, and Hal Smith as Otis Campbell. Guests included Dan Tobin as Gentleman Dan Caldwell, and Mike Steen as the Sergeant.

ANDY AND THE NEW MAYOR 69th episode filmed and 66th episode broadcast. Original broadcast date was October 15, 1962. It was written by Harvey Bullock and Ray Allen Saffian. It was directed by Bob Sweeney. Regulars included Andy Griffith, Don Knotts, and Ronny Howard. Guests included Parley Baer as Mayor Stoner, Roy Engel as Jess Morgan, Helen Kleeb, and Janet Stewart.

ANDY AND THE WOMAN SPEEDER 35th episode filmed and broadcast. Original broadcast date was October 16, 1961. It was written by Jack Elinson and Charles Stewart, and directed by Bob Sweeney. Regulars included Andy Griffith, Frances Bavier, Ronny Howard, Don Knotts, and Howard McNear. Guests included Jean Hagen as Elizabeth Crowley, and Dick Elliot as Mayor Pike.

ANDY DISCOVERS AMERICA 86th episode filmed and broadcast. Original broadcast date was March 4, 1963. It was written by John Whedon, and directed by Bob Sweeney. Regulars included Andy Griffith, Ronny Howard, Don Knotts, and Frances Bavier. Guests included Aneta Corsaut (in her first appearance as Helen Crump), Joey Scott as Howard, Dennis Rush as Whitey, and Richard Keith as Johnny Paul Jason.

ANDY FORECLOSES 28th episode filmed and broadcast. Original broadcast date was April 24, 1961. It was written by Ben Gershman and Leo Solomon, and directed by Bob Sweeney. Regulars included Andy Griffith, Don Knotts, Ronny Howard, and Frances Bavier. Guests included Will Wright as Ben Weaver, Sam Edwards as Lester Scoby, Margaret Kerry as Helen Scoby, Hope Summers as Bertha, Bob McQuain as Bill, Joy Ellison as Mary Scoby, and Jack Prince.

"ANDY GUMP" (47F/B) Comic strip Barney read every week in the Sunday paper.

ANDY ON TRIAL 61st episode filmed and broadcast. Original broadcast date was April 23, 1962. It was written by Jack Elinson and Charles Stewart, and directed by Bob Sweeney. Regulars included Andy Griffith, Don Knotts, and Hal Smith as Otis. Guests included Ruta

Lee as Jean Boswell, Richard Vath, Robert Brubaker, Sally Mansfield, and Byron Morrow.

ANDY SAVES BARNEY'S MORALE 16th episode filmed and 20th episode broadcast. Original broadcast date was February 20, 1961. It was written by David Adler, and directed by Bob Sweeney. Regulars included Andy Griffith, Don Knotts, Francis Bavier, Ronny Howard, and Howard McNear. Guests included Hal Smith as Otis Campbell, Burt Mustin as Jud Fletcher, Florence MacMichael as Hilda Mae, and Dick Elliot as Mayor Pike.

ANDY SAVES GOMER 119th episode filmed and 118th episode broadcast. Original broadcast date was March 16, 1964. It was written by Harvey Bullock, and directed by Jeffrey Hayden. Regulars included Andy Griffith, Ronny Howard, Frances Bavier, and Howard McNear. Guests included Jim Nabors as Gomer Pyle.

ANDY, THE MARRIAGE COUNSELOR 18th episode filmed and broadcast. Original broadcast date was February 6, 1961. It was written by David Adler, and directed by Gene Reynolds. Regulars included Andy Griffith, Don Knotts, Frances Bavier, and Ronny Howard. Guests included Jesse White as Fred Boone, Claudia Bryar as Jennie Boone, Forrest Lewis, Norman Leavitt, and Tim Stevenson.

ANDY THE MATCHMAKER 9th episode filmed and 7th episode broadcast. Original broadcast date was November 14, 1960. It was written by Arthur Stander, and directed by Don Weis. Regulars included Andy Griffith, Don Knotts, Ronny Howard, and Elinor Donahue as Ellie Walker. Guests included Amzie Strickland as Miss Rosemary, and Jack Mann as Tracy Crawford.

ANDY'S ADDRESS (50F/B) (87F/B) (201F/204B) In 50F/B, 24 Elm Street. In 87F/B, 332 Maple Road, and in 201F/204B, 14 Maple Street.

ANDY'S "BAD DAY" (161F/160B) The following series of events caused Andy to come home upset: the Leonard boy got mad at his brother, stole his car, drove it to the marsh and set it on fire. It took all day to put out. Also, someone kept calling the courthouse looking for Ethel, and Otis got gassed and drove his car through the Hoopers' rose garden, leveling it. Finally, Andy came home to find out that Opie had wrecked his "pretty new" bike.

ANDY'S BEGINNINGS (137F/B) (148F/B) In 137F/B, it's stated that Andy started as sheriff in Mayberry in 1952. In 148F/B, the year 1953 is given.

ANDY'S ENGLISH VALET 89th episode filmed and broadcast. Original broadcast date was March 25, 1963. It was written by Harvey Bullock, and directed by Bob Sweeney. Regulars included Andy Griffith, Don Knotts, Frances Bavier, and Ronny Howard. Guests included Bernard Fox as Malcolm Merriweather, and Bob McQuain.

ANDY'S FAVORITE DISH (92F/B) Leg of lamb. (Although in 180F/B, he said pork chops were "a favorite.")

ANDY'S FORTUNE (209F/210B) At Aunt Bee's Canton Palace: "Try to avoid temptation in the coming week."

ANDY'S INVESTMENT 231st episode filmed and 230th episode broadcast. Original broadcast date was November 20, 1967. It was written by Michael Morris and Seamon Jacobs, and directed by Alan Rafkin. Regulars included Andy Griffith, Ronny Howard, Frances Bavier,

Aneta Corsaut, Jack Dodson, and Paul Hartman. Guests included Ken Lynch as Inspector Rogers, Roy Jenson as Trooper Leroy Miller, Richard Collier as Mr. Giddings, Ceil Cabot as Alpha Porter (her credit lists her character simply as "Woman"), Maudie Prickett as Mrs. Larch, and Jesslyn Fax as Mrs. LeGrande.

ANDY'S LAST WORDS (241F/249B) In response to Sam Jones' observation that Sam was going to be eating a lot of "Chicken Polinisi" (since he had decided to let the Vincente family live with him), Andy replied, "Yeah, it looks like."

ANDY'S OLD GIRLFRIEND 207th episode filmed and 209th episode broadcast. Original broadcast date was January 30, 1967. It was written by Sid Morse, and directed by Lee Phillips. Regulars included Andy Griffith, Aneta Corsaut, and Jack Dodson. Guests included Joanna McNeil as Alice Harper.

ANDY'S PHONE NUMBER (AT HOME) (239F/238B) Mayberry 426.

ANDY'S RICH GIRLFRIEND 67th episode filmed and 65th episode broadcast. Original broadcast date was October 8, 1962. It was written by Jim Fritzell and Everett Greenbaum, and directed by Bob Sweeney. Regulars included Andy Griffith, Don Knotts, Frances Bavier, and Betty Lynn. Guests included Donald Lawton, Warner Jones, and Joanna Moore as Peggy McMillan.

ANDY'S RIVAL 163rd episode filmed and 161st episode broadcast. Original broadcast date was September 20, 1965. It was written by Laurence Marks, and directed by Peter Baldwin. Regulars included Andy Griffith, Frances Bavier, Ronny Howard, George Lindsey, and Aneta Corsaut. Guests included Charles Aidman as Frank Smith. Aneta Corsaut's wardrobe was by California Girl.

ANDY'S SHOPPING LIST (206F/B) When Aunt Bee and Opie were both away, Andy shopped for a feast. He bought wild mushrooms, canned oysters in chili sauce, pickled avocados, chocolate syrup, and shrimp enchiladas. He never got to eat any of it, instead being forced to eat three spaghetti dinners, thanks to Goober's jumbling of a phone message.

ANDY'S TRIP TO RALEIGH 226th episode filmed and 223rd episode broadcast. Original broadcast date was October 2, 1967. It was written by Joseph Bonaduce, and directed by Lee Phillips. Regulars included Andy Griffith, Jack Dodson, Aneta Corsaut, George Lindsey, and Paul Hartman. Guests included Whitney Blake as Attorney Lee Drake.

ANDY'S VACATION 118th episode filmed and 117th episode broadcast. Original broadcast date was March 9, 1964. It was written by Jim Fritzell and Everett Greenbaum, and directed by Jeffrey Hayden. Regulars included Andy Griffith, Don Knotts, Frances Bavier, and Jim Nabors. Guests included Allan Melvin, Dabbs Greer, James Seay, and Molly Dodd.

"ANIMAL CRACKERS" (15F/B) Song Barney offered to play for Wilbur Finch on the harmonica.

"ANJ" OR "ANGE" (82F/B) Many times throughout the early episodes of the show, Barney referred to Andy as "Anj." Although the reason for this diminutive nickname was never explained, it is my feeling that the answer was given in "Class Reunion" (82F/B), in the scene where Andy and Barney looked through their old yearbook,

"The Cutlass." There, under Andy's entry, it states that Andy's full name was "Andrew Jackson Taylor." Barney, of course, would know his cousin's middle name, and it is quite reasonable to assume that what Barney was doing was combining the "An" from Andrew and the "J" from Jackson to come up with his affectionate nickname for his cousin.

"THE ANTEATERS FROM OUTER SPACE" (163F/161B) Movie that was coming to Mayberry.

RHODA APFEL (136F/B) Woman who Andy correctly guessed was getting married. Barney read it in Red Akins' "Mayberry After Midnight" newspaper column.

APHIDS (203F/201B) The enemy of the Mayberry Garden Club, according to Mr. Simmons of the Simmons Seed Catalogue.

APPLE CRUMB PIE (109F/108B) Helen Crump brought one to the town picnic.

APPLE DUMPLING (60F/B) Horse who came in at 10 to 1.

APPLE PIE (32F/B) (40F/38B) (108F/107B) In 32F/B, Opie's favorite. In 40F/38B, Dave the Hobo stole one from Mrs. Tilman's window sill. In 108F/107B, Opie took one from Aunt Bee to bring to Wary Willy the Hobo.

"APPLE PIE ORDER" (143F/B) How Bee kept her house, according to Barney.

APPLES (73F/70B) (196F/203B) In 73F/70B, 8¢ a pound as sold by Neil and Matt from the back of their truck. In 196F/203B, 25¢.

APRICOT FESTIVAL (72F/71B) Yearly Mayberry social event.

APRON (54F/B) Aunt Bee's purchase from Bert Miller, the peddler. It cost eighty-seven cents and she told Andy to pay for it.

MRS. ARBESTER (138F/B) The woman Barney suggested as a replacement for Clara Edwards in the role of "Lady Mayberry" when Clara couldn't play the part. The idea was vetoed, however, because Mrs. Arbester was too small.

THE ARCADE (119F/118B) Raleigh game center. Barney and his cousin, Virgil, went there during Barney's vacation. They played four games of skiball and bought a tin inkblot.

CAPTAIN ARDELL (30F/B) State police. Ardell called to tell Andy that Eddie Brooks had escaped again and was heading for Mayberry.

"THE ARISTOCRATS" (116F/115B) The name Eleanora Poultice suggested for Andy, Barney, and Gomer when their choral "trio" went over so well at the concert. (It was supposed to be a solo.)

ARKANSAS (37F/40B) The home state of Thelma Lou's cousin, Karen Moore.

GEORGE ARKIS (172F/170B) The crook, Jack, said he was Arkis, a state police officer, in order to get the keys to the state mobile museum from Warren.

ARMY STORY #17 (29F/B) The story during which Sam Becker's son, Andy, was born. The stories were being swapped by Barney and Sam.

THE ARREST OF THE FUN GIRLS 155th episode filmed and broadcast. Original broadcast date was April 5, 1965. It was written by Richard M. Powell, and directed by Theodore J. Flicker. Regulars included Andy Griffith, Don Knotts, Frances Bavier, Aneta Corsaut, Hal

Smith, and Betty Lynn. Aneta Corsaut's wardrobe was by Suivante. Guests included Joyce Jameson as Skippy, and Jean Carson as Daphne.

ART (50F/B) (53F/B) First seen in 50F/B. In 53F/B, Art was a Mayberry butcher who got involved with Andy in honoring a stranger in order to interest "outsiders" in Mayberry. (Somehow, that seemed a little ridiculous, considering the character of the town.) Art was deputized for the "guest of honor" parade as Badge #2.

THE ART OF JUDO (18F/B) Book written by Professor Matsumata. Barney read it in the courthouse.

THE ART OF KARATE (56F/B) A book Barney read. From his reading, he showed Andy three moves: "The Hawk," "The Bull Elk," and "The Rattlesnake."

ARTHUR (125F/124B) Man who called Andy to solicit his help in forcing Nelvin to take down the quarantine signs he had put up on his property.

ARTISTIC COMMITTEE (208F/212B) Subdivision of the Civic Improvement Committee appointed to oversee the construction of the statue of Seth Taylor. Bee Taylor was chairperson; Clara Edwards, co-chairperson.

ASA (102F/B) He worked in the Mayberry Hotel.

ASHEVILLE, NORTH CAROLINA (166F/B) Bee's cousin, Evan Moore, lived there.

ATLANTA (30F/B) (224F/221B) In 30F/B, it was the town from which Eddie Brooks escaped. In 224F/221B, Lou Jenkins went there on business, thus necessitating a replacement for the bowling team.

MRS. ATZELL (176F/B) She played sax with Carl Benson's Wildcats on a regular basis, except on Friday nights when the library was open.

AUBURN COUNTY (240F/B) The locale Chief Dewhurst suggested for the US/USSR summit meeting before Mayberry was agreed upon.

AUGUST (4F/6B) George Foley's birth month.

AUGUST 1953 (106F/B) The month Barney was sworn in as deputy, although this seems to be in conflict with other information given. In "The New Housekeeper," Barney was just starting as Andy's deputy. In "Aunt Bee and the Lecturer," Aunt Bee stated that she'd been with Andy and Opie since 1959. These two episodes together have Barney starting in 1959, yet in "Citizen's Arrest" it's said that Barney started in 1953. Also, in 131F/129B, "Barney's Physical," Barney stated that he "joined the sheriff's department" on May 16, 1959.

AUGUST 9, 1946: 11:25 A.M. (152F/B) The arrest date and time of Charlie Foley and Floyd Lawson for the original "case of the punch in the nose."

AUGUST 3 AND 4, 1959 (244F/243B) On August 3, the photo of Helen being arrested ran in the "Kansas City Chronicle." On August 4, she was arraigned on the felony charges, which included one for associating with a known hoodlum. The charges were later dropped.

AUGUST 21 (171F/172B) Clara Cartwright's birthday.

AUNT BEE AND THE LECTURER 230th episode filmed and 229th episode broadcast. Original broadcast date was November 13, 1967. It was written by Seamon Jacobs, and directed by Lee Phillips. Regulars included Andy Griffith, Frances Bavier, Aneta Corsaut, George Lindsey, Jack Dodson, Hope Summers, and Ronny Howard. Guests included Edward Andrews as Professor Hubert St. John.

AUNT BEE LEARNS TO DRIVE 180th episode filmed and broadcast. Original broadcast date was February 7, 1966. It was written by Jack Elinson, and directed by Lee Phillips. Regulars included Andy Griffith, Frances Bavier, George Lindsey, Ronny Howard, Aneta Corsaut, and Howard McNear. Guests included Raymond Kark as Lowell.

AUNT BEE ON TV 165th episode filmed and 169th episode broadcast. Original broadcast date was November 15, 1965. It was written by Fred Freeman and Lawrence J. Cohen, and directed by Alan Rafkin. Regulars included Andy Griffith, Frances Bavier, Aneta Corsaut, Ronny Howard, George Lindsey, and Howard McNear. Guests included Hope Summers as Clara Edwards, Amzie Strickland as Myra Tucker, and William Christopher as Mr. Heathcote.

AUNT BEE TAKES A JOB 171st episode filmed and 172nd episode broadcast. Original broadcast date was December 6, 1965. It was written by Bill Idelson and Sam Bobrick, and directed by Alan Rafkin. Regulars included Andy Griffith and Frances Bavier. Guests included Jack Burns as Warren Ferguson, James Milhollin as Arnold Finch, Milton Frome as Ralph Kingsley, Herbie Faye as Mr. Clark, Maggie Magennis as Violet Rose Schumaker, Jason Johnson as Mr. Weaver, and Don Gazzaniga as Jones.

AUNT BEE THE CRUSADER 111th episode filmed and 110th episode broadcast. Original broadcast date was January 20, 1964. It was written by John Whedon, and directed by Coby Ruskin. Regulars included Andy Griffith, Frances Bavier, Don Knotts, and Ronny Howard. Guests included Hal Smith as Otis, Charles Lane as Mr. Frisby, Mary Lansing, and Noreen Gammill.

AUNT BEE THE JUROR 223rd episode filmed and 226th episode broadcast. Original broadcast date was October 23, 1967. It was written by Kent Wilson, and directed by Lee Phillips. Regulars included Andy Griffith, Frances Bavier, Ronny Howard, and George Lindsey. Guests included Jack Nicholson as Marvin Jenkins, Jim Begg as Mr. Keyes, Tom Palmer as the District Attorney, Rhys Williams as Judge Cranston, Henry Beckman as Mr. Gilbert the Prosecutor, Tol Avery as the Jury Foreman, Richard Chambers as Mr. Granger, Arthur Hansen as Mr. Smith, Pete Madsen as the Clerk, and Alan Dexter, Emory Parnell, and Frederic Downs as Jurors.

AUNT BEE, THE SWINGER 160th episode filmed and 163rd episode broadcast. Original broadcast date was October 4, 1965. It was written by Jack Elinson, and directed by Larry Dobkin. Regulars included Andy Griffith, Frances Bavier, Ronny Howard, Aneta Corsaut, and Howard McNear. Guests included Charles Ruggles as John Canfield. This was the very first episode broadcast in color.

AUNT BEE THE WARDEN 55th episode filmed and broadcast. Original broadcast date was March 12, 1962. It was written by Jack Elinson and Charles Stewart, and directed by Bob Sweeney. Regulars included Andy Griffith, Don Knotts, and Frances Bavier. Guests included Hal Smith as Otis Campbell, Hope Summers as Clara, Mary Lansing as Mary, Orville Sherman, Bob McQuain, and Paul Bakanas.

AUNT BEE'S BIG MOMENT 243rd episode filmed and 242nd episode broadcast. Original broadcast date was February 12, 1968. It was written by Dick Bensfield and Perry Grant, and directed by Lee Phillips. Regulars included Andy Griffith, Frances Bavier, Ronny Howard, George Lindsey, Aneta Corsaut, Jack Dodson, and Paul Hartman. Guests included John McLiam as Mac.

AUNT BEE'S BRIEF ENCOUNTER 38th episode filmed and 41st episode broadcast. Original broadcast date was December 4, 1961. It was written by Leo Solomon and Ben Gershman, and directed by Bob Sweeney. Regulars included Andy Griffith and Frances Bavier. Guests included Doodles Weaver, George Cisar, Sherwood Keith, and Edgar Buchanan as Henry Wheeler.

AUNT BEE'S "CANTON PALACE" (209F/210B) Aunt Bee's Chinese restaurant. She was partners with Charlie Lee, she invested $400, and she sold out to Charlie's nephew, Jack. The menu included Moo Moo Gai Pan, Lee Chi Chi, Chow Mein, and fortune cookies. Aunt Bee served as hostess.

AUNT BEE'S COUSIN 234th episode filmed and 232nd episode broadcast. Original broadcast date was December 4, 1967. It was written by Dick Bensfield and Perry Grant, and directed by Lee Phillips. Regulars included Andy Griffith, Frances Bavier, Ronny Howard, Aneta Corsaut, George Lindsey, Jack Dodson, Hope Summers, and Paul Hartman. Guests included Ann Morgan Guilbert as Ella, and Jack Albertson as Bradford J. Taylor.

AUNT BEE'S CROWNING GLORY 194th episode filmed and broadcast. Original broadcast date was October 10, 1966. It was written by Ronald Axe, and directed by Lee Phillips. Regulars included Andy Griffith, Frances Bavier, Howard McNear, Ronny Howard, Hope Summers, and Aneta Corsaut. Guests included Ian Wolfe as Reverend Leighton, Carol Veazie as Mrs. Larch, Ruth Thom as Maggie Peters, and Janet Stewart as Bernice.

AUNT BEE'S INVISIBLE BEAU 154th episode filmed and broadcast. Original broadcast date was March 29, 1965. It was written by Ben Joelson and Art Baer, and directed by Ted Flicker. Regulars included Andy Griffith, Don Knotts, Frances Bavier, Ronny Howard, Aneta Corsaut, and Hope Summers. Guests included Woodrow Chamblis as Orville Hendricks, Bobby Diamond as Evan Hendricks, and Lyle Latell as Farley Thurston. Aneta Corsaut's wardrobe was by Suivante.

AUNT BEE'S LICENSE PLATE NUMBER (199F/196B) (219F/B) In 199F/196B, AY-321. In 219F/B, GP-780.

AUNT BEE'S MEDICINE MAN 87th episode filmed and broadcast. Original broadcast date was

March 11, 1963. It was written by John Whedon, and directed by Bob Sweeney. Regulars included Andy Griffith, Frances Bavier, Don Knotts, and Ronny Howard. Guests included Kathryn Hart, Noreen Gammill, Jewel Rose, Mary Lansing, Ruth Packard, and John Dehner as Colonel Harvey.

AUNT BEE'S RESTAURANT 209th episode filmed and 210th episode broadcast. Original broadcast date was February 2, 1967. It was written by Ronald Axe and Les Roberts, and directed by Lee Phillips. Regulars included Andy Griffith, Frances Bavier, George Lindsey, Jack Dodson, and Aneta Corsaut. Guests included Keye Luke as Charlie Lee, Lloyd Kino as Jack, Ruth Thom as the Wife (although she's called "Ella" in the show), and Jason Johnson as the Man.

AUNT BEE'S ROMANCE 130th episode and 132nd episode broadcast. Original broadcast date was October 19, 1964. It was written by Harvey Bullock, and directed by Howard Morris. Regulars included Andy Griffith, Frances Bavier, Ronny Howard, and Howard McNear. Guests included Wallace Ford as Roger Hanover.

AUSTRALIA (234F/232B) Bradford Taylor claimed he had a 41,000-acre sheep ranch there.

"AN AUSTRALIAN BULLWHIP" (202F/196B) Arnold said he'd carry one instead of a gun when he became a sheriff like Andy.

AUTO SHOW (242F/241B) It was held at the convention center in Raleigh. Goober, Andy, Bee, and Opie went to see the new models. Goober met Roy Swanson there. He had gone to auto trade school with Roy. Roy pretended he was a Senior Vice President with Amalgamated Motors, but in reality he was only a mechanic. Goober found out later, after his self-confidence had almost been destroyed. The truth brought his self-esteem back, though, and he compassionately didn't let Roy know he knew the real story.

AUTO TRADE SCHOOL (242F/241B) Goober's alma mater.

"AVIATION JOURNAL" (243F/242B) Magazine read by Aunt Bee under the dryer in the beauty parlor.

AVOCADO SALAD AND HOT ROAST BEEF SANDWICHES (225F/224B) Opie's lunch at the Hollander's.

"AWAY IN A MANGER" (11F/B) Sung by Andy and Ellie in the courthouse during the Christmas party.

AY-321 (115F/114B) (129F/130B) (199F/196B) In 115F/114B, the license plate number of Otis Campbell's car. In 129F/130B, the plate number of Ollie and Nora's car. In 199F/196B, Aunt Bee's plate number.

B AVERAGE (231F/230B) The grades needed for admission to the University of North Carolina at Chapel Hill.

B+ (103F/B) Opie's grade on the first math test he took after originally failing the subject.

"BABY DOLL" (3F/B) The name Bobby Fleet derogatorily called the waitress at the Diner.

A BABY IN THE HOUSE 184th episode filmed and broadcast. Original broadcast date was March 7, 1966. It was written by Bill Idelson and Sam Bobrick, and directed by Alan Rafkin. Regulars included Andy Griffith, Frances Bavier, Aneta Corsaut, Ronny Howard, and George Lindsey. Guests included Jim Connell as Darryl, Candace Howard as Martha, Ronny Dapo as Pete, and Alvy Moore as the Salesman. The infant, Evie Joy, was uncredited.

"BACK BAY BOSTON" (113F/112B) The area where Mrs. Wiley thought Ernest T. Bass came from.

BACK TO NATURE 127th episode filmed and 126th episode broadcast. Original broadcast date was May 11, 1964. It was written by Harvey Bullock, and directed by Coby Ruskin. Regulars included Andy Griffith, Don Knotts, Ronny Howard, Howard McNear, and Jim Nabors. Guests included Willis Bouchey as Fletch, David A. Bailey as Trey Bowden, Richard Keith as Johnny Paul Jason, and Dennis Rush as Whitey.

BACKROOM OF THE COURTHOUSE (104F/105B) Barney moved into the backroom after being evicted from Mrs. Mendlebright's boarding house. It didn't work out, though, and Andy eventually orchestrated the reconciliation between Barney and Mrs. Mendlebright after they saved her from the con man, Mr. Fields.

BACON (91F/B) (104F/105B) (120F/119B) (135F/B) (162F/164B) (180F/B) (192F/191B) (196F/203B) In 104F/105B, 39¢. In 91F/B and 120F/119B, 99¢. In 135F/B, 97¢. In 162F/164B, 25¢. In 180F/B, 192F/191B, and 196F/203B, 59¢.

BADGE #3 (53F/B) Floyd Lawson was deputized "Badge #3" for the "guest of honor" celebration.

BADGE #2 (53F/B) Art Crowley, the butcher, was deputized "Badge #2" for the "guest of honor" celebration.

ARNOLD BAILEY (220F/B) (228F/227B) Opie's friend. In 220F/B, he had a thirteenth birthday party. Opie invited Mary Alice Carter to the party, she accepted, and then stood him up for Fred Simpson. In 228F/227B, Arnold instigated the trouble Opie and he got into by recording the crook Eddie Brooks' private conversation with his lawyer.

DOC BAILEY (228F/227B) Mayberry doctor, Arnold's father.

JOHN JUDSON BAILEY (47F/B) Ronald's father and an important figure in North Carolina.

MRS. BAILEY (228F/227B) Arnold's mother, Doc Bailey's wife.

RONALD BAILEY (47F/B) "Bailey's bad boy." Nineteen-year-old wise guy who sped through Mayberry on his way to Miami, and got caught by Andy. Bailey sideswiped Fletch Dillbeck and then fled the scene. Andy made Bailey stay over in the Mayberry jail for a trial before Judge Parker. At first Ronald was a blustering, threatening jerk, but eventually Mayberry's ways straightened him out

and he left a better man.

BAILEY'S BAD BOY 47th episode filmed and broadcast. Original broadcast date was January 15, 1962. It was written by Leo Solomon and Ben Gershman, and directed by Bob Sweeney. Regulars included Andy Griffith, Don Knotts, Hal Smith, Frances Bavier, and Ronny Howard. Guests included Bill Bixby as Ronald Bailey.

BAKED ALASKA (42F/B) The dessert that came out "since it became a state," as explained by Barney to the members of the Esquire Club.

JIM BAKER (42F/B) Member of the Esquire Club. Andy and Barney were introduced to him at one of the meetings. Jim's golf score was "95, 96." Barney thought he should try to break a hundred sometime.

KEVIN BAKER (116F/115B) Mayberry tenor who Barney thought might be his replacement in the choir.

RALPH BAKER (32F/B) Classmate of Opie's. Opie handcuffed Ralph to the flagpole during lunch, much to the chagrin of Aunt Bee and the principal.

RALPH BAKER (33F/34B) Friend of Andy's. Baker sent Bob Rogers to Mayberry to watch law enforcement in action.

BAKER STREET (200F/197B) Howard suggested building the new bridge over Parker Creek on Baker Street instead of on Ranch Road. This would save Mayberry $3,628.

THE BALL GAME 195th episode filmed and 193rd episode broadcast. Original broadcast date was October 3, 1966. It was written by Sid Morse from a story by Rance Howard, Ronny's father. It was directed by Lee Phillips. Regulars included Andy Griffith, Ronny Howard, Frances Bavier, Aneta Corsaut, George Lindsey, Howard McNear, and Jack Dodson. Guests included John Reilly as Billy.

"THE BALLAD OF ANDY AND BARNEY" (41F/39B) Folk song also called "The Gangster's Mistake." The lyrics were written by Barney Fife, and it was sung to the tune of "Frankie & Johnny."

1. Andy and Barney were lawmen
Bravest you ever did see
Warned every crook in the record book
To stay out of Mayberry
They were the law
And they didn't know fear

2. Pretty Boy Floyd come a ridin'
Dillinger too big as life
They weren't alone there was Al Capone
And in back old Mack the Knife
They broke the law
They broke the law

BALTIMORE (71F/72B) Madeline Grayson was on her way to Palm Beach from Baltimore. She planned on stopping in Mayberry to see Floyd on her way.

THE BAMBOO PODS (230F/229B) Mt. Pilot nightclub. Bee wanted to take Professor Hubert St. John there.

BANANAS (84F/B) (91F/B) (162F/164B) (180F/B) 9¢. In 180F/B, the price went up to 10¢.

BAND FESTIVAL (72F/71B) Yearly event in Raleigh that the Mayberry Band usually attended. They'd been participating in the festival for ten years.

BANGKOK (234F/232B) Bradford Taylor claimed he was called to go there, a story he made up as an excuse to leave Mayberry.

BANJO-PLAYING DEPUTY 159th episode filmed and broadcast. Original broadcast date was May 3, 1965. It was written by Bob Ross, and directed by Coby Ruskin. Regulars included Andy Griffith, Ronny Howard, Frances Bavier, and Howard McNear. Guests included Jerry Van Dyke as Jerry Miller, Herbie Faye as the Manager, Sylvia Lewis as Flossie, Hope Summers as Miss Bedloe, Mary Lansing as Miss Roundtree, Jean Inness as the Woman, Robert Carricart as Frankie, Lee Van Cleef as Skip, Tom Steele as the 1st Character and Bill Catching as the 2nd Character.

"BANK HOLD-UP FOILED HERE" (78F/76B) Headline of the "Gazette" after Andy and Barney stopped a bank robbery. Beneath it was "Sheriff Andy Taylor and Deputy Barney Fike Nip Robbery In The Bud." Barney complained to Mr. Butler about the misspelling. Butler called Barney "Howie." This was the third time Butler had written "Fike."

THE BANK JOB 78th episode filmed and 76th episode broadcast. Original broadcast date was December 24, 1962. It was written by Jim Fritzell and Everett Greenbaum, and directed by Bob Sweeney. Regulars included Andy Griffith, Don Knotts, and Jim Nabors. Guests included Warren Parker as Mr. Meldrim, Clint Howard as Leon, Al Checco, Mary Lansing, Lee Krieger, Frances Osborne, and Charles Thompson as Asa.

THE BANK POEM (9F/7B) Some of the bigger boys wrote the following poem on the wall of the Mayberry Security Bank. Barney was so upset he resigned.

> There once was a deputy called Fife
> Who carried a gun and a knife
> The gun was all dusty
> The knife was all rusty
> 'Cause he never caught a crook in his life

Barney originally accused Opie, but Andy knew Opie couldn't have done it: the boy couldn't write.

BANNER STREET (5F/8B) Street used as a border for one of the five sections Annabelle Silby divided Mayberry into for fund-raising purposes. The entire section was "From Grover's Place over to Banner Street then around Cornwall's Gas Station up to Tate Warren's store."

THE BANQUET ROOM (240F/B) Room at the Blue View Motel that Barney suggested as a possible site for the US/USSR summit meeting.

A BARBECUE FIESTA (227F/222B) Clara had one after her return from Mexico.

THE BARBERSHOP QUARTET 191st episode filmed and 192nd episode broadcast. Original broadcast date was September 26, 1966. It was written by Fred S. Fox, and directed by Lee Phillips. Regulars included Andy Griffith, Frances Bavier, Ronny Howard, Howard McNear, and Jack Dodson. Guests included Hamilton Camp as Jeff Nelson, Burt Mustin as Burt (although the credits for his character read "Jud"), Blackie Hunt as Wally, Sam Edwards as Tom Bedlowe, Vernon Rich as Mr. Johnston, Harry Arnie as Kelly, and Ken Mayer as Sheriff Blake Wilson (although the credits for his character read "Sheriff Blake").

GROVELY BARCH (64F/73B) According to Andy, the name of the Spirit of Air.

BARCLAY'S JEWELRY STORE (53F/B) (81F/B) Mayberry retailer. In 53F/B, the "guest of honor," Sheldon Davis, attempted to rob the store and was caught by Andy and Barney. In 81F/B, the store was seen in the background of a scene.

DETECTIVE BARDOLLI (57F/B) The hotel detective in the Capitol City hotel where Andy and Barney stayed when they went to the "big city." Barney thought Bardolli was a jewel thief.

BARGAIN DAY 120th episode filmed and 119th episode broadcast. Original broadcast date was March 23, 1964. It was written by John Whedon, and directed by Jeffrey Hayden. Regulars included Andy Griffith, Frances Bavier, Ronny Howard, and Jim Nabors. Guests included Frank Ferguson as Mr. Foley, and Hope Summers as Clara Johnson.

CAPTAIN BARKER (2F/B) State police captain in charge of the "manhunt." He came to Mayberry to take over the hunt from Andy and Barney.

"BARN" (69F/66B) How Barney referred to himself when talking to Juanita.

BARN PAINT (110F/109B) Opie and Trey Bowden used barn paint to seal their bond as blood brothers.

BARNEY AND THE CAVE RESCUE 109th episode filmed and 108th episode broadcast. Original broadcast date was January 6, 1964. It was written by Harvey Bullock, and directed by Dick Crenna. Regulars included Andy Griffith, Don Knotts, Aneta Corsaut, Betty Lynn, Ronny Howard, and Jim Nabors. Guests included Warren Parker as Mr. Meldrim, Roy Engel, and Joe Hamilton.

BARNEY AND THE CHOIR 52nd episode filmed and broadcast. Original broadcast date was February 19, 1962. It was written by Jack Elinson and Charles Stewart, and directed by Bob Sweeney. Regulars included Andy Griffith, Don Knotts, and Betty Lynn. Guests included Olan Soule as John Masters, the choir director.

BARNEY AND THE GOVERNOR 76th episode filmed and 78th episode broadcast. Original broadcast date was January 7, 1963. It was written by Bill Freedman and Henry Sharp, and directed by Bob Sweeney. Regulars included Andy Griffith, Don Knotts, and Hal Smith. Guests included Parley Baer as Mayor Stoner, Carl Benton Reid, Joe Hamilton, Bob McQuain, Rance Howard, and Burt Mustin as Jud.

BARNEY AND THELMA LOU, PHFFTT 126th episode filmed and 125th episode broadcast. Original broadcast date was May 4, 1964. It was written by Bill

Idelson and Sam Bobrick, and directed by Coby Ruskin. Regulars included Andy Griffith, Don Knotts, Jim Nabors, and Betty Lynn.

BARNEY AND THELMA LOU'S FIRST MEETING (131F/129B) They first met at Wilton Blair's funeral in 1960.

BARNEY AND THELMA LOU'S "ROUTINE" (134F/B) Sunday, they went to church; Tuesday, her house for TV; Thursday, the Diner for the special; and Fridays when he was working, she came by for coffee.

BARNEY COMES TO MAYBERRY 212th episode filmed and 208th episode broadcast. Original broadcast date was January 23, 1967. It was written by Sid Morse, and directed by Lee Phillips. Regulars included Andy Griffith and Frances Bavier. Guests included Don Knotts as Barney Fife, Diahn Williams as Teena Andrews, Chet Stratton as Carson, Patty Regan as Renee, Christine Burke as Harriet, Luana Anders as Miss Clark, Ollie O'Toole as The Man On The Train, and Steve Dunne as The Announcer.

"BARNEY FIFE FOR SHERIFF, THE MAN FOR THE JOB, WIN WITH FIFE" (148F/B) Barney had a speaker truck recite this when he ran against Andy for the sheriff's position.

"BARNEY FIFE, M.D." (57F/B) The way Barney signed his name; the "M.D." stood for "Mayberry Deputy."

BARNEY FIFE, REALTOR 143rd episode filmed and broadcast. Original broadcast date was January 4, 1965. It was written by Bill Idelson and Sam Bobrick, and directed by Peter Baldwin. Regulars included Andy Griffith, Don Knotts, Ronny Howard, and Frances Bavier. Guests included Amzie Strickland as Lila Simms, Dennis Rush as Howie Williams, and Harlan Warde as Mr. Williams.

THE BARNEY FIFE SUBCONSCIOUS PROBER PRIMER (44F/B) The book Andy and Otis said Barney should write after Barney attempted to elicit the location of Rafe Hollister's still by probing Otis's subconscious while Otis was (supposedly) asleep.

"BARNEY FIFE THE BULKHEAD" (30F/B) Barney said he became a bulkhead when he (accidentally) captured the escaped crook, Eddie Brooks.

BARNEY GETS HIS MAN 30th episode filmed and broadcast. Original broadcast date was May 8, 1961. It was written by Leo Solomon and Ben Gershman, and directed by Bob Sweeney. Regulars included Andy Griffith, Don Knotts, Ronny Howard, and Betty Lynn. Guests included Barney Phillips, Bob McQuain, Mike Steen, Burt Mustin, Joseph Hamilton, and Norman Leavitt.

BARNEY HOSTS A SUMMIT MEETING 240th episode filmed and broadcast. Original broadcast date was January 28, 1968. It was written by Aaron Ruben, and directed by Lee Phillips. Regulars included Andy Griffith, Frances Bavier, and George Lindsey. Guests included Ben Astar as Mr. Vasilievich, Alan Oppenheimer as Mr. Ruskin the Interpreter, Michael Higgins as Mr. Clifford, Paul Fix as Mr. McCabe, Richard X. Slattery as Captain Dewhurst, Hollis Morrison as Jenkins, and Charles Horvath as Peterson. Also, credited as "Special Guest Star," was Don Knotts as Barney Fife in a role for which he won his fifth Emmy.

BARNEY MENDS A BROKEN HEART 68th episode filmed and 69th episode broadcast. Original broadcast date was November 5, 1962. It was written and produced by Aaron Ruben, and directed by Bob Sweeney. Regulars included Andy Griffith, Don Knotts, Ronny Howard, Frances Bavier, and Betty Lynn. Guests included Joanna Moore as Peggy McMillan, Josie Lloyd as Lydia Crosswaithe, Joyce Jameson as Skippy, Jean Carson as Daphne, Fred Beir, and Michael Ross.

BARNEY ON THE REBOUND 36th episode filmed and 37th episode broadcast. Original broadcast date was October 30, 1961. It was written by Jack Elinson and Charles Stewart, and directed by Bob Sweeney. Regulars included Andy Griffith, Don Knotts, and Betty Lynn. Guests included Jackie Coogan as Mr. Stevens.

BARNEY RUNS FOR SHERIFF 148th episode filmed and broadcast. Original broadcast date was February 8, 1965. It was written by Richard M. Powell, and directed by Alan Rafkin. Regulars included Andy Griffith, Don Knotts, Ronny Howard, Howard McNear, Aneta Corsaut, Betty Lynn, George Lindsey, and Frances Bavier.

"BARNEY THE BEAST" (73F/70B) Andy told the two farmers selling on the side of the road that Barney was known as "the Beast" in order to frighten them into obeying the deputy.

BARNEY'S ADDRESS (44F/B) 411 Elm Street.

BARNEY'S BEGINNINGS (131F/129B) May 16, 1959. This was given as the day Barney joined the Mayberry sheriff's department. However, in 106F/B, "Citizen's Arrest," it was said that Barney was sworn in as of August 1953. To further confuse matters, in 230F/229B, "Aunt Bee and the Lecturer," Bee stated that she'd been with Andy since 1959. And in 1F/B, "The New Housekeeper," which took place on the day Aunt Bee moved in with Andy and Opie, Barney had just started as Andy's deputy.

BARNEY'S BLOODHOUND 128th episode filmed and 133rd episode broadcast. Original broadcast date was October 26, 1964. It was written by Bill Idelson and Sam Bobrick, and directed by Howard Morris. Regulars included Andy Griffith, Don Knotts, and Howard McNear. Guests included Arthur Batanides as Ralph Neal, James Seay as the first Trooper, and Brad Trumbull as the second Trooper.

BARNEY'S BREAKFAST (99F/98B) Orange juice, bowl of cereal, stack of wheats, three eggs over (not runny), bacon on the crisp side, white toast buttered, hash brown potatoes, and coffee.

BARNEY'S CAR (4F/6B) Andy attempted to push a car identified as Barney's in front of a fire plug as a joke. However, in 90F/B, "Barney's First Car," it was said that the car Barney bought in that episode was his very first.

BARNEY'S COFFEE (37F/40B) (177F/B) In 37F/40B, Barney took his coffee with two sugars. Apparently, the two lumps didn't make his coffee sweet enough because by 177F/B, he was taking his coffee with three lumps and a little cream. In 177F/B, Warren somehow knew that the former deputy was now up to three lumps.

BARNEY'S "CRIME WAVE" (137F/B) In order to convince Andy to stay on as sheriff, Barney created this "crime wave": Goober pretended he was robbed of forty dollars by a "big and tough" guy with a "big shotgun," who was driving a "little red sports car." The culprit wore a "big black mask," and had "two beady eyes." Then, Goober pretended to be a "bunch of wild kids whooping and hollering." Finally, Floyd pretended he, too, was robbed.

BARNEY'S DEN (126F/125B) While walking Main Street one night, Barney and Thelma Lou stopped in front of a furniture store and daydreamed about the future. Barney liked the leather chair and said he wanted his den to smell like real leather, pipe tobacco, books, and a dog. Thelma Lou, in a lapse, said she wouldn't bother Barney in his den. This was one of the few times Barney and Thelma Lou talked about marriage.

BARNEY'S FIRST CAR (90F/B) A 1954 Ford sedan, license plate number MP-3791. (See also BARNEY'S CAR)

BARNEY'S FIRST CAR 90th episode filmed and broadcast. Original broadcast date was April 1, 1963. It was written by Jim Fritzell and Everett Greenbaum, and directed by Bob Sweeney. Regulars included Andy Griffith, Don Knotts, Jim Nabors, Frances Bavier, Ronny Howard, and Betty Lynn. Guests included Ellen Corby as Myrt Lesh, Hallene Hill as Rose Temple, Allan Melvin, and Tom Allen.

BARNEY'S FRIENDSHIP QUOTE (134F/B) "So deep a friendship hath one man for another, that no female caress shall ever tear it asunder."

BARNEY'S GEAR (9F/7B) When Barney resigned after a derogatory poem was written on the bank wall about him, he turned in the following equipment: badge, notebook, pencil, gunbelt, holster, revolver, bullet, whistle, tieclip, tie, cap, and flashlight.

BARNEY'S GIFTS TO THE TAYLORS (176F/B) When Barney came to Mayberry for the class reunion, he brought Opie an "official" ink pad, Bee, handkerchiefs imported from Tijuana, and a tie clip for Andy.

BARNEY'S HELMET (112F/111B) Barney got upset when Andy tried on his motorcycle helmet. He said he couldn't stand to wear a hat after it had been on someone else's head. He said his mother was like that. Andy remembered that about Barney's mother.

BARNEY'S LETTER TO ANDY (144F/B) While on vacation in Raleigh, Barney sent the following letter home:

"Dear Andy: It certainly is exciting up here in Raleigh. Really havin' a ball. My head hasn't hit the pillow before 11:15 since I got here. Catchin' all the shows. Saw that Italian picture we read about in the paper: "Bread, Love, and Beans" and it was pretty risqué let me tell you. The food here in the cafeteria is terrific and I've been eatin' up a storm. The breakfast special is unbelievable. Three hotcakes, two strips of bacon, one egg—any style—juice and coffee, all for 35¢. It's served only between 5 and 6 A.M. but I can't sleep late anyway. I ran into a fellow on the street the other day who tried to sell me an iron deer for my front lawn, but I don't know. Well, it's almost five, so I better get down to breakfast. Love to Aunt Bee, Opie, Floyd, Goober and all the boys. 10-4, over and out, Barney. P.S. I'm not saying anything but there's an awful lot of pretty women up here. Ha, Ha."

BARNEY'S LETTER TO THE GANG (119F/118B) While on vacation in Raleigh with his cousin, Virgil, Barney sent this letter to the gang:

"Dear Peasants: (Ha ha) Would have written sooner but Virgil and I have been on the go every minute since we got here and checked in at the Y. It sure isn't like Mayberry, where they roll up the sidewalks every night. Ha ha.

Last night was really wild. We went to the Arcade and played four games of skiball. There was a magic store there, and I bought a tin inkblot that looks just like the real thing. Can't wait to put it on Aunt Bee's tablecloth and watch her face. Ha ha.

Next, Virgil had a tie painted for him while I shot at a tin bear with an air rifle. Let me tell you, ol' sharpshooter Barn really pinged up the place! Then we went in a booth where you get four pictures taken for a quarter. I was going to send you one but it turned all brown later.

After that we had supper at a waffle shop where the waitresses all dress alike in peekaboo blouses and let me tell you . . . (Andy read this part to himself—with Floyd looking over his shoulder—because there happened to be an inquisitive young boy named Opie there who wanted to know what 'peekaboo' meant. He was sure it had something to do with babies.)

Have to close now. Having fun but money sure doesn't last. Been here only three days and already gone through ten dollars.

Well, see you in the funny papers. Ha ha.

Barney"

BARNEY'S MIDDLE NAME AND/OR INITIAL (25F/B) (82F/B) (103F/B) (114F/B) (122F/121B) In 25F/B, Oliver. In 82F/B, Milton. In 103F/B, 114F/B, and 122F/121B, "P."

BARNEY'S MOTHER'S STOMACH (124F/123B) Barney explained to Andy that because of his "low blood sugar content" he had to eat by noon or he got a headache and he was no good to anybody. Barney said his mother was like that, and that they both had clocks in their stomachs. Andy told him that Aunt Bee once had an elephant with a clock in its stomach. Barney said, "Don't kid about my mother's stomach."

BARNEY'S #1 JOB (73F/70B) According to Barney, his #1 job was "stalking."

BARNEY'S PHONE MANNERS (4F/6B) Barney answered the phone thusly: "Mayberry Sheriff's Office. Town Headquarters. Andy Taylor Sheriff. Deputy Barney Fife speaking, hello?"

BARNEY'S PHONE NUMBER (22F/B) 431.

BARNEY'S PHYSICAL 131st episode filmed and 129th episode broadcast. Original broadcast date was September 28, 1964. It was written by Bob Ross, and directed by Howard Morris. Regulars included Andy Griffith, Don Knotts, Frances Bavier, Betty Lynn, Ronny Howard, and Howard McNear. Guests included Larry Thor as Mr. Bronson, Charles Thompson as Asa Bascomb, Richard Keith as Johnny Paul Jason, and Dennis Rush as Howie.

BARNEY'S REPLACEMENT 33rd episode filmed and 34th episode broadcast. Original broadcast date was October 9, 1961. It was written by Jack Elinson and Charles Stewart, and directed by Bob Sweeney. Regulars included Andy Griffith, Don Knotts, Ronny Howard, and Betty Lynn. Guests included Hope Summers as Clara Johnson, Cheerio Meredith as Emma Brand, and Mark Miller as Bob Rogers.

BARNEY'S RIDDLE (36F/37B) This is the riddle Barney told Melissa Stevens and her "Daddy": "What's yellow, has four legs, flys, and weighs a 1,000 pounds?" Answer: "Two 500-pound canaries."

BARNEY'S SIDECAR 112th episode filmed and 111th episode broadcast. Original broadcast date was January 27, 1964. It was written by Jim Fritzell and Everett Greenbaum, and directed by Coby Ruskin. Regulars included Andy Griffith, Don Knotts, Frances Bavier, and Ronny Howard. Guests included Virginia Sale, Rodney Bell, Joe Hamilton, Ray Kellogg, Hal Landon, and Jerry Brutsche.

BARNEY'S "SON" (79F/77B) Fictitious offspring Barney brought up whenever he disapproved of the way Andy was raising Opie. Andy usually teased him with questions like "Who's the mother?"

BARNEY'S TRICK SHOTS (WITH A SLINGSHOT) (101F/96B) His trick shots included "Over The Mountain," "Behind The Barn," "Under The Bridge," and his best shot, "Tail-Gunner."

BARNEY'S TWO WAYS (TO TELL A GIRL YOU LIKE HER) (132F/128B) Barney's advice to Opie: 1. Play hard to get. 2. Poetry and romance. Opie, however, only knew two poems: "I had a dog and his name was Spot," and "The boy stood on the burning deck." Barney helped out by taking the following poem out of his book, *Poems of Romance* by T. Jonathan Osgood. He told Opie to read it to his "girl," who Barney didn't know was Helen: "When you and I are far apart, I no longer live. My heart is bursting from within with all my love to give. Lovesick as I am. . ."

BARNEY'S UNIFORM 135th episode filmed and broadcast. Original broadcast date was November 9, 1964. It was written by Bill Idelson and Sam Bobrick, and directed by Coby Ruskin. Regulars included Andy Griffith, Don Knotts, Frances Bavier, and Ronny Howard. Guests included Allan Melvin as Fred Plummer, Yuki Shimoda as Mr. Izamoto, and William Keene as Reverend Tucker.

BARNEY'S VACATION (65F/67B) (118F/117B) On two occasions, Barney did the following on his vacation: he got the corner room at the Y in Raleigh, put on his pongee shirt, got a haircut and a shoeshine, hung around the lobby of the Y and watched some ping pong games, and then had supper at the coffee shop. He had the special: Vienna sausages with tomato sauce. Then he stayed at the Y and took in one of their shows, either a movie or a lecture on sportsmanship and cleanliness. Finally, he'd have a tapioca and a hot chocolate. By then it was time for bed.

BARNEY'S WEIGHT (131F/129B) 138 to 138 1/2 pounds.

"BARON VON RICHTOFEN" (112F/111B) The moniker Andy gave Barney when Barney arrived "suited up" to ride his motorcycle. He was wearing goggles and a helmet.

ALVIN BARROWS (226F/223B) A lawyer Howard Sprague knew in Raleigh.

GEORGE BARSTOW (178F/B) The Taylors' egg man. He had been in the Taylor house just prior to the disappearance of Aunt Bee's pin. Andy refused to consider George a suspect, and Warren reluctantly agreed to rule him out.

EFFIE BARTLETT (13F/B) Orville Monroe had her in the backroom of his funeral parlor/TV repair shop; her picture tube had gone on the blink.

CINDY BARTON (247F/246B) Infant daughter of Mrs. Barton. Sam Jones kissed Cindy during a campaign stop.

MRS. BARTON (247F/246B) Woman Goober and Sam visited for a campaign call. Goober made Sam kiss her infant daughter, Cindy.

ASA BASCOMB (131F/129B) Because of a pinched nerve in Asa's back, Doc Harvey gave him a stretching harness which increased his height over half an inch.

BASEBALL (161F/160B) Opie pretended he wanted to play baseball so Mr. Doakes would fire him and give the delivery boy job to Billy Crenshaw. Billy's dad had been sick and they had some bills.

BASS (225F/224B) Andy took George Hollander and his friends fishing for bass at Myer's Lake. Andy got four, Hollander got five.

ERNEST T. BASS (94F/B) (99F/98B) (113F/112B) (133F/131B) (164F/162B) Mayberry's resident lunatic and compulsive rock (and brick) thrower. Throughout the run of the series, Ernest T. Bass hurled twenty-one projectiles. The count is as follows:

FOURTEEN ON-SCREEN THROWS
(broken down by episode)
"Mountain Wedding" (94F/B)—five throws

All five throws were through windows in the Darlings' cabin. (Although it's quite possible that Ernest T. broke many more than just five. In the episode called "Ernest T. Bass Joins The Army," Briscoe Darling states that in "Mountain Wedding" Ernest T. "broke every window in [the Darlings'] house." There were three windows in the Darlings' cabin, each of which held twelve panes of glass. Therefore, if Briscoe was correct and not simply exaggerating, Ernest T. can be held responsible for thirty-six broken panes in this episode.)
"Ernest T. Bass Joins The Army" (99F/98B)—two throws

One was through the front window of the Mayberry courthouse and one was through the window of an unnamed Main Street business. (For this business, the throw was seen, but the breaking of the window was not.)
"My Fair Ernest T. Bass" (113F/112B)—one throw

This one throw was through the front window of Mrs. Wiley's house.
"The Education Of Ernest T. Bass" (133F/131B)—
three throws

One was through the right front window of the Mayberry courthouse, one was through the left front window of Helen Crump's house, and one was through the front window of an unnamed Main Street business.
"Malcolm At The Crossroads" (164F/162B)—three throws

A rock was thrown at a passing car, a brick was thrown at a passing pickup truck, and another brick was thrown through the window of an unnamed Main Street business.

SEVEN OFF-SCREEN THROWS
(broken down by episode)

"Ernest T. Bass Joins The Army" (99F/98B)—six throws

One went through the front window of the recruiting office, one broke a streetlight in front of Miss Mingus' house, two broke a couple of panels in Hannah Lou Smith's greenhouse, one broke the window of Richie Ferraro's hardware store, and one broke the front window of an unnamed Main Street business.

"My Fair Ernest T. Bass" (113F/112B)—one throw

This one throw was through the front window of Hoggette Winslow's house.

FIVE MESSAGE ROCKS
(broken down by episode)

Of the above twenty-one throws, five were message projectiles (i.e., they had a note tied to them).

1. Through the window of the Darling house in "Mountain Wedding" (94F/B). Message: "Charlene, I still love you and want you. Ernest T. Bass."

2. Through a front window of the Darling house in "Mountain Wedding" (94F/B). Message: "Maybe you gonna have a preacher and maybe you gonna have a altar but maybe you not gonna have a bride. Did you ever think of that?"

3. Through the right front window of the Mayberry courthouse (when facing the courthouse) in "Ernest T. Bass Joins The Army" (99F/98B). Message: "It's all your fault I didn't get my uniform, sheriff, and I'm gonna break every window in the state to get even. Ernest T. Bass, ex-serviceman."

4. Through the front window of Hoggette Winslow's house in "My Fair Ernest T. Bass" (113F/112B). Message: A request for a date (wording not specified).

5. Through the left front window of Helen Crump's house (when facing the house) in "The Education Of Ernest T. Bass" (133F/131B). Message: "I love you."

We first met Ernest T. in "Mountain Wedding" (94F/B) and the very first person to ever mention the crazy mountain man is another mountain man, Briscoe Darling. Ernest T.'s first appearance was when he crept out from behind a bush up at the Darlings' cabin. Ernest T. refused to accept that Charlene Darling was really wed to Dud Wash (because Andy wasn't no preacher), so Andy and Barney had to go up to the Darlings' place to stop Ernest T. from bothering Charlene. He was described in this episode in the following manner:

Andy: "A strange and weird character."
Briscoe: "Just plain ornery."
Barney: "He's a nut."

We next meet Ernest T. in the episode "Ernest T. Bass Joins The Army" (99F/98B). In this episode, Ernest T. tried to join the Army so's he could get a uniform and impress the girls back home. When the recruiting officer turned him down, he went on a rock-throwing, window-breaking rampage through Mayberry and the only way Andy could calm him down was to give him one of Barney's uniforms so he'd go back to the woods and leave everybody alone. He was described in this episode in the following manner:

Andy: [He's] "a strange one." Also, [he's "high-strung."

Recruiting sergeant: [He's] "a wild man."
Barney: "He's a nut."

We are next treated to a visit by Ernest T. Bass in the episode "My Fair Ernest T. Bass" (113F/112B). In this episode, Ernest T. came to town looking for a woman. Andy tried to civilize him but, in the end, nothing could change Ernest T. He began a relationship with Ramona Anchram in this episode, and we also learn that Hoggette Winslow was going to marry a taxidermist that sewed up her head after Ernest T. hit her with his "date request" rock.

Next—in the episode "The Education Of Ernest T. Bass" (133F/131B)—Ernest T. decided he wanted an "ejacation" because the "love of his life," Ramona, turned down his marriage proposal. The reason? He wasn't book-learned. Even though Ernest T. knew "the whole front part of the alphabet: A, B, C, F, L, G," it wasn't enough. (He had even shaved the back of his head "slickety," and had had a sign painter put gold leaf on his front tooth for a dollar, but all this still wasn't enough to convince Ramona to marry him.) Andy solved the problem by having Helen award him a "Special Award for Learning." It didn't do any good. Ramona still wouldn't marry him, now because he didn't have enough money for a honeymoon.

We found out about Ernest T.'s honeymoon problems in the last Ernest T. episode (and the only Ernest T. episode in color), "Malcolm at the Crossroads" (164F/162B). In this episode, Ernest T. came into Mayberry prepared: he brought a big burlap sack filled with rocks and bricks; after Andy fired him from his school crossing job for throwing rocks at passing cars, he made short work of the bag's contents.

The next time we see Ernest T. Bass, it's more than twenty years later. One of Ernest T.'s first obligations when back in Mayberry was to throw a rock at the front window of the courthouse—just as Barney was opening the door. The rock sailed right between Barney's legs. That throw was the only Ernest T. projectile in "Return To Mayberry" and it was also the last time we see Ernest T. throw anything (although I'm sure we'll be seeing—and hearing—from Ernest T. again! (See additional entries beginning with the word "ERNEST")

[Author's Note: Very special thanks to my friend, Jim Clark—presiding Goober of "The Andy Griffith Show" Rerun Watchers Club and co-author of the super *The Andy Griffith Show Book*—for suggesting the slant of the above entry. My sincere appreciation to Jim and Ken Beck for all their scholarship regarding Mayberry! (See the interview with Jim Clark in this book)]

BASTILLE DAY (17F/B) Holiday used by the customers of the Morrison sisters as an excuse to buy the sisters' moonshine. The sisters would only sell their "Special Elixir" for "recognized" holidays.

ELLA BATKINS (203F/201B) She won second prize in the pansy division at the Mayberry Garden Club flower show.

THE BATTLE OF MAYBERRY (188F/B) Classic battle that took place in May of 1762, the details of which changed through the years in the course of retelling. It seemed that everyone in town had an ancestor in this glorious battle, and they were all colonels. Farley Upchurch, publisher of the "Mayberry Gazette," sponsored an essay competition for the paper's fiftieth anniversary.

The theme was the Battle, and first prize was a gold medal and publication of the essay on the front page of the "Gazette." Opie went to the library in Raleigh and found the original newspaper report of the Battle, which follows. It caused more than a little dismay.

"Dear readers, there was no Battle of Mayberry. The only casualties were one scrawny cow, three deer, and one mule who had the misfortune to look like a deer. The whole fracas began with the death of Bessie Lawson. Bessie was their mean old cow that an Indian shot by accident. The next day the Mayberryites sent the women and children away, and fifty settlers found themselves facing fifty Cherokee braves, who had about as much desire to fight as they did. Taunts and insults filled the air but no bullets or arrows. Then out of the stockade stepped Lieutenant Edwards. He approached the Indians in a wavering course holding a fearsome weapon in his hand: A jug of Mayberry's finest corn liquor. One drink led to another and when they were all happy and friendly, they went into the woods together to shoot some deer to pay Lawson for Old Bessie. That's how the mule got killed. Those were the only shots fired in the Battle of Mayberry. Both sides realized that the true story of the Battle would be a sorry tale to tell their womenfolk. So, the story of the bloody Battle of Mayberry was conceived and born after the last shot had been fired."

THE BATTLE OF MAYBERRY 188th episode filmed and broadcast. Original broadcast date was April 4, 1966. It was written by Paul David and John L. Greene, and directed by Alan Rafkin. Regulars included Andy Griffith, Aneta Corsaut, Ronny Howard, Frances Bavier, Howard McNear, George Lindsey, and Hope Summers. Guests included Norm Alden as Tom Strongbow, Clinton Sundberg as Farley Upchurch, and Arthur Malet as Purvis.

"THE BATTLE OF THE SEXES" (37F/40B) The battle in which Andy said he came in second, after Karen Moore beat him at skeetshooting.

MR. BAXTER (15F/B) Andy and Barney had to take a ride out to Baxter's house. A trespasser stole his "No Trespassing" sign.

THE BAZAAR 162nd episode filmed and 164th episode broadcast. Original broadcast date was October 11, 1965. It was written by Art Baer and Ben Joelson, and directed by Sheldon Leonard. Regulars included Andy Griffith, Frances Bavier, Ronny Howard, and George Lindsey. Guests included Jack Burns as Warren Ferguson, Hope Summers as Clara Edwards, Amzie Strickland as Myra, Mary Lansing as Dorothy, Janet Stewart as Martha, Claudia Bryar as Ruth, Joe di Reda as Harlan, Pam Ferdin as Corlis, and Sam Edwards as Fred.

"BE YOURSELF" (225F/224B) A Ralph Waldo Emerson quotation Andy used. Emmett thought Andy was referring to Fletcher Emerson, who once owned the hardware store.

"THE BEAGLES" (229F/228B) The way Goober referred to "The Beatles."

BEANS (54F/B) (84F/B) (91F/B) (133F/131B) (162F/164B) In 54F/B and 91F/B, 26¢. In 84F/B, 19¢. In 133F/131B, and 162F/164B, 35¢.

A BEARSKIN RUG (246F/245B) Howard had one delivered after his mother moved to Mt. Pilot with her new husband, George. He bought it to help transform his "Old Homestead" into a swinging bachelor pad. It didn't work.

JAMES ARTHUR BEASLOW (163F/161B) Goober was concerned that James Arthur might be sweet on his girlfriend, Lydia Crosswaithe.

"THE BEAST OF THE FOURTH FLOOR" (132F/128B) Mrs. VonRoder, one of Andy's and Barney's teachers. They tormented her.

"THE BEAST THAT ATE MINNESOTA" (140F/B) Movie at the theater (along with "The House of Blood") that Opie wanted to see. Barney felt as though he should get Andy's OK before allowing Opie to see it.

"BEASTO MARISTO" (139F/B) Halcyon Loretta Winslow, according to Barney.

"BEAUTY AND THE BEAST" (32F/B) Story Andy told Opie when the boy came to the courthouse after school.

THE BEAUTY CONTEST 20th episode filmed and 16th episode broadcast. Original broadcast date was January 23, 1961. It was written by Jack Elinson and Charles Stewart, and directed by Bob Sweeney. Regulars included Andy Griffith, Frances Bavier, Howard McNear, Ronny Howard, and Elinor Donahue as Ellie Walker. Guests included Lillian Bronson as Erma Bishop, Dick Elliot as Mayor Pike, Josie Lloyd as Josephine Pike, Frank Ferguson, Elvia Allman, Gail Lucas, and Yvonne Adrian.

"THE BEAVER" (112F/111B) Mrs. Beggs' sister Tilly's nickname in school. It was brought on by her long teeth, the result of a gum condition.

BEAVER DAM (110F/109B) Andy escorted the queen of the state Apricot Festival to the dam when she visited Mayberry.

ANDREW BEAZLEY (152F/B) Bobby Gribbel used to go with Andrew's daughter. Bobby ended up marrying Emma Larch instead.

CHARLIE BEAZLEY (7F/5B) Andy told Charlie he had good muscles in order to put Charlie on Ellie Walker's trail. (Andy thought Ellie was after him.)

EDGAR BEAZLEY (103F/B) Acquaintaince of Andy's who was always "braggin' on his young 'uns." After Opie mistakenly got all A's on his report card, Andy said he wanted to take Opie's picture and send it to Edgar with the report card.

GOOBER BEAZLEY (150F/B) Goober Pyle's name in an earlier episode.

JUANITA BEAZLEY (28F/B) Girl who worked at the Junction Cafe, a popular truck stop. The phone number of the Cafe was 142R. She later went to work at the Bluebird Diner. Barney dated Juanita. He also sang "Juanita" to her. (See the entry JUANITA)

AL BECKER (105F/104B) Mayberry man who was in Norman's Groceteria when a shaved collie came up to Mrs. Spears.

ANDY BECKER (29F/B) The newborn son of Sam and Lily Becker. He was delivered by Andy Taylor, and he weighed in at eight pounds nine ounces.

LILLIAN BECKER (82F/B) Classmate of Andy's and Barney's. They were in the Class of 1945 at Mayberry Union High.

LILY BECKER (29F/B) Sam's wife. Lily (with the help of Andy) gave birth—offscreen—to Andy Becker. Lily was never seen.

SAMUEL W. BECKER (29F/B) "Quiet Sam." Mayberry farmer who lived at the old Birch place. Because he was quiet and a loner, Barney assumed he was a shady character, perhaps even to the point of being a marijuana grower. It turned out that Sam's wife was pregnant and ready to deliver, and that Sam had been preoccupied with worry about her. Andy and Barney lent a hand: Barney kept Sam occupied by swapping army stories, and Andy delivered the baby. The Beckers named the child "Andy" in honor of our favorite sheriff.

HARRY BECTORIS (82F/B) Ramona Wiley's husband.

THE BED JACKET 75th episode filmed and broadcast. Original broadcast date was December 17, 1962. It was written by Ray Allen Saffian and Harvey Bullock, and directed by Bob Sweeney. Regulars included Andy Griffith, Frances Bavier, Ronny Howard, and Hope Summers. Guests included Dabbs Greer, Mary Lansing, and Parley Baer as Mayor Stoner.

MISS BEDLOW (159F/B) One of the women who insisted that Andy shut down the "goochie-hoochie" show at the carnival.

TOM BEDLOW (191F/192B) (192F/191B) In 191F/192B, he auditioned for tenor a Howard Sprague's replacement in the barbershop quartet competition. In 192F/191B, he was shown to be one of the members of the Regal Order of the Golden Door to Good Fellowship.

BEE, AUNT see AUNT BEE

"BEE TAYLOR FOR CITY COUNCIL" (200F/197B) Banner the ladies hung on Andy's house.

BEE TAYLOR'S BIRTHDAY (75F/B) (171F/172B) In 75F/B, December 19, a Saturday. In 171F/172B, March 17.

BEE'S BEGINNINGS (230F/229B) With Andy and Opie: 1959.

BEE'S FORTUNE (209F/210B) At Aunt Bee's Canton Palace: "Beware of new business ventures, they can prove costly." This worried Bee, as she had just invested $400 to open the Canton Palace.

"BEE'S HOMEMADE ICE CREAM" (234F/232B) The trade name Bradford Taylor suggested for Aunt Bee's ice cream, which he planned on marketing.

BEE'S PURSE (159F/B) When Bee's purse was cut off her arm at the carnival, it contained the following: sixteen dollars, a leather wallet, a gold ring Bertha gave her, her membership card to the woman's club, a rhinestone buckle she meant to have fixed, a package of bobby pins, and a brand new orangewood stick. The bag cost her $8.50.

BEN BEECHAM (236F/237B) Martha Clark's brother. He owned the Ben Beecham Insurance Agency. He convinced Emmett to work for him selling insurance. The arrangement didn't work out.

BEEF CASSEROLE (237F/236B) The first dish Bee prepared on the air for her cooking show, "The Mayberry Chef."

BEEF STEW (124F/123B) One of the dishes Malcolm Merriweather prepared for supper. It contained "double dollops of cooking sherry." Barney was aghast; he was on duty that night.

THE BEEMANS (129F/130B) Mayberry family Andy greeted on their way to church. The family consisted of Claude Sr., Claude Jr., Plain Claude, and Claudette. Plain Claude was called Plain because he wasn't a Junior or a Senior. Bee thought he was called Plain because he was so homely. Andy said he wasn't homely, he just had the Beeman overbite, a family characteristic.

BEER CAN OPENER WITH AN UMBRELLA ON IT (117F/116B) One of the items sold by Weaver's Department Store. Barney remarked that it would make a nice gift, and Andy suggested "for Mother's Day."

MRS. BEGGS (112F/111B) Woman who burst into the courthouse with the following tale: she was on Highway 6 doing 35 when a car doing 45 or 50 sped past her. There was a woman driving. She was wearing a "green hat trimmed with pink baby roses and a beige cloth with bitty bone buttons with furring and medals." Mrs. Beggs' sister, Tilly, had the same type of buttons on her jacket. Tilly was a tall woman with long teeth, the result of a gum condition. Her father took her to a dentist in Nashville. The dentist's office was in the back of a store and he "warn't no good." In school they called Tilly, "The Beaver."

BEGONIAS (245F/244B) Martha Clark told Andy she was having trouble with hers.

HARVEY BELFAST (215F/B) The most popular kid in town when Andy was a boy.

THE BELFASTS (125F/124B) On the night of Andy's and Helen's "engagement party," Aunt Bee sent Opie to the Belfasts' for the night.

"OTTO BELL" (104F/105B) One of Mr. Field's aliases.

BELL PEPPERS (73F/70B) 2¢ each as sold by Neil and Matt from their truck.

"RALPH BELLAMY" (105F/104B) Before the chamber of commerce dance, Andy told Gomer his hair wasn't just right and directed him to make it "like Ralph Bellamy."

"BELLE OF THE BALL" (246F/245B) Helen said she felt like one when she found out she'd be the only girl at Howard's "swinging party."

GORDON BELLFIELD (13F/B) Mayberry man who went on vacation to Hollywood one year. He was told to get off Gary Cooper's lawn.

BELMONT PICTURE STUDIO (166F/B) The Hollywood studio that made the movie "Sheriff Without A Gun," which was based on Andy. As a partial payment for the rights to use Andy's story, they sent him a check for $1,000 which he used to take the family to Hollywood. Art Spiegel signed the check.

BEN BEECHAM AGENCY (236F/237B) Martha Clark's brother's insurance agency.

BRYAN BENDER (167F/B) The star who played Andy in the "Sheriff Without A Gun" movie.

"BENJY" (37F/40B) The nickname Andy gave to a blind date Barney once arranged for him. Andy said she looked like Benjamin Franklin.

DR. BENNETT (199F/196B) (201F/204B) In 199F/196B, he was the Mayberry physician who treated Goober's imaginary whiplash. The doctor made Andy massage Goober's neck for twenty minutes, five to six times a day for six weeks. In 201F/204B, he retired from his

Mayberry practice after forty years. Bee figured he must have delivered all the babies in Mayberry. Dr. Thomas Peterson took over his practice.

HENRY BENNETT (49F/B) The jinx. Through a series of misfortunes that seemed to be his doing, Henry got the undeserved reputation of being a jinx. With Barney as the ringleader, the town teased Henry unmercifully. Eventually, as usually happens with these things, the situation got out of control and Henry planned on leaving town to start over somewhere else. Realizing their error, the town rigged a raffle to let Henry win a TV, thinking this would prove to him that he wasn't a jinx. The ruse failed, though, when Henry pulled his hat size out of the hat instead of the winning ticket. Henry then felt it inevitable that he was doomed to jinxhood. But the town rallied around Henry, awarded him the TV, and he decided to stay in Mayberry.

CHIEF BENSON (95F/B) Police official who told Andy that crooks would be held in Mayberry.

MR. BENSON (244F/243B) He had a vegetable stand. Wally Crenshaw backed into it.

DR. ROBERT BENSON (24F/B) The "new doctor" who came to Mayberry to start a practice. He was the youngest doctor ever to practice in Mayberry and he relied on Ellie Walker to help him through his first few days in town. Barney, as usual, read this situation incorrectly and convinced Andy he'd better make his move or he'd risk losing Ellie. Andy proposed, found out the doctor was engaged, and was relieved when Ellie refused his marriage proposal.

SAM BENSON (153F/B) Man Andy greeted on Main Street.

SPOOKY BENSON (219F/B) Man Goober got to take care of the filling station while he tried to straighten out his "Grab Bag for Cash" prize error.

MILES BENTLEY (228F/227B) Attorney from Jonesboro who represented the crook, Eddie Blake.

NEIL BENTLEY (141F/142B) Mt. Pilot attorney who convinced Otis to sue the county for $5,000. Bentley's office was in room 205.

"BERNARD P. FIFE, ATTORNEY AT LAW" (122F/121B) The pose Barney adopted when he sent a "lawyer letter" to the Miracle Salve Company after they mailed Trey Bowden a "blacklist" scare letter.

BERNICE (194F/B) Hairdresser who talked Bee into buying a blonde wig.

BERNICE (220F/B) At Arnold's thirteenth birthday party, Opie told Bernice she had a nice dress.

"BERNIE" (68F/69B) (123F/122B) The name Skippy called Barney.

BERNIE THE FURRIER (245F/244B) Flora's friend. He had a shop in Mt. Pilot. Flora took Emmett there to help him get a fur for Martha.

BERRIES FOR WOMEN'S HATS (39F/36B) Frank Myers used to make berries for women's hats. His career went down the drain when women stopped wearing them. When Frank discovered what he thought was a valuable bond, he still had an inventory of fifty boxes of berries just waiting for a comeback. He had logenberry, strawberry, blueberry, blackberry, and huckleberry.

BERT (198F/200B) He fished for Old Sam at Tucker's Lake.

"BERT AND SQUIRT" (69F/66B) Barney angrily called Andy and Opie "Bert and Squirt" when they both told him his cologne, "Nuit de Paris," smelled like paint.

BERTHA (45F/B) Jeff Pruitt's neighbor and potential girlfriend. According to Jeff, Bertha was strong: she milked cows and was good at calling hogs and picking tobacco. Jeff went home to Bertha after failing to score with Thelma Lou in Mayberry.

BESS (216F/B) The cow in Howard Sprague's joke: A farmer got up earlier than usual to milk his cow, Bess, who was still asleep. She woke up and said, "Thank heavens it's you! I thought I was being robbed!"

BESSIE see under LAWSON, BESSIE

"BEST BETS" (213F/B) A section of the TV directory used in Mayberry. One night, Andy noted that they had a documentary on forest rangers listed there.

"BEST COOK IN MAYBERRY" (194F/B) Bee, according to Helen Crump.

"BEST DANCER IN MAYBERRY" (226F/223B) Howard Sprague, according to Andy.

BEST MAN (67F/65B) Andy's best man was Barney.

"BEST SALESMAN IN MAYBERRY" (54F/B) Andy Taylor, according to Ben Weaver.

BETH (165F/169B) Mayberry hairdresser. She lived in back of the shop. Clara told her she wanted an upswept Italian look.

BETSY (218F/B) Classmate of Opie's. Betsy wanted to write about her uncle for her "most unforgettable character" essay. He had one brown eye and one blue eye.

BETTY ANN (152F/B) Andy got a call from her. Somebody punched her, and Andy attributed it to the violent climate created by Barney, thanks to the deputy's reopening of the "case of the punch in the nose."

"THE BIG BOMB" (134F/B) The fight Barney had with Thelma Lou, as described by Barney. She claimed he never took her anywhere. Barney offered this to Andy as a defense: Sunday, they went to church; Tuesday, it was her house for TV; Thursday, the Diner for the special; and Friday nights when he was working, she came by for coffee.

THE BIG BROTHER MOVEMENT (217F/B) Promotion organized by the sheriff's department. Howard got involved and became a big brother to Tommy Parker, but ended up falling in love with Tommy's sister, Betty.

BIG BROTHERS 217th episode filmed and broadcast. Original broadcast date was March 27, 1967. It was written by Fred S. Fox, and directed by Lee Phillips. Regulars included Andy Griffith, Howard McNear, George Lindsey, and Jack Dodson. Guests included Elizabeth MacRae as Betty Parker, Peter Hobbs as Mr. Tracy, and Scott Lane as Tommy Parker.

BIG FISH IN A SMALL TOWN 198th episode filmed and 200th episode broadcast. Original broadcast date was November 28, 1966. It was written by Bill Idelson and Sam Bobrick, and directed by Lee Phillips. Regulars included Andy Griffith, Jack Dodson, Ronny Howard, Howard McNear, and George Lindsey. Guests included Sam Reese as the Photographer.

"THE BIG FREEZE" (68F/70B) The treatment Barney said he'd give the state inspector called in to look into all the cow thefts in Mayberry. Barney warmed up when it turned out the inspector had read some of Barney's reports to the state and was very impressed.

"BIG HOUSE" (123F/122B) The game Daphne wanted to play when she locked herself and Andy in a cell.

THE BIG HOUSE 95th episode filmed and broadcast. Original broadcast date was May 6, 1963. It was written by Harvey Bullock, and directed by Bob Sweeney. Regulars included Andy Griffith, Don Knotts, and Jim Nabors. Guests included George Kennedy, Lewis Charles, Billy Halop, Jack Lambert, Bob McQuain, Richard Angarola, and Arthur Kendall.

CLINT BIGGERS (93F/B) The real owner of the eleven stray "dogs, dogs, dogs" Opie brought to the Mayberry courthouse.

TOM BIGGERS (45F/B) Mayberry realtor. Andy told Jeff Pruitt that Tom had three houses for sale. It wasn't said if Tom and Clint were related.

BIGGS DEPARTMENT STORE (169F/165B) (179F/B) In 169F/165B, the department store across the street from the Mayberry courthouse. In 179F/B, people ran into the store when Clarence Earp challenged Andy to a duel at high noon on Main Street.

A BIKE (161F/160B) Red and white bike with two headlights, and foxtails on the handlebars. This bike was Opie's planned purchase with the money he would earn working at Mr. Doakes' market.

BILL (28F/B) Barney showed him a coat—imported from Richmond—at the Save the Scoby House Fund rummage sale.

BILLY (1F/B) (18F/B) (190F/B) (203F/210B) Friend of Opie's. In 1F/B, Opie remembered him in his prayers. In 18F/B, Billy was the young man with whom Opie had an argument. In 190F/B, it was Billy who told Floyd and Goober that Cynthia gave Opie his black eye. In 203F/201B, Billy was the boy who passed the football to Opie, which Opie missed, and which then broke Aunt Bee's prize rose.

BILLY RAY (80F/B) Mayberry mailman. He delivered to the courthouse. In 80F/B, he refused to hand Andy the mail, insisting instead on slipping it through the slot in the door. He said Andy wasn't "an authorized receptacle."

"BILLY THE KID" (4F/6B) The character Opie was dressed as while playing on Main Street with Tommy and Steve.

BIOLOGY CLASS (29F/B) Class Andy flunked in the spring of 1938. It was taught by Miss Webster.

THE BIRCH PLACE (29F/B) House on the outskirts of Mayberry where Sam and Lily Becker lived.

"A BIRD IN THE HOUSE MEANS A DEATH IN THE FAMILY" (101F/96B) Barney remembered this old saying when Opie adopted the three orphan songbirds.

ERMA BISHOP (20F/16B) Seamstress who always volunteered to make the costumes for the Founder's Day celebrations. In 20F/16B, she worked on the costumes for the beauty pageant and was truly the unsung hero of the show. Andy recognized her contributions and extricated himself from the difficult situation of having to choose one of the girls by crowning Erma "Miss Mayberry."

MRS. BIXBY (25F/B) One of the ladies of the Women's Historical Society who discovered that living in Mayberry was a direct descendant of the Revolutionary War hero, Nathan Tibbs. It was Otis Campbell.

A BLACK DAY FOR MAYBERRY 102nd episode filmed and broadcast. Original broadcast date was November 11, 1963. It was written by John Whedon, and directed by Jeffrey Hayden. Regulars included Andy Griffith, Don Knotts, Frances Bavier, Ronny Howard, and Jim Nabors. Guests included Rance Howard (Ronny's father), Ken Lynch, Clint Howard, (Ronny's brother) Joe Hamilton, Roy Engel, Charles P. Thompson, Doodles Weaver, Phil Arnold, Alex Barringer, and Leslie Barringer.

BLACK JELLYBEANS (55F/B) Andy's favorite.

BLACKIE (66F/64B) The name of Opie's imaginary horse. Blackie had a silver saddle and a long tail.

MRS. BLAIR (247F/246B) The woman who called Andy to tell him Sam Jones won the head of city council election by 405 votes.

WILTON BLAIR (131F/129B) Barney first met Thelma Lou at Wilton's funeral in 1960.

EDDIE BLAKE (228F/227B) Small-time crook who pulled off the Raleigh bank robbery and was arrested and held at the Mayberry jail.

HARRY BLAKE (216F/B) He wanted to get Howard Sprague to entertain at the Elk's "Annual Hijinks."

PAT BLAKE (150F/B) The production assistant for the "Sheriff Without A Gun" TV show. She set up Andy with flattery in order to rob the Mayberry Security Bank.

ROSE BLAKE (15F/B) According to Aunt Bee, Rose went to Raleigh to buy a new set of teeth.

THE BLAKE BOY (190F/B) A bully. Andy figured that he was the one who gave Opie his black eye. Helen's niece, Cynthia, actually did it.

MISS BLANCHARD (244F/243B) Reporter for the "Kansas City Chronicle" who gave Andy the information he requested about Helen's arrest.

BLANCHE (92F/B) One of the potential "wives for Andy" that Barney sent over to Andy's house.

EDITH BLESSING (84F/B) She and Mrs. Rosenbach had been talking about Mrs. Tarbochs when Arnold Winkler, the "spoiled kid," rode by and knocked over Mrs. Rosenbach.

"BLOCKHOUSE LOOKOUT" (95F/B) The Mayberry courthouse roof.

BLOOD BROTHERS (64F/73B) Andy and Opie were blood brothers, as were Opie and Peggy McMillan. They became brothers by marking an "X" on the inside of their wrists with ashes and then rubbing their wrists together. Opie had suggested cutting their wrists with a knife.

"BLOOD WILL TELL" (113F/112B) What Barney said when Andy told him that Ramona Anchram was the granddaughter of Rotten Ray Anchram. Barney was surprised that Ernest T. and Ramona had hit it off, but understood when he was told of Ramona's lineage.

"BLOODHOUND OF THE LAW" (148F/B) Floyd said that Barney looked like he "smelled something" in the picture used on Barney's "Honest, Fearless" campaign poster, hence the "Bloodhound of the Law" nickname.

"BLOODY MARY" (55F/B) Aunt Bee, according to Otis, after she took over as his warden.

BLUE (10F/12B) Lucy Matthews' favorite color.

BLUE (128F/133B) The name of Barney's bloodhound.

"BLUE BOY" (211F/207B) The painting on the wall of Barney's room in Ma Parker's boarding house.

BLUE CONVERTIBLE (176F/B) 1960 automobile with a 1961 grill. It backfired. Barney drove it from Raleigh to Mayberry for the class reunion.

"BLUE MOONLIGHT" (239F/238B) Cologne sold at Mr. Crawford's drugstore. Four ounces cost sixty-four dollars. Opie broke a sample bottle and, thinking it was the real thing, bought a new one rather then tell Mr. Crawford. His decision to withhold the truth was due in large part to Arnold's "advice." The truth came out, though, and Crawford paid Opie back. Andy bought the cologne for Helen.

BLUE ROBES (238F/239B) What Aunt Bee and Clara Edwards wanted to buy with the $500 willed to All Souls Church. The robes were made of heavy polished cotton with a detachable collar made of poplin, guaranteed wrinkle-proof. They cost $37.50 each.

BLUE ROCK CAVERNS (233F/231B) Howard wanted to go to the King Arthur Pageant and then the Blue Rock Caverns in Morgantown for his and Millie's honeymoon.

"BLUE STEEL BABY" (150F/B) The name Barney called his gun.

BLUE SUIT, PEARLS, HAT, AND WHITE GLOVES (225F/224B) Bee's outfit when she dropped off Opie at the Hollanders. She told the maid she was "not exactly dressed for visiting" when the maid invited her in.

BLUE THUNDERBIRD (202F/199B) Car driven by Mr. Garland, the character played by Jack Nicholson. His wife abandoned their son on the courthouse steps.

BLUE VIEW MOTEL (136F/B) (240F/B) In 136F/B, Barney took Phoebe Gilbert to the Banquet Room at the motel for dinner. In 240F/B, Barney suggested the Banquet Room in the motel as a possible site for the US/USSR summit meeting.

"BLUEBERRY" (168F/B) The name Pat Michaels called Mayberry.

BLUEBERRY PIE (184F/B) Pete and Opie fed Evie Joy blueberry pie. Her lips turned blue and Bee panicked.

BLUEBIRD DINER (85F/B) (102F/B) (132F/128B) Mayberry eatery where Juanita worked. Frank usually answered the phone when Barney called, and Barney invariably said "Hi, Sweetie" to Frank. In 85F/B, Barney called there to make an eight o'clock date with Juanita. In 102F/B, Barney called Juanita there to "not tell" her about the gold shipment coming through Mayberry. Juanita had guessed it was a rocket.

"THE BLUEPRINT STAGE" (61F/B) In his attempt at impressing the student/reporter, Jean Boswell, Barney explained that the following were in the "blueprint stage" for the Mayberry jail: a crime lab, a wing of cell blocks, a dispensary, a recreation hall, and a chapel.

MR. BLUETT (183F/182B) Mayberry citizen who said the gypsies must have had something to do with the rain because it did, in fact, rain. Mr. Bluett told the gypsies they could stay in Mayberry.

BERTIE BLUSH (97F/101B) Gomer told Jason a fish story about Bertie that took place near Lover's Leap Rock. As Gomer told the story, he ignored Wally's customers. Wally fired him, which caused Gomer to become Andy's "house guest."

LEONARD BLUSH (116F/115B) (128F/133B) The "Masked Singer." Leonard Blush became something of a legend in Mayberry and the surrounding towns. It's not really clear whether or not Blush actually came from Mayberry, although it's likely because he, like Barney, was a voice student of Mayberry's Eleanora Poultice. Eleanora took pride in reminding people that two years after she met Leonard Blush he sang the "Star-Spangled Banner" at the opening of the county insecticide convention. He was called the "Masked Singer" because he would wear a black mask while singing. (He wore the mask until his skin condition cleared up.) He was a favorite of Andy's and Barney's. He had a nasal voice and usually sang with just a piano accompaniment. In 128F/133B, he sang on station WMPD, "the voice of Mt. Pilot."

BLYNKEN (101F/96B) One of the three songbirds Opie adopted (along with Wynken and Nod) after he accidentally killed their mother with a slingshot. Blynken was "wiry."

BO (111F/1110B) Mr. Frisby's rooster. His full name was Beauregard. When Frisby was forced to leave his land, he gave Bo to Opie.

BOB (165F/169B) The real name of the Taylors' chauffeur in Hollywood. His stage name was John. Bee called him Bob.

BOBBY FLEET AND HIS BAND WITH A BEAT (3F/B) (24F/B) Musical group that came through Mayberry on occasion. In 3F/B, Andy convinced Bobby Fleet to hire Jim Lindsey for the band. The group consisted of five guys; they played trumpet, trombone, clarinet and drums, with Bobby on lead vocals. In 24F/B, they were the band playing at the Saturday night social.

"BOIL THAT CABBAGE DOWN" (121F/120B) Song Andy performed with the Darlings.

BOILED BEEF (229F/228B) Dish Aunt Bee prepared. She made it because Mr. Bronson had a special on it.

BOLOGNA (54F/B) (76F/78B) 25¢.

BOND (39F/36B) Issued by the Town of Mayberry in 1861. It's face was $100 and it was at 8 1/2 percent interest. Frank Myers inherited it through his family, and in 1961 it was worth $349,119.27. Frank demanded payment on the bond and this threatened to bankrupt Mayberry. Eventually, however, it was discovered to be worthless because it had originally been bought with Confederate money.

THE BOOKIE BARBER 60th episode filmed and broadcast. Original broadcast date was April 16, 1962. It was written by Ray Allen Saffian and Harvey Bullock, and directed by Bob Sweeney. Regulars included Andy Griffith, Don Knotts, Howard McNear, Frances Bavier, and Ronny Howard. Guests included Herb Vigran as Bill Medwin the bookie barber, and Cheerio Meredith as Emma Watson.

FRED BOONE (18F/B) Mayberry man who fought—constantly and violently—with his wife, Jennie. When their neighbors complained about the dish-throwing and the noise, Andy stepped in and taught them to be civil to each other. The result, however, was that they then become rotten to all their friends. Andy allowed them to go back to fighting because somehow, illogically, the Boones expressed their affection by being horribly cruel to each other all the time.

JENNIE BOONE (18F/B) Fred's wife and sparring partner.

BOOSTER'S CLUB (200F/197B) Clara set up a speaking engagement for Bee at a Booster's luncheon during her city council campaign.

JEAN BOSWELL (61F/B) Reporter for J. Howard Jackson. Jackson sent Boswell to Mayberry to "get the dirt" on Andy after Andy forced Jackson to return to Mayberry to pay a fifteen-dollar speeding ticket. Boswell posed as a college student doing a thesis on small town administration and "seduced" Barney into revealing things about Andy that he found unprofessional.

HARRY BOSWORTH (172F/170B) Head of the Mayberry Department of Water and Power. He gave the welcoming speech to Governor Handley at the Founder's Day parade.

AGENT BOUTON (98F/97B) Federal agent with the Alcohol Control Division. He was familiar with "Big Jack" Anderson, the moonshiner.

FREDERICK BOWDEN III (110F/109B) Andy and Opie's pal, Trey. Trey came from Erie, Pennsylvania, with his mother to visit Clara Edwards. When Andy took a special interest in Trey, Opie got jealous and had to make adjustments and develop maturity. Among the things that annoyed Opie was the fact that Andy let Trey use his fishing pole, sleep in his bed, and he brought him milk and pie in bed. In 153F/B, Trey forgot to bring his lunch to school. This bit of news warranted a mention in Opie's newspaper, "The Mayberry Sun."

TREY BOWDEN (110F/109B) (122F/121B) (127F/126B) Frederick Bowden III. Trey was his nickname. Trey and Opie were blood brothers. In 122F/121B, Trey sent back his Miracle Salve after failing to sell it. The company sent him a "blacklist" scare letter which prompted Barney to pose as U.T. Pendyke, D.V.M. In 127F/126B, Trey told Andy that Opie was gone from the camping trip.

BOWLING ALLEY (109F/108B) The mother of Sarah, the operator, broke her hip there.

"BOY WANTED AFTER SCHOOL AND SAT. APPLY INSIDE" (161F/160B) Sign in the window of Mr. Doakes' market.

"BOYS AT THE LAB" (113F/112B) Fictitious associates of Barney's. He wanted to send Ernest T. Bass's rock to them for fingerprinting.

BOY'S DAY (51F/B) Mayberry event, presumably yearly, in which the boys in town competed in athletic events for medals. Andy was usually finish line judge, and Barney, the official starter.

BOY'S DETECTIVE DISGUISE KIT (50F/B) The present to Opie from Horton, the state investigator.

BOYSINGER'S BAKERY (222F/225B) Main Street bakery where Millie Hutchins worked, across the street from the courthouse.

MERLIN BRACEY (99F/98B) He called the courthouse to tell Andy he saw Ernest T. Bass break a streetlight in front of Miss Mingus's house.

NATE BRACEY (82F/B) Classmate of Andy's and Barney's. He and his wife took dance lessons.

BRADBURY BUSINESS COLLEGE (231F/230B) Howard Sprague's alma mater. It was in Mt. Pilot on the third floor of the Essex Bank Building. Howard took the year-and-a-half course.

"BRADFORD INTERNATIONAL ICE CREAM" (234F/232B) The trade name Bradford Taylor suggested for Bee's ice cream, which he planned on marketing.

CHARLIE BRADSHAW (238F/239B) Member of the Building and Safety Committee. He was out of town when Howard called the meeting regarding the tilting of the church.

HERB BRADSHAW (247F/246B) The head of the Mayberry City Council. His resignation opened up the seat, which prompted Sam Jones to run for and win it. Herb resigned to become head teller for the Raleigh Security Bank. It wasn't said whether Herb was related to either Charlie Bradshaw or the Widow Bradshaw.

THE WIDOW BRADSHAW (164F/162B) Ernest T. Bass thought she was after him. It wasn't said if she was related to Charlie Bradshaw. Since Charlie was said to be alive in 238F/239B, "The Church Benefactors," she couldn't be his widow. Therefore, if there was a relationship, she might have been Charlie's mother.

BILL BRADY (38F/41B) Brother of Mary Brady. He lived with his sister in Mt. Pilot, and was a former "victim" of Henry Wheeler.

MARY BRADY (38F/41B) Woman in Mt. Pilot who lived with her brother, Bill Brady. Henry Wheeler moved in with the Bradys and sponged off them for quite a while.

MR. BRADY (26F/B) Inspector Ralph Case's superior. Case called him to Mayberry to view Andy's atrocious ways of running the courthouse and the jail. When Brady saw how well Andy handled the moonshiner, Luke Rainer, he realized that Case was all wet.

PURCELL BRANCH (106F/B) (160F/163B) Tyler's dad. He was arrested in 1931 by Sheriff Pinckley for disturbing the peace: he drove down Main Street with the cutout open on his REO Flying Cloud. In 160F/163B, Purcell lived across the street from Andy and he stared at Andy and Helen while they sat on the porch of Andy's house.

TYLER BRANCH (106F/B) Purcell's son.

EMMA BRAND (1F/B) (2F/B) (6F/4B) (15F/B) In 1F/B, Barney arrested Emma for jaywalking on Maple Street. Emma scolded him, saying, "Naughty deputy." When Andy released Emma, Barney asserted that Mayberry was becoming a "regular sin town." In 2F/B, she was a Mayberry citizen with sciatica who made a batch of pies just about every day. She was held hostage by the escaped prisoner, Dirksen, in "The Manhunt." She was later known as "Emma Watson." In 6F/4B, Fred Walker had been selling Emma ten-cent blue sugar pills for years. They acted as a placebo for her sciatica. When Ellie Walker refused to sell them to Emma without a prescription, Emma took to her bed and everyone hated Ellie. Ellie relented and everybody was happy. In 15F/B, Emma was one of the women who gossiped in the drugstore about Millie Parsons' putting blonde streaks in her hair. (The other women there were Clara Linsey and Bee Taylor.) Emma bought toothpaste for 60¢, rubbing alcohol for 29¢, and peroxide for 45¢. The ladies also discussed Rose Blake's trip to Raleigh to buy a new set of teeth.

JUDGE BRANSON (244F/243B) Judge friend of Andy's who lived in Mt. Pilot. Andy went to see him to get more information about Helen's arrest.

BRASS MEDALLION (39F/36B) Memento Frank Myers had from the St. Louis World's Fair of 1906.

BRAZIL (234F/232B) The place where Bradford Taylor claimed he had a plantation.

"BREAD, LOVE, AND BEANS" (44F/B) The movie Barney saw while on vacation in Raleigh. It was "pretty risque let me tell you."

BREAD PUDDING (240F/B) The US and USSR ambassadors ate it in Bee's kitchen late at night during the summit meeting.

"THE BREADWINNER" (161F/160B) Andy's role, according to Andy. He brought up this rather obvious fact on the day Opie wrecked his bike while trying to impress Sharon Porter.

BREAKFAST FOR OTIS (55F/B) Barney fixed the following for one of Otis' "morning-after" breakfasts: two soft-boiled eggs (four minutes), one piece of toast, coffee, black with one sugar.

MARTIN BRECKINRIDGE (225F/224B) The biggest real estate operator in North Carolina; a friend of George Hollander's.

DR. HARRISON EVERETT BREEN (100F/99B) The visiting preacher from New York City who gave the sermon called "What's Your Hurry?" in All Souls Church.

ASA BREENY (117F/116B) Ben Weaver's night watchman.

"BRIAN JACKSON STONE MASON HEAD STONES + ART OBJECTS" (208F/212B) Jackson's sign.

BRICE'S DEPARTMENT STORE (223F/226B) Mt. Pilot department store that was the site of a nighttime burglary. The items stolen were "two typewriters, several toasters, a waffle iron, a large stereo combination, and a TV set." Also, as was later revealed, a radio was stolen. Marvin Jenkins was arrested and charged with the robbery. Aunt Bee was a juror at his trial. He was later acquitted, thanks to some detective work by Andy.

GEORGE BRICKER (38F/41B) Mayberry mailman. Because of all the work being done on it, Bricker asked Andy if he was selling his house.

MRS. BRIGGS (239F/238B) Opie made her a sandwich at Mr. Crawford's soda fountain. She tipped him ten cents.

"BRINGING IN THE SHEAVES" (47F/B) Song Barney sang to Otis in order to lull him to sleep.

"BRINGING NELLIE HOME" (59F/B) Song sung at Mary Simpson's house by Andy, Barney, Mary, and Thelma Lou.

BRINGING UP OPIE 32nd episode filmed and broadcast. Original broadcast date was May 22, 1961. It was written by Jack Elinson and Charles Stewart, and directed by Bob Sweeney. Regulars included Andy Griffith, Ronny Howard, Don Knotts, Frances Bavier, and Hal Smith. Guests included Mike Brent.

BRISCOE DECLARES FOR AUNT BEE 96th episode filmed and 100th episode broadcast. Original broadcast date was October 28, 1963. It was written by Jim Fritzell and Everett Greenbaum, and directed by Earl Bellamy. Regulars included Andy Griffith, Frances Bavier, and Ronny Howard. Guests included Denver Pyle as Briscoe Darling, and The Dillards as The Darling Boys.

MR. BRISTOL (218F/B) Eggman. Bee suggested him as a possible subject for Opie's essay, "My Most Unforgettable Character."

CLIFF BRITTEN (42F/B) Member of the Esquire Club. Andy and Barney were introduced to him at one of the meetings.

GEORGE BRONSON (42F/B) Member of the Esquire Club. Andy and Barney were introduced to him at one of the meetings.

MR. BRONSON (131F/129B) The Civil Service regional director. He had to verify that the deputies of North Carolina met the new height and weight requirements.

MR. BRONSON (229F/228B) Mayberry butcher. He ran a special on the cut of meat Aunt Bee used to prepare boiled beef.

GEORGE BROOKFIELD (226F/223B) A lawyer Howard Sprague knew in Raleigh.

EDDIE BROOKS (30F/B) Small-time crook who escaped from Atlanta and ended up passing through Mayberry, where he was unwittingly captured by Barney. Eddie was a "three time loser doing twenty years." Eddie swore revenge on Barney and escaped again. He came back to Mayberry looking for Barney and was captured once again, this time through Andy's maneuverings (although Barney was allowed the credit).

"THE BROTHERS THREE" (116F/115B) The name Eleanora Poultice suggested for Andy, Barney, and Gomer after their vocal "trio" went over so well at the concert. It was supposed to be a solo.

ELLEN BROWN (48F/B) "The manicurist" and a "centerfold come to life." When Ellen left her boyfriend, Pierre, she got on a bus and got off in Mayberry because she saw the sign that said, "Welcome to Mayberry, the Friendly Town." The ladies in town weren't so friendly when Floyd gave her a job in the barbershop and Ellen actually held the hands of the Mayberry men (all in the line of duty, of course). Eventually, she made up with Pierre and went back and married him. But not before she had a chance to give the Mayberry guys the nicest looking nails in the South.

HARRY BROWN (244F/243B) The hoodlum that Helen Crump associated with (while undercover) and was arrested with in 1959.

WILSON BROWN (229F/228B) Rhythm guitarist in Opie's band, "The Sound Committee."

DAVID BROWNE (40F/38B) Hobo friend of Opie's who came to Mayberry and proceeded to set a bad example for the boy. He taught Opie how to get out of work, and how to steal gumballs. Andy told Browne he was doing harm to Opie, so Dave pretended to steal Aunt Bee's purse so he'd look bad in Opie's eyes. Opie called him "Mr. Dave."

"BROWNEYED MARY" (60F/B) Horse that Sarah thought was a girl after she overheard Bill Medwin's horse-betting phone calls.

BROWNIE RECIPE (223F/226B) Judge Cranston requested Bee's in a letter to her after the Brice's Department Store trial.

BROWNIES AND HOT CHOCOLATE (208F/212B) Clara Edwards served them at the meeting of the Civic Improvement Committee held at her house.

BRUCE (129F/130B) Ollie and Nora's son.

BRUCE (181F/B) Floyd gave Bruce a haircut for the school party. The boy told him that his mother said Floyd had cut it too short last time.

ROGER BRYANT (213F/B) Publishing company owner, editor, and publisher. His house—Bryant Publishing Company—put out Helen Crump's first book, *Amusing Tales of Tiny Tots*.

BRYANT PUBLISHING COMPANY (213F/B) The publishing house that published Helen Crump's book, *Amusing Tales of Tiny Tots*, under the pseudonym Helene Alexian Dubois. The company was headed by Roger Bryant, Robling Flask was the flamboyant cover designer, and Harold Mosley was promotion director. Bryant sent Helen a $1,000 advance for her book.

ORVILLE BUCK (173F/174B) Aunt Bee's first blind date. They went ice-skating. He had weak ankles and Bee had to hold him up all night. He was killed later in an explosion.

BUCKET ISSUE (107F/127B) Gomer Pyle was issued a bucket upon his induction into the Marines. It was "to be filled with personal items such as soap, toothbrush, razor blades, etc." Sergeant Carter used the bucket to cover Gomer's head when Gomer talked in the ranks.

SHERIFF DALE BUCKLEY (106F/B) The sheriff of Mayberry before Andy Taylor.

"BUDDY" (53F/B) The name Barney called Sheldon Davis.

HASTY BUFORD (121F/120B) Mountain man with whom Dud Wash went fox hunting. They didn't return for a week. This, and Dud's grinning at Idele Bushy during the preacher's sermon, were the reasons Charlene Darling divorced Dud.

BUGLE (72F/71B) The prize Opie won—along with ten free lessons—at the movie house.

"BUGS AND WORMS AND THINGS" (101F/96B) Opie's breakfast for his three adopted sons, the songbirds Wynken, Blynken, and Nod.

BUILDING AND SAFETY COMMITTEE (238F/239B) Committee with Howard Sprague as chairman, and Charlie Bradshaw and Emmett Clark as members. When Jarrad Hooper willed $500 to All Souls Church, Howard called a meeting of the committee to mobilize efforts to correct the tilting of the church.

HARVEY BUNKER (213F/B) He had to quit being scoutmaster after he dated Mavis Neff.

MRS. BUNTLEY (10F/12B) Mother of the twins, Robert and William. She was surprised when the "stranger in town," Ed Sawyer, knew all about her and could tell the difference between her two boys.

ROBERT BUNTLEY (10F/12B) One of the Buntley twins.

WILLIAM BUNTLEY (10F/12B) One of the Buntley twins. William had a mole on his right ear.

BURFORD'S (245F/244B) The Mayberry department store where Emmett bought a genuine thermaweave woolen bathrobe for Martha.

KAREN BURGESS (91F/B) Girl Opie was sweet on. She couldn't care less about him, though, until he started hanging around with Thelma Lou, much to the dismay of Barney.

DR. BURNSIDE (185F/B) In 185F/B, a Mayberry physician. Mrs. Sprague assured Howard that Burnside was as close as the phone during her fake "illness."

DR. BURNSIDE (231F/230B) In 231F/230B, he was a Mayberry dentist. He suggested that Opie might be able to take over his practice when he decided to retire.

BURSITIS (23F/B) (54F/B) In 23F/B, Bee's cousin Edgar's wife, Maude, got it when she slept with the window open. This necessitated Bee going to Mt. Pilot to help. In 54F/B, it was one of Bert Miller's ailments. He had it in his left shoulder.

BURT (187F/186B) Crewman for the Foster Furniture Polish commercial in which Bee almost starred.

BURT (191F/192B) Member of the Mayberry Barbershop Quartet.

MR. BURTON (81F/B) The blast engineer in charge of dynamiting the new Mayberry underpass, which was being built for the benefit of Mayor Stoner's brother.

IDELE BUSHY (121F/120B) Girl Dud Wash grinned at during preaching. This was the reason Charlene Darling divorced him. It wasn't said if Idele was related to Nate Bushy.

NATE BUSHY (105F/104B) Mayberry man who took his mother to the annual chamber of commerce dance.

"BUSINESSMAN'S SPECIAL" (78F/76B) Luncheon special at the Diner. It consisted of a hollowed-out tomato stuffed with avocado and raisins, topped off with a lemon phosphate. Andy suggested Barney go have one and then take a walk over to the Grand and watch them change the marquee.

"BUSTER" (53F/B) The name Barney called Sheldon Davis.

BUSTER (184F/B) Goober's teddy bear.

"BUT BARNEY, I'M YOUR MOTHER" (2F/B) The only line ever spoken by Barney's mother, said during her only appearance on the show. She said it because Barney stopped her during a roadblock while on the "manhunt."

MR. BUTLER (78F/76B) Newspaper man who spelled Barney's name "Fike."

BUTTERSCOTCH PECAN (103F/B) Opie's favorite pie.

A BUTTONHOOK (39F/36B) One of Frank Myers' "valuables."

C+ AVERAGE (231F/230B) Opie's grades at the time of this episode. A "B" average was needed for admission to the University of North Carolina at Chapel Hill.

CABBAGE (73F/70B) 12¢ a head as sold by Neil and Matt from the back of their truck.

THE CACAYA TRIBE (183F/182B) Murillos, the gypsy leader, hypothesized that the band of gypsies that had previously passed through Mayberry—and cheated people—was the Cacaya tribe.

THE CAFE (96F/100B) Mayberry eatery. The Darlings caused trouble when they went there to eat. Briscoe Darling wanted to sit in the kitchen and watch them prepare his meal.

CAL (2F/B) Mayberry citizen stopped by Barney during the "manhunt" roadblock.

BUNNY CALDWELL (118F/117B) Woman who complained to Andy that Gomer gave her a parking ticket. Andy explained that there was no parking between 9:30 and 11:00 in the morning on Tuesdays and Thursdays so that Mr. Martinelli could sweep out his meat market.

GENTLEMAN DAN CALDWELL (21F/B) "Gentleman" con man who Andy had to hold in the Mayberry jail for a day or two. His specialties were forgery, swindling, and con games. He had bilked women in Bowling Green, Kentucky, and Jacksonville, Florida. Caldwell had his cigars made in Tampa. He swept Bee off her feet with compliments, and won Opie over by telling him the story of Baby Face Nelson and John Dillinger. Caldwell stole Barney's gun to escape but Andy laughed him off, convincing Caldwell that Barney never kept his gun loaded. The laugh was on Andy, though, because after Andy took the gun from Caldwell, he fired a live round into the ceiling.

CALIFORNIA (210F/211B) The Robinson family of Mayberry moved there.

"CALIFORNIA, HERE WE COME" (166F/B) The song the Mayberry Band played as Andy, Bee, and Opie boarded the bus to the airport for their Hollywood trip.

FRED CALLAHAN (191F/192B) The tenor Burt suggested as Howard Sprague's replacement for the barbershop quartet competition. Fred couldn't participate, though, because he was dead.

MR. CALVIN (247F/246B) Man who lived on Elm Street. Bee and Helen visited him in an attempt to get his vote for Sam Jones as head of city council.

CAMP WILSON (107F/127B) Gomer Pyle's Marine Corps boot camp.

CAMP WINOKE (225F/224B) Boy's camp. It was twenty-two acres on lovely Lake Winoke. Andy sent Opie there for summer Saturdays. The cost was ten dollars a day, and the activities included tennis and waterskiing. It was there that Opie met Billy Hollander.

CLAUDIA CAMPBELL (248F/247B) Heather's sister. She was named after her mother's mother. She and Mike Jones became an item.

HEATHER CAMPBELL (248F/247B) Girl who moved next door to Opie. Opie hit it off with her, much to the chagrin of Mike Jones—Sam's son—who had become attached to Opie. She was from West Virginia, was named after her father's sister, and she took piano lessons.

OTIS CAMPBELL (101F/96B) (137F/B) (175F/B) Mayberry's lovable town drunk. In 101F/96B, Otis forgot his radio at the courthouse. In 137F/B, he was Deputy #3, as deputized by Barney. In 175F/B, Warren attempted to teach Otis to make mosaic tile pictures. Otis took to it, and did a horrible picture of a cow for Andy and Aunt Bee. He also insisted that they hang it over their fireplace. Because of Otis's successful rehabilitation through tile art, Warren arranged for him to talk before the art class. He was to explain how art saved him from drinking. Otis found out, however, that Andy had taken down his picture, and so he showed up at the class drunk. The next day he presented another picture, this one lovely and scenic, that he had done when "a little gassed." He now had two hobbies, he explained: drinking and art. Otis was a town drunk when heavy drinking was still cute. A portrayal such as that of Otis Campbell simply would not be shown today. Right or not, though, Otis was a gentleman, and an uproariously funny guy. (See additional entries beginning with the word "OTIS" or "OTIS'S")

RALPH CAMPBELL (63F/B) Otis Campbell's brother. He came to visit Otis, and Andy agreed to deputize Otis to impress Ralph. It turned out that Ralph was the town drunk back home.

VERLAINE CAMPBELL (63F/B) Ralph Campbell's wife.

CONGRESSMAN JOHN CANFIELD (160F/163B) Another beau of Bee's who was seen once and forgotten. Canfield had been living in Washington, D.C., as a congressman from North Carolina. He retired and moved back to Mayberry. Andy invited him to dinner and he asked Bee out. Because of a mistaken notion on her part that he'd find her too slowpaced after his life in Washington, she made it a point to go out every night and keep ridiculously busy. It turned out that she was tiring him out and that he didn't want that kind of hectic life anymore. His return to Mayberry was announced in the "Mayberry Gazette" with the headline "Congressman John Canfield Returning To Mayberry."

CANNON (14F/B) (172F/170B) Gun in the town square. In 14F/B, in order to sell it, Andy made up the following story about it for the antique dealer, Ralph Mason: it fired the first shot at Fort Sumter, the crack in the muzzle came from a direct hit while Teddy Roosevelt was a'draggin' her up San Juan Hill, it was Teddy's favorite cannon, and the initials T.R. scratched in the cannon by Tracy Rupert were actually Roosevelt's. In 172F/170B, a cannonball was stuck in it. Warren fired it and shot the station wagon that held the two crooks, Jack and Stella.

THE CANNON 172nd episode filmed and 170th episode broadcast. Original broadcast date was November

22, 1965. It was written by Jack Elinson, and directed by Alan Rafkin. Regulars included Andy Griffith, Frances Bavier, George Lindsey, Howard McNear, and Jack Burns. Guests included Justin Smith as John, Byron Foulger as Harry Bosworth, Vaughn Taylor as Frank Chase, J. Edward McKinley as Governor George C. Handley, Sally Mansfield as Stella, Robert Carnes as Jack, and Douglas McCairn as the Driver.

"CANNONBALL" (5F/8B) The nickname Andy called Opie as they played catch in front of the courthouse.

"CANNONBALL EXPRESS" (3F/B) The name Bobby Fleet derogatorily called the waitress at the Diner. Apparently, she wasn't moving fast enough for him.

CANTEEN (5F/8B) A social gathering Annabelle Silby and the ladies club organized for the boys back from the war. It took place every Saturday night.

CANTON PALACE see AUNT BEE'S "CANTON PALACE"

CAPITOL CITY (57F/B) North Carolina "big city" where Andy and Barney went to request funds for Mayberry from the commissioner. Barney thought that the hotel detective was a jewel thief, and that the jewel thief was a newspaper owner. Andy figured everything out and once again extricated Barney from a tangled mess. They stayed in room 920.

THE CAPONE GANG (40F/38B) Barney thought that Dave the Hobo might be "Mr. Big" of the Capone gang.

CAPRICORN (10F/12B) Lucy Matthews' sign.

CARBURETOR RECORD (182F/183B) Goober's record for dismantling a carburetor was thirty-eight minutes twelve seconds.

CARL (72F/71B) First clarinet in the Mayberry Band. Andy told him to "Andy Gump" his mouth more on his clarinet.

CARL (216F/B) Howard Sprague's uncle. He used to come out with "humorous quips."

CARL BENSON'S WILDCATS (82F/B) (176F/B) In 82F/B, the band that played at the Class of 1945 Mayberry Union High class reunion. Carl's mother played sax. In 176F/B, the band that played at the class reunion. Mrs. Atzell played regularly with the band, except on Friday nights when the library was open.

CARP (41F/39B) Andy caught one and told the boys at the barbershop about it.

MR. CARP (41F/39B) Margaret Williamson, the reporter, heard that Andy killed a "Mr. Carp." She was aghast. Of course, Mr. Carp was a fish.

CARROLL'S OF MAYBERRY (45F/B) Men's clothier where Andy took Jeff Pruitt to buy him a suit.

CARROTS (73F/70B) 15¢ a bunch as sold by Neil and Matt from the back of their truck.

DOC CARRUTHERS (24F/B) (52F/B) In 24F/B, he was mentioned as an early doctor in Mayberry. In 52F/B, he told Barney that his throat was well enough for the deputy to sing.

MARTHA CARRUTHERS (187F/186B) Girl from Pleasantville who took over as the Foster Lady after Bee withdrew.

ELMER CARSON (185F/B) Denise Graber's first cousin.

HAROLD CARSON (212F/208B) Teena Andrews' manager and publicity man. He suggested that Barney—as a publicity stunt—escort Teena to the premiere of her movie.

THE CARSON SHACK (204F/202B) The shack where Otis hid his spirits. Also, the two crooks, Fred and Larry, hid out there after their Mt. Pilot bank robbery.

CARTER (79F/77B) One of Opie's friends. He was with Opie when Steve Quincy broke a street lamp with an apple core and blamed Opie.

HANNAH CARTER (8F/9B) Young girl whose family had been feuding with the Wakefields for eighty-seven years. She wanted to marry Josh Wakefield, and Andy fixed it so she could.

MARY ALICE CARTER (220F/B) Opie's "first love." He had been stuck on her since first grade. He asked her to Arnold's thirteenth birthday party, she accepted, and then stood him up for Fred Simpson. Opie went "stag" and ended up with Mary Alice anyway. Simpson was so conceited that he ignored her all night.

MR. CARTER (8F/9B) His family had been feuding with the Wakefields for eighty-seven years.

MR. CARTER (85F/B) Man who accused Jim Morgan—the boy who worked for him making deliveries—of stealing a battery. Jim did take the battery, but he only borrowed it to see if a motor he had made worked. A new battery cost $12.95.

GUNNERY SERGEANT VINCE CARTER (107F/127B) Gomer Pyle's boot camp drill instructor in the pilot episode, "Gomer Pyle, U.S.M.C.," and later in Gomer's own show of the same name.

CLARA CARTWRIGHT (171F/172B) Bee told Andy that Clara had gotten a job stuffing jelly donuts at the bakery three days a week. The name of the bakery wasn't given, but it was probably Boysinger's. Bee told Andy about Clara to open up the subject of getting a job herself. Clara's birthday was August 21.

"A CARY GRANT MOVIE" (123F/122B) Thelma Lou and Helen wanted Andy and Barney to take them to "a Cary Grant movie" on the night the boys were doing inventory at the courthouse. Andy refused, suggesting that they could all go to the dance the following night. The poster for the movie said, "A rollicking new romantic comedy."

THE CASCADE CLUB (74F/B) Club in Toledo where Al hung out. Al was a friend of the "convicts at large" and had a "dumb face, weak chin, and round shoulders." The cons said Barney reminded them of Al.

INSPECTOR RALPH CASE (26F/B) State inspector sent to Mayberry instead of Andy's friend, Sam Allen. Case was a real "by-the-book" guy who was aghast at Mayberry's laid-back "not-so-by-the-book" ways. Case called his superior, Mr. Brady, to Mayberry to see just how bad things were, but Brady was impressed with Andy's handling of the moonshiner, Luke Rainer. Rainer was shooting at people and Andy simply walked up, scolded him for acting like a young 'un, and arrested him.

CASE (111F/110B) The make of bulldozer the county sent to knock down Frisby's farm.

"THE CASE OF THE PIGHEADED DEPUTY WHO WAS KILLED BY A BERSERK SHERIFF" (162F/164B) After Warren, the "pigheaded" deputy," arrested the whole Ladies Auxiliary for gambling, Andy told Warren he obviously had not read this story.

THE CASE OF THE PUNCH IN THE NOSE 152nd episode filmed and broadcast. Original broadcast date was March 15, 1965. It was written by Bill Idelson and Sam Bobrick, and directed by Coby Ruskin. Regulars included Andy Griffith, Don Knotts, Ronny Howard, Frances Bavier, George Lindsey, and Howard McNear. Guests included Frank Ferguson as Mr. Foley, and Larry Hovis as Gilly Walker.

CASH REGISTER BANK (51F/B) Opie had one.

CASHEW FUDGE (114F/113B) The snack Thelma Lou made for herself and Barney to eat while watching a George Raft movie.

CASPER TICE AND HIS LATIN RHYTHMS (226F/223B) The band that played at the Harvest Ball.

CASSINO (26F/B) One of the games Barney played against himself.

CATCHER'S MITT (11F/B) The gift the reformed Ben Weaver gave to Billy Muggins.

"CATCHING THE WINNING TOUCHDOWN PASS" (243F/242B) Andy's "big moment."

CATFISH CASSEROLE (125F/124B) The Friday night special at the Diner.

CAULIFLOWER (162F/164B) 10¢.

CB & Q RAILROAD (108F/107B) Wary Willy the Hobo claimed he worked for the railroad as a fireman and got a "multiple fracture of the petulla oblongata" on the job (a bad leg). He had used this questionable injury for years as an excuse not to work.

CELERY (84F/B) (91F/B) (120F/119B) (186F/187B) (201F/204B) (203F/201B) 19¢.

CELL #1 (109F/108B) (118F/117B) Facing the cells, the right cell in the Mayberry courthouse.

CELL #2 (109F/108B) (118F/117B) Facing the cells, the left cell of the Mayberry courthouse.

CENTENNIAL SIGN (138F/B) "Mayberry Centennial Pageant Tryouts Tonight Town Hall 8:30." Andy posted it on the courthouse bulletin board.

CENTERVILLE (16F/20B) Andy had to go to the Centerville, North Carolina, courthouse on business. During Andy's absence, Barney arrested the whole town.

CENTRAL HIGH (153F/B) Barney's high school. In earlier episodes, it was said that Barney and Andy both attended Mayberry Union High. But in 153F/B, it was said that Barney went to Central. It wasn't indicated whether Barney went to two high schools or if Mayberry Union High and Central High were the same school.

CHAMBER OF COMMERCE DANCE (105F/104B) Annual Mayberry event, "The Biggest Dance of the Year." The dance had Japanese lanterns, a buffet supper, and a door prize. Barney arranged for Gomer to take Thelma Lou's cousin, Mary Grace Gossage. As they were all sitting in Thelma Lou's house before the dance, Gomer suddenly jumped up and left. The girls were all upset and their night was a flop. When they returned to Thelma Lou's, they found Gomer dancing with Mary Grace; he only ran out to get her a corsage because she was the only girl who didn't have one.

CHAMPION HAND WRESTLER (182F/183B) Goober, for four years in a row.

CHANNEL 12 (237F/236B) Siler City TV station owned by Carl Phillips. Channel 12 ran Bee's cooking show, "The Mayberry Chef."

CHARITY DANCE (135F/B) Andy put a sign for the dance on the courthouse window. The sign read, "Charity Dance Wed. 8 P.M. Tickets Here $3 Per Couple." Barney planned on wearing his salt-and-pepper suit, but then decided on his uniform after Fred Plummer told him he'd beat him up if he ever caught him out of uniform.

"CHARLIE" (3F/B) (68F/69B) In 3F/B, the name Bobby Fleet called Andy. In 68F/69B, the name Skippy called Barney.

CHARLIE (16F/20B) Man Andy greeted as he came out of the cell after Barney arrested the whole town.

CHARLIE (31F/B) Member of the Mayberry Drum and Bugle Corp. His assignment, with Ralph, was to carry the banner. Charlie always let his end drop.

CHARLIE (66F/64B) Mr. McBeevee told Travers he needed Charlie to help him with the stringer line.

CHARLIE (79F/77B) He owned the house on Grove Street that the Quincys rented.

CHARLIE (186F/187B) Counterman at the Diner.

CHARLIE (192F/191B) Member of the Regal Order of the Golden Door to Good Fellowship, the Mayberry men's lodge.

CHARLIE (197F/198B) The man who did the lights for "The Senior Play."

CHARLIE (237F/236B) Production person on Bee's cooking show, "The Mayberry Chef." The director consulted with Charlie via headphones during the show.

"CHARLIE CHASE" (74F/B) Sally, one of the "convicts at large," called Floyd "Charlie Chase."

"CHARLIE MONEYBAGS" (5F/8B) The name Andy called Opie when he heard that his son's donation of three cents to the Underprivileged Children's Charity Drive was the lowest amount given.

CHARLOTTE (5F/8B) Opie's girlfriend. Opie saved up to buy her a winter coat.

CHARLOTTE (94F/B) Barney and his mother went on a bus trip to Charlotte, North Carolina.

CHARLOTTESVILLE (5F/8B) Annabelle Silby told everyone that her husband, Tom, got run over by a taxicab in Charlottesville while on a business trip.

FRANK CHASE (172F/170B) He planned the Mayberry Founder's Day parade, which included Sharon Dobbins—the Potato Queen—wearing a bathing suit while riding in a convertible, and Sam Effley riding his motorcycle.

"CHECKPOINT CHICKIE" (112F/111B) The speed trap Barney set up on Highway 6, near Turner's Grade.

CHESTER (76F/78B) One of the "regulars" who hung around outside the Post Office. When he threw a gum wrapper on the sidewalk—in plain sight of Deputy Fife—Barney gave Chester a "Nip It" speech. (See NIP IT)

CHICAGO (82F/B) The town where Sharon Duspaine lived and worked.

CHICKEN (40F/38B) Dave the Hobo stole a chicken from Jes Crawford.

CHICKEN (240F/B) The US and USSR ambassadors ate Bee's chicken in her kitchen late at night.

"THE CHICKEN" (135F/B) The nickname Mr. Izamoto gave Barney, not because he was afraid (even though he was) but because Barney's bones were like chicken bones: thin. They would snap.

CHICKEN A LA KING (153F/B) Dish made by Mrs. Foster. It tasted like wallpaper.

CHICKEN AND DUMPLINGS (3F/B) The dish Aunt Bee prepared for Jim Lindsey on the day Andy arrested him for disturbing the peace.

CHICKEN AND DUMPLINGS AND SWEET TATER PIE (44F/B) The meal Andy promised Aunt Bee would prepare for Rafe Hollister on his first night in jail.

CHICKEN CASSEROLE (223F/226B) Clara made it for Andy and Opie for the Wednesday and Thursday Bee would be on jury duty.

CHICKEN FRICASEE (225F/224B) The dish the Diner was offering at noon the day Opie had Billy Hollander over for lunch.

CHICKEN IN A POT (237F/236B) The dish Aunt Bee prepared on the air the second day of her cooking show, "The Mayberry Chef."

CHICKEN OR POT ROAST (65F/67B) Aunt Bee left these two meals for Andy and Opie when she went to visit her Aunt Louise for three or four days.

CHICKEN PAPRIKASH (228F/227B) The recipe Aunt Bee wanted to make at the close of this episode.

CHICKEN WIRE FENCE (44F/B) Andy's solution to Osgood's and Huey Welch's fight over the spike fence Osgood built on their mutual property line. The fence prevented Huey's laying hens from getting enough sun.

CHICKEN WITH CRUST (65F/67B) Opie said it was Andy's favorite.

"CHICKIE-BABY" (72F/71B) Barney started to call Andy "chickie-baby" after he hung around the Freddy Fleet band too long. Barney got his "cool" talk from Phil Sunkel in the band.

"CHIEF" (78F/76B) Barney called Andy "chief" whenever he saw a crime movie. In 78F/76B, the movie he saw was "G-Men," with Glenn Ford.

"CHILDISH" (134F/B) Helen called Thelma Lou childish during the four-way fight which involved them, Andy, and Barney.

CHILI (104F/105B) The dish that Barney cooked in his room. Cooking caused his eviction from Mrs. Mendlebright's boarding house.

CHIMNEY ROCK (207F/209B) Locale near Myer's Lake.

"CHINATOWN" (87F/B) (160F/163B) (227F/222B) In 87F/B, Aunt Bee and members of the Ladies Aid church committee sang "Chinatown" after they all got drunk on Colonel Harvey's Indian Elixir. In 160F/163B, Bee sang the song after her first date with John Canfield. In 227F/222B, Bee sang it as she prepared for her trip to Mexico.

CHING LEE'S (192F/191B) Mrs. Sprague had reservations for herself and Howard at Ching Lee's the night Andy invited Howard to the lodge meeting. Howard went to the lodge meeting.

CHIPPED BEEF PUFFS (228F/227B) The recipe Bee gave Clara over the phone.

"CHIRIBIRIBIN" (83F/B) Barney's audition song for the Ladies League musicale.

CHIROPRACTOR (71F/72B) When he posed as Floyd's son, "Andrew Paul Lawson," Andy told Madeline Grayson he was still in school learning to be a chiropractor.

CHOCOLATE LAYER CAKE (136F/B) Andy's favorite cake.

CHOCOLATE STAIN (58F/B) Aunt Bee had one on her dress. She brought the dress to Fred Goss, the cleaner.

CHOIR MEETING (114F/113B) The meeting Andy planned on attending the night the "prisoner of love" came to Mayberry. The purpose of the meeting was to vote on new choir robes. Cissy Noonan wanted white robes with black collars. Fred Henry wanted black robes with white collars.

CHONEY (109F/108B) Mayberry citizen who was at the town picnic when the Old Mine Caves collapsed, sealing Andy and Helen inside. After the "rescue," Andy told Choney that if it had been him in the mine, he probably wouldn't have been so quick to tease Barney about stopping Mr. Meldrim from opening his own bank. (Barney thought it was a robbery.)

"CHOPPER" (50F/B) According to Barney, one of his nicknames.

"CHRISTMAS, HA!" (11F/B) The phrase Ben Weaver used to show his disdain for the Christmas season. It was meant to echo "Bah, Humbug!" for a character that was essentially a Mayberry Ebenezer Scrooge.

CHRISTMAS STORY 11th episode filmed and broadcast. Original broadcast date was December 19, 1960. It was written by David Adler, and directed by Bob Sweeney. Regulars included Andy Griffith, Don Knotts, Frances Bavier, Ronny Howard, and Elinor Donahue as Ellie Walker. Guests included Will Wright as Ben Weaver, Sam Edwards as Jim Muggins, and Margaret Kerry as Bess Muggins.

COLONEL CHUMLEY (89F/B) (164F/162B) Malcolm Merriweather was a gentleman's gentleman for the colonel for eleven years. In 164F/162B, Malcolm stated that he was also the colonel's valet and falconkeeper.

CHURCH BASEMENT (238F/239B) Where the men's club meetings were held.

THE CHURCH BENEFACTORS 238th episode filmed and 239th episode broadcast. Original broadcast date was January 22, 1968. It was written by Earl Barrett and Robert C. Dennis, and directed by Lee Phillips. Regulars included Andy Griffith, Frances Bavier, Ronny Howard, Aneta Corsaut, Jack Dodson, and Paul Hartman. Guests included William Keene as Reverend Hobart Tucker, Mary Lansing as Martha, and Vince Barnett as Elmo.

THE CHURCH ORGAN 174th episode filmed and 173rd episode broadcast. Original broadcast date was December 13, 1965. It was written by Paul Wayne, and directed by Lee Phillips. Regulars included Andy Griffith, Frances Bavier, Ronny Howard, and Howard McNear. Guests included Jack Burns as Warren Ferguson, Hope Summers as Clara Edwards, William Keene as Reverend Tucker, Woodrow Chambliss as Harlan Robinson, Bert

Remsen as Jim Slater, Pitt Herbert as Rudy, and Robert B. Williams as Sam.

CHURCH SOCIAL (55F/B) (181F/B) Yearly Mayberry social event. In 55F/B, at the social, Opie danced with Sharon Porter and "stomped" all over her. In 181F/B—in 1962—Bee, Clara, and Mary made eighteen cakes for the social. The previous year, fourteen cakes were not enough.

BILLY CINCIPAUL (216F/B) Man who called Bee to complain about Howard Sprague's comedy routine on "Colonel Tim's Talent Time" amateur show.

CINEMASCOPE CAFE (13F/B) The Diner changed its name to The Cinemascope Cafe after a Hollywood movie was scheduled to be made in Mayberry.

"CIRCUS" (11F/B) The sign in the alley next to the courthouse.

CITIZEN'S ARREST 106th episode filmed and broadcast. Original broadcast date was December 16, 1963. It was written by Jim Fritzell and Everett Greenbaum, and directed by Dick Crenna. Regulars included Andy Griffith, Don Knotts, Frances Bavier, Jim Nabors, and Hal Smith. Guests included Roy Engel and Joe Hamilton.

CITY STATUTE "249A, V" (84F/B) "No bikes on the sidewalk."

CIVIC IMPROVEMENT COMMITTEE (208F/212B) Bee Taylor, Andy Taylor, Clara Edwards, Howard Sprague, Goober Pyle, and Floyd Lawson. Howard was chairman. They met to determine what to do with the $200 in their treasury.

CIVIC IMPROVEMENT LEAGUE (223F/226B) Probably the same as the Civic Improvement Committee of 208F/212B. In 223F/226B, Bee was mentioned as the head of the league.

CIVIL SERVICE BUILDING DIRECTORY (131F/129B) The directory in the lobby of the Mt. Pilot building read as follows: "McGarre 607, Smith, Steve Noon 603, A Wedget 612, Glenn Ross, I. Rock."

MRS. CLAREBURN (159F/B) She parked illegally on Main Street and Andy told her to move her car after she refused to obey the "banjo-playing deputy," Jerry Miller.

CLARENCE (29F/B) Mayberry man who Barney drafted for the posse that went out to Sam Becker's place.

EMMETT CLARK Emmett was a testy sort of guy who took over the location of Floyd's Barbershop to open a fix-it shop. He was a fairly good friend of Andy's but not as close as, say, Goober, Gomer, or even Howard. A few episodes were devoted to Emmett but basically he was a "Floyd replacement." The boys needed somewhere to hang around, didn't they? Emmett tended to be a bit abrasive at times. He was married to Martha, and they had no children. He ran for head of city council in 247F/246B, and was soundly beaten by Sam Jones. (See additional entries beginning with the word "EMMETT'S")

MARTHA CLARK (245F/244B) Emmett's wife. She suggested that Mrs. Pendleton stay with Andy when Aunt Bee had to go out of town.

MISS CLARK (211F/207B) (212F/208B) Secretary of the detective bureau for the Raleigh police. Barney referred to her as "sweetheart" and "our gal Friday."

In 212F/208B, Barney took her to the policeman's ball, he as Jack, she as Jill. She agreed to go with him after Barney was pictured in the paper escorting Teena Andrews to the premiere of her movie.

MR. CLARK (171F/172B) A customer of the counterfeiters, Ralph Kingsley and Arnold Finch. When he picked up his bogus money, he told Bee they were wedding and birth announcements. "Clark" was probably an alias.

THE CLARKS (143F/B) Mayberry family to whom Barney tried to sell the Mortonsen's house.

CLASS PRESIDENT (190F/B) Opie, in Class 7A.

CLASS REUNION 82nd episode filmed and broadcast. Original broadcast date was February 4, 1963. It was written by Jim Fritzell and Everett Greenbaum, and directed by Charles Irving. Regulars included Andy Griffith and Don Knotts. Guests included Peggy McCay and Paul Smith.

CLASS VALEDICTORIAN (10F/12B) (163F/161B) In 10F/12B, Lucy Matthews was valedictorian at the time that Ed Sawyer came to town. In 163F/161B, it was said that Andy was valedictorian of his high school class.

CLAUDE (165F/169B) Mayberry man who worked at the Post Office. He told Clara that a package from Darcy Furs in Hollywood was delivered to Bee.

CLAUDE (229F/228B) Clara Edwards' musician brother. He played with Hippie Harrison.

CLAUSE 6 (210F/211B) The clause in Floyd's new lease that raised his rent from $50 to $65 per month. Floyd didn't like this clause.

JESSIE CLAYTON (229F/228B) The drummer in Opie's band, "The Sound Committee."

HARRIET CLEAVER (231F/230B) Friend of Bee's. She was from South Bend. Harriet told Bee about Louise's boy, Willis Spooner.

CLETE (192F/191B) Member of the Regal Order of the Golden Door to Good Fellowship, the Mayberry men's lodge.

CLEVELAND (80F/B) Luke Comstock owned a chain of television stores in Cleveland.

CLIFF (18F/B) Fred Boone's and Gil's card partner for hearts.

MR. CLIFFORD (240F/B) American ambassador who participated in the US/USSR summit meeting held at Andy's house. He was referred to as the "distinguished representative" of the U.S.A.

CLINT (142F/141B) Mayberry postal worker. Andy ran into Clint on the day that Opie's fingerprint set arrived in town on the late bus. Andy delivered the kit to the courthouse, fulfilling another of the wishes Opie made to Count Iz Van Talecki.

THE CLUBHOUSE (202F/199B) (203F/201B) Ramshackle shed in Andy's backyard that Opie and his friends used for secret meetings, etc. In 202F/199B, it's where Opie and Arnold brought the abandoned baby boy they found on the courthouse steps. In 203F/201B, it was seen.

THE CLUBMEN 42nd episode filmed and broadcast. Original broadcast date was December 11, 1961. It was written by Fred S. Fox and Iz Elinson, and directed by Bob Sweeney. Regulars included Andy Griffith, Don

Knotts, Frances Bavier, Ronny Howard, and Howard McNear.

CODE 404B (145F/B) The violation Barney arrested Otis on when Otis got drunk and rode a cow through Mayberry.

CODE 421 (16F/20B) Unlawful assembly and inciting to riot. Barney arrested Aunt Bee for violation of this code.

CODE 721-8 (16F/20B) Disturbing the peace. Barney arrested Jud Fletcher for violation of this code.

"CODE OF THE WEST" (179F/B) "The man who can fight is the man who's right." Clarence Earp lived by it. Opie and his friends were so impressed by Clarence that they used his code as an excuse to fight in an alley.

MR. COEFIELD (210F/211B) He owned a chain of barbershops and considered opening a shop in Floyd's location. He offered Howard $70, then $75 per month rent.

COFFEE (135F/B) (162F/164B) A two pound can was sixty-five cents.

THE COFFEE SHOP (37F/40B) Barney conspired to have Andy meet Thelma Lou's cousin, Karen, at "the coffee shop" at 3:00 P.M. It wasn't said if the coffee shop was the Bluebird Diner.

FLOYD COLBY (13F/B) Mayberry barber. Floyd Colby became Floyd Lawson later in the series. When Mayberry went "Hollywood," Floyd changed the name of his barbershop to "Colby's Tonsorial Parlor," offering "Cary Grant haircuts."

COLD CHICKEN AND POTATO SALAD (65F/67B) Peggy McMillan brought cold chicken and potato salad for Andy's and Opie's lunch.

COLD STREAM GUARDS (164F/162B) In England, Malcolm Merriweather was a Guard. Goober pronounced it "Cold Cream Guards."

EDGAR COLEMAN (146F/B) Thelma Lou had to glue covers on hymn books with Edgar, so she couldn't see Barney.

MRS. COLITA (125F/124B) A woman Andy greeted as he walked Main Street. He complimented her on her "mighty pretty black oilcloth coat."

COLLARD GREENS (94F/B) 10¢.

COLLEGIATE DICTIONARY (231F/230B) Aunt Bee gave one to Willis Spooner on the occasion of his going off to college.

COLONEL TIM see under TIM

"COLONEL TIM'S TALENT TIME" (216F/B) Amateur show broadcast out of Station WASG (the "Andy Griffith Show" initials transposed) in Raleigh. Colonel Tim's show launched the careers of Ozzie Snake, Rosamae Johnson, and Jughead Peters & His Aristocrats. Howard Sprague went on the show and did his comedy routine. His act aggravated everyone in town because he poked gentle fun at the people of Mayberry. The show was hosted by Colonel Tim.

COMMERCIAL ART COURSE (223F/226B) A correspondence course. Opie got a mail solicitation for the course. It consisted of twelve lessons for $98.50.

COMMODORE HOTEL (242F/241B) The Raleigh hotel where Andy, Bee, Goober, and Opie stayed when they went to the auto show.

"COMPELSHION" (60F/B) The way Barney pronounced "compulsion."

LUKE COMSTOCK (80F/B) Man Andy wounded in a gas station holdup in 1952. Andy got a letter eleven years later reading: "Been wantin' to see you for a long time to set things straight between us." Barney said the letter spelled "revenge." Barney then overreacted, deputizing Gomer and Otis in an attempt to protect Andy. It turned out Luke came to Mayberry to thank Andy for setting him straight and changing his life, and to present him with a hunting shotgun. Luke owned a chain of television stores in Cleveland.

"CONCEALING A .38 REVOLVER" (244F/243B) One of the charges Helen Crump was arraigned on in 1959.

"CONCERT TONIGHT—RELAX TO MUSIC UNDER THE STARS" (100F/99B) The sign Barney made to announce the band concert. He and Andy ended up deciding not to put it up.

CONFEDERATE MONEY (39F/36B) Frank Myers owned an 1861 Town of Mayberry bond that was bought with Confederate money.

JUDGE CONNOLLY (226F/223B) Raleigh judge who asked Andy to go see a lawyer on Elm Street regarding a case.

NAOMI CONNORS (74F/B) One of the "convicts at large," Naomi was five foot four and 115 pounds, slender, blonde, and also known as "Jaylene Naomi Connors." Her prison number was 5831.

FLIP CONROY (215F/B) Mayberry man who left town to go to college and who then played pro ball with the Giants for ten years. He left the Giants and came back to Mayberry to work in his father's business. He took over coaching Opie's football team, which caused a conflict between Opie's new piano practice hours and football practice. When Flip heard about Opie's problem, he came to Andy's house and played the piano for Bee and Andy, showing them that, with a little scheduling, football and piano lessons could be combined in one boy.

A.J. CONSIDINE (167F/B) The director of the movie about Andy, "Sheriff Without A Gun."

"CONSTABLE" (89F/B) The title Malcolm Merriweather called Andy.

CONTEMPT (35F/B) Andy fined Elizabeth Crowley, the woman speeder, for contempt; he fined her ten dollars, twice.

CONVERTIBLE (31F/B) (71F/72B) (225F/224B) In 31F/B, Jim Lindsey's leased red car was a convertible. In 71F/72B, Madeline Grayson's rented car was also a convertible. And in 225F/224B, Aunt Bee's car was likewise.

CONVICTS AT LARGE 74th episode filmed and broadcast. Original broadcast date was December 10, 1962. It was written by Jim Fritzell and Everett Greenbaum, and directed by Bob Sweeney. Regulars included Andy Griffith, Don Knotts, and Howard McNear. Guests included Reta Shaw as Maude Tyler, Jane Dulo as Naomi Connors, Jean Carson as Sally, and Willis Bouchey as Charlie O'Malley.

JONAS CONWAY (5F/8B) Mayberry farmer who bred prize pigs.

CLARK COOPER (154F/B) In 154F/B, Clara Edwards had been dating him for five years. Bee asked her if he still "cuts the slits in his shoes."

MRS. COREY (144F/B) She called Andy to have him tend to some unspecified task.

CORLIS (162F/164B) Daughter of Harlan and Ruth. When Ruth was arrested with the Ladies Auxiliary, Harlan brought Corlis to Andy's house for supper.

CORN (73F/70B) 25¢ a dozen as sold by Neil and Matt from the back of their truck.

CORN MASH MOONSHINE (111F/110B) The moonshine that Frisby, the egg man, was making on his farm.

CORN ON THE COB (248F/247B) Goober's favorite vegetable.

CORNED BEEF HASH (237F/236B) The dish Andy burned in one of his cooking attempts while Aunt Bee was doing her cooking show, "The Mayberry Chef."

CORNISH PASTRY (124F/123B) The lunch Malcolm Merriweather prepared for Andy and Barney. It consisted of half meat and potatoes, and half plum pudding. With it he also brought salad, pickles, and olives. The lunch was so good Barney figured that Malcolm must have cooked for the king of England.

CORNWALL'S GAS STATION (5F/8B) Early service station in Mayberry. It was used as a border for one of the five sections Annabelle Silby divided Mayberry into for fund-raising purposes. The section was "From Grover's Place over to Banner Street then around Cornwall's Gas Station up to Tate Warren's store." It's not said whether Cornwall's became Wally's later on or if it was a different service station altogether.

CORSAGE (105F/104B) Gomer abruptly left Thelma Lou's to get Mary Grace Gossage a corsage. He had to go to a couple of places to get one with pink in it.

THE COSGROVE BOY (190F/B) A Mayberry bully. Goober asked if it was the Cosgrove boy who gave Opie his black eye. Actually, it had been Helen's niece, Cynthia.

"A COTTON MILL IN SAVANNAH" (36F/37B) George Stevens told Barney he was involved in a cotton mill along with his shipping interests.

"THE COUNT OF MONTE CRISTO" (113F/112B) Barney called Ernest T. Bass the Count of Monte Cristo. He was referring to the elusive way Ernest T. entered and left both rooms and jail cells.

THE COUNTY CLERK 185th episode filmed and broadcast. Original broadcast date was March 14, 1966. It was written by Bill Idelson and Sam Bobrick, and directed by Alan Rafkin. Regulars included Andy Griffith, Ronny Howard, Jack Dodson, and Aneta Corsaut. Guests included Nina Shipman as Irene Fairchild, Mabel Albertson as Mrs. Sprague, Jim Begg as the Young Man, and Coleen O'Sullivan as the Young Girl.

COUNTY EMPLOYMENT OFFICE (108F/107B) The government bureau Andy said could find a job for Wary Willy the Hobo.

THE COUNTY FAIR (21F/B) (234F/232B) (237F/236B) (243F/242B) In 21F/B, Aunt Bee won a blue ribbon for her rhubarb pie. In 234F/232B, Bee won first prize for her homemade strawberry ice cream. In 237F/236B, it was mentioned that Bee won cooking contests at the fair. In 243F/242B, Goober won the pancake eating contest by eating fifty-seven pancakes.

"COUNTY HAS NO HEART" (111F/110B) Sign Bee and the women carried at Frisby's farm when the county men came to bulldoze the place.

COUNTY INSECTICIDE CONVENTION (116F/115B) Two years after the voice teacher, Eleanora Poultice, met Leonard Blush, he sang the "Star-Spangled Banner" at the opening of the county insecticide convention. Miss Poultice was especially proud of this achievement of Leonard's.

COUNTY LEGAL DEPARTMENT (141F/142B) The bureau Andy called when he found out Otis was suing the county. They told him the county could be liable for his "injuries."

COUNTY LINE CAFE (115F/114B) Otis went there at 5:00 P.M., bought a bottle of redeye, and then went to Charlie Varney's house.

THE COUNTY NURSE 56th episode filmed and broadcast. Original broadcast date was March 19, 1962. It was written by Jack Elinson and Charles Stewart, and directed by Bob Sweeney. Regulars included Andy Griffith and Don Knotts. Guests included Julie Adams as Mary Simpson the county nurse and Jack Prince as Rafe Hollister.

COUNTY PENMANSHIP CONTEST (67F/65B) Barney came in second to Andy's first when they were in school.

"COUPLE OF THE YEAR" (82F/B) Andy Taylor and Sharon Duspaine in their junior and senior years at Mayberry Union High School.

COURTHOUSE STEPS (202F/196B) Where Arnold Bailey and Opie found the abandoned Garland baby boy.

ROGER COURTNEY (42F/B) Member of the Esquire Club and a fishing buddy of Andy's. Roger invited Andy to a meeting of the club.

"COUSIN" ANDY (2F/B) (4F/6B) (103F/B) In 2F/B and 4F/6B, Barney referred to Andy as his cousin. These were the only references to their relationship. This cousin relationship seemed to have been either forgotten by the producers or deliberately eliminated, as it was never mentioned or acknowledged past the first season. Exactly how they were related was never explained. However, in 103F/B, Barney asked Andy how he voted. To persuade Andy to tell him, Barney said, "It's not as if I'm a stranger, I'm your friend." No mention at all was made that Andy and Barney were kin. Instead, Barney seemed to want to emphasize that they were the best of friends, rather than being related.

COUSIN VIRGIL 62nd episode filmed and broadcast. Original broadcast date was April 30, 1962. It was written by Phillip Shukin and Johnny Greene, and directed by Bob Sweeney. Regulars included Andy Griffith, Don Knotts, Frances Bavier, Ronny Howard, and Hal Smith as Otis Campbell. Guests included Michael J. Pollard as Cousin Virgil.

THE COW THIEF 70th episode filmed and 68th episode broadcast. Original broadcast date was October 29, 1962. It was written by Ray Allen Saffian and Harvey Bullock, and directed by Bob Sweeney. Regulars included Andy Griffith, Don Knotts, and Ronny Howard. Guests included Malcolm Atterbury, Ralph Bell, Jon Lormer, and Parley Baer as Mayor Stoner.

"COWBOY" (110F/109B) Andy called Trey Bowden "cowboy."

COWLICK (161F/160B) Andy had one. This part of Andy's hair always upset Floyd.

COWSILL FLAT (17F/B) The locale where Ben Sewell's farm was situated.

MRS. COX (60F/B) Second grade teacher of Opie's. Opie and Joey said Barney looked like Mrs. Cox when he dressed in drag to try and catch Bill Medwin, the bookie barber.

"CRABMONSTER" (199F/196B) Goober's favorite comic book character.

CRANBERRY SAUCE (135F/B) 47¢

JUDGE CRANSTON (223F/226B) The judge at Marvin Jenkins' trial in Mt. Pilot.

CRANSTON'S FARM (183F/182B) Farm on the outskirts of Mayberry, just over the county line. The gypsies camped near there after Andy ran them out of town.

JES CRAWFORD (40F/38B) Dave the Hobo stole Jes's chicken.

MR. CRAWFORD (239F/238B) Mayberry druggist. He hired Opie to run his soda fountain when Elroy Dockins left the drugstore to work in Mt. Pilot.

TRACY CRAWFORD (9F/7B) Chattanooga man who Barney arrested for the fictitious Walker Drugstore robbery. After Andy checked out Crawford, it turned out that he was wanted back in Tennessee on five counts. Barney's picture was run in the paper with the headline, "Deputy Barney Fife Cracks Walker Robbery"; next to the photo was this headline: "Dangerous Criminal Captured Single-Handed Through The Clever Sleuthing Of Our Local Deputy." Under his photo was the caption, "Deputy Fife—Hero."

"CRAZY GUN BARNEY" (73F/70B) Barney's nickname, according to Andy. He invented it and told it to the two roadside farmers, Neil and Matt, in order to scare them into obeying the deputy.

CREAM BUN (222F/225B) Andy pretended he had a craving for a cream bun in order to give Howard Sprague an excuse to go into Boysinger's Bakery and meet the new girl, Mille Hutchins. (Howard was sweet on Millie.)

BILLY CRENSHAW (161F/160B) Youngster who applied for the delivery boy job at Mr. Doakes' market at the same time as Opie. Doakes gave them both a job for a one week trial period. Opie finally got the job, but when he found out that Billy needed it more to help his family pay bills, Opie pretended he'd rather play baseball so Doakes would let him go and hire Billy instead.

WALLY CRENSHAW (244F/243B) Wally backed his pickup truck into Mr. Benson's vegetable stand. It wasn't said if Wally and Billy were related.

THE CRIME PATTERN IN MAYBERRY (33F/34B) According to Bill Rogers' chart, in 33F/34B, the following would take place in Mayberry before the month was up: twelve traffic violations, three breaking and enterings, one wife beating case, and one vagrancy.

CRIME-FREE MAYBERRY 41st episode filmed and 39th episode broadcast. Original broadcast date was November 20, 1961. It was written by Paul Henning, and directed by Bob Sweeney. Regulars included Andy Griffith and Don Knotts. Guests included Hal Smith as Otis Campbell.

"CRIMINAL LOOKS" (29F/B) This is what a criminal looked like, according to Barney: "narrow chin, eyes close together, slack jaw with a prominent overbite." Andy said that sounded like a description of Barney.

GLENN CRIPES (52F/B) Bass in the choir who Andy wanted to sing in Barney's place.

MRS. CRIPPS (202F/196B) Elderly woman. Opie asked her to take in the abandoned Garland baby he and Arnold found on the courthouse steps. Mrs. Cripps later called Aunt Bee to complain about Opie.

"THE CRISIS OF 1874" (208F/212B) Undisclosed fiscal crisis Mayberry went through in 1874. They were "rescued" by Andy's ancestor, Seth Taylor, who lent the town money.

LYDIA CROSSWAITHE (68F/69B) (147F/B) In 68F/69B, Lydia was a girlfriend of Thelma Lou's. Barney and Thelma Lou arranged for Andy to meet Lydia after Peggy McMillan cancelled her date with Andy. Lydia worked in Mt. Pilot, she didn't play bridge, her name meant "native of Lydia," and she was from Greensboro, North Carolina. She hated the outdoors—when she went out in the sun she got the herpes—she hated guitar and chit-chat, and she liked the clarinet and the sax. In 147F/B, it was mentioned that her father used to work in a lumber plant. Also in that episode, Barney called her an "albatross," and she was fixed up with Goober. Her house number was 598.

CROUCH'S WOODS (108F/107B) The woods where Opie and his "merry men" met Wary Willy the Hobo. It was down by Myer's Lake.

MRS. CROUTE (118F/117B) Her cat, Queenie, got stuck up a tree.

CROW (5F/8B) Andy said he was eating crow after he found out that Opie was saving up to buy his girlfriend, Charlotte, a coat and that's why Opie donated only three cents to the Underprivileged Children's Charity Drive.

ELIZABETH CROWLEY (35F/B) The woman speeder. She was from Washington, D.C., and Andy arrested her for doing 70 mph on the 45 mph road outside Myer's Lake. When she refused to pay the fine, Andy jailed her for mayor's court. She swayed everybody—including Aunt Bee and Opie—against Andy, and convinced the mayor to acquit her. In the end, though, she realized she was wrong and let Andy catch her speeding again, only this time she paid *both* fines and Andy respected her.

HERB CROWLEY (28F/B) Andy figured he could get Herb's old porch furniture for the Save the Scoby House Fund rummage sale. It wasn't specifically noted whether Herb was "Old Man" Crowley, although it's likely.

OLD MAN CROWLEY (176F/B) Barney couldn't wait to see the look on Crowley's face when he saw Barney back in Mayberry. The old man just walked by and said "Hi, Andy, Barney," not the least bit surprised.

CROWLEY'S MARKET (45F/B) (53F/B) (61F/B) In 45F/B, Crowley's was the market where Andy said Jeff Pruitt could get a job working in the vegetable department. In 53F/B, it was where the tour of the merchant's stores began. In 61F/B, Andy made a grocery delivery for Art Crowley.

CROWN PRINCE OF DENMARK (234F/232B) Bradford Taylor claimed he was the financial adviser to the prince.

HELEN CRUMP Mayberry schoolteacher, Andy's girlfriend, and later, wife. She came to town in 86F/B, "Andy Discovers America," and Andy aggravated her before he even met her. When she let him know that she was peeved that he had told Opie that his history homework wasn't that important, he made it up to her by getting Opie and his friends interested in history. Andy began dating her in that episode and they eventually married in the first episode of "Mayberry, R.F.D." Later in that series they had a child, a son. Helen was a quiet, pretty companion for Andy, and was very often willing to subordinate her own feelings in order to make Andy happy. She did not have the liberated attitudes of Ellie Walker, for instance. In a number of episodes (especially 190F/B), she even voiced her opinion that sometimes a woman had to do things to look bad so men wouldn't feel threatened. Helen published a children's book during the series. (See additional entries beginning with the word "HELEN" or "HELEN'S")

CRYSTAL BALL (183F/182B) Murillos and his clan of gypsies had a crystal ball that Murillos claimed was 600 years old.

CRYSTAL CREEK ROAD (2F/B) Road "down by the lake" (either Myer's or Tucker's) past the old summer place where Andy trapped the escaped prisoner, Dirksen.

"LA CUCARACHA" (59F/B) Song Barney learned to play on the bongo drums.

CUCUMBERS (73F/70B) (135F/B) In 73F/70B, 1¢ each as sold by Neil and Matt from the back of their truck. In 135F/B, 5¢.

"CUFF SLAPPING" (118F/117B) The skill that Gomer was practicing when he handcuffed himself to Barney.

A CURRENCY CONVERTER (227F/222B) Clara gave Bee one as a going away present after Bee won the trip to Mexico.

"CURSE OF THE CLAW" (46F/B) The punishment that would be inflicted on any member of the Wildcats who revealed any doings of the club.

BEN CURTIS (214F/B) The dairyman who took over Walt Simpson's route during Walt's vacation.

CUSTOM SEDAN (90F/B) 1958 auto offered to Barney by Myrt Lesh. She offered him the car in exchange for him forgetting about her robbing him on the first car he had bought from her earlier.

"THE CUTLASS" (82F/B) Andy and Barney's Mayberry Union High School yearbook. Aunt Bee gave Andy's to a disease drive. (See the entries under YEARBOOK ENTRY)

CYMBAL CITY (72F/71B) The store where Barney bought his Andre Kostalanez Marchers cymbals.

CYNTHIA (190F/B) Helen's niece. She did everything better than Opie. This rapidly destroyed Opie's ego, and he finally had a fistfight with her and she gave him a black eye. She later played down her talents in order to feed Opie's ego (after a sexist talk with Helen), and the two youngsters ended up friends. Cynthia was from Wheeling, West Virginia.

CYRANO ANDY 22nd episode filmed and broadcast. Original broadcast date was March 6, 1961. It was written by Jack Elinson and Charles Stewart, and directed by Bob Sweeney. Regulars included Andy Griffith, Don Knotts, Betty Lynn as Thelma Lou, and Elinor Donahue as Ellie Walker.

71

D

"D'S & E'S" (153F/B) The letters Opie and Howie ran out of when editing their newspaper, "The Mayberry Sun."

"DAME" (134F/B) Barney said, "Take the dame's side" regarding an argument with Helen, and Andy got very mad: "Helen is not a dame!"

"DAN TUCKER" (96F/100B) Song Opie sang with Andy when the Darlings ate at Andy's house.

JOHN DANBY (42F/B) Member of the Esquire Club. Andy and Barney were introduced to him at one of the club's meetings.

"DANCE TILL YOUR STOCKINGS ARE HOT AND RAVELIN'" (94F/B) Song performed by the Darlings.

DANCING (10F/12B) One of Lucy Matthews' favorite pastimes.

"DANGEROUS CONDEMNED MINE" (32F/B) Sign on the abandoned Johnson mine.

DAPHNE (68F/69B) (155F/B) One of the fun girls from Mt. Pilot. When Andy and Peggy McMillan had a fight, Barney arranged for him and Andy to meet Skippy and Daphne at the Tip-Top Cafe, twelve miles away in Mt. Pilot. In 155F/B, she and Skippy sped through Mayberry, and then arrested themselves as a way to get next to Andy and Barney.

DARCY FURS (165F/169B) Hollywood furrier. They supplied the genuine ranch mink Aunt Bee won on "Win Or Lose."

REVEREND DARGOOD (138F/B) The minister who was in charge of the production of "The Little Princess," in which Bee played the part of Alice.

BRISCOE DARLING (121F/120B) Father of Charlene Darling Wash. He came to Mayberry to enforce Charlene's divorce from Dud Wash and Andy's impending marriage to Charlene.

CARL DARLING (184F/B) Jed Darling told him there was no Santa Claus. This started a big fight.

CHARLENE DARLING (88F/B) (121F/120B) Daughter of Briscoe, wife of Dudley J. Wash. In 88F/B, Charlene married Dud (then called Dudley A. Wash). In 121F/120B, she divorced him and decided—much to Andy's chagrin—to marry the sheriff.

DEAN DARLING (193F/195B) One of Briscoe's sons. Briscoe brought him to Mayberry to marry him off.

DOUG DARLING (193F/195B) He used to have to sit on the hood of the car holding a lantern until Andy told Briscoe to put headlights on their car.

JED DARLING (184F/B) Jed told Carl Darling there was no Santa Claus. This started a big fight.

MITCH DARLING (193F/195B) One of Briscoe's sons. Mitch had chiseled features (he got hit in the head with a chisel when he was younger).

RODNEY DARLING (193F/195B) Rodney was jittery about getting married. He was the fun-loving Darling.

THE DARLING BABY 139th episode filmed and broadcast. Original broadcast date was December 7, 1964. It was written by Jim Fritzell and Everett Greenbaum, and directed by Howard Morris. Regulars included Andy Griffith, Don Knotts, Ronny Howard, and Frances Bavier. Guests included Denver Pyle as Briscoe Darling, Maggie Peterson as Charlene Darling Wash, and The Dillards as The Darling Boys.

THE DARLING FORTUNE 193rd episode filmed and broadcast. Original broadcast date was October 17, 1966. It was written by Jim Parker and Arnold Margolin,, and directed by Lee Phillips. Regulars included Andy Griffith, Frances Bavier, Aneta Corsaut, and George Lindsey. Guests included Denver Pyle as Briscoe Darling, Maggie Peterson as Charlene, and The Dillards as Doug, Rodney, Dean, and Mitch Darling.

THE DARLINGS (184F/B) Andy had to stay up all night during one of their fights. Jed had told Carl that there was no Santa Claus. This started the fight.

THE DARLINGS ARE COMING 88th episode filmed and broadcast. Original broadcast date was March 18, 1963. It was written by Jim Fritzell and Everett Greenbaum, and directed by Bob Sweeney. Regulars included Andy Griffith. Guests included Denver Pyle as Briscoe Darling, Margaret Ann Peterson as Charlene Darling, Olan Soule as John Masters the Reservation Clerk, Hoke Howell, and The Dillard Brothers as The Darling Boys.

"DARN CUTE" (153F/B) How Barney described—more than once—Opie's newspaper, "The Mayberry Sun."

DARRYL (184F/B) Martha's husband. Martha was Bee's niece. Darryl was a wimpy-looking guy who was a stickler about his infant daughter's eating and sleeping schedules.

A DATE FOR GOMER 105th episode filmed and 104th episode broadcast. Original broadcast date was November 25, 1963. It was written by Jim Fritzell and Everett Greenbaum, and directed by Dick Crenna. Regulars included Andy Griffith, Don Knotts, Betty Lynn, Aneta Corsaut, Frances Bavier, and Ronny Howard. Guests included Mary Grace Canfield as Thelma Lou's cousin, Mary Grace Gossage.

DAVE THE HOBO (40F/38B) David Browne.

DAVE'S HONG KONG (173F/174B) Mt. Pilot Chinese restaurant. On Bee's suggestion, Andy and Helen planned on eating there, but Helen wanted to double-date because Chinese food was more fun if there were more than two people.

JEFFERSON DAVIS (39F/B) President of the Confederacy. Frank Myers had a letter from him.

OLD MAN DAVIS (145F/B) He sold Otis a horse—which was really a cow—for twenty dollars.

SHELDON DAVIS (53F/B) The "guest of honor" who, as "Thomas A. Moody," got picked by Mayberry to be honored. It turned out he was a small-time crook who planned on robbing Barclay's Jewelry Store.

Sheldon was thrown out of Pierce County for stealing the chief of police's watch. He said he was a traveling salesman.

DAVIS COUNTY (240F/B) Locale suggested, then ruled out, as a possible site for the US/USSR summit meeting eventually held in Mayberry.

DAVIS' STORE (12F/10B) Mayberry retailer. When Ellie ran for city council, the men tried to get back at the women by cutting off their charge accounts. Otis Campbell's wife had a charge account at Davis'. It's not said if Old Man Davis owned the store.

DC-254 (38F/41B) The license plate number of Henry Wheeler's truck.

DC-269 (6F/4B) (33F/34B) In 6F/4B, the license plate number of the squad car. (This was the only time the plate number of the squad car was not JL-327.) In 33F/34B, the plate number of Bob Rogers' car.

MRS. DEACON (130F/132B) Woman from the Raleigh Ladies Auxiliary. Bee incorrectly guessed that a letter she received was from Mrs. Deacon.

"DEAD EYE ANDY" (41F/39B) The nickname Floyd gave Andy to dramatize his image as a lawman and crime fighter.

"THE DEADLY GAME" (30F/B) According to Barney, the "deadly game" was being a deputy. He was in it "for keeps."

A DEAL IS A DEAL 122nd episode filmed and 121st episode broadcast. Original broadcast date was April 6, 1964. It was written by Bill Idelson and Sam Bobrick, and directed by Jeffrey Hayden. Regulars included Andy Griffith, Don Knotts, Frances Bavier, Ronny Howard, and Jim Nabors. Guests included George Petrie, Lewis Charles, Richard Keith, Dennis Rush, Ronnie Dapo, and David A. Bailey as Trey Bowden.

"DEALING CARDS AT AN ILLEGAL GAMING HOUSE" (244F/243B) One of the charges Helen Crump was arraigned on in 1959.

MERLE DEAN (97F/101B) His shocks were squeaking so he came by Andy's house in the middle of the night to let Gomer (Andy's "house guest") listen while he jumped up and down on the bumper.

DECEMBER 19 (75F/B) Aunt Bee Taylor's birthday. She was born on a Saturday.

"DECK THE HALLS" (11F/B) Carol sung by Andy, Barney, Ellie, Aunt Bee, Opie, and the Muggins family in the courthouse as they trimmed the tree and prepared the Christmas Eve dinner.

"DEEP PINK ECSTASY" (203F/201B) The name of Aunt Bee's rose; it was a Mrs. Pinkney Variegated Red cross-pollinated with an Alma Swarthouse Sunset Pink.

"DEFENDER OF THE UNDERDOG" (248F/247B) The name Bee gave Opie after he helped Mike Jones out of a bully problem.

DELI-TIME SNACK BAR (210F/211B) Deli that was next door to Floyd's new barbershop in Mt. Pilot.

"THE DELUXE SPECIAL" (132F/128B) At Morelli's restaurant, the deluxe special consisted of minestrone and Pounded Steak a la Morelli. It sold for $1.85.

CLARENCE "KID" DEMPSEY (179F/B) The role Clarence Earp took after Andy revealed that he wasn't related to Wyatt Earp.

MRS. DENNIS (83F/B) Swanky lady who introduced Rafe Hollister's performance at the Ladies League musicale.

THE DENVER MINT (102F/B) The gold shipment that passed through Mayberry was from the Denver Mint on its way to Fort Knox. The shipment was worth over $7 million.

THE DEPARTMENT OF PUBLIC WORKS (137F/B) The Mayberry office Barney called when George got his head stuck in a sewer on Maple Street.

THE DEPOT (164F/162B) Mayberry train or bus station where Fletch Roberts worked.

"DEPUTY FIFE HERO" (50F/B) The caption beneath the photo of Barney that ran with the headline, "Deputy Fife Hero In Cave Rescue." In 50F/B, the photo was hanging on the courthouse wall.

"DEPUTY FIFE HERO IN CAVE RESCUE" (109F/108B) (123F/122B) (211F/207B) Headline of the "Mayberry Gazette" edition put out after Barney "rescued" (with Andy's help) Andy and Helen from the Old Mine Cave collapse. In 123F/122B, the paper was hanging on the wall of the courthouse backroom. In 211F/207B, the paper was hanging on Barney's bedroom wall in the Parker's house.

"THE DEPUTY OATH" (80F/B) To protect Andy from Luke Comstock, Barney deputized Gomer and Otis. He used this oath: "As a deputy of the County of Mayberry, I swear to uphold the laws and regulations therein set to by Statute 426E County Rules and Regulations, put there by this date, City of Mayberry, County of Mayberry thereon."

DEPUTY OTIS 63rd episode filmed and broadcast. Original broadcast date was May 7, 1962. It was written by Fred S. Fox, and directed by Bob Sweeney. Regulars included Andy Griffith, Don Knotts, and Hal Smith as Otis Campbell. Guests included Stanley Adams as Ralph Campbell and Dorothy Neumann as Verline Campbell.

THE DEPUTY PHYSICAL REQUIRE-MENTS (131F/129B) When Barney's job was put under Civil Service, the new physical requirements became five feet eight inches in height and a weight of 145 pounds. Barney didn't meet them.

DETECTIVE AGENCY (36F/37B) Barney told Melissa Stevens and her "Daddy" that he'd eventually like to open his own detective agency.

DETECTIVE BUREAU (211F/207B) (240F/B) Office in Raleigh where Barney worked after leaving Mayberry. He was "in fingerprints" before moving to the detectives bureau.

DETROIT (37F/40B) (74F/B) (243F/242B) (246F/245B) In 37F/40B, the hometown of Melinda Keefer. In 74F/B, Charlie O'Malley was in Detroit when the "convicts at large" took over his house. In 243F/242B, Goober had auto parts air-freighted in from Detroit. That's why he was at the airfield the day Aunt Bee took her five-dollar demonstration flight from MacDonald's Flying School. In 246F/245B, Shirley was leaving for Detroit when Howard called and asked her to his "swinging party."

CHARLIE DEVEREAUX (99F/98B) When Barney remarked that Mrs. Devereaux was "ugly as homemade soap," Andy remarked that Charlie was "no prize."

CLIFF DEVEREAUX (71F/72B) Mayberry man who had Andy watch his house while he and his family were in New Orleans. Andy allowed Floyd to use Cliff's house to pose as a rich widower when Madeline Grayson visited Floyd.

MRS. DEVEREAUX (99F/98B) Barney remarked that Mrs. Devereaux was "ugly as homemade soap." Andy countered that her husband Charlie was "no prize."

WAYNE DEVEREAUX (58F/B) He brought a garment in to Fred Goss, the cleaner. It had a picture of Myrna Loy in the pocket. It wasn't said if he was related to Cliff, Charlie, or Mrs. Devereaux.

M.L. DEWHURST (211F/207B) (240F/B) Barney's captain at the Raleigh Detective Bureau.

DEXTER STREET (73F/70B) Neil and Matt sold produce from a truck parked behind Dexter Street.

DF-153 (89F/B) (90F/B) In 89F/B, it was the license plate number of Mrs. Edwards' car. The car was parked in Andy's driveway. Aunt Bee explained that she would be parking the car there for the few days that Aunt Bee was out of town. In 90F/B, it was the plate number of the tow truck that came to tow "Barney's first car" back into town. The truck was owned by Myrt Lesh.

"DIAMOND JIM" (5F/8B) The name Andy called Opie when he heard that Opie's donation of three cents to the Underprivileged Children's Charity Drive was the lowest given.

DIAMOND JIM'S (120F/119B) A new discount butcher shop that opened in Mayberry. The butcher wore a straw hat and sleeve bands, and there was sawdust on the floor. Clara Johnson told Bee the prices there were ten cents a pound lower than at Foley's. She persuaded Bee to buy a whole side of beef, which Bee couldn't store because her "bargain" freezer didn't work. The meat was terribly tough anyway; Andy hated it. The side weighed fifty pounds, and it cost Bee $133.50.

DIAMONDS (41F/39B) Barney didn't want them set in his "crime-free" medal. (Rubies were OK, though. They were his birthstone.)

DIANA (153F/B) Classmate of Opie's and the best friend of Cindy Ames. Diana wasn't invited to Cindy's birthday party.

"DICE ARE LOADED AGAINST THE EVIL-DOER" (135F/B) The title of a sermon Reverend Tucker gave that Andy found particularly enjoyable.

DICK (162F/164B) Father of Pansy. After Warren arrested Dick's wife, Dick showed up at Andy's house, with Pansy, for supper.

DICK (171F/172B) He called Andy to tell him that fake ten dollar bills were as close as Siler City.

DICK (237F/236B) Studio assistant at Channel 12 in Siler City. He carried in Aunt Bee's grocery bags for her show, "The Mayberry Chef."

DICKIE (1F/B) Opie's bird, probably a parakeet. Aunt Bee left his cage door open and he flew away. Aunt Bee then prepared to leave because she felt she wasn't wanted by Opie. Opie called her back, however, and that night Dickie flew back into his cage.

FLETCH DILLBECK (47F/B) Man sideswiped by Ronald Bailey on a road on the outskirts of Mayberry.

JOHN DILLINGER (108F/107B) Barney thought John Dillinger might have read "Robin Hood."

DILLON see "MARSHALL DILLON," "SHERIFF MATT DILLON"

THE DINER LUNCH (99F/98B) Barney especially enjoyed the eighty-cent special: "Three Vienna sausages, heavy on the tomato puree, slice of bread and butter on a paper dish, and a more than ample portion of succotash." Olive was the waitress. She was a widow with four children, and Andy and Barney both left her a quarter tip.

THE DINER LUNCH SPECIAL (133F/131B) Chicken wings, rice, and mixed vegetables. Barney said they gave you two wings from a "chicken that's done a lot of flying."

DINER PHONE NUMBER (51F/B) 242.

DINNER AT EIGHT 206th episode filmed and broadcast. Original broadcast date was January 9, 1967. It was written by Budd Grossman, and directed by Lee Phillips. Regulars included Andy Griffith, Frances Bavier, Ronny Howard, George Lindsey, Jack Dodson, and Aneta Corsaut. Guests included Emory Parnell as Uncle Edward, and Mabel Albertson as Mrs. Sprague.

"DIPSY-DOODLE" (55F/B) Song Otis sang when drunk.

DIRKSEN (2F/B) The escaped prisoner and object of the "manhunt."

"A DISHCLOTH SALESMAN" (153F/B) The Widow Saunders was seen with a dishcloth salesman at the Half Moon Roadhouse. They ate New York-cut steak, and she got in at 1:00 A.M.

"DISTURBING THE PEACE" (3F/B) (106F/B) In 3F/B, the charge for which Andy arrested Jim Lindsey because he'd played guitar in front of Orville Monroe's funeral parlor. In 106F/B, the misdemeanor Sheriff Pinckley arrested Purcell Branch for in 1931. He drove down Main Street with the cutout open on his REO Flying Cloud.

DIVORCE INCANTATION, "MOUNTAIN STYLE" (121F/120B) This is the spell Charlene Darling Wash used to divorce herself from Dudley J. Wash: "Beak of owl, strip of swine, tooth of comb, take mine from thine, Canaba in, Canaba out, Canaba in, and roundabout." She then drew a circle on the ground around the sack she buried which contained "the beak of an owl, four tailfeathers from a chickenhawk, a piece of bacon and a broken comb." From the time of the incantation till the moon comes full was the waiting period. She was divorcing Dud because she caught him looking and grinning at Idele Bushy during preaching. Also, Dud went hunting foxes with Hasty Buford and didn't come home for a week.

DIVORCE, MOUNTAIN STYLE 121st episode filmed and 120th broadcast. Original broadcast date was March 30, 1964. It was written by Jim Fritzell and Everett Greenbaum, and directed by Jeffrey Hayden. Regulars included Andy Griffith, Don Knotts, and Howard McNear. Guests included Denver Pyle as Briscoe Darling, Maggie Peterson as Charlene Darling Wash, Bob Denver as Dudley J. Wash, and The Dillards as The Darling Boys.

DOAKES MARKET (161F/160B) Grocery store on Main Street. Doakes' was the market where Opie and Billy Crenshaw both applied—and competed—for the same delivery boy job.

OLD MAN DOBBINS (172F/170B) Sharon's father. Sharon was the Mayberry Potato Queen.

SHARON DOBBINS (172F/170B) The Mayberry Potato Queen. She wore a bathing suit and rode in a convertible in the Founder's Day parade.

COUNCILMAN DOBBS (44F/B) Member of the Greendale, North Carolina, town council.

DOC (95F/B) One of the crooks brought to the Mayberry jail. Tiny was the other one.

ELROY DOCKING (239F/238B) Nineteen-year-old who used to run Mr. Crawford's soda fountain. Elroy left Crawford to work in Mt. Pilot.

"A DOCTOR" (161F/160B) Floyd thought Opie might grow up to be a doctor.

THE DOCTORS OF MAYBERRY (24F/B) (29F/B) (55F/B) (66F/64B) (87F/B) (131F/129B) (190F/B) (218F/B) (228F/227B) (232F/233B) In 24F/B, Doc Carruthers, Doc Green, Doc MacKenzie, and Dr. Robert Benson. In 29F/B, Doc Winters. In 55F/B, Doc Zach. In 66F/64B and 131F/129B, Doc Harvey. In 87F/B, Doc Andrews. In 190F/B, Dr. Anderson. In 218F/B and 228F/227B, Doc Bailey. In 232F/233B, Doc Roberts.

MR. DODSON (161F/160B) Mayberry man Opie greeted as he made his rounds delivering groceries for Doakes Market.

"DOES THE SHERIFF RUN THE TOWN OR DOES THE TOWN RUN THE SHERIFF?" (61F/B) The headline Jean Boswell used as the lead off in her smear campaign against Andy.

"DOGS, DOGS, DOGS" 93rd episode filmed and broadcast. Original broadcast date was April 22, 1963. It was written by Jim Fritzell and Everett Greenbaum, and directed by Bob Sweeney. Regulars included Andy Griffith, Don Knotts, Ronny Howard, and Hal Smith as Otis Campbell. Guests included Robert Cornthwaite as Mr. Somerset, and Roy Barcroft as Clint Biggers. The dogs were uncredited.

DOGWOOD DAIRY FARMS (214F/B) The company for which Walt Simpson and Dolly, his horse, worked delivering dairy products. Andy and Aunt Bee were among his customers.

DOLL (11F/B) The Christmas gift from Ben Weaver to Effie Muggins.

"A DOLLAR AND A QUARTER" (2F/B) Andy wouldn't take a dollar and a quarter for his rowboat, Gertrude. (Even though she leaked.)

DOLLY (214F/B) Walt Simpson's horse. Dolly pulled Walt's dairy wagon and knew what houses to stop at for deliveries. When Walt went on vacation, Opie took over the feeding of Dolly. Dolly wouldn't eat, however, and it was discovered that the horse missed both Walt and pulling the wagon. The company replaced Dolly with a truck. Walt solved the problem by letting Dolly walk behind the new truck.

DOMINOES (245F/244B) Ethel Pendleton told Andy to set up a table for dominoes after supper.

DON (68F/69B) An old college friend of Peggy McMillan's. She once shared a lab in chemistry class with him. He stopped to see Peg on his way to a pharmacy convention in Miami. Because of Don's visit, Peg broke a date with Andy. Andy got mad.

DON'T MISS A GOOD BET 205th episode filmed and broadcast. Original broadcast date was January 2, 1967. It was written by Fred S. Fox, and directed by Lee Phillips. Regulars included Andy Griffith, Frances Bavier, George Lindsey, Howard McNear, Ronny Howard, and Aneta Corsaut. Guests included Roger Perry as George Jones, and Dick Ryan as Mr. Wilson.

"DON'T PATRONIZE THIS JAIL" (111F/110B) The sign Bee and the other women carried when they picketed the courthouse to protest Frisby's eviction from his land.

PETE DOOLEY (95F/B) Gomer saw Pete splash mud on Miss Fletcher. Gomer saw all this from the courthouse roof.

"DOPEY" (79F/77B) The name Steve Quincy, the bully, called Opie.

"DOPEY THE DWARF" (8F/9B) Andy said he felt like Dopey the Dwarf when he had to put on a nightshirt and nightcap for his middle-of-the-night marriage ceremonies.

DORIS (249F/248B) Sam Jones' girlfriend.

DOROTHY (245F/244B) The waitress who relieved Flora Mallerby. She was late for work the night Flora and Emmett went to Mt. Pilot to look for a fur for Martha, Emmett's wife.

DOROTHY (246F/245B) The girl Howard invited to his swinging party. It's not said if she was the same Dorothy as the waitress who relieved Flora in 245F/244B. Howard called her "Dot."

CLARIE DORSETT (7F/5B) In 7F/5B, the last time Barney had worn his tweed suit was at Clarie Dorsett's funeral.

DOUBLE-BREASTED SUIT (113F/112B) The suit Ernest T. Bass wore on his introduction to Mayberry's social set at Mrs. Wiley's Saturday night singles social.

"DOWN AT THE DOUBLE EAGLE" (72F/71B) The song Barney played on his Andre Kostalanez Marchers cymbals.

"DOWN IN THE VALLEY" (65F/67B) Song Andy and Peggy McMillan sang after supper.

MORGAN DOWNEY (116F/115B) The tenor who Barney thought might be his replacement at the choir recital. It wasn't indicated whether Morgan owned the store called "Downey's" of 147F/B.

DOWNEY'S (147F/B) Andy sent Goober there to buy a box of assorted deluxe chocolates.

DOWNTOWN BUSINESSMAN'S CLUB (205F/B) Floyd was the secretary.

D-QUEEN JUNCTION (67F/65B) One summer, Andy and Barney set out on a trip to New Orleans in Andy's old Model A. The car burned out a bearing "about D-Queen junction." Andy later sold the car for twelve dollars.

DRAFT BEER (67F/65B) Andy ordered a draft to drink at the restaurant in Raleigh where he took Peggy McMillan.

ATTORNEY LEE DRAKE (226F/223B) The lawyer in Raleigh who Andy had to go see regarding a court case. Drake said—regarding lady lawyers—"we are rare." Helen got jealous when Andy tried to conceal Lee's attractiveness.

DRESS BLUES (107F/127B) Gomer's recruit "buddies" convinced him to put on Sgt. Carter's dress blues. Sgt. Carter was not pleased.

DRESSING (121F/120B) (180F/B) (196F/203B) (201F/204B) 35¢.

THE "DRINKING FOUNTAIN SCANDAL" (200F/197B) Scandal that occurred during the four "stormy" years Floyd served on the Mayberry City Council. Someone ran hot water into the water fountain and tried to cover it up.

ALICE DRUMHILLER (151F/B) Talk of the town in '49. She was supposed to marry Horace Frisey but he left her at the altar. She took to drink; her brother found her under the sink nipping at the elderberry wine. She was singing. Alice finally married Horace. She got fat and dyed her hair blonde; it came out orange.

MRS. DRUMM (116F/115B) She had her battery charged by Gomer.

DRY WELL (228F/227B) The well on Ferguson's farm where Eddie Blake hid the money he stole.

DUANE (138F/B) The author of the Mayberry Centennial Pageant.

DUBOIS, HELENE ALEXIAN see "HELENE ALEXIAN DUBOIS"

PURLIMAE DUBOIS (82F/B) Classmate of Andy's and Barney's, Mayberry Union High Class of 1945. When Barney saw her picture in their yearbook, "The Cutlass," he said "Oh, wow!"

SHARON DUSPAINE (82F/B) (176F/B) High school sweetheart of Andy's. She and Andy were voted Couple of the Year their junior and senior years in school. After high school, she moved to Chicago, where she was working at the time of the "class reunion." At the reunion, Andy and Sharon talked about getting back together, but the same problem that broke them up back then cropped up again: to Andy living and working in Mayberry was all he needed. As he put it, "I've found what I want." But to Sharon, it wasn't enough. Barney called Andy and Sharon "One of the great natural romances of all time." In 176F/B, it was said that she and Andy were in civics class together.

EAGLE (107F/127B) Gomer wanted an eagle tattooed on his arm before he joined the Marines. He wanted "Mother" under it.

"EAGLE-EYE ANNIE" (75F/B) Andy's fishing pole. The pole served as the pivotal bargaining piece in his dealings with Mayor Stoner over the bed jacket Aunt Bee wanted for her birthday.

"EAGLE-EYE BARNEY" (76F/78B) Barney's self-description.

EAGLE ROCK (37F/40B) Rock at Finnegan's Flats that looked like an eagle.

EARL (123F/122B) Bandleader at the dance the "fun girls" attended with Andy and Barney.

"EARLY, EARLY, URCHIN FREE" (240F/B) The game Barney used to play in Old Man McCabe's front yard.

CLARENCE EARP (179F/B) Star of Gibson's Wild West Show and alledgedly the great-nephew of Wyatt Earp. Clarence was a scrawny guy with horn-rimmed glasses who was actually very strong (he beat Warren at arm wrestling and he beat up Goober), and also an expert in gun-twirling. The truth came out—thanks to Andy—that his manager, Fred Gibson, had made up the story that Clarence was related to Wyatt. Clarence accepted the truth, but then he and Fred changed his name to Clarence "Kid" Dempsey.

EARP, WYATT see "WYATT EARP"

EARRINGS (183F/182B) Murillos, the gypsy leader, sold Aunt Bee and Clara each a pair of earrings that he claimed were 400 years old and were once owned by Queen Vincenta. Murillos told Bee that she was the "living image" of the queen. The earrings cost $4.50.

"EAST TO WEST, GIBSON'S THE BEST" (179F/B) The slogan of Gibson's Wild West Show.

EASTMONT, NORTH CAROLINA (4F/6B) George Foley's hometown.

EAT YOUR HEART OUT 182nd episode filmed and 183rd episode broadcast. Original broadcast date was February 28, 1966. It was written by Art Baer and Ben Joelson, and directed by Alan Rafkin. Regulars included Andy Griffith, George Lindsey, Howard McNear, and Aneta Corsaut. Guests included Alberta Nelson as Flora Mallerby.

"EBUM SHUBUM SHUBUM SHUBUM" (139F/B) The incantation Andy recited before he signed the Andelina Darling/Opie Taylor wedding agreement with disappearing ink. Andy told the Darlings that there was a little witching on his ma's side.

ED (60F/B) (76F/78B) In 60F/B, Ed was a customer Floyd told to come back later. In 76F/78B, Ed was the first name of the governor.

ED (204F/202B) Ed called Andy to inform him of a Mt. Pilot bank robbery in which $6,000 was taken.

ED'S REFRIGERATION (120F/119B) Service company that worked on Bee's "bargain" freezer on March 3, 1951.

EDDIE (112F/111B) Edgar J. Masters, the trucker Barney stopped and gave a warning for speeding. Barney called him "Eddie."

"AN EDDIE BRACKEN MOVIE" (213F/B) Andy and Helen planned on watching an Eddie Bracken movie after they watched a documentary on forest rangers.

E

EDGAR (23F/B) Aunt Bee's cousin from Mt. Pilot. His wife, Maude, slept with the window open and got "the vursitis." Bee had to go to Mt. Pilot to help Edgar function.

EDGAR (70F/68B) Andy asked him to print descriptions of the stolen cows in the newspaper. It wasn't said if Edgar was the editor of the paper or if he just worked there.

MR. EDINGER'S CARPENTER SHOP (66F/64B) Mr. McBeevee gave Opie a hatchet. Andy thought he got it from Edinger's.

THE EDUCATION OF ERNEST T. BASS 133rd episode filmed and 131st episode broadcast. Original broadcast date was October 12, 1964. It was written by Jim Fritzell and Everett Greenbaum, and directed by Alan Rafkin. Regulars included Andy Griffith, Don Knotts, Ronny Howard, and Aneta Corsaut. Guests included Ronda Jeter as Sharon, and Howard Morris as Ernest T. Bass.

UNCLE EDWARD (206F/B) Helen Crump's. Uncle Edward was invited for dinner the night Goober mixed up Andy's phone message and Andy ended up having to eat three spaghetti dinners. Uncle Edward made a special spaghetti sauce of which the secret ingredient was oregano. (See OREGANO)

BERTHA EDWARDS (23F/B) Lady friend of Aunt Bee's, the forerunner of first, Clara Johnson, and then, Clara Edwards. Andy sent Opie to Bertha's to borrow some dishes.

CLARA EDWARDS (89F/B) (110F/109B) (165F/169B) (203F/201B) Aunt Bee's lifelong lady friend. In 89F/B, her car was parked in Andy's driveway and her license plate number was shown as DF-153. In 110F/109B, Trey Bowden's mother was visiting Clara. In 165F/169B, Clara got jealous when Bee was the sweepstakes winner on the Hollywood show, "Win Or Lose." In 203F/201B, Clara had won the flower show competition for seven years. Clara was sort of snooty, although in a number of episodes a real warmth and sensitivity showed through. I, for one, was surprised that she supported Bee in her bid for the role of Lady Mayberry in the Founder's Day pageant. Clara taught piano and made superb pickles.

COLONEL EDWARDS (188F/B) Clara's ancestor and a hero of the Battle of Mayberry.

DIXIE BELL EDWARDS (141F/142B) She went to the Great Dismal Swamp with Mary Pleasance to hunt black bear.

GAYLE EDWARDS (154F/B) Clara's son.

SAM EFFLEY (172F/170B) He rode his motorcycle at the end of the Mayberry Founder's Day parade.

JACK EGBERT (82F/B) Jack didn't like Barney so he blackballed him from the Philomathian Society at Mayberry Union High.

EGGNOG (11F/B) The drink Ellie Walker brought to the Christmas Eve party held at the courthouse.

EGGS (160F/163B) (161F/160B) (183F/182B) (186F/187B) 25¢ a dozen.

EIGHT (43F/B) (100F/99B) In 43F/B, eight was the number of quarts of pickles Bee made. In 100F/99B, eight was the number of members in the Mayberry Band.

8:00 A.M. (43F/B) (115F/114B) In 43F/B, the time Barney always picked Andy up for work. In 115F/114B, the time Otis wanted to get up on the day he bought his "hot rod."

8:00 A.M.-5:30 P.M. (225F/224B) The hours of Camp Winoke.

8 1/2 PERCENT, COMPOUNDED ANNUALLY (39F/36B) The rate of payout on Frank Myers' 1861 Town of Mayberry bond.

8 ¢ (73F/70B) Cost of a pound of apples as sold by Neil and Matt from the back of their truck.

$8.00 (105F/104B) (183F/182B) (224F/221B) The price of the shoes Gomer bought to take Mary Grace Gossage to the dance. The shoes had brass buckles on the side. (See entry GOMER'S OUTFIT) In 183F/182B, the cost of the shawl that Murillos, the gypsy leader, sold Aunt Bee. He claimed it was once worn by Princess Teronoya. In 224F/221B, the bowling shirts for the "Mayberry Rollers" cost Emmett's Fix-It Shop eight dollars each. The total cost for the shirts was Emmett's entire ad budget.

$850.00 (245F/244B) The last coat that Bernie the Furrier showed Emmett cost $850. Emmett bought it. Bernie described the coat as "not a mink you wear in the light."

895 (163F/161B) Helen Crump's house number.

EIGHT PLACES (161F/160B) In 161F/160B, Opie applied to eight places looking for a job.

8 LBS., 9 OZ. (29F/B) Andy Becker's birth weight.

EIGHT QUARTERS (39F/36B) Frank Myers was eight quarters behind in his property taxes.

8:28 A.M. (34F/33B) The time Opie turned the corner at Fifth and Elm Streets on his way to his confrontation with Sheldon the Bully. He had three blocks to go before he would see Sheldon.

8216 (74F/B) Big Maude Tyler's prison number.

EIGHT YEARS (244F/243B) It was eight years since Helen had looked at the history outline she had Andy pull down from the closet shelf. That was how Andy found the photo of Helen being arrested.

EIGHTEEN (38F/41B) Bee Taylor's age when her family moved to Peoria.

$18.50 (72F/71B) The cost of Barney's Andre Kostalanez Marchers cymbals, bought at Cymbal City.

$1,800.00 (245F/244B) Emmett's price for the ranch mink coat Bernie the Furrier showed him. It retailed for $3,000.

1890 (62F/B) The year the Feed and Grain Store was established.

1870 (113F/112B) The year Rotten Ray Anchram came down from the hills and burned down Mayberry.

1864 (138F/B) The year Mayberry was founded.

1861 (39F/36B) The issue year of Frank Myer's Town of Mayberry bond.

EIGHTH GRADE (243F/242B) The grade in which Helen Crump won the state spelling bee championship in Kansas when she was a kid.

80¢ (60F/B) The amount Bill Medwin, the bookie barber, charged for a shampoo.

81 (53F/B) The room Sheldon Davis stayed in at the Mayberry Hotel.

87¢ (54F/B) The cost of the apron Aunt Bee bought from Bert Miller, the peddler. She told Andy to pay for it.

EKMONDWIGHT (89F/B) Malcolm Merriweather's hometown. It was "up Arbeshire way."

EL CARP (240F/B) Locale suggested as possible site for the US/USSR summit meeting. This was before Mayberry was agreed upon.

ELDERBERRY WINE (230F/229B) Andy made his own. Bee offered some to Professor Hubert St. John.

ELDERBERRY WINE STAINS (58F/B) Mrs. Doug Palmer brought in clothes to Fred Goss, the cleaner, with elderberry wine stains on them.

"ELECTRONICALLY-CONTROLLED" (202F/196B) Arnold claimed the blankets he and Opie used to cover the abandoned baby were "electronically-controlled." He said this to keep Andy from looking in the clubhouse.

"ELECTRONILLY" (85F/B) The way Barney wanted to modernize the courthouse.

11 (43F/B) Bee's jar number at the county fair pickle competition.

ELEVEN (88F/B) (243F/242B) In 88F/B, Mr. Darling said it usually took eleven hatfuls of water to fill his truck's radiator when it overheated. He dipped his hat in the David Mendlebright Memorial Horse Trough ("Let no horse go thirsty") to get the water. In 243F/242B, Bee had taken eleven flying lessons when Mr. McDonald decided it was time for her to solo.

11:00 A.M. (100F/99B) Sunday preaching began at 11:00 A.M. at All Souls Church.

ELEVEN BOYS (127F/126B) The number of boys Andy, Barney, and Gomer took "back to nature."

$1,100.00 (245F/244B) The price to Emmett for the shorthaired mink coat Bernie the Furrier showed him.

$1,150.00 (245F/244B) Emmett saw some mink coats in a catalogue that cost $1,150.

11:00 P.M. (29F/B) The time Barney always made his nightly patrol rounds.

ELEVEN SPEED WARNINGS (112F/111B) The number of warnings Barney issued from his motorcycle at Checkpoint Chickie on Highway 6.

ELEVEN YEARS (43F/B) Clara Johnson won the blue ribbon for her pickles at the county fair eleven years in a row.

ELI (129F/130B) Man Andy greeted on his way to church. Andy told Eli he'd enjoy the services.

ELLA (209F/210B) A customer at Aunt Bee's Canton Palace. She ate with her husband. Their bill was $3.80.

ELLA (234F/232B) She wrote the society column in the "Mayberry Gazette."

ELLEN (206F/B) Bee's sister. In 206F/B, Bee went to visit her in Raleigh. Ellen had a lot planned: luncheon, then a handicraft exhibit at the Old People's Home, then dinner at the Armenian restaurant, Shabob's. At Shabob's they wrapped everything in grape leaves.

ELLIE COMES TO TOWN 6th episode filmed and 4th episode broadcast. Original broadcast date was October 24, 1960. It was written by Jack Elinson and Charles Stewart, and directed by Don Weis. Regulars included Andy Griffith, Don Knotts, Frances Bavier, and Ronny Howard. Guests included Elinor Donahue as Ellie Walker, Cheerio Meredith as Emma Brand, and Harry Antrim as Fred Walker.

ELLIE FOR COUNCIL 12th episode filmed and 10th episode broadcast. Original broadcast date was December 12, 1960. It was written by Jack Elinson and Charles Stewart, and directed by Bob Sweeney. Regulars included Andy Griffith, Frances Bavier, Don Knotts, Ronny Howard, Hal Smith as Otis, and Elinor Donahue as Ellie Walker. Guests included Frank Ferguson, Mary Treen, Forrest Lewis, Dorothy Neumann, and Florence MacMichael as Hilda Mae.

ELLIE SAVES A FEMALE 27th episode filmed and broadcast. Original broadcast date was April 17, 1961. It was written by David Adler, and directed by Bob Sweeney. Regulars included Andy Griffith, Don Knotts, Ronny Howard, and Elinor Donahue as Ellie Walker. Guests included R.G. Armstrong, Edris March, and Bob McQuain.

ELM CITY (39F/36B) A visitor to Mayberry actually thought he was in Elm City.

ELM CITY DELIVERY SERVICE (32F/B) After Aunt Bee foolishly forbade him to visit Andy in the courthouse, Opie went wandering and fell asleep in an Elm City Delivery Service truck.

ELM STREET (50F/B) (52F/B) (153F/B) (200F/197B) (226F/B/223B) In 50F/B, the street on which Andy lived (see ANDY'S ADDRESS). In 52F/B, the street on which John Masters, the choir director, lived. In 153F/B, the Mayberry street where Opie delivered copies of his and Howie's newspaper, "The Mayberry Sun." In 200F/197B, Bee wanted to beautify Elm Street as part of her campaign for city council. In 226F/223B, the street in Raleigh where attorney Lee Drake lived.

ELM STREET PLAYGROUND (153F/B) The playground where Karen Folker fell down while chasing Bruce Newdell.

ELMO (227F/222B) (232F/233B) (238F/239B) In 227F/222B, he was the proprietor of the film-developing store on Main Street. In 232F/233B, Goober gave him a ticket for turning without a signal. In 238F/239B, Elmo suggested that the finance committee use the $500 willed to the church to buy a pool table for the men's club meetings in the church basement.

JARVIS ELRIDGE (82F/B) Classmate of Andy's and Barney's at Mayberry Union High, Class of 1945.

THE EMANCIPATION PROCLAMATION (86F/B) Barney pretended he knew all about it in an attempt to impress Helen Crump with his knowledge.

EMBASSY DANCE CLUB (217F/B) The club in Siler City where Betty Parker worked nights.

"EMBRYONIC MEGALOPOLIS" (163F/161B) According to Frank Smith, Raleigh was becoming one.

FLETCHER EMERSON (225F/224B) Mayberry man who used to own the hardware store. When Andy said that Emerson (he meant Ralph Waldo) said "Be yourself," Emmett thought he meant Fletcher.

EMILY (234F/232B) Mayberry woman who felt that Bee's reception for her cousin, Bradford Taylor, was the most exciting party in Mayberry.

EMMETT'S ANNIVERSARY 245th episode filmed and 244th episode broadcast. Original broadcast date was February 26, 1968. It was written by Perry Grant and Richard Bensfield, and directed by Lee Phillips. Regulars included Andy Griffith, Frances Bavier, Ronny Howard, George Lindsey, and Paul Hartman. Guests included Ruth McDevitt as Mrs. Pendleton, Mary Lansing as Martha Clark, Alberta Nelson as Flora Mallerby, and Ronnie Schell as Bernie the Furrier.

EMMETT'S BROTHER-IN-LAW 236th episode filmed and 237th episode broadcast. Original broadcast date was January 8, 1968. It was written by the award-winning James L. Brooks, the writer now known for "The Mary Tyler Moore Show" and the film "Terms Of Endearment." This episode was one of his earliest television projects. It was directed by Lee Phillips. Regulars included Andy Griffith, Aneta Corsaut, Jack Dodson, Paul Hartman, and Mary Lansing as Martha Clark. Guests included Dub Taylor as Martha's brother, Ben Beecham.

EMMETT'S FIX-IT SHOP (224F/221B) Main Street repair business owned and operated by Emmett Clark. Emmett opened his shop in the location of Floyd's Barbershop after Floyd closed. The Fix-It Shop became the new gathering spot for the Mayberry men. Emmett's sponsored the bowling team, consisting of Andy, Goober, and Emmett, called the "Mayberry Rollers."

EMMIE (8F/9B) Jedediah Wakefield's mule. Jedediah was admitted to the hospital on September 14, 1908, after Emmie bit him on the behind.

"EMPTYING TRASHCANS ON THE CITY STREETS" (11F/B) Andy eventually arrested Ben Weaver on this littering charge.

ENCYCLOPEDIA EUROPA (231F/230B) A classified ad Andy read. The ad was for a salesman.

"AN ENGLISH OTIS" (124F/123B) The name Barney called Malcolm Merriweather when Malcolm served cold soup (with the cover in the bowl), and spilled the silver drawer all over the floor. Malcolm pretended to be drunk on sherry because he realized that Bee felt left out because he was so efficient. He had actually dumped the sherry down the sink.

ERECTOR SET (136F/B) Opie looked at one in a catalogue and Andy told him that he had had one once. He had gotten it for Christmas and he built a drawbridge over a creek near his house. He had boats in the water, a steam engine with pulleys to raise and lower the bridge, and a little wind-up tractor to go across the bridge. Opie said he'd like to build one like that and Andy said maybe he would. Barney chimed in with, "Will you help us?!"

ERIE, PENNSYLVANIA (110F/109B) Hometown of Trey Bowden.

ERNEST T. BASS JOINS THE ARMY
99th episode filmed and 98th episode broadcast. Original broadcast date was October 14, 1963. It was written by Jim Fritzell and Everett Greenbaum, and directed by Dick Crenna. Regulars included Andy Griffith and Don Knotts. Guests included Allan Melvin, Paul Smith, Alice Backes, Tom Myers, David Lipp, and Howard Morris as Ernest T. Bass.

ERNEST T. BASS'S PHYSICAL PROWESS (99F/98B) Ernest T. was proud of being able to chin twenty times with one hand, pick a watermelon out of a barrel with his jaws, and tote a jackass five miles to the doctor.

ERNEST T. BASS'S "SENTENCE" (133F/131B) Ernest T. wrote the following sentence as part of his "ejacation": "No hunt beware open and closed no credit."

ESCARGOT AND BRAINS (57F/B) The meal Barney ordered in Capitol City by pointing out things on the menu to the waiter. He wouldn't admit he couldn't read French.

ESCARGOT BOURGINOIN (67F/65B) Peggy McMillan ordered snails for both herself and Andy at the restaurant in the state capital. Andy wouldn't eat his.

THE ESQUIRE CLUB (42F/B) Andy's friend, Roger Courtney, belonged to this swanky club. Roger asked Andy to come to a meeting as a possible new member and Andy brought Barney. Andy got accepted but they didn't want Barney. Andy turned down membership to spare Barney's feelings, but stayed friends with Roger. The Esquire Club met Thursdays at 8:00 P.M. in Raleigh.

ESSEX BANK BUILDING (231F/230B) Mt. Pilot building where the Bradbury Business College (Howard Sprague's alma mater) was located. It was on the third floor.

ESTELLE (197F/198B) The female lead in "The Senior Play."

ETHEL (125F/124B) A little girl that Helen walked home. Helen reminded Ethel to have her mother put something on her sty.

ETHEL (161F/160B) Somebody kept calling the courthouse one day asking for Ethel.

"THE ETHEL PAGE ORGAN RECITAL" (116F/115B) Radio program. Leonard Blush did all the vocals on the show. Ethel used to have a canary with her but she dropped the bird. She hadn't had the canary with her since she sang Sunday afternoons at the Pot 'O Honey Restaurant.

"EVERYTHING IN TIME OF NEED" (24F/B) Sign on the window of Orville Monroe's funeral parlor.

EVIE JOY (184F/B) Daughter of Martha and Darryl. Martha was Bee's niece. She asked Bee to care for Evie Joy while they went to Jersey City for a wedding. Evie Joy cried every time Bee picked her up. Opie and Pete fed the baby blueberries, Bee panicked (thinking the baby was sick), grabbed her out of the crib, and the baby didn't cry. Andy finally figured out that the baby had been sensing Bee's nervousness and reacting to it.

"EXTRASENSITIVE PERCEPTION" (142F/141B) The way Barney pronounced "extrasensory perception."

F (103F/B) Opie's actual grade in arithmetic. Helen Crump mistakenly gave him an A.

F. WAKEFIELD BEAUTY SALON (75F/B) Mayberry beauty parlor.

"FACE ON THE BARROOM FLOOR" (35F/B) Barney sang it after Elizabeth Crowley—the "woman speeder"—told him he looked like Frank Sinatra.

"FACITIOUS" (115F/114B) The way Barney pronounced "facetious."

"THE FACTS OF LIFE" (202F/199B) Bee wanted Andy to tell Opie the facts of life after the boy started going around town asking people if they wanted a baby. Actually, he and Arnold were trying to find a good home for the abandoned Garland baby.

"A FADING FLOWER OF FORGOTTEN LOVE" (96F/100B) Poem by Alice Ellicott Strong that Bee recited for Briscoe Darling. In this episode, Andy revealed that Bee used to recite this poem with her sister, Florence, when they were younger.

MISS FAIN (213F/B) Publisher Roger Bryant's secretary.

"FAIR AND SQUARE SAM" (247F/246B) The slogan Goober suggested for Sam Jones' campaign for head of city council.

"A FAIR DEAL FOR THE FAIR SEX" (12F/10B) Ellie Walker's campaign slogan. Even though Andy realized his sexism in opposing Ellie's campaign for city council member, after the campaign was over Andy teased Ellie by singing "Elinor Walker Councilman/Won the election and away she ran/Everybody knows she's just a filly/Runnin' for Council's just plain silly." Ellie got mad whenever he called her efforts "silly."

IRENE FAIRCHILD (185F/B) The new county health officer. Irene took over Howard Sprague's old office when Howard moved to a larger one. Howard was embarassed when Irene found his T-shirt and returned it to him. He had removed it on an especially hot day and stuck it in a file cabinet drawer. Andy and Helen arranged a date between Irene and Howard. They went to Morelli's. Howard's mother did not like the idea of her boy dating and she faked illness to get them to cut the date short.

THE FAMILY DINNER FOR ONE (51F/B) The meal Barney and Juanita had the night they went to Mt. Pilot for Chinese. The bill came to $2.75.

FAMILY VISIT 129th episode filmed and 130th broadcast. Original broadcast date was October 5, 1964. It was written by Jim Fritzell and Everett Greenbaum, and directed by Howard Morris. Regulars included Andy Griffith, Ronny Howard, Frances Bavier, and Howard McNear. Guests included James Westerfield as Ollie, Maudie Prickett as Nora, Richard Keith as Johnny Paul Jason, Kenneth Butts as Bruce, Forrest Lewis as Mr. Mundt, and Billy Booth as Roger.

FANCY GAP (17F/B) (155F/B) In 17F/B, the locale Andy and Barney considered as a possible still site. In 155F/B, the highway department called Andy to tell him to expand the 50 mph zone as far as Fancy Gap.

THE FAR EAST (234F/232B) Bee's cousin, Bradford Taylor, claimed he was called away to the Far East by the State Department for a shipping crisis.

FARLEY (234F/232B) Mayberry postal worker.

He delivered the special delivery letter to Aunt Bee from her cousin, Bradford Taylor.

EVAN FARLEY (247F/246B) Mrs. Farley's son. He was a cub scout.

MRS. FARLEY (122F/121B) (247F/246B) In 122F/121B, she was the woman who called Bee because she needed help getting her cat down from a tree. The cat got down by itself, however. In 247F/246B, Mrs. Farley called Emmett to complain about the moving of the cub scout meeting from the school to the building behind the firehouse.

THE FARMER TAKES A WIFE 45th episode filmed and broadcast. Original broadcast date was January 1, 1962. It was written by Jack Elinson and Charles Stewart, and directed by Bob Sweeney. Regulars included Andy Griffith, Don Knotts, Frances Bavier, and Betty Lynn. Guests included Adoree Evans, Bob McQuain and Alan Hale as Jeff Pruitt.

TOMMY FARRELL (14F/B) Opie traded his cap pistol to Tommy for "licorice seeds."

JIMMY FARRINGTON (124F/123B) Opie went to his birthday party. Malcolm Merriweather took him to the party in his chauffeur's uniform.

"A FAST-BACK WIRE-WHEELED COUPE" (153F/B) The dishcloth salesman's car. The Widow Saunders was seeing him.

"FAST GUN FIFE" (41F/39B) Nickname Barney personally claimed in order to enhance his image as a lawman.

FAT KNEES (37F/40B) Along with talking a lot, fat knees was one of the negatives about Melinda Keefer, a blind date Barney once arranged for Andy.

FATBACK (54F/B) (74F/B) (76F/78B) 17¢ a pound.

HAROLD FAWCETT (249F/248B) Juanita was going to Myer's Lake every night with Harold to "discuss business," or so Goober thought.

THE FBI (36F/37B) Barney told Melissa Stevens he'd thought of joining the FBI.

"FEARLESS FIFE" (73F/70B) According to Barney, one of his nicknames.

FEBRUARY 7 (106F/B) One of the dates Barney resigned as deputy.

THE FEED AND GRAIN STORE (62F/B) Store owned by Oscar Skinner, established in 1890. In 62F/B, Otis remarked that he might have a job working for Oscar. The store was behind the courthouse.

HOWARD FELCHER (136F/B) He and Lorraine were getting divorced.

LORRAINE FELCHER (136F/B) Barney found out about her and her husband Howard's impending divorce from Phoebe Gilbert, Lemley Gilbert's sister, when Barney took Phoebe to the Blue View Motel for dinner. Lorraine was a drinker. Phoebe worked at the beauty parlor.

MRS. FELDON (237F/236B) The woman who Aunt Bee called in to cook for Andy and Opie while she did her cooking show, "The Mayberry Chef."

"FELIX THE CAT" (42F/B) The name Barney angrily called Andy after the sheriff hid Barney's shoes while the deputy was napping.

MRS. FENTON (176F/B) She was one of Barney's teachers. At the class reunion, she asked him if he still got nosebleeds.

MISS FENWICK (61F/B) J. Howard Jackson's secretary.

FERDIE (189F/B) Clara Edwards' nerdy nephew. He played the accordion and the ladies brought him with them to "re-audition" their song, "My Home Town," for Keevy Hazleton in his hotel room.

HARLAN FERGUS (39F/36B) Mayberry banker whose bank machines figured that Frank Myers' hundred-year-old bond was worth $349,119.27. Harlan was a member of the town council. The council voted to evict Frank for nonpayment of taxes.

DEPUTY WARREN FERGUSON (169F/165B) (173F/174B) (174F/173B) Floyd's nephew, his sister's son. In 169F/165B, Warren believed he was gifted with ESP, and proceeded to make Andy's life miserable. In 173F/174B, it was mentioned that he came from Boston. In 174F/173B, it was stated that he was in the wholesale fish business before becoming a deputy. Warren was intended to be a Barney Fife replacement. The casting didn't work. He was too abrasive at most times.

THE FERGUSON GIRL (210F/211B) Mayberry girl who beat up Harold Lovitt. That incident was the last occurrence of bad blood in Mayberry until the Howard Sprague/Floyd Lawson fight over a rent increase in 1967.

FERGUSON'S FARM (228F/227B) Abandoned farm on Orchard Road where Eddie Blake hid the $25,000 he stole from the Raleigh Bank. He hid the money in a dry well. It wasn't said if the farm was owned by the Ferguson girl's family.

RICHIE FERRARO (99F/98B) Ernest T. Bass broke a window in Richie's hardware store.

MR. FERRIS (143F/B) Andy's plumber. He told Andy he might need a whole new plumbing system.

A FEUD IS A FEUD 8th episode filmed and 9th episode broadcast. Original broadcast was December 5, 1960. It was written by David Adler, and directed by Don Weis. Regulars included Andy Griffith, Frances Bavier, and Ronny Howard. Guests included Arthur Hunnicut, Chubby Johnson, Claude Johnson, and Tammy Windsor as Hannah Carter.

"BARNEY FICE" (150F/B) The way Barney's name was spelled in the "Sheriff Without A Gun" article in "Law And Order" magazine.

MISS FICKETT (86F/B) Former teacher of Andy's and Barney's. Barney said she had to be 107 years old: it would take that long to get that mean.

FIDO (214F/B) The name of Howard Sprague's pony when Howard was a kid.

MR. FIELDS (104F/105B) Stranger in Mayberry who came into town and began to court Barney's landlady, Mrs. Mendlebright. When Mrs. Mendlebright evicted Barney for cooking in his room, she gave his room to Mr. Fields. Before long, Fields convinced the old lady to marry him and withdraw all her money from the bank to use as a down payment on a new house in Raleigh. Andy and Barney got suspicious and eventually exposed him as a crook and con artist. His aliases included Oscar Fields, Otto Bell, and Norman Feldspar. He had been associated in the past with extortion and bigamy.

"OSCAR FIELDS" (104F/105B) One of Mr. Fields' aliases.

BARNEY FIFE "Fearless Fife." "Fife the Fierce." "Reliable Barney Fife." "Barn." Opie may have been the real child but Barney Fife was the spiritual child of Mayberry. He was Andy's best friend, his little brother, his son, his cousin, and his continual annoyance. At times, Barney could be infuriatingly dense, and then heartbreakingly considerate. One always felt that nothing could be finer than to have Barney Fife as a friend. Even when he apparently turned his back on Andy (as in "Andy On Trial"), his subsequent redemption was obviously a major turning point for him. His opinion of himself was as changing as the weather. One minute he was Super Deputy, Casanova, and Don Quixote. The next he was worthless, a whimpering loser. He was a lover, a genius, and a shrewdy. And then there were times when he was too naive to believe. Barney Fife was the epitome of the child in us all. When he left Mayberry, he broke the town's heart. I'm not sure Mayberry ever forgave him. (See other entries beginning with the word "BARNEY" or "BARNEY'S")

MRS. FIFE (2F/B) Barney's mother, played by Lillian Culver. Her only appearance on the show was in "The Manhunt," when Barney stopped her at a roadblock and frisked her. Her only line on the show was, "But, Barney, I'm your mother!"

FIFE REALTY (143F/B) Barney's short-lived real estate company. When all the deals he had cooking fell through, he claimed he had lost $3,478 in commissions.

"FIFE THE FIERCE" (73F/70B) Barney's nickname, according to Andy, who told it to the two roadside farmers, Neil and Matt, to scare them into obeying Barney.

"FIFI THE UPSTAIRS MAID" (71F/72B) According to Andy, Aunt Bee looked like Fifi when she dressed up and posed as a maid to help Floyd convince Madeline Grayson that he was a rich widower.

FIFTEEN (119F/118B) Andy pretended he did fifteen pushups a day.

$15.00 (61F/B) (75F/B) (210F/211B) In 61F/B, $15 was the fine Andy imposed on J. Howard Jackson. In 75F/B, Mayor Stoner's final offer for Andy's fishing pole, "Eagle-Eye Annie," was $15. In 210F/211B, the rent increase Howard wanted from Floyd—after he bought the building in which Floyd's shop was located—was $15. He said he needed the increase in order to make five percent on his money.

$1,500.00 DOWN (210F/211B) The amount that was required to buy the building on Main Street in which Floyd's Barbershop was located.

FIFTEEN MINUTES, MORNING AND NIGHT (207F/209B) How Howard Sprague used his toothbrush.

$15,000.00 (236F/237B) Ben Beecham claimed that $15,000 was the potential income as an insurance salesman for the Mayberry, Mt. Pilot, Siler City area. Fifteen thousand would be more than twice Emmett's income.

$15,000.00 FOR FOUR YEARS (231F/230B) In 231F/230B, the cost of a college education.

THE 15TH (122F/121B) The date of the "blacklist" scare letter the Miracle Salve Company sent Trey Bowden.

FIFTH AND ELM (34F/33B) The corner Opie turned at 8:28 A.M. on his way to his confrontation with Sheldon the Bully.

FIFTH GRADE (153F/B) The class Opie was in when he and Howie produced their newspaper, "The Mayberry Sun."

FIFTY BOXES (39F/36B) The number of boxes of decorative berries Frank Myers had in storage while he waited for the day when women would once again start wearing berries on their hats.

$50.00 (31F/B) (136F/B) (210F/211B) In 31F/B, the fine Bobby Fleet imposed on Jim Lindsey for missing thirty hours of rehearsal time. In 136F/B, the money Opie found in Parnell Rigsby's purse. In 210F/211B, Floyd was paying the Robinson family $50 a month rent before Howard Sprague bought the building.

FIFTY-FIVE MILES (67F/65B) The distance from Raleigh, the capital of North Carolina, to Mayberry.

$54.20 (208F/212B) The amount of money that was left in the treasury of the Civic Improvement Committee after they paid for the statue of Seth Taylor.

FIFTY PERCENT (228F/227B) The cut Eddie Blake offered his lawyer from the money he stole.

FIFTY-SEVEN PANCAKES (243F/242B) The number of pancakes Goober ate to win the pancake eating contest at the county fair.

$50,000.00 (150F/B) The amount of money that was in the Mayberry Security Bank on Fridays.

$52.50 (28F/B) Lester Scoby's mortgage payment. In 28F/B, he fell one month behind. Ben Weaver wanted to foreclose so he could build a warehouse on the property. Andy played the heavy and made Ben realize what he was doing. Ben ended up giving Lester a job working for him at his department store.

FIFTY-YARD DASH (51F/B) The race Opie entered at the Boy's Day competition. The winners of the race were: first place, Billy Johnson; second place, Aaron Harrison; and third place, Freddy Pruitt. When Barney was young, he won a fifty-yard dash.

"FIKE" (78F/76B) (118F/117B) In 78F/76B, Mr. Butler of the "Mayberry Gazette" spelled Barney's name "Fike" in the paper. In 118F/117B, this was also the way the "Gazette" spelled Barney's last name after the escaped prisoner was caught.

FILLMORE (240F/B) Locale suggested, then ruled out, as a possible site for the US/USSR summit meeting. Mayberry was finally agreed upon to be the site of the meeting.

FINANCE COMMITTEE (238F/239B) Committee consisting of Andy Taylor as chairman, Martha Clark, and Reverend Hobart Tucker. They met to decide what to do with the $500 willed to the church by Jarrod Hooper.

ARNOLD FINCH (171F/172B) Counterfeiter who came to Mayberry with his partner, Ralph Kingsley. Aunt Bee went to work for them as a clerk. They operated out of Hansen's Print Shop's location at 177 Main Street. Hansen's had gone out of business at that location.

AUGUSTA FINCH (87F/B) Lady friend of Aunt Bee's. Augusta died at ten-thirty on the morning of the day Colonel Harvey came to town. Her death upset Bee so much, she became an easy sale for Colonel Harvey, who sold her two bottles of his Indian Elixir. She got drunk on it. Bee and Augusta were the same age.

WILBUR FINCH (15F/B) Shoe salesman for the Manhattan Shoe Company. Bee and Emma Brand started a rumor that he was a talent scout for "Manhattan Showtime." The men in town sent all kinds of acts to his hotel room, both to buy shoes and to perform. In the end, the truth came out and the ladies proved that "those gossipin' men" were just as bad as women when it came to rumor-propagating.

"FINGERS" (50F/B) According to Barney, one of his nicknames.

"FINICULI FINICULA" (15F/B) (36F/37B) In 15F/B, the song Barney offered to play for Wilbur Finch on the harmonica. In 36F/37B, he offered to play it for Melissa Stevens and her "Daddy."

FINISH LINE JUDGE (51F/B) Andy's role at the yearly Boy's Day competition.

FINNEGAN FLATS (37F/40B) Rural area on the outskirts of Mayberry where Andy took Karen Moore crow shooting.

THE FINNEYS (222F/225B) Mayberry couple. Mr. Finney, not liking Mrs. Finney, threw a rock through her window.

"FIRE BY CONSTRICTION" (127F/126B) Barney claimed he started a campfire by this method when he rubbed two sticks together.

"FIREBUG" (129F/130B) The name Ollie, Aunt Bee's brother-in-law and Andy's uncle, called Mr. Mundt for parking in front of a fire hydrant.

THE FIREHOUSE (119F/118B) Carter French called Andy to tell him that there was a boiled dinner and then cribbage down at the firehouse.

FIREWORKS DISPLAY (42F/B) Andy told Barney he looked good enough to get taken to the fireworks display.

FIRST AND THIRD STREETS (200F/197B) Rather than installing new sewers on Main Street, Howard suggested repairing the 200-foot run between First and Third Streets.

"THE FIRST BASH OF THE MAYBERRY SOCIAL SEASON" (246F/245B) The way Howard described his "swinging" party.

"THE FIRST BORN CHILD OF THE MAN THAT SAVED MY LIFE" (119F/118B) Opie's title, as bestowed upon him by Gomer.

FIRST PRIZE (234F/232B) Bee won first prize at the county fair for her homemade strawberry ice cream.

FISHER'S POND (111F/110B) Waterhole near Mr. Frisby's farm. Fire trucks and ambulances had to drive around it and then cross a "wobbly old bridge" in order to get to certain places, and all because Frisby's farm was right in the middle of the road. The state wanted to bulldoze Frisby's farm so they could extend the highway.

"THE FISHIN' HOLE" Theme to "The Andy Griffith Show." Lyrics were by Everett Sloane, and music by Earle Hagen and Herbert Spencer:

I Well now, take down your fishin' pole
And meet me at the fishin' hole
We may not get a bite all day
But don't you rush away
What a great place to rest your bones
And mighty fine for skippin' stones
You'll feel fresh as a lemonade
A settin' in the shade
Whether it's hot, whether it's cool
Oh what a spot
For whistlin' like a fool
What a fine day
To take a stroll
And wander by the Fishin' Hole
I can't think of a better way
To pass the time o' day

II We'll have no need to call the roll
When we get to the Fishin' Hole
There'll be you, me and Old Dog Trey
To doodle time away
If we don't hook a perch or bass
We'll cool our toes in dewy grass
Or else pull up a weed to chaw
And maybe set and jaw
Hangin' around
Takin' our ease
Watchin' that hound
A-scratchin' at his fleas
Come on, take down your fishin' pole
And meet me at the Fishin' Hole
I can't think of a better way
To pass the time o' day

These are the original lyrics. They were never sung on the show, although there was a vocal version of the song released in 1985 on Rhino Records (#RNC 703 BT 18809). The song was also on a CBS Special Products album called "The TV Theme Song Sing-Along Album," and this "big-bandish" version of "The Fishin' Hole " was sung by none other than Andy Griffith! This cut was originally a Capitol Records release, although the year is uncertain. Copyright 1960, 1961, 1966 by Larrabee Music.

FISHING POLE (136F/B) Opie bought one with part of the fifty dollars he found in Parnell Rigsby's purse. He later returned it when Mr. Rigsby appeared to claim the money.

FITZ (135F/B) The name of the guy in Siler City who mistakenly received Barney's salt-and-pepper suit.

"5" (131F/129B) The numeral that was engraved on the back of the watch Barney was presented with on his fifth anniversary as deputy. It was given to him by Andy, Opie, Aunt Bee, and Thelma Lou.

5¢ (5F/8B) The second lowest amount given to the Underpriviliged Children's Charity Drive. It was donated by Roy Pruitt. He was one of the underpriviliged children. The lowest amount given was three cents by Opie Taylor.

FIVE CHAIRS (42F/B) The number of chairs the Raleigh barbershop had, according to Floyd.

FIVE DAYS IN JAIL (106F/B) The punishment Barney chose rather than pay a fine after Andy forced him to write himself a ticket. Gomer made a "citizen's arrest" of Barney after the deputy made an illegal U-turn.

$5.00 (30F/B) (243F/242B) In 30F/B, the amount the crook, Eddie Brooks, offered Barney to get him to forget about a parking violation. In 243F/242B, the cost of a demonstration flying lesson at MacDonald's Flying School.

$5.00 PER MAN (229F/228B) The fee Mrs. Roach paid for Opie's band, "The Sound Committee," to play at her daughter Brenda's birthday party.

5831 (74F/B) Naomi Connors' prison number.

FIVE FEET EIGHT INCHES (131F/129B) The height requirement Barney had to fulfill to remain a deputy. He borrowed Asa Bascomb's stretching harness to "hang" himself to get the extra height.

FIVE FEET FOUR INCHES TALL, 115 POUNDS, SLENDER, BLONDE" (74F/B) The description of Naomi Conners, one of the "convicts at large."

FIVE FEET NINE INCHES (53F/B) Sheldon Davis's height.

FIVE FEET SIX INCHES TALL, DARK HAIR, 175 LBS" (74F/B) The description of Big Maude Tyler, leader of the "convicts at large."

FIVE HOURS (236F/237B) The length of time it took to drive from Mayberry to Raleigh. (A bit strange, as the distance to Raleigh is given as fifty-five miles in 67F/65B.)

$500.00 (238F/239B) The amount of money Jarrod Hooper willed to All Souls Church when he died at the age of 93.

FIVE INCHES (238F/239B) All Souls Church was tilted five inches out of plumb.

FIVE MILES (4F/6B) The number of miles George Foley figured he could hike a day.

598 147F/B) Lydia Crosswaithe's house number.

596 (117F/116B) Thelma Lou's phone number.

5:00 P.M.-8:00 P.M. (237F/236B) The time Bee was gone from the house every day to do her cooking show, "The Mayberry Chef."

FIVE PERCENT (210F/211B) Howard wanted to make five percent on his money after buying the Main Street building in which Floyd's Barbershop was located.

FIVE SECTIONS (5F/8B) The number of sections Annabelle Silby divided Mayberry into for fund-raising purposes.

$5,000.00 (19F/B) The first royalty check Mr. Maxwell brought to Mayberry from National Records for the album of folk songs, "Music From Mayberry." The royalty rate for Maxwell was 25¢ per record, for the investors, 3¢. Barney invested $40.

FIVE YEARS (24F/B) (104F/105B) (116F/115B) (231F/230B) In 24F/B, the time Andy considered proper as an engagement period. In 104F/105B, the length of time Barney lived in Mrs. Mendlebright's rooming house before she evicted him for cooking in his room. In 116F/115B, Barney said that Gomer's voice was five years from performance level. In 231F/230B, Cyrus Whitley was serving five years for embezzlement.

FLAG DAY (189F/B) The holiday for which Aunt Bee and Clara Edwards wrote their magnum opus, "My Hometown." (See entry "MY HOMETOWN")

FLAMENCO DANCER (227F/222B) During Bee's Mexican trip, the dancer's first show started at midnight.

ROBLING FLASK (213F/B) Flamboyant cover designer for Bryant Publishing Company who was assigned to do the cover for Helen Crump's book, *Amusing Tales Of Tiny Tots*. Robling "let his pastels run wild" for Helen's cover.

"FLEET AND LINDSEY" (31F/B) Jim Lindsey wanted to change the name of "Bobby Fleet and his Band with a Beat" to "Fleet and Lindsey."

FLETCH (127F/126B) He brought the boys roasted chicken and archery equipment for their "back to nature" camping trip. The chicken was from Aunt Bee.

JUD FLETCHER (16F/20B) Barney arrested Jud for violation of Code 721-8, disturbing the peace; Jud had hollered at Chester Jones. Jud was seventy-four, and it was not said if he was related to Tate.

MISS FLETCHER (95F/B) Gomer saw Pete Dooley splash mud on Miss Fletcher. Gomer watched this happen from the courthouse roof.

MRS. FLETCHER (241F/249B) Sam Jones's cook. She quit after Sophia Vincente took over the kitchen.

TATE FLETCHER (68F/70B) The farmer whose cows were stolen by Luke Jensen.

FLEUR DE LIS BEAUTY SALON (30F/B) Main Street beauty parlor.

FLIGHT 17 (227F/222B) The flight Bee, Clara, and Myrtle took to Mexico. It left from Gate 12.

FRANKIE FLINT (27F/B) Francis Flint, daughter of Old Man Flint. She was Flint's only child, and he wouldn't let her use makeup or perfume. He insisted her chores were more important. Andy convinced him that if he let Frankie become Francis, he'd end up with both a daughter and a strong young son-in-law. Ellie Walker started the "makeover" of Frankie.

OLD MAN FLINT (27F/B) Frankie's father. Andy convinced him to let Frankie become Francis.

IRENE FLOGG (212F/208B) The original name of former Mayberry resident Teena Andrews, who became a big movie star.

HORACE FLOOD (186F/187B) He was studying electronics during the day and so couldn't cover for Goober at the filling station. Goober wanted to go trout fishing.

FLORA (245F/244B) Flora Mallerby. Waitress at the Diner. She knew Bernie the Furrier in Mt. Pilot, and offered to get Emmett forty percent off on a mink for his wife's anniversary gift.

FLORENCE (96F/100B) Aunt Bee's sister and Andy's aunt. In 96F/100B, it was stated that Bee and Florence used to recite poetry together when they were younger, specifically, "A Fading Flower of Forgotten Love" by Alice Ellicot Strong.

FLORIDA (240F/B) The Russian ambassador was in Florida when Barney arranged for the US/USSR summit meeting to be held in Mayberry.

FLOSSIE (159F/B) The "Sultan's Favorite." Flossie was the dancer in the carnival show that Jerry Miller (the "banjo-playing deputy") played in as the one-man band.

FLOWER SEEDS (122F/121B) Andy and Barney both sold them when they were kids. The seeds were guaranteed to bloom night and day. In 122F/121B, Barney still had five packets. He tried to sell them to Andy.

BRUCE FLOWERS (116F/115B) Mayberry tenor who could only sing high after a fight with his mother.

FLOY (146F/B) Goober's aunt. He sent her a copy of the "lucky letter." He also sent one to Gomer in the Marines.

PRETTY BOY FLOYD (3F/B) "A wanted poster to be proud of." Andy tried to convince Talbott, the postmaster, that his possession of a Pretty Boy poster made his bulletin board better than Barney's.

FLOYD LAWSON AND CALVIN COOLIDGE (130F/132B) Andy told Floyd that Mark Twain said, "Everybody complains about the weather, but no one does anything about it." Floyd said he thought Calvin Coolidge said that. Andy told him no, and Floyd asked, "What *did* Calvin Coolidge say?"

"FLOYD LAWSON ENTERPRISES" (71F/72B) The company name Floyd used as the business name and mailing address for his lonely hearts club correspondence.

FLOYD LAWSON'S CAREER (10F/12B) (71F/72B) (210F/211B) Floyd's Barbershop—the only barbershop in Mayberry—gave Floyd Lawson a very nice living in the town of Mayberry. In 10F/12B, his posted prices were $1 for a haircut, 35¢ for a shave, 75¢ for a shampoo, and 25¢ for a shine. At this time, the population of Mayberry was 1,800. (See entry MAYBERRY'S POPULATION.) We can assume that half the population consisted of men and boys. We can also assume that in conservative Mayberry, a haircut every three or four weeks for most men and boys would not be out of the ordinary. That would come out to thirteen haircuts a year per male. We can then calculate that 900 males times thirteen haircuts equals 11,700 haircuts done by Floyd in a year. Assuming he worked six days a week for a total of 312 working days, that comes out to about thirty-eight haircuts a day. Floyd was a pretty busy barber, averaging four haircuts an hour in an eight hour day. With that kind of schedule, where did he find the time to sit in front of his shop and talk with Andy? That kind of business also gave him an annual income of almost $12,000, a rather nice living for that period and area. Floyd was grossing about $225 a week at this point in the series. Later on in the series, starting around 71F/72B, Floyd raised his prices to $1.75 for a haircut, $2 for a flat top, $2 for a butch, 75¢ for a shampoo, and 50¢ for a shave. He also began charging 25¢ extra for tonic. He had been giving it away before this. These prices were in effect through Floyd's last appearance in 210F/211B. Throughout this period, the population also rose, topping out at about a

300 percent growth rate. (See entry MAYBERRY'S POPULATION again.) Using the same formulas, Floyd's haircut business would have jumped to about a hundred a day, an impossibility even for a hard worker like Floyd. It is my opinion that at this point, Floyd was losing about half his business to Mt. Pilot barbers. If we assume that he was up to fifty haircuts a day, and that he decided to work an even longer day to get the work done, his income—at $1.75 a head—would have jumped to almost $28,000 a year, over $500 a week gross! And that's what he made on haircuts alone! Up until Howard raised his rent in 210F/211B, Floyd had only been paying $50 a month, a total of $600 a year. Floyd's Barbershop was a goldmine! I wonder what he did with his money, don't you?

FLOYD, THE GAY DECEIVER 71st episode filmed and 72nd episode broadcast. Original broadcast date was November 26, 1962. It was written by Aaron Ruben, and directed by Bob Sweeney. Regulars included Andy Griffith, Howard McNear, Frances Bavier, and Ronny Howard. Guests included Doris Dowling as Madeline Grayson.

FLOYD'S BARBERSHOP 210th episode filmed and 211th broadcast. Original broadcast date was February 13, 1967. It was written by Jim Parker and Arnold Margolin, and directed by Lee Phillips. Regulars included Andy Griffith, Howard McNear, George Lindsey. Jack Dodson, Ronny Howard, and Frances Bavier. Guests included Dave Ketchum as Harry, George Cisar as Cyrus Tankersley, James O'Rear as Mr. Coefield, and William Chalee as the Checker Player.

FLOYD'S ENGAGEMENT CARD TO ANDY AND HELEN (125F/124B) He wrote, "Andy and Helen, congratulations. May all your troubles be little ones."

FLOYD'S TONSORIAL PARLOR (35F/B) Early name of Floyd's Barbershop.

FLUFFY (80F/B) Mrs. Peterson's cat. She called Andy to tell him that Fluffy was on the roof.

BUZZ FLUHART (49F/B) According to Barney, Mr. Fluhart discovered the "jinxing ray."

CHARLIE FOLEY (120F/119B) (152F/B) (157F/B) Owner/butcher of Foley's Market. He told Bee she could store her "bargain" meat in his freezer. Years previous to Andy's and Barney's administration, Foley and Floyd Lawson had an argument over whether or not Charlie had asked for a shave. They came to blows and supposedly Floyd hit Charlie in the nose. Sheriff Poindexter straightened it out, but the "case of the punch in the nose" was never officially closed. Barney, through his meddlesome ways, reopened both the case and old wounds. Charlie and Floyd were both arrested August 9, 1946 at 11:25 A.M. Otis Campbell was a distant kin of Foley's. Foley was Johnny Paul Jason's uncle. In 157F/B, Charlie Foley told Aunt Bee that Einstein was a dropout.

GEORGE FOLEY (4F/6B) Little boy who ran away from home and met Opie, who brought him home to Andy. George liked to be called Tex, and was heading for Texas or Wyoming. George was really from Eastmont, North Carolina, and the Eastmont sheriff described George as "eight years old, blonde hair, blue eyes, blue-jeans."

FOLEY'S MARKET (120F/119B) (171F/172B) (202F/199B) In 120F/119B, the store where Bee wanted to store her "bargain" meat. In 171F/172B, counterfeit bills showed up at Foley's. In 202F/199B, Arnold and Opie used one of Foley's market baskets (shopping carts) to transport the abandoned baby they found on the courthouse steps.

CRAIG FOLGER (161F/160B) Mayberry man who, like Andy, had a cowlick. Floyd, however, knew the truth about Craig. His wife Millie caught him sneaking in late one night and hit him with a broom handle, thus the cowlick.

MILLIE FOLGER (161F/160B) Craig's wife. She caught him sneaking in late one night and hit him with a broom handle, giving him a permanent cowlick.

CLARENCE FOLK (35F/B) Mayberry attorney mentioned as possible counsel for Elizabeth Crowley, the woman speeder. He was considered available because he didn't start umpiring ball games until June.

KAREN FOLKER (153F/B) Classmate of Opie's. She became the subject of a piece in Opie's newspaper, "The Mayberry Sun." She fell down in the Elm Street playground while chasing Bruce Newdell.

FOOT POWDER (227F/222B) During their Mexican trip, Myrtle went to a Mexican farmacia to buy foot powder.

FOOTLORE TOUR (227F/222B) During Bee's Mexican trip, the tour started at 8:00 A.M.

"FOR RENT BY OWNER HOWARD SPRAGUE CALL MAYBERRY 397" (210F/211B) Sign Howard put on Floyd's Barbershop.

"FOR SALE HARRY WALKER REAL ESTATE CO. DON'T DISTURB TENANT" (210F/211B) Sign Harry put up on Floyd's Barbershop.

"4 SALE $295" (180F/B) The sign Goober put on the car he wanted to sell. Aunt Bee bought it. It was standard shift. It's license plate number was AY-321, and the car once belonged to Jed Koontz. Goober explained that the seats were nicely broken in; Jed weighed over 290 pounds.

DONNA FORBES (130F/132B) She and her husband owned a cabin on the outskirts of Mayberry. They moved to Raleigh. Donna had arthritis.

THE FORBES (128F/133B) (130F/132B) In 128F/133B, the Forbes owned the cabin that the escaped con, Ralph Neal, broke into and in which he held Barney hostage. In 130F/132B, Bee guessed incorrectly that a letter she received from Raleigh was from Donna Forbes. They had moved to Raleigh the previous May. Donna had arthritis.

FORD SEDAN (90F/B) 1954 automobile in a classified ad. The car was "only driven to Aunt Martha's." The phone number of the owner was MP-3791. It was owned by Myrt Lesh, who claimed she was selling it to pay the funeral expenses of her late husband, Bernard. She said she owed the Pilot Pines Funeral Parlor $140. Andy offered Myrt $100, Barney ended up giving her $300, his life savings: $297.50 for the car, and $2.50 for Mr. Lesh's "favorite charity." The car's license plate number was GP-780, and it was a bomb that broke down the first time Barney took it out. He had Andy, Bee, Opie, Gomer, and Thelma Lou in the car at the time. Barney had Gomer and Wally go through the car and, as Gomer said, Wally "went through her with as fine-a-tooth comb as you can imagine." They found the following wrong with it: "Plugs, points, bearings, valves, rings, starter switch, ignition wires, water pump, fuel pump, oil pump, clutch, clutch bearings, clutch plate, brake linings, brake shoes, brake drums, radiator hose, and radiator hose cover."

HOWIE FORMAN (196F/203B) Friend of Opie's who chewed up the pencil Opie gave Andy for Andy's adult education class in history.

MR. FORSYTH (226F/223B) He refused to postpone a court case for Lee Drake.

FORT LAUDERDALE (104F/105B) Mrs. Mendlebright's mother's dresser came from Ft. Lauderdale by bus. Barney hid his chili in the dresser. Mrs. Mendlebright was aghast and evicted Barney.

40¢ (105F/104B) The cost of the ice cream Barney brought Thelma Lou from Murphy's House of the Nine Flavors. It was West Indian Licorice Mocha Delight, and Barney made Thelma Lou pay.

$40.00 TO $10.00 (224F/221B) The amount the Truckers Cafe bowling team bet the Mayberry Rollers that Howard couldn't bowl a perfect 300. Howard did it.

FORTY-FIVE-MINUTE EGGS (1F/B) The breakfast specialty Opie made to prove to Andy that they didn't need Aunt Bee to care for them.

FORTY-FIVE MILES PER HOUR (35F/B) The speed limit on the road outside Myer's Lake.

41,000 ACRES (234F/232B) The size of Bradford Taylor's nonexistent sheep ranch.

FORTY PERCENT OFF (245F/244B) Flora told Emmett she could get him a forty percent discount on a fur stole for Martha through her friend, Bernie the Furrier.

FORTY WATTS (104F/105B) The maximum bulb size Mrs. Mendlebright allowed to be used in her rooming house. Barney used a seventy-five watt bulb and fell asleep with it on. Mrs. Mendlebright caught him. He called her a "snoop."

EARL FOSTER (214F/B) Earl lived out near Walt Simpson, the dairyman. Earl had a busted fuel pump, which was why Goober was out that way on the day Opie had to feed Walt's horse. It wasn't said if Earl was related to Jubell Foster, Miss Foster, or Mrs. Foster.

JUBELL FOSTER (46F/B) Cantankerous old moonshiner who accidentally burned down his own barn. He blamed Opie and his fellow Wildcat club members. Andy, after he found Opie with the club's "sacred candle," believed Jubell. But the truth was discovered—thanks to Barney—when Andy and Barney went to Jubell's to pay for the barn and Barney got immediately drunk on what he thought was water. It wasn't said if Jubell was related to Miss Foster, Mrs. Foster, or Earl Foster.

MISS FOSTER (244F/243B) Mayberry history teacher. Helen Crump took her class for two weeks.

MRS. FOSTER (153F/B) Mayberry woman whose chicken a la king tasted like wallpaper. It wasn't said if she was the same Foster woman (now married) whose class Helen Crump took over for two weeks in 244F/243B.

PRESTON FOSTER (127F/126B) Gomer's favorite actor. Gomer didn't want to go on the "back to nature" camping trip because he planned to stay home and watch a Preston Foster movie.

WILLARD FOSTER (187F/186B) Founder of the Foster Furniture Polish Company in Raleigh. His car broke down after he ditched it to avoid hitting a cow on

Juniper Road, a mile-and-a-half from the (unnamed) lake. He had a mobile phone, #KG62114, and his license plate number was SD-61. Andy invited him for lunch (tuna stuffed tomatoes), and he was so taken by Bee's praise of his polish that he offered her a job as the Foster Lady, his commercial spokesperson. She didn't work out, though, and when they wanted to play her for comedy, Andy talked her out of doing the commercial. Foster lived at 403 Elm Street, Raleigh.

FOSTER FURNITURE POLISH (187F/186B) Polish manufactured in Raleigh.

"THE FOSTER JINGLE" (187F/186B) Bee wrote the following jingle for the Foster Furniture Polish commercial. It was sung to the tune of "Harvest Moon."

"Shine on, Foster's Polish
That's the one to try
You ain't had such shinin'
Since January, February, June, or July"

THE FOSTER LADY 187th episode filmed and 186th episode broadcast. Original broadcast date was March 21, 1966. It was written by Jack Elinson and Iz Elinson, and directed by Alan Rafkin. Regulars included Andy Griffith, Frances Bavier, Ronny Howard, George Lindsey, and Howard McNear. Guests included Robert Emhardt as Willard Foster, Ronnie Schell as Jim Martin, Marc London as Bob Saunders, Sid Hickox as Sid Hickox the Cameraman, Burt Taylor as Burt the Crewman, and Eva Kryger as Eva Kryger the Makeup Artist. (Sid Hickox was the real Director of Photography on the show, Robert Saunders the Assistant Director, Burt Taylor, a Crewman, and Eva Kryger the Hair Stylist.)

FOUNDER'S DAY (53F/B) Annual Mayberry holiday. In 53F/B, the "guest of honor" celebration was in honor of Founder's Day.

FOUNDER'S DAY PICNIC (179F/B) Warren was arm wrestling champ at the picnic. He won a month's supply of mint jelly.

4 (43F/B) (119F/118B) Clara Johnson's jar number at the county fair pickle competition was 4. In 119F/118B, Barney and Virgil played four games of skiball at the Arcade.

4-A (110F/109B) The grade (fourth) in which Andy and Barney started hanging out together.

FOUR BEDROOMS AND ONE-AND-A-HALF BATHROOMS (240F/B) The layout of Andy Taylor's house.

$4.00 A HEAD (183F/182B) Andy sarcastically said that lettuce was $4 a head after Bee and Helen blamed him for the dry spell that caused tomato prices to shoot to 43¢ a pound.

$4.50 (183F/182B) The price of the allegedly 400-year-old earrings that Murillos, the gypsy leader, sold Aunt Bee and Clara.

411 (114F/113B) Otis was arrested on this violation; he was "drunk and disorderly."

411 ELM STREET (44F/B) Barney's address.

"FOUR EYES" (74F/B) The name Sally, one of the "convicts at large," called Floyd.

400 (5F/8B) The number of needy boys in Mayberry County. That averaged out to one-and-a-half needy boys per square mile, making Mayberry County approximately 267 miles square. Opie, upon hearing this, remarked that he'd never seen half of a boy. Andy explained to him that that was "a ratio." Opie asked, "Horatio who?"

400 YEARS OLD (183F/182B) The alleged age of the earrings Murillos, the gypsy leader, sold Aunt Bee and Clara for $4.50.

403 (167F/B) The room in the Piedmont Hotel in Hollywood where Andy, Opie, and Aunt Bee stayed.

403 ELM STREET, RALEIGH, NORTH CAROLINA (187F/186B) Willard Foster's address.

"FOUR OR FIVE" (225F/224B) The number of bass Andy caught when he went fishing with George Hollander at Myer's Lake.

"FOUR OR NINE" (4F/6B) The number of sandwiches George Foley, "the runaway kid," figured he could eat in a day.

4:30 A.M. (207F/209B) The time Andy and Alice Harper got lost by Myer's Lake on their nocturnal walk. Helen didn't like this one bit. .

439-7123 (129F/130B) Racine Tyler's phone number.

431 (22F/B) Barney's phone number.

4-10 SPLIT (224F/221B) Howard made a 4-10 split during one of his Thursday night bowling practice sessions.

426 (239F/238B) Andy's phone number.

"FOUR YEARS LAST OCTOBER" (36F/37B) That's when George Stevens nonexistent wife died, according to George.

FOUR YEARS OLD (29F/B) The age Nat Pike was when he told Opie that a penny hit by lightning was worth six cents.

14 (110F/109B) The number on Opie's football shirt.

14-A (52F/B) The song number of "Welcome Sweet Springtime," a song in the Mayberry Choir's repertoire.

$14.50 (72F/71B) The cost of the lesser pair of cymbals Barney could have bought at Cymbal City instead of the Andre Kostalanez Marchers. They only had leatherette.

14 MAPLE STREET (201F/204B) Andy's address in this episode. (See ANDY'S ADDRESS)

"FOURTEEN TIMES IN TWO DAYS" (24F/B) The number of times the new Dr. Benson went into Walker's Drugstore, according to Barney's count. Barney was looking out for Andy's best interests. (Ellie Walker worked in her uncle's drugstore.)

4TH AND MAIN (137F/B) The Mayberry intersection where there was a wreck. A big garbage truck collided with a hook-and-ladder.

"FOURTH QUARTER, FOUR SECONDS TO GO, FOURTH DOWN" (243F/242B) Andy's "big moment"; this was when he caught the winning pass against Mt. Pilot High.

FOX STOLE (245F/244B) Goober suggested a fox stole as an anniversary gift for Emmett's wife.

"FOXY FIFE" (9F/7B) After Barney captured Tracy Crawford, he called himself "Foxy Fife."

FRANK (132F/128B) Owner or employee of the Bluebird Diner. Frank usually answered the phone when

Barney called Juanita, but Barney invariably said "Hi, Sweetie" to Frank. In all likelihood, Frank probably owned the place.

FRANK (151F/B) Andy's "cousin" Gloria's ex-fiancee. Andy got them back together.

"FRANKIE AND JOHNNY" (41F/39B) The tune to which "The Ballad of Andy and Barney" was sung.

MR. FRANKLIN (249F/248B) Associate of Dr. Edith Gibson's at Scientific Introductions, Inc.

FRANKLIN HOLLOW (55F/B) Locale in the hills where the Gordon brothers ran their still.

FRANKLIN WOODS (59F/B) Andy asserted the woods would be a nice place for a picnic. There was a lake nearby, either Myer's or Tucker's, and a berry patch. It wasn't said if Franklin Woods and Franklin Hollow were near each other.

FRANKLYN PHARMACY (62F/B) (78F/76B) Mayberry drugstore. It's not said if Franklyn's was originally Walker's or if there were two drugstores in Mayberry. In 62F/B, there was a bus stop in front of the store where the Macon bus carrying Barney's cousin, Virgil, stopped. In 78F/76B, it was shown as being directly across the street from the Mayberry Security Bank.

FRANKS (84F/B) (91F/B) (135F/B) (203F/201B) (237F/236B) 49¢ per pound.

FRASER'S (69F/66B) Barney sent Opie there to buy a licorice whip.

FRED (32F/B) Owner/operator of the Elm City Delivery Service. He called Andy to tell him that Opie fell asleep in his truck and that he was all right.

FRED (53F/B) The man who told Andy that Thomas A. Moody was actually a crook. Fred told Andy during a phone call.

FRED (114F/113B) The state trooper who took away the "prisoner of love."

FRED (149F/B) Mayberry hotel clerk.

FRED (162F/164B) After Warren arrested Fred's unnamed wife for gambling with the Ladies Auxiliary, Fred showed up at Andy's house for supper with two unnamed kids. It wasn't said if this Fred was the same Fred that worked at the hotel as a clerk.

FRED (204F/202B) One of the two crooks who robbed a Mt. Pilot bank of $6,000. He and Larry hid out in the Carson shack.

FREDDY FLEET AND HIS BAND WITH A BEAT (72F/71B) (105F/104B) (147F/B) Band which passed through Mayberry on occasion. In 72F/71B, Andy enlisted their help in convincing Mayor Stoner to let the Mayberry Band go to Raleigh for the band festival. It's not said if Freddy was the same person as Bobby Fleet of earlier episodes or if they were brothers. In 105F/104B, Freddy's was the band playing at the annual chamber of commerce dance.

A FREE RADIATOR FLUSH (196F/203B) Goober promised Floyd a free flush for not charging him to trim his new beard.

FREEBERGER (106F/B) Early sewer inspector of Mayberry. He wore a uniform and a badge, and once arrested Barney's father for speeding.

FREEZER (120F/119B) Appliance Aunt Bee bought at an auction, claiming she saved $100. Andy called it a "$100 mousetrap."

CARTER FRENCH (95F/B) (119F/118B) In 95F/B, Carter thought he saw the two escaped crooks, Doc and Tiny. In 119F/118B, he was the man who called Andy to tell him that there was a boiled dinner down at the firehouse, and then after they were all going to play cribbage.

"FRESH FARM PRODUCE" (196F/203B) Sign on the grocery store window.

"FRICK AND FRACK" (60F/B) When Floyd and Andy teased Barney about his almost nonexistent sideburns, the deputy said they should call themselves "Frick and Frack."

FRIDAY EVENING AT EIGHT O'CLOCK (234F/232B) The day and time of Bee's reception for her cousin, Bradford Taylor.

FRIED CHICKEN AND CORNBREAD (31F/B) Jim Lindsey's favorite meal, especially as prepared by Aunt Bee.

FRIED CHICKENS (109F/108B) Helen Crump and Thelma Lou made four fried chickens to bring to the town picnic.

OFFICER DEAN FRIENDLY (57F/B) Cop in Capitol City who showed Andy a book of mug shots.

"THE FRIENDLY CITY" (53F/B) Mayberry, North Carolina.

MR. FRISBY (111F/110B) Egg man who was being driven off his land so the county could extend the highway. Bee became outraged and started a crusade against Andy's wishes. Turned out Frisby was running a still on his land and Bee was defending a moonshiner. Andy admitted he never liked Mr. Frisby.

HORACE FRISEY (151F/B) He was supposed to marry Alice Drumhiller but he left her at the altar. He did eventually marry her, however.

FROG (35F/B) Barney's "catch" on the day he, Andy, Floyd, and Opie caught "the woman speeder." He caught it at his special "secret" place.

FROM THE CRADLE TO JUNIOR COLLEGE (184F/B) Book by Dr. Walker. It sold over 65,000 copies. Bee read it when she agreed to take care of her niece Martha's daughter, Evie Joy.

FROSTED CHERRY BERRY BON BON (27F/B) Lipstick color Ellie Walker offered Frankie Flint.

FRUITCAKE (87F/B) Bee wouldn't allow it in the house. Andy said it was because of her brother, the unspoken implication being that he was a drinker.

FRUITS AND VEGETABLES (108F/107B) The food Johnny Paul Jason brought Wary Willy the Hobo. He raided his mother's fruit and vegetable bin.

FRYERS (196F/203B) 29¢

BLANTON FULLER (195F/193B) Sports columnist for the "Mayberry Gazette." He had to cover the fishing derby in Siler City, so Howard—who usually wrote the garden column—had to cover the ball game between the Mayberry Giants and the Mt. Pilot Comets. (See the entry HOWARD'S DEFENSE OF ANDY)

"FULLY LET OUT RANCH MINK" (245F/244B) The fur that Bernie the Furrier showed Emmett. It sold for $3,000, but Emmett's price was $1,800.

FUN GIRLS 123rd episode filmed and 122nd episode broadcast. Original broadcast date was April 13, 1964. It was written by Aaron Ruben, and directed by Coby Ruskin. Regulars included Andy Griffith, Don Knotts, Frances Bavier, Aneta Corsaut, Betty Lynn, George Lindsey, and Jim Nabors. Guests included Joyce Jameson as Skippy, Jean Carson as Daphne, and Dick Winslow.

FUN IN THE GARAGE ON A RAINY DAY (139F/B) Book by Seymour Schreck, author of *Twenty Scientific Tricks A Boy Can Do At Home.*

FUND SOLICITING COMMITTEE (5F/8B) A branch of the Underpriviliged Children's Charity Drive. Annabelle Silby asked Andy to serve on the committee.

FURNACE CREEK (17F/B) Locale where Rube Sloan's still was located.

FURNITURE FACTORY (28F/B) (110F/109B) (175F/B) In 28F/B, Lester Scoby couldn't get a job at the factory. In 110F/109B, the furniture factory was where Andy escorted the queen of the state Apricot Festival. In 175F/B, it was mentioned that Otis Campbell was a glue-dipper at the factory.

"FURNITURE NEW AND USED" (237F/236B) (248F/247B) Sign on storefront window on Main Street.

FURNITURE STORE (126F/125B) Main Street business. Barney and Thelma Lou stopped in front of the store one night while out walking. On the window was lettered, "Household Appliances Home Furnishings Hardware." In the window was a sofa with a sign on it that read, "Lamp Shades Made To Order." The sofa was blue on a green rug. Thelma Lou told Barney the color combination was "the latest." Barney thought the furniture looked "spindly."

G

SKEETS GALLAGHER (177F/B) Sidekick to Tailspin Tommy. Skeets was Barney's idol.

"THE GANGSTER'S MISTAKE" (41F/39B) The other title of "The Ballad of Andy and Barney."

"GARDEN CITY OF THE STATE" (208F/212B) Mayberry, according to Floyd Lawson.

GARDEN CLUB MEETING (245F/244B) Martha Clark wore her new fur coat to the meeting. She received it from Emmett for their anniversary.

"THE GARDEN SPOT OF MAYBERRY" (39F/36B) Frank Myers' house after the townsfolk helped renovate it.

"GARDEN SPOT OF THE STATE" (208F/212B) Mayberry.

"A GARDENIA BLOSSOM" (27F/B) After Ellie sprayed Andy with Midnight Madness cologne, Opie and Barney both said Andy smelled like "a gardenia blossom."

MR. GARLAND (202F/199B) He and his wife had a fight. This prompted his wife to abandon their infant son on the Mayberry courthouse steps. Opie and Arnold found the baby. (Mr. Garland was played by Jack Nicholson.)

MRS. GARLAND (202F/199B) She had a fight with her husband, which led to the abandonment of their infant son on the Mayberry courthouse steps. Opie and Arnold found the baby.

GAS HEATER (119F/118B) Andy pretended to fix the gas heater in the courthouse and pass out so that Gomer could "save" him, thereby evening the score.

THE GAS WORKS (129F/130B) Factory in Mayberry that had a new blacktop done for its employees. Andy showed it to Ollie and Nora when he took them on a tour of Mayberry.

GATE 12 (227F/222B) Bee's flight to Mexico—Flight 17—left from Gate 12.

"THE GATEWAY TO MONTE CARLO" (60F/B) The name Barney said Mayberry should be called after it was discovered that Bill Medwin—the bookie barber—was taking wagers on horse races in Floyd's Barbershop.

"GEM HOTEL—ROOMS" (196F/203B) Sign on hotel wall. The only hotel in Mayberry apparently changed its name to "Gem" in this episode.

GENERAL STORE (235F/234B) The gathering spot for the locals on St. Benedict's Island in the Caribbean. They sold, among other things, ships in bottles, which were created by the locals. They were not big sellers. St.Benedict's Island was where Howard started his "new life."

GENESIS 6:10 (238F/239B) The Bible verse mentioned by Reverend Tucker regarding the tilting of the church.

GENUINE THERMAWEAVE (245F/244B) Emmett Clark bought his wife, Martha, a bathrobe made of this material.

GENUINE WHALEBONE NAPKIN RING (39F/36B) One of Frank Myers' "valuables."

GEORGE (137F/B) Little boy who got his head stuck in a sewer on Maple Street.

GEORGE (140F/B) (166F/B) Helen's TV repairman. In 140F/B, Barney brought George out to Myer's Lake, interrupting "Andy's & Helen's Day." George wanted to bring Helen's set into the shop for repair and Barney wanted Helen's okay before letting him take it. In 166F/B, Goober told George about Andy's $1,000 "Sheriff Without A Gun" check.

GEORGE (156F/B) Mayberry plumber.

GEORGE (220F/B) Boy who went to Arnold's thirteenth birthday party. George said that what Mary Alice Carter did to Opie (standing him up) was dirty.

GEORGE (221F/235B) Man who worked for Goober when he bought Wally's Service Station. George quit because of Goober's tyrannical ways.

GEORGE (246F/245B) Mrs. Sprague's beau and, later, husband. They were married in 246F/245B, and moved to Mt. Pilot where George lived and had a business. George didn't want Howard to call him "Dad."

"A GEORGE RAFT MOVIE" (68F/69B) (114F/113B) Daphne said she and Skippy could have been watching "a George Raft movie" the night they met Andy and Barney at the Tip-Top Cafe in Mt. Pilot. In 114F/113B, Barney planned on watching a George Raft movie at Thelma Lou's the night the "prisoner of love" came to Mayberry.

GEORGE SAFFERLY'S SERVICE STATION (10F/12B) Gas station George sold to the "stranger in town," Ed Sawyer, who probably then sold it to Wally, who later sold it to Goober Pyle. Ed was never seen past 10F/12B, so he probably sold the station to Wally immediately after making the purchase.

"GERONIMO" (192F/191B) The password at the Regal Order of the Golden Door to Good Fellowship, the Mayberry men's lodge.

GERTRUDE (2F/B) Andy's rowboat. She leaked. Andy wouldn't take "a dollar and a quarter" for her.

GERTRUDE (189F/B) Mayberry lady who loved Keevy Hazleton.

GETTYSBURG (124F/123B) Malcolm Merriweather was heading to Gettysburg when he passed through Mayberry and caused a traffic jam.

DR. EDITH GIBSON (249F/248B) The "girl for Goober." She started a computer dating service called Scientific Introductions, Inc. Goober filled out one of their questionnaires and, thinking the "number of books read a month" meant comic books, put down thirty. He also said he liked painting, thinking it meant house and room painting. Gibson decided he was right for her and arranged a date. At Morelli's, she realized they were hopelessly mismatched, but that Goober was a pleasant conversationalist, and they had a good time anyway. Gibson later changed the questionnaire to make it a bit more specific.

FRED GIBSON (179F/B) Manager of Wild West star, Clarence Earp. His show was called Gibson's Wild West Show, and its slogan was "East to West, Gibson's the best." The truth was that he named Clarence Earp himself; the boy was not related to Wyatt. He had known Clarence's family and had adopted the boy when he was young.

GIBSON'S WILD WEST SHOW (179F/B) Show owned and operated by Fred Gibson, with Clarence Earp as its star. The show's slogan was "East to West, Gibson's the best."

MR. GIDDINGS (231F/230B) Realtor who rented Andy the store Andy used for his Laundercoin franchise.

THE GIGOLO CLUB (68F/69B) Club in Yancey where, according to Daphne, "they got a floor show."

GIL (18F/B) In 18F/B, Gil played hearts with Fred Boone and Cliff.

GILBERT (156F/B) Newton Monroe's cousin. He was a dental technician.

LEMLEY GILBERT (136F/B) Phoebe's brother.

MR. GILBERT (223F/226B) Court prosecutor at the Mt. Pilot municipal court. He attempted to prove the guilt of Marvin Jenkins in the burglary of Brice's Department Store.

PHOEBE GILBERT (136F/B) Lemley's sister. Barney found out about Lorraine and Howard Felcher's impending divorce from Phoebe when he took her to dinner at the Blue View Motel. Phoebe worked at the beauty parlor.

EARLY GILLY (49F/B) (186F/187B) (195F/193B) (219F/B) In 49F/B, Early skimped on caulking Andy's boat, Gertrude. She sank. In 186F/187B, it was said he had a filling station on the other side of Mt. Pilot. Goober thought he could get a job with Early after Flora took over his job at Wally's. In 195F/193B, Early was sick, so Andy had to umpire the softball game between the Mayberry Giants and the Mt. Pilot Comets. In 219F/B, it was mentioned that Early's filling station directly competed with Goober's. He was running a very successful promotion called "Line Up For Loot."

GIN RUMMY (115F/114B) (183F/182B) In 115F/114B, the card game Andy and Barney played in the courthouse. Andy collected spades. Otis came in and told Barney what to discard. Andy won and Barney got mad. In 183F/182B, the card game Murillos and Sylvio were playing when Andy and Helen came upon their camp in the woods.

GINNY (246F/245B) A girl Goober invited to Howard's "swinging" party. She turned him down because she was engaged.

A GIRL FOR GOOBER 249th episode filmed and 248th episode broadcast. Original broadcast date was March 25, 1968. The teleplay was written by Bruce Howard from a story by Bob Ross. It was directed by Lee Phillips. This was the final episode filmed. Regulars included Andy Griffith, Aneta Corsaut, George Lindsey, Ken Berry, and Ronny Howard. Guests included Nancy Malone as Dr. Edith Gibson, Tod Andrews as Mr. Franklin, Maggie Peterson as

Doris, Richard Poston as the Waiter, Yvonne Shubert as the Girl, and George Sawaya as the Man.

GIRL-SHY 173rd episode filmed and 174th episode broadcast. Original broadcast date was December 20, 1965. It was written by Bill Idelson and Sam Bobrick, and directed by Lee Phillips. Regulars included Andy Griffith, Frances Bavier, Aneta Corsaut, and George Lindsey. Guests included Jack Burns as Warren Ferguson.

GLADIOLA (203F/201B) Blue ribbon category at the Mayberry Garden Club flower show.

FRANK GLENDON (225F/224B) Friend of George Hollander's and owner of the Glendon Grocery Stores chain.

GLORIA (151F/B) Andy's gorgeous "cousin," who wasn't really his cousin. Bee and Gloria's mother had been close friends for years. Gloria came to stay with Bee to get over her breakup with Frank. She and Andy became an item in Helen's eyes, and Helen's resulting jealousy caused fireworks. Andy solved the problem by bringing Frank to Mayberry.

GLORIA (222F/225B) Goober Pyle's girlfriend. He took her to Myer's Lake but she refused to go in his truck.

GLUE-DIPPER (175F/B) Otis's job at the furniture factory.

"GOLDBRICK WHEELER" (38F/41B) The name Sheriff Mitchell called Henry Wheeler when he heard that Andy had taken Wheeler into his home. Mitchell was a Mt. Pilot sheriff.

THE GOLDEN PALACE (242F/241B) Very swanky—and expensive—Raleigh restaurant. In order to impress his old friend Roy Swanson, Goober took Roy, Andy, Aunt Bee, and Opie there for dinner. When Andy heard that Goober wanted to pick up the tab, he said the bill would cost Goober "no more than a week's pay," if he was lucky. Goober ordered Silver Ribbon champagne and didn't know how to taste it.

GOLF BALL (120F/119B) Along with a mousetrap, Gomer found a golf ball in Aunt Bee's freezer.

"GOLLLLY!" (107F/127B) Another of Gomer Pyle's all-purpose expletives and expressions of amazement. Surprisingly—for such a notable trademark—we can only find one instance of Gomer using "Golllly!" in the entire run of the original "Andy Griffith Show" series. That was in the pilot for his own show, "Gomer Pyle U.S.M.C." (107F/127B). However, he did use "Golllly!" frequently in the "Gomer Pyle" series and that, plus the ubitquitousness of the syndicated "Andy Griffith Show" reruns, has given us the impression that it was used in Mayberry more often than it actually was. "Golllly!" was likely heard more often at Camp Henderson than in Mayberry. Gomer Pyle reprised "Golllly!" in "Return To Mayberry" on two occasions, and at the very beginning of the movie he improvised a variation on the "Golllly!" theme by saying "Well, I'lllll be!" upon Andy's arrival at the G & G Garage.

"THE GOLLYWOBBLER" (40F/38B) Dave the Hobo's invention to catch fish.

GOMER PYLE, U.S.M.C. 107th episode filmed and 127th episode broadcast. Original broadcast date was May 19, 1964. It was written and directed by Aaron Ruben. Regulars included Andy Griffith and Jim Nabors. Guests included Alan Reed Jr., Eddie Ryder, Frank

Albertson, Karl Lukas, Charles Myers, and Frank Sutton as Sgt. Vince Carter.

GOMER THE HOUSE GUEST 97th episode filmed and 101st episode broadcast. Original broadcast date was November 4, 1963. It was written by Jim Fritzell and Everett Greenbaum, and directed by Earl Bellamy. Regulars included Andy Griffith, Jim Nabors, Frances Bavier, and Ronny Howard. Guests included Trevor Bardette, Lee Krieger, Forrest Lewis, Roy Engel, and Joe Hamilton.

GOMER'S OUTFIT (105F/104B) For the annual chamber of commerce dance (the dance to which he was taking Thelma Lou's cousin, Mary Grace Gossage), Gomer purchased the following ensemble: yellow socks, a brown belt with a horseshoe buckle made of imitation mother-of-pearl, a purple tie with acorns on it, and shoes with brass buckles on the side.

GOOBER AND THE ART OF LOVE 147th episode filmed and broadcast. Original broadcast date was February 1, 1965. It was written by Fred Freeman and Lawrence J. Cohen, and directed by Alan Rafkin. Regulars included Andy Griffith, Don Knotts, Aneta Corsaut, Betty Lynn, and George Lindsey as Goober. Guests included Josie Lloyd as Lydia Crosswaithe.

GOOBER GOES TO AN AUTO SHOW 242nd episode filmed and 241st episode broadcast. Original broadcast date was February 5, 1968. It was written by Joseph Bonaduce, and directed by Lee Phillips. Regulars included Andy Griffith, George Lindsey, Ronny Howard, and Frances Bavier. Guests included Noam Pitlik as Roy Swanson, Jack Good as the Salesman, Patty Regan as the Manicurist, Freddy Roberto as the Waiter, and Don Sturdy as the Counterboy.

GOOBER MAKES HISTORY 196th episode filmed and 203rd episode broadcast. Original broadcast date was December 19, 1966. It was written by Paul David and John L. Greene, and directed by Lee Phillips. Regulars included Andy Griffith, Frances Bavier, Ronny Howard, George Lindsey, Aneta Corsaut, and Howard McNear. Guests included Richard Bull as Bill Lindsay and Christina Burke as Edna.

GOOBER TAKES A CAR APART 144th episode filmed and broadcast. Original broadcast date was February 11, 1965. It was written by Bill Idelson and Sam Bobrick, and directed by Peter Baldwin. Regulars included Andy Griffith, Ronny Howard, Howard McNear, Frances Bavier, and George Lindsey. Guests included Larry Hovis as Gilly Walker, Buck Young as Deputy Joe Watson, Wally Engelhardt as Sheriff Jackson, Tom Jacobs as The Man, Stanley Farrar as Man #1, and Johnny Coons as Man #2.

GOOBER THE EXECUTIVE 221st episode filmed and 235th episode broadcast. Original broadcast date was December 25, 1967. (Wouldn't it have been great to spend Christmas night in Mayberry?) It was written by Seamon Jacobs and Michael Morris, and directed by Lee Phillips. Regulars included Andy Griffith, George Lindsey, Ronny Howard, and Paul Hartman. Guests included David Ketchum as Fred Michaels, George Cisar as Cyrus Tankersley, Bo Hopkins as George, James McCallion as Harry, and Sam Green as the Man.

GOOBER'S BEGINNINGS (152F/B) Goober was born in 1941.

GOOBER'S BEST FRIEND (196F/203B) Floyd Lawson.

GOOBER'S CONTEST 219th episode filmed and broadcast. Original broadcast date was April 10, 1967. It was written by Ron Friedman and Pat McCormick, and directed by Lee Phillips. Regulars included Andy Griffith, George Lindsey, Ronny Howard, and Frances Bavier. It also starred Howard McNear in what was his last episode. He died shortly after filming "Goober's Contest." Guests included Rob Reiner as Joe, Owen Bush as Mr. Hammond, and Edgar Hess as the Man.

GOOBER'S FAVORITE VEGETABLE (248F/247B) Corn on the cob.

GOOBER'S FORTUNE (209F/210B) At Aunt Bee's Canton Palace: "You are going to meet a tall handsome stranger."

GOOBER'S "GUSHER OF GOLD" (219F/B) The original name of Goober's filling station promotion, "Grab Bag For Cash."

GOOBER'S IMPERSONATIONS (123F/122B) (197F/198B) He could do Cary Grant ("Judy, Judy, Judy"), Edward G. Robinson, and he could walk like Chester of "Gunsmoke" fame.

GOOBER'S PHONE NUMBER (AT HOME) (77F/79B) 371J.

GOOBER'S REPLACEMENT 186th episode filmed and 187th episode broadcast. Original broadcast date was March 28, 1966. It was written by Howard Merrill and Stan Dreben, and directed by Alan Rafkin. Regulars included Andy Griffith, Ronny Howard, George Lindsey, and Howard McNear. Guests included Alberta Nelson as Flora Mallerby, Cliff Norton as Wally, Jason Johnson as Mr. Weaver, Charles Smith as the Counterman, Maudie Prickett as Mrs. Larch, Burt Mustin as the Old Geezer, and David Azar as the Man.

GOOBER'S SERVICE (221F/235B) The name Goober gave to the filling station after he bought it from Wally. He bought it with a borrowed and co-signed $2,000. (The note was co-signed by Andy and Emmett.) George worked for him and Goober made up two mottos: "Free Air With A Smile," and "Free Water With A Smile."

"GOOD EVENING" (113F/112B) One of the phrases Andy taught Ernest T. Bass to say correctly.

GOODBYE, DOLLY 214th episode filmed and broadcast. Original broadcast date was March 6, 1967. It was written by Michael L. Morris and Seamon Jacobs, and directed by Lee Phillips. Regulars included Andy Griffith, Ronny Howard, Frances Bavier, Jack Dodson, and George Lindsey. Guests included Tom Tully as Walt Simpson, and Sheldon Golomb as Arnold.

"GOODBYE MR. CHIPS" (245F/244B) 1939 movie that Martha Clark asked Ethel Pendleton about. She wanted to know if Ethel saw Greer Garson in the film.

GOODBYE, SHERIFF TAYLOR 137th episode filmed and broadcast. Original broadcast date was November 23, 1964. It was written by Fred Freeman and Lawrence J. Cohen, and directed by Gene Nelson. Regulars included Andy Griffith, Don Knotts, Frances Bavier, Howard McNear, Hal Smith, and George Lindsey. Guests included Burt Mustin as Judd, Janet Stewart as Mrs. Jackson, and Andrew Duncan as the Truck Driver.

GOOSEBERRY PIE (37F/40B)   Andy's favorite pie.

GOOSEDOWN PILLOW (129F/130B) Ollie's favorite pillow. Nora forgot to bring it when they visited Bee and Andy.

GORDON (60F/B) One of Floyd's customers.

BILLY GORDON (55F/B) One of the Gordon boys who ran a still at Franklin Hollow. Barney, in an attempt to rehabilitate the boys, told Billy he could have been a great architect.

IKE GORDON (55F/B) One of the Gordon boys who ran a still at Franklin Hollow. Barney, in an attempt to rehabilitate the boys, told Ike he could have been a great violinist.

JUNIOR GORDON (55F/B) One of the Gordon boys who ran a still at Franklin Hollow. Barney, in an attempt to rehabilitate the boys, told Junior he could have been a dancer.

SHERMAN GORDON (55F/B) One of the Gordon boys who ran a still at Franklin Hollow. Barney, in an attempt to rehabilitate the boys, told Sherman he could have been a dentist.

THE GORDON BOYS (55F/B) Ike, Billy, Sherman, and Junior. They ran a still at Franklin Hollow. After the boys were caught by Andy and Barney, the two lawmen realized that if they jailed the boys with Otis (who the Gordon boys believed snitched on them), they'd kill him. So, Andy brought Otis home and made Aunt Bee his warden. While they were in the Mayberry jail, Barney attempted to rehabilitate the Gordons. He brought the boys a woodcarving set, a leathercraft set, a metalcraft set, and a Mr. Potato set. (See individual "GORDON" entries.)

FRED GOSS (58F/B) (135F/B) Mayberry drycleaner and tailor who had a romantic interest in Aunt Bee. Bee encouraged him, thanks to some meddling by Clara Edwards. Because of Clara's insinuations, Aunt Bee actually thought that Andy wanted her out of his house, and that she was preventing him from marrying Helen. Goss was loud, crude, and a gossip. He frequently sprinkled cigarette ashes on people's clothes. In 135F/B, he lost Barney's salt-and-pepper suit. It was sent to a guy named Fitz in Siler City.

H. GOSS (50F/B) (58F/B) Mayberry tailor who later became Fred Goss. In 58F/B, he offered three-hour service.

MARY GRACE GOSSAGE (105F/104B) Thelma Lou's cousin. Barney and Thelma Lou arranged for Gomer to take Mary Grace to the annual chamber of commerce dance. The night of the dance, Gomer jumped up and left Thelma Lou's house just before they were all ready to leave. The girls were aghast; they cut the dance short and fought with Andy and Barney. When they returned to Thelma Lou's, they found Gomer dancing and having a good old time with Mary Grace. He had only run out to get her a corsage. This was Gomer's first date. It wasn't said if Mary Grace was related to Oliver Gossage, Andy's cousin. If they were, that would have made Andy and Thelma Lou kin.

OLIVER GOSSAGE (113F/112B) Andy's cousin from Raleigh. Andy attempted to pass off Ernest T. Bass as Oliver at Mrs. Wiley's Saturday night social. It wasn't said if Oliver was related to Mary Grace Gossage.

"GOVERNMENT" (61F/B) Reporter Jean Boswell's major in her fictitious pose as a college student.

THE GOVERNOR (76F/78B) (188F/B) In 76F/78B, Barney ticketed him to prove that he didn't play favorites. The governor, instead of firing him, came to Mayberry to congratulate Barney, much to the surprise of Mayor Stoner. The governor's first name was Ed. In 188F/B, the governor made a radio broadcast praising Opie and Mayberry for printing the true story of the Battle of Mayberry.

GP-780 (90F/B) (219F/B) In 90F/B, the license plate number of Barney's car. In 219F/B, the plate number of Aunt Bee's car.

"GRAB BAG FOR CASH" (219F/B) The promotion Goober ran at Wally's filling station to compete with Early Gilly's "Line Up For Loot." The contest was set up as follows: three $10 winners, fourteen $5 winners, twenty $3 winners, and twenty $2 winners. The total prize pool was $200, but Hammond Printers thought that that figure was an additional prize and so listed a $200 prize as well. Floyd won the big prize which, of course, Goober couldn't pay. Floyd then threatened suit on fraud charges. Andy solved it by arresting Goober, which forced Floyd to realize his unreasonableness in holding Goober to the error. He then dropped the charges and his prize demand.

DENIECE GRABER (185F/B) A young couple went to Howard Sprague for a marriage license but had a fight because the groom insisted on inviting Deniece to the wedding. He had no choice: Deniece was Elmer Carson's first cousin. The problem for the bride, however, was that the groom had dated Deniece for three years.

GRACE (134F/B) The alias Barney invented for Helen for her blind date with Andy.

GRACE (184F/B) Martha's sister. She and Martha were Bee's nieces. Martha went to Grace's wedding in Jersey City.

THE GRAND (50F/B) (59F/B) (78F/76B) (188F/B) Mayberry theater. In 59F/B, Andy asked Mary Simpson to see a movie there. In 188F/B, seats cost 35¢ for the orchestra and 25¢ for the balcony.

GRAND MARSHAL (31F/B) Barney's role in the escort parade that welcomed Jim Lindsey back to Mayberry.

GRANGER (223F/226B) The real thief in the Brice's Department Store burglary. His lighter was found at the scene. Andy made the connection, thereby exonerating the man accused of the crime, Marvin Jenkins.

GRANITE (208F/212B) The material Brian Jackson used to sculpt the statue of Seth Taylor. He used a five foot seven granite block.

GRAPEFRUIT JUICE (246F/245B) The drink Howard offered at his "swinging" party.

BILLY GRAY (79F/77B) Friend of Opie's. Steve Quincy singled out Billy to throw an apple core at, yelling "Apple core, Baltimore, Billy!"

MADELINE GRAYSON (71F/72B) A widow Floyd met through his lonely hearts club correspondence. He had pretended he was a big shot businessman, so he maneuvered Andy into posing as his son and letting him use Cliff Devereaux's house as his own when Madeline came to visit. Turned out Madeline was a con artist looking to fleece rich old boys. Andy got rid of her, and Floyd was never told.

THE GREAT DISMAL SWAMP (141F/142B) Mary Pleasance went there to hunt black bear with Dixie Bell Edwards.

THE GREAT FILLING STATION ROBBERY (85F/B) Wally's filling station was robbed of four flashlights, six fan belts, and two sets of battery clips by Pothrow Henson. He hid in the trunk of his car and came out after the place was closed.

THE GREAT FILLING STATION ROBBERY 85th episode filmed and broadcast. Original broadcast date was February 25, 1963. It was written by Harvey Bullock, and directed by Bob Sweeney. Regulars included Andy Griffith, Don Knotts, Ronny Howard, and Jim Nabors. Guests included Pat Colby, Jack Shea, Johnny Silver, and Willis Bouchey as Mr. Carter.

THE GREAT MANDRAKE (179F/B) The last show that passed through Mayberry before Clarence Earp came to town. Mandrake was a fire-eater and the fire department had to keep putting him out.

THE GREATER MAYBERRY HISTORICAL SOCIETY AND TOURIST BUREAU, LTD. (41F/39B) Organization chaired by Bee Taylor which was set up to promote "crime free Mayberry," and specifically, Andy and Barney.

DOC GREEN (24F/B) Early doctor of Mayberry.

GREEN (10F/12B) Room 216 at the Mayberry Hotel had recently been painted green, and the "stranger in town," Ed Sawyer, knew it.

THE GREEN RIVER ORDINANCE (33F/34B) The law cited by Bob Rogers which required door-to-door salesman in Mayberry to be licensed. The ordinance originated in 1924 in Green River. Violating the ordinance was a Code 304. Rogers wanted to charge Barney with the code for selling vacuum cleaners door-to-door after Barney quit as deputy.

GREENDALE CITY HALL (44F/B) Erected in 1902, this was the building where the Greendale city council decided to offer Barney the position of sheriff in Greendale, North Carolina.

GREENLAND (183F/182B) Base of Station CQL, the weather station Murillos, the gypsy leader, listened to for his "magical" weather prediction abilities.

GREENSBORO, NORTH CAROLINA (68F/69B) Hometown of Lydia Crosswaithe.

"A GREER GARSON MOVIE" (245F/244B) Ethel Pendleton and Martha Clark set out to see "a Greer Garson movie" on the night before Emmett's and Martha's twenty-fifth anniversary.

"GREETINGS FROM STATE PRISON" (11F/B) The message beneath the photo of the Hubacher brothers in the Christmas card they sent Andy and Barney. (In the episode, Andy incorrectly read it as "Merry Christmas from state prison.")

"GREGORY PECK MOVIES" (104F/105B) Andy took Opie to see three Peck movies on the night Barney entertained Thelma Lou in his new "pad," the backroom of the courthouse.

NED GRESHAM (216F/B) Ned told Floyd he looked tired.

MISS GRETHAM (62F/B) Mayberry woman who got off the same Macon bus that carried Barney's cousin, Virgil. Andy greeted her by name.

ROBERT GRIBBEL (152F/B) He and Emma Larch announced their engagement in the "Mayberry Gazette." Floyd remembered that eleven years previous Bobby had written, "Bobby Gribbel hates Emma Larch" in the cement outside his barbershop.

TOMMY GRIEF (153F/B) Classmate of Opie's. He gave Trey Bowden a pear when Trey forgot his lunch.

SKINNY GRIFFIN (105F/104B) He kept telling Gomer the muskrat would bite him.

HAROLD GRIGSBY (153F/B) Mayberry man who owned "half the sawmill." Harold set tongues wagging when he married a young blonde named Sue.

SUE GRIGSBY (153F/B) Harold's young blonde wife. According to Barney, Sue was a "genuine blonde right out of a bottle."

GROVE STREET (79F/77B) The Quincys rented a house owned by Charlie that was on Grove Street.

GROVER (235F/234B) Former Detroit lawyer who became a bum on St. Benedict's Island in the Caribbean. Howard met him when he started his "new life."

GROVER'S PLACE (5F/8B) Street in Mayberry used as a border for one of the five sections Annabelle Silby divided the town into for fund-raising purposes. The section went "From Grover's Place over to Banner Street then around Cornwall's Gas Station up to Tate Warren's Store."

GUEST IN THE HOUSE 151st episode filmed and broadcast. Original broadcast date was March 8, 1965. It was written by Fred Freeman and Lawrence J. Cohen, and directed by Coby Ruskin. Regulars included Andy Griffith, Ronny Howard, Frances Bavier, George Lindsey, Howard McNear, and Aneta Corsaut. Guests included Jan Shutan as Gloria, and George Spence as Frank.

GUEST OF HONOR 53rd episode filmed and broadcast. Original broadcast date was February 26, 1962. It was written by Bob Ross, and directed by Aaron Ruben. Regulars included Andy Griffith, Don Knotts, and Howard McNear. Guests included Jay Novello as Sheldon Davis, the "guest of honor."

GUIDED MISSILES (41F/39B) Andy told Barney they didn't have them, and they didn't need them, at the Mayberry jail.

GUITAR PLAYER 3rd episode filmed and broadcast. Original broadcast date was October 17, 1960. It was written by Jack Elinson and Charles Stewart, and directed by Don Weiss. Regulars included Andy Griffith and Don Knotts. Guests included James Best as Jim Lindsey, and Henry Slate as Bobby Fleet.

THE GUITAR PLAYER RETURNS 31st episode filmed and broadcast. Original broadcast date was May 15, 1961. It was written by Jack Elinson and Charles Stewart, and directed by Bob Sweeney. Regulars included Andy Griffith, Ronny Howard, Don Knotts, Frances Bavier, Howard McNear, and Elinor Donahue as Ellie Walker. Guests included Dick Elliot as Mayor Pike, James Best as Jim Lindsey, Tom Browne Henry, Herb Ellis, and Phil Chambers.

GULLIVER (1F/B) Opie's never-seen dog.

GUMBALLS (40F/38B) Dave the Hobo stole them from a machine on Main Street with his so-called "magic" word, "Tuscorora." Opie was quite impressed.

CECIL GURNEY (99F/98B) He had two sets of false teeth and wouldn't admit it.

THE GYPSIES (183F/182) Band of travelers who came to Mayberry and proceeded to sell worthless junk under false pretenses. Andy told them to leave town, and they put a curse on the town. (See the entry THE GYPSY CURSE) They were Sylvio, Queen La Farona, Sabella and the leader, Murillos.

THE GYPSIES 183rd episode filmed and 182nd episode broadcast. Original broadcast date was February 21, 1966. It was written by Roland MacLane, and directed by Alan Rafkin. Regulars included Andy Griffith, Frances Bavier, Ronny Howard, Aneta Corsaut, George Lindsey, and Hope Summers. Guests included Vito Scotti as Murillos, Francesca Bellini as Sabella, Argentina Brunetti as La Farona the Gypsy Queen, Jason Johnson as Mr. Bluett, and Jamie Farr (Corporal Klinger of M*A*S*H fame) as Sylvio, although the credits incorrectly listed his character as "Grecos."

THE GYPSY CURSE (183F/182B) Murillos, the gypsy leader, put the following curse on Mayberry: "According to the divine will of our gypsy queen, La Farona, there will be not one drop of rain in this beautiful town until the harmless gypsies are allowed to return." He cursed them because Andy threw them out of town for selling junk.

"THE GYPSY SONG" (183F/182B) Sylvio played the guitar and sang the following with Murillos and La Farona as Sabella danced:

> "Through the forest wild and free
> Come the gypsy melody
> Ever dancing as they say
> None so merry, none so gay"

H

H141Q5 (109F/108B) License plate number of the truck that gave Andy and Helen a ride back to town on the day they got trapped in the Old Mine Cave collapse.

VIRGIL HAAS (49F/B) Virgil was pitching a beautiful game of horseshoes until Henry Bennett, the "jinx," patted him on the back. Virgil lost. Barney offered this story as proof that Henry was indeed a jinx.

JESSE EARLE HAGEN (172F/170B) John told Andy that Jesse Earle Hagen was coming in from Mt. Pilot to play bass with the Mayberry Band for the Founder's Day parade. It was Earle Hagen who actually wrote all of the music for "The Andy Griffith Show."

"HAIL TO THEE MISS MAYBERRY" (20F/16B) The song Floyd Lawson wrote for the Founder's Day beauty pageant. It was sung to the tune of "O, Christmas Tree." The lyrics:

"Hail to thee Miss Mayberry
Hail to thee all hail
Your loveliness, your majesty
Brings joy to every male
All hail, all hail, all hail all hail."

MR. & MRS. RALPH HAINES (82F/B) Couple who attended the Class of '45 reunion of Mayberry Union High. Barney mistook Ralph Haines for Jack Sweet. Mrs. Haines was "in debate" at Paul Revere High School in Chicago. Andy said Mrs. Haines reminded him of Edna Thope. Edna was "in debate" at Mayberry Union High.

HALF HOUR (245F/244B) The length of time it took to drive to Mt. Pilot from Mayberry.

HALF MOON ROADHOUSE (153F/B) Restaurant where the dishcloth salesman took the Widow Saunders. He drove a fast-back, wire-wheeled coupe. They ate New York-cut steak.

HALF MOON TRAILER PARK (50F/B) Trailer camp on outskirts of Mayberry where Barney cornered Doc Molloy and his girlfriend. It was on River Road; it wasn't said if there was any connection between the Trailer Park and the Half Moon Roadhouse of 153F/B.

HAM (2F/B) (108F/107B) In 2F/B, Andy used ham as bait while out fishing with Opie in Gertrude, Andy's rowboat. In 108F/107B, Whitey Porter stole a ham from his mother to bring to Wary Willy the Hobo.

"HAM, CAKE, EGGS AND PLENTY OF MILK" (89F/B) The food Aunt Bee left for Andy and Opie when she went out of town for a few days. The boys ended up not needing her provisions. Malcolm Merriweather came to Mayberry and caused a turmoil, doing forty dollars worth of damage in an accident. He didn't have the money, so

Andy put him to work in the Taylor household. He was a superb "gentleman's gentleman," and an excellent cook.

HAM LOAF AND GREEN BEANS CHINESE STYLE (101F/96B) The meal Aunt Bee prepared the night Opie killed the mother songbird. Opie didn't eat his supper.

MR. HAMPTON (197F/198B) School principal. He gave Helen a hard time about the "senior play." He was a stuffy old gentleman who thought that the contemporary music Helen wanted to use in the play was immoral and wrong. Helen reminded him what the music of *his* generation was all about (the Charleston, etc.), and he realized his error in judging so harshly. The show went on.

HAMS (91F/B) (135F/B) In 91F/B, 39¢ a pound. In 135F/B, 43¢.

"HAND-TO-HAND" (128F/133B) How Barney defined "vis-a-vis."

AUNT HANNAH (233F/231B) Millie Hutchins' aunt. Howard met her the day he and Millie called off their wedding.

ROGER HANOVER (130F/132B) An old friend of Bee's with whom she used to "keep company." After Bee received a letter from Roger, she invited him to Mayberry for a visit. Roger was a practical joker and Andy couldn't stand him. He said he "just got over the grip" after he stepped over his suitcase; he told Andy to "hang it on the wall" when Andy put his hand out to shake; and he thought it was funny to put on a monster mask—at Andy's breakfast table—and say "Take me to your leader." He was also crude and a know-it-all: he took over fixing a lamp cord from Andy and broke it. After exposing Andy to his "ways," he told the sheriff that he'd like to go to Florida, but he needed $400. He implied that if Andy didn't give him the money, the sheriff would have a new "uncle." Andy called his bluff and Roger left on the noon train, with Aunt Bee none the wiser.

LARS HANSEN (17F/B) Moonshine customer of the Morrison sisters. Lars said he was a Moslem so the sisters would sell him moonshine (the ladies only sold their "Special Elixir" for special occasions and religious holidays). Lars was actually a Lutheran.

HANSEN'S PRINT SHOP (171F/172B) Business at 177 Main Street that went broke. Old Man Hansen had owned and operated the business. The two counterfeiters, Ralph Kingsley and Arnold Finch, opened up a money factory in this location, with Aunt Bee as their clerk/receptionist.

HANSON (131F/129B) Deputy approved by Mr. Bronson, the Civil Service regional director, who evaluated him regarding the new deputy height and weight requirements.

HANSON'S HILL (186F/187B) Area above Martin's Cottages. Goober went fishing at Martin's.

"HAPPINESS" (174F/173B) Theme of the sermon at All Souls Church the day the old organ went bad and Clara ran out in tears.

"HAPPY VALLEY" (138F/B) The original name of Mayberry.

"HARBORING A RUNAWAY" (4F/6B) The crime Barney accused Andy of committing when the deputy found out that Andy allowed the runaway, George Foley, to stay with him without calling the boy's parents.

HARD STUFF (246F/245B) Cider that had started to turn. Howard had some and offered it at his "swinging" party.

HARDWARE AND APPLIANCES (222F/225B) Main Street business next to another storefront called Lamps And Shades.

HARDWARE STORE (38F/41B) Henry Wheeler's business before he went on the road as a traveling handyman.

MR. HARKINSON (237F/236B) Former butcher of Mayberry who never gave Aunt Bee a problem about cutting the fat off her pot roasts before weighing them. The new butcher refused to do the same. Bee remembered that Mr. Harkinson "was a gentleman."

HARLAN (162F/164B) Husband of Ruth, father of Corlis. After Warren arrested the Ladies Auxiliary for gambling, Harlan went to Andy's house with Corlis to eat supper. Ruth was a member of the Auxiliary.

HARLEY (118F/117B) (137F/B) Mayberry man whom Andy gave "one hour to knock that thing down or I come out there with a stick of dynamite." The reason Andy was so adamant? As he explained it to Harley: "It's not yours, Harley—it's the county's." Apparently there was a road on Harley's property that Mayberry Township used by right of eminent domain. Harley—determined to protect his land from interlopers—must have erected some kind of fence or barrier to prevent passage. Andy wouldn't stand for it, thus the dynamite threat.

VICKI HARMES (91F/B) Barney was sweet on Vicki when he was in school. She was stuck up because her father was in the Civil Service. Barney would wait for her outside the ice cream parlor and every time he offered her a lick of his raspberry sno-cone, she would bite off the bottom and suck out all the juice.

MR. HARMON (13F/B) Film producer who came to Mayberry to make a movie. He wanted to film the small town naturalness of the place, but instead the people went crazy and began to "Hollywoodize" Mayberry. Harmon came back to town to start filming and was appalled at the changes they had made, not the least of which was the plan to cut down what many felt was the centerpiece of the town, the old oak tree. He told them they were wearing "trick or treat" outfits, and to put the town back the way it was or he wouldn't make the movie there. The people obliged and the movie was never mentioned again.

"HARNESS RACING" (11F/B) Sign in the alley next to courthouse.

HARNET (68F/69B) Place where there was dancing, according to Skippy.

KATHRYN HARNEY (151F/B) An ex-girlfriend of Andy's. He followed her to the prom and watched her dance with Vern Harris.

ALICE HARPER (207F/209B) Former Mayberry woman who left town in 1957 to move to New York. Alice was an old girlfriend of Andy's. In 207F/209B, she said she was moving back to Mayberry but, like Ed Sawyer (the "stranger in town"), she came back to Mayberry and was never seen again.

THE HARPERS (161F/160B) Otis got gassed and drove through their rose garden, leveling it. Apparently Otis went back on his word: in 115F/114B, "Hot Rod Otis,"

he swore to never drive drunk, but in this episode, "Opie's Job," he obviously did.

HARRIET (78F/76B) Teller for Mr. Meldrim at the Mayberry Security Bank.

HARRIET (212F/208B) Teena Andrews' secretary.

ARTHUR HARRINGTON (47F/B) Ronald Bailey's attorney.

JOHNNY HARRIS (199F/196B) After Goober got rear-ended, Floyd told him that Johnny Harris had been injured the same way, and had ended up with whiplash. He couldn't raise or lower his elbows and they had to bury him in a wide coffin because his arms were stuck out. Andy clarified later that Johnny had gotten kicked in the head by a mule.

AARON HARRISON (51F/B) Boy who won second place in the fifty-yard dash at the annual Boy's Day competition.

HIPPIE HARRISON (229F/228B) Professional musician. Clara's brother, Claude, played with Hippie.

HARRY (16F/20B) Andy greeted him as he came out of the cell after Barney arrested the whole town.

HARRY (221F/235B) Goober's accountant.

HARRY (222F/225B) Man who bothered Millie Hutchins while she was working at Boysinger's Bakery. Harry punched Howard Sprague in the stomach when Howard came to Millie's defense.

HARRY (247F/246B) Man Emmett greeted on Main Street. Harry was going to Miller's Pond.

HARRY (247F/246B) Man who owned the Diner. To get his vote, Emmett hinted that he'd put a bus stop in front of his diner.

HARRY'S POND (129F/130B) New trout pond two miles east on Miles Road. Andy sent Ollie there to get him out of the courthouse. They'd rent Ollie a rod at the pond, according to Andy.

FRED HARTLEY (214F/B) When Dolly, the horse, started kicking Andy's garage wall, he said it sounded like Fred Hartley was building something. Fred was probably one of Andy's neighbors.

LILLIAN HARTZELL (200F/197B) She would play sax for Bee during her speaking engagement at the Literary Guild. Lillian's version of "Flight of the Bumblebee" really livened up a crowd.

"THE HARVARDS, THE YALES" (67F/65B) The guys Barney asserted rich girls hung out with, guys named Freddy, and Binky, and Bobo.

HARVEST BALL (226F/223B) (246F/245B) Yearly social event. In 246F/245B, it was the social event where Emmett reached the finals in the dance competition.

HARVEY (154F/B) Man Goober got to fill in for him at the filling station.

HARVEY (227F/222B) (232F/233B) In 227F/222B, he was the telegraph clerk who came to tell Aunt Bee she had won the Tampico Tamale contest. In 232F/233B, he made a U-turn on Main Street during Mayberry Safety Week. Andy gave him a ticket.

COLONEL HARVEY (87F/B) He came to Mayberry selling alcoholic Indian Elixir. Bee bought two bottles and got drunk on them. She also invited him to dinner, where he showed Opie "Indian smoke signals." Bee said meeting Colonel Havey was "the greatest experience" in her life since "being baptized."

DOC HARVEY (66F/64B) (92F/B) (131F/129B) In 66F/64B, Doc Harvey was the Mayberry physician Barney called to attend Andy when Andy said he believed Opie about Mr. McBeevee. Barney thought Andy was crazy. In 92F/B, Opie was told that if he didn't let Andy clean his skinned knee, Opie might have to go over to Doc Harvey's and get a shot. In 131F/129B, Doc Harvey gave Asa Bascomb a stretching harness for a pinched nerve in his neck. The harness made Asa over a half inch taller.

MR. HARVEY (150F/B) Supposedly worked on the "Sheriff Without A Gun" TV show.

HARVEY WILLICK'S SHOE STORE (45F/B) Andy said that Jeff Pruitt could work at Harvey's store as a clerk.

HASH ROAD (17F/B) Locale in Cowsill Flats where Ben Sewell's farm was located.

MRS. HASKINS (137F/B) Goober—acting as temporary deputy and traffic cop—caused a giant traffic jam in front of the courthouse involving a lumber truck and a milk truck when he let Mrs. Haskins through.

C. J. HASLER (57F/B) Jewel thief in Capitol City who pretended he was C. J. Hoffman, a newspaper owner, in order to get Barney's help in pulling off a jewelry robbery. His mug shot number was 75249.

HAT (227F/222B) Bee sent Andy a hat from Mexico.

THE HAUNTED HOUSE 98th episode filmed and 97th episode broadcast. Original broadcast date was October 7, 1963. It was written by Harvey Bullock, and directed by Earl Bellamy. Regulars included Andy Griffith, Don Knotts, Ronny Howard, Hal Smith, and Jim Nabors. Guests included Ronnie Dapo and James Seay.

KATHY HAWKINS (224F/221B) She was "due any day" and that was why Doc Spring couldn't bowl.

HAWKINS CREEK (202F/199B) Arnold claimed he almost caught a shark in this creek.

HAWK'S POINT (17F/B) Barney thought there might be a still there.

HAZEL (39F/36B) The name of Frank Myers' chicken.

HAZEL (52F/B) (116F/115B) The piano player for the choir and the Mayberry Chorale.

KEEVY HAZELTON (189F/B) Rock-and-roller who performed Bee's and Clara's song, "Mayberry, My Hometown," on TV. The ladies didn't like his original version; it was too (heaven forfend!) rock-and-roll. He finally slowed it down and everyone was happy.

"HE'S UGLY, BUT HE AIN'T STUPID" (109F/108B) Gomer Pyle's description of his cousin, Goober Pyle.

HEAD OF CITY COUNCIL (247F/246B) Heated race in Mayberry that pitted Emmett Clark against Sam Jones. Sam won by 405 votes.

HEADS (65F/67B) In Andy's and Opie's coin toss to determine whether they ate chicken or pot roast, "heads" was pot roast.

"HEARTBREAK ALLEY" (67F/65B) (138F/B) In 67F/65B, Barney told Andy he was headed for "Heartbreak Alley" if he continued to see Peggy McMillan.

In 138F/B, Barney called the professional theater, "Heartbreak Alley."

HEARTS (18F/B) Card game Fred Boone played with Cliff and Gil.

"HEATER" (110F/109B) The name Barney called his gun.

AGENT HEATHCOTE (165F/169B) IRS agent who came to Mayberry with the news that the tax due on Aunt Bee's "Win or Lose" game show winnings of $4,850 was $1,138.72. His license plate number was IR51957, and he knew that Goober had paid all his taxes.

"THE HEATHEN CANNIBALS" (66F/64B) They taught Mr. McBeevee how to make smoke come out of his ears.

HEATING PAD (234F/232B) Emmett fixed Clara's. She needed it for her neuralgia. He charged her fifty cents.

HELEN CRUMP'S HOUSE NUMBER (163F/161B) 895.

HELEN CRUMP'S PHONE NUMBER (168F/B) 2389.

HELEN, THE AUTHORESS 213th episode filmed and broadcast. Original broadcast date was February 27, 1967. It was written by Douglas Tibbles, and directed by Lee Phillips. Regulars included Andy Griffith, Aneta Corsaut, Howard McNear, George Lindsey, Frances Bavier, Ronny Howard, and Jack Dodson. Guests included Keith Andes as Roger Bryant, Elaine Joyce as Mavis Neff, and Laurie Main.

HELEN'S FORTUNE (209F/210B) At Aunt Bee's Canton Palace: "Spend the day with good friends."

HELEN'S PAST 244th episode filmed and 243rd episode broadcast. Original broadcast date was February 19, 1968. It was written by Douglas Tibbles, and directed by Lee Phillips. Regulars included Andy Griffith, Aneta Corsaut, George Lindsey, and Jack Dodson. Guests included Ruth McDevitt as Mrs. Pendleton, Peter Hobbs as Mr. Lockridge, Connie Sawyer as Miss Blanchard, Monty Magretts as Mrs. Crane, and Michael Freeman as Hollis.

"HELENE ALEXIAN DUBOIS" (213F/B) The pen name Helen Crump uncomfortably adopted at the urging of her publisher, Roger Bryant, for the publication of her book, *Amusing Tales Of Tiny Tots.*

"A HELIACOPTER" (41F/39B) Barney was upset; Mayberry didn't have one.

"HELLO, DOLL" (123F/122B) Daphne's trademark way of greeting Andy.

HEN HOUSE (29F/B) Sam Becker backed into a hen house and got spurred by a rooster.

"A HEN PARTY" (45F/B) How Barney described the ladies party that Thelma Lou had at her house.

"RALPH HENDERSON" (74F/B) One of Big Maude Tyler's aliases.

EVAN HENDRICKS (154F/B) Orville's son.

MR. HENDRICKS (195F/193B) (209F/210B) In 195F/193B, he was the bases umpire at the softball game between the Mayberry Giants and the Mt. Pilot Comets. In 209F/210B, he owned the Sparerib Tavern on Main Street. It went out of business.

ORVILLE HENDRICKS (154F/B) Aunt Bee's "invisible beau." Hendricks was Bee's butter and egg man. She pretended she was dating him because of Clara's insinuation that Bee was getting in the way of Andy's and Helen's romance. She didn't know he was married. Andy and Barney confronted Hendricks, who told them the truth. Andy then explained to Bee that she was not in the way. Hendricks refused to sell to them anymore. He was from Mt. Pilot. Barney called him a "Chicken Coop Casanova" before he found out the truth.

"HENNESSEY" (149F/B) The alias a crook used to convince Barney he was with the FBI. He gave Barney the secret "FBI handshake" and talked about the fictitious "McAllister case."

WILBUR HENNESSEY (10F/12B) Mayberry man who got drunk and fell out of room 209 at the Mayberry Hotel.

FRED HENRY (114F/113B) (153F/B) In 114F/113B, Fred wanted all black choir robes with white collars. In 153F/B, Fred told Barney about the Widow Saunders and the dishcloth salesman.

HENS (104F/105B) (120F/119B) (121F/120B) (186F/187B) 29¢.

JED HENSON (85F/B) He and his brother, Pothrow, parked their car in Wally's garage while Wally was in the Jefferson county seat.

POTHROW HENSON (85F/B) He and his brother parked their car in Wally's garage while Wally was in the Jefferson county seat. Pothrow hid in the trunk and stole things from the filling station every night. He stole, among other things, four flashlights, six fan belts, and two sets of battery clips. Jim Morgan was falsely accused of the thefts but he redeemed himself by wiring the cash register to car batteries and catching Pothrow red-handed.

"HERE COMES THE BRIDE" (1F/B) Barney played it on the harmonica at Rose's wedding.

HIALEAH (60F/B) The track where the horse, Ladybug, did very well for Bill Medwin, the bookie barber.

"A HICK JOB IN A HICK TOWN" (41F/39B) How Barney described his job in a moment of anger.

SID HICKOX (187F/186B) Cameraman on the Foster Furniture Polish commercial.

MR. HIGBY (214F/B) Piano tuner who came through Mayberry on occasion.

SALLY HIGGINS (214F/B) Woman Bee ran into one afternoon.

HIGH NOON IN MAYBERRY 80th episode filmed and broadcast. Original broadcast date was January 21, 1963. It was written by Jim Fritzell and Everett Greenbaum, and directed by Bob Sweeney. Regulars included Andy Griffith, Don Knotts, Frances Bavier, Ronny Howard, Hal Smith, and Jim Nabors. Guests included Dub Taylor and Leo Gordon.

HIGHWAY 43 (77F/79B) The road where Malcolm Tucker's car broke down. It had a clogged fuel line. Tucker was the "man in a hurry."

HIGHWAY 6 (112F/111B) The road Mrs. Beggs was driving on when a woman speeder passed her. It was on the outskirts of Mayberry, and on the highway was Turner's Grade.

HIGHWAY 214 (129F/130B) The road Ollie took to Andy's house instead of Highway 7. He saved seventy miles. Ollie got gas in Freeport.

"HIGHWAYS ARE KILLERS" (111F/110B) Sign Bee and the women carried when they picketed the jail to protest Mr. Frisby's eviction from his land.

HILDA MAE (11F/B) (12F/10B) (16F/20B) In 11F/B, she was an early girlfriend of Barney's. She called him "Barney-Parney-Poo." In 12F/10B, she convinced Barney to sign the "Ellie Walker for Council" petition by sweet-talking him. In 16F/20B, she tried to console Barney after he made a fool of himself by arresting the whole town. Instead, she ended up laughing at him when she mussed his hair; he looked ridiculous.

HILLSIDE UNIVERSITY (61F/B) School in Raleigh where the reporter, Jean Boswell, claimed she was a student majoring in government. Barney believed her.

HIP (109F/108B) Sarah's mama broke her hip at the bowling alley.

"HIRAM" (3F/B) The name Bobby Fleet derogatorily called Andy.

HI-TEST (110F/109B) The gasoline Andy and Barney used in the squad car.

WARDEN HIX (177F/B) Warden on the county work farm. He called Andy to tell him Avery Noonan had escaped. Barney had originally sent Noonan to jail.

MAJOR HOBART (112F/111B) Tank driver from the 22nd Division who Andy stopped on Highway 6, thinking it was Barney with a new tank bought at an auction.

LORILEE HOBBS (102F/B) Gomer found out about the gold shipment from Lorilee. She worked "up at the dime store."

THE HOFBRAU (155F/B) Restaurant Helen suggested. Andy and Barney couldn't go because they were expecting a conference call from the highway department at 10:00 P.M.

C. J. HOFFMAN (57F/B) The alias that C. J. Hasler—the jewel thief—used to convince Barney he was a newspaper owner.

HOGARTH DETECTIVES (137F/B) Firm in Raleigh that offered Andy a job. Herb Mason, a friend of Andy's, made the offer.

HOGBACK (118F/117B) According to Naylor, hogback was all that Maudie cooked.

BILLY HOLLANDER (225F/224B) George and Laura's son. Billy told Opie that supper should be called dinner. Opie invited Billy for lunch, and Bee made shrimp and duck.

GEORGE HOLLANDER (225F/224B) Well-to-do businessman from Walnut Hills. His son, Billy, became friends with Opie at Camp Winoke. George was the director of five different banks.

LAURA HOLLANDER (225F/224B) George's wife.

HOLLIS (244F/243B) Goober tried to patch his bike tire but he popped it instead.

MARTHA HOLLISTER (44F/B) (83F/B) Rafe's wife. In 44F/B, she stubbed her toe and complained about it a lot. In 83F/B, it was mentioned that she and Rafe lived on Willow Creek Road.

RAFE HOLLISTER (44F/B) (56F/B) (83F/B) Mayberry moonshiner. In 56F/B, he accepted his tetanus shot from the county nurse after Andy showed him what a hero he'd be when he died as a result of refusing the shot. In

83F/B, Rafe did a solo vocal performance at the Ladies League musicale. He was arrested in April of 1962. His case number was 68456735.

"HOLLYWOOD COMES TO MAYBERRY" (13F/B) Headline of the "Mayberry Gazette" after it was announced that the producer, Mr. Harmon, would be making a movie in Mayberry. Under the headline was the smaller line, "Local Citizens To Be In Movies."

"HOLLYWOOD FUNERALS" (13F/B) The new name Orville Monroe used for his funeral parlor after Mayberry was picked as the site for a Hollywood movie.

THE HOLLYWOOD MARQUEE (168F/B) The hotel Darlene Mason stayed at in Hollywood during the filming of "Sheriff Without a Gun." The hotel's phone number was 27399.

THE HOLLYWOOD PARTY 168th episode filmed and broadcast. Original broadcast date was November 8, 1965. It was written by Fred Freeman and Lawrence J. Cohen, and directed by Alan Rafkin. Regulars included Andy Griffith, Ronny Howard, Frances Bavier, and Aneta Corsaut. Guests included Ruta Lee as Darlene Mason, and Sid Melton as Pat Michaels.

HOLMES, SHERLOCK see "SHERLOCK HOLMES"

"HOLY JUMPING CATFISH!" (136F/B) What Barney exclaimed when Opie brought in the man's purse he found with fifty dollars in it. The purse would become Opie's if the owner didn't appear within a week.

"HOME DECOR" (243F/242B) Magazine read by a lady under a dryer in the beauty parlor.

"HOMELY AT THE CRADLE, PRETTY AT THE TABLE" (101F/96B) The adage Barney remembered as he and Andy discussed the three orphan songbirds Opie adopted.

HOMER (197F/198B) The lead in the "senior play."

HOMINY GRITS (54F/B) (104F/105B) (112F/111B) (115F/114B) (135F/B) (180F/B) (183F/182B) (201F/204B) In 54F/B, 10¢. In all the other episodes listed, 19¢.

"HONEY" (3F/B) The name Bobby Fleet derogatorily called the waitress at the Diner.

"HONEYPIE" (45F/B) The name Jeff Pruitt called Thelma Lou.

HONG KONG SUITS (231F/230B) Classified ad read by Andy in his search for an investment.

"THE HONOR SYSTEM" (11F/B) System the state penal commission recommended for state prisoners.

JARROD HOOPER (238F/239B) Mayberry man who died at the age of ninety-three, willing $500 to All Souls Church.

HOOT OWL (125F/124B) The imitation Gomer used as a signal to tell the surprise party that Andy and Helen had arrived.

OLD HUGO HOPFLEISH (118F/117B) Old German soldier who gave Barney advice on soldiering. Hugo was in the Army in "'18."

EILEEN HOPKINS (166F/B) She asked Andy to get her an autograph of Tony Curtis when the Taylors went to Hollywood.

HOPKIN'S CREEK (205F/B) Creek three miles outside of Mayberry. George Jones claimed he had a map which showed Ross's Treasure was buried there.

HOPKIN'S LAKE (189F/B) Lake Goober suggested to Keevy Hazleton as a fishing spot. According to Goober, it had the "finest trout fishing in the county."

"HORATIO WHO?" (5F/8B) The question asked by Opie when Andy explained that the statement "there are one-and-a-half needy boys per square mile" in the county was a ratio.

THE HORSE TRADER 14th episode filmed and broadcast. Original broadcast date was January 9, 1961. It was written by Jack Elinson and Charles Stewart, and directed by Bob Sweeney. Regulars included Andy Griffith, Don Knotts, Ronny Howard, and Elinor Donahue as Ellie Walker. Guests included Dick Elliot as Mayor Pike, and Casey Adams as Ralph Mason.

HORSEHAIR (121F/120B) One of Barney's allergies.

HORTON (50F/B) Man from the state bureau of investigation who came to Mayberry to tell Andy about the robbery of the furniture company's payroll by Doc Molloy.

HOT BULLION (161F/160B) Soup Aunt Bee offered Andy when he came home after having a bad day.

HOT FUDGE SUNDAES (10F/12B) One of Lucy Matthew's favorite foods.

HOT ROD OTIS 115th episode filmed and 114th broadcast. Original broadcast date was February 17, 1964. It was written by Harvey Bullock, and directed by Earl Bellamy. Regulars included Andy Griffith, Don Knotts, and Hal Smith as Otis.

HOTEL BAR AND RESTAURANT (164F/162B) (183F/182B) Restaurant across the street from the Mayberry courthouse.

"HOUDINI" (118F/117B) After Gomer locked himself to Barney while playing with the handcuffs, Barney called him "Houdini."

"THE HOUSE OF BLOOD" (140F/B) Movie that was playing at the Grand Theater along with "The Beast That Ate Minnesota." Barney insisted on getting Andy's OK before he would allow Opie to see it.

"HOW DO YOU DO, MRS. WILEY" (113F/112B) One of the conversational bons mots Andy taught Ernest T. Bass to say. Ernest T. then said it to everyone he met, including Barney.

"HOW IT FEELS TO PULL THE SWITCH" (104F/105B) One of the stories in "True Blue Detective" magazine. Barney had bound copies of the magazine.

"HOW TO MAKE FRIED CHICKEN AND JOHNNYCAKE" (10F/12B) According to Andy, one of Mayberry's "secrets."

"HOW TO MAKE POSSUM PIE" (10F/12B) According to Andy, one of Mayberry's "secrets."

"HOW TO MAKE TURNIP JAM" (10F/12B) According to Andy, one of Mayberry's "secrets."

"HOW TO TELL IF A WATERMELON'S RIPE" (196F/203B) During his "beard stage," Goober pompously explained to Aunt Bee how to tell if a watermelon was ripe.

HOWARD (86F/B) A friend of Opie's and a member of the history troupe, "The Mayberry Minutemen."

HOWARD AND MILLIE 233rd episode broadcast and 231st episode broadcast. Original broadcast date was November 27, 1967. It was written by Joseph Bonaduce, and directed by Peter Baldwin. Regulars included Andy Griffith, Aneta Corsaut, Jack Dodson, George Lindsey, and Ronny Howard. Guests included Arlene Golonka as Millie Hutchins, Elizabeth Harrower as Mrs. Hutchins, Steve Pendleton as Mr. Hutchins, Robert B. Williams as Uncle Phil, Ida Mae MacKenzie as Aunt Hannah, Carol Veazie as the Customer, and Roy Engel as the Conductor.

HOWARD THE BOWLER 224th episode filmed and 221st episode broadcast. Original broadcast date was September 18, 1967. It was written by Dick Bensfield and Perry Grant, and directed by Lee Phillips. Regulars included Andy Griffith, Frances Bavier, Jack Dodson, George Lindsey, Aneta Corsaut, and Paul Hartman. Guests included Norman Alden as Hank, and Bob Becker as George.

HOWARD THE COMEDIAN 216th episode filmed and broadcast. Original broadcast date was March 20, 1967. It was written by Michael Morris and Seamon Jacobs, and directed by Lee Phillips. Regulars included Andy Griffith, Jack Dodson, Frances Bavier, Ronny Howard, Hope Summers, George Lindsey, and Howard McNear. Guests included Dick Haynes as Colonel Tim, Dick Curtis as Bill Hollenback, and Tol Avery as the Driver.

HOWARD'S COMEDY ROUTINE (216F/B) This was the routine that Howard Sprague did on "Colonel Tim's Talent Time." At first, the citizens were outraged at what they thought were insults, but later, after they became "famous" because of the jokes, they loved it and started to give Howard material.

"Mayberry is so small they had to widen Main Street to put a white line down the middle. Andy Taylor is so relaxed the sheriff's office has an unlisted telephone number. When Goober takes a girl out, he drives with his feet. In Mayberry, there's three forms of communication: telephone, telegraph, tell Floyd. A customer told Floyd to take up the violin—it would give his chin a rest. Aunt Bee's family came over on the Mayflower—in those days the immigration laws weren't so strict. Miss Edwards' father fought with Pershing. Her grandfather fought with Teddy Roosevelt, and her great-grandfather fought with General Lee. Her folks couldn't get along with anybody."

HOWARD'S DEFENSE OF ANDY (195F/ 193B) After the entire town of Mayberry turned against Andy for his calling Opie out in a critical play during "The Ball Game," Howard wrote the following editorial for the "Mayberry Gazette":

"Although this reporter was assigned to cover today's Mayberry-Mt. Pilot baseball game, he must admit frankly that he has very little knowledge of baseball. However, after witnessing this game, it appears that more important than the knowledge of baseball is a knowledge of people. For instance, why does a man take on a job as umpire and expose himself to all kinds of abuse? I know why one man in particular did it. [Aunt Bee continues to read from here.] His reason is because he was asked to, as a favor. He wasn't particularly

anxious to do it because his son happened to be playing on the team and he didn't want to run the risk of not being completely impartial. [Goober continues reading from here.] It seems to me that once a man is asked to handle a job like that, any decisions he makes—right or wrong—should be accepted in the spirit of good sportsmanship. [Helen concludes the piece, reading from here.] If any of you critics want the job of umpire at next year's game, let him speak up loud and clear. Frankly, I don't think we'll get too many offers."

This article did the trick, and everyone, including Coach Goober, apologized to Andy for treating him so shabbily.

HOWARD'S FORTUNE (209F/210B) At Aunt Bee's Canton Palace: "Be considerate of others, it will return manyfold."

HOWARD'S MAIN EVENT 222nd episode filmed and 225th episode broadcast. Original broadcast date was October 16, 1967. It was written by Earl Barret and Robert C. Dennis, and directed by Lee Phillips. Regulars included Andy Griffith, Jack Dodson, George Lindsey, and Aneta Corsaut. Guests included Arlene Golonka as Millie Hutchins, Alan Melvin as Clyde Plaunt, and Wayne Heffley.

HOWARD'S NEW LIFE 235th episode filmed and 234th episode broadcast. Original broadcast date was December 18, 1967. It was written by Richard Bensfield and Perry Grant, and directed by Lee Phillips. Regulars included Andy Griffith, Ronny Howard, Frances Bavier, Jack Dodson, Paul Hartman, and George Lindsey. Guests included Harry Dean Stanton as the Proprietor, Don Keefer as Grover, Sam Greene as Wes, Sir Lancelot as the Man, and Mark Brown as Sebastian.

HOWARD'S PHONE NUMBER (210F/ 211B) Mayberry 397.

HOWARD'S SHOPPING LIST (206F/B) His mother wanted: oatmeal, two quarts whole milk, a dozen brown eggs, a container of yogurt, and three dozen oranges.

HOWIE (78F/76B) One of the crooks who tried to rob the Mayberry Security Bank. Mort was the other crook.

ELMER HUBACHER (26F/B) Elmer was out on parole but he ended up back in jail.

JUNIOR HUBACHER (63F/B) One of the Hubacher brothers. When Junior was in the Mayberry jail, he sang "My Little Grey Home In The West." It was touching.

THE HUBACHER BROTHERS (11F/B) (26F/B) Three brothers Andy and Barney sent to North Carolina State Prison for an undisclosed crime, which was probably moonshining. They sent Andy and Barney a Christmas card every year. Elmer was the youngest (Barney said, "He's the baby"), and in the Christmas card photo, Elmer was in the middle. In 26F/B, Andy and Barney got a package from them; the brothers made Andy a wallet and Barney a leather bookmark.

"HUBCAPS LESH" (90F/B) Myrt Lesh's alias.

HUCKLEBERRY SMASH (73F/70B) New soda flavor that was put in the cooler at Wally's Service Station.

MRS. HUDGINS (146F/B) Andy and Barney found one of her grocery lists in the dump while searching for the "lucky letter." She had pies, cakes, and cookies on the list. She had claimed her weight problem was "glandular."

SY HUDGINS (81F/B) Farmer who owned Jimmy, the "loaded goat." Sy brought Jimmy to town because he had promised the goat a trip for a long time. While in Mayberry, Jimmy ate a case of dynamite and it was up to Andy and Barney to lead Jimmy safely out of town. It wasn't said if Sy was related to Mrs. Hudgins.

ROCK HUDSON (87F/B) Barney combed his hair in the mirror while watching a framed picture of Rock Hudson. He fancied himself a Rock lookalike.

HUDSON TERRAPLANE (90F/B) 1949 automobile in a classified ad. Barney considered buying the car. Its price was twelve good laying hens.

HUDSON TERRAPLANE (121F/120B) Barney had his picture taken sitting on his uncle's Hudson rather than on a pony because even when he was young he was allergic to horsehair.

WEDDY HUFF (70F/68B) Man whose cow was stolen.

CHARLES HUMBONE (216F/B) Man who called Bee to complain about Howard Sprague's comedy routine on "Colonel Tim's Talent Time." The routine poked gentle fun at Mayberry and its people.

"HUSH" (99F/98B) When the doctor at the recruiting office looked into Ernest T.'s ears, Ernest T. said "Ahhh" because that's what the doctor asked him to say when he looked into Ernest T.'s throat. The doctor told him not to say "Ahhh." Ernest T. asked what he should say instead, and the doctor angrily said "Hush!" Ernest T. then said "Hush" as the doctor examined his ears.

MILLIE HUTCHINS (222F/225B) (233F/231B) Young girl from Mt. Pilot who moved to Mayberry in 222F/225B and worked at Boysinger's Bakery. Howard Sprague was sweet on Millie. In 233F/231B, Howard proposed to Millie, and she accepted. After a testy train ride to Wheeling, however, all of their individual "ways" surfaced and they decided to call off the wedding. Millie couldn't function in the morning before she had her coffee. Howard, on the other hand, was a "morning person." He aggravated Millie by being so annoyingly perky at such an early hour.

MR. AND MRS. HUTCHINS (233F/231B) Millie's parents. Millie and Howard went to see them in Wheeling with plans of marrying there, but they called it off at the last minute.

I KNOW SOUTH AMERICA (230F/229B) Book written by Professor Hubert St. John. He lectured on the book for the Mayberry women's club.

"I MARRIED A FINK" (104F/105B) One of the stories from "True Blue Detective" magazine. Barney had bound copies of the magazine.

"I PICKED A POCKET AND PAID" (104F/105B) One of the stories from "True Blue Detective" magazine. Barney had bound copies of the magazine.

"I'M JUST A VAGABOND LOVER" (15F/B) (31F/B) Song Barney offered to play for Wilbur Finch on the harmonica. In 31F/B, he offered to play it for Bobby Fleet.

ICE CREAM SODAS (38F/41B) Aunt Bee and Henry Wheeler had them after the movies.

IDEAL CONSTRUCTION COMPANY (122F/121B) Mt. Pilot company that was in the same building and on the same floor as the Miracle Salve Company.

IF I HAD A QUARTER-MILLION 149th episode filmed and broadcast. Original broadcast date was February 15, 1965. It was written by Bob Ross, and directed by Alan Rafkin. Regulars included Andy Griffith, Don Knotts, George Lindsey, and Howard McNear. Guests included Hank Patterson, Byron Folger, and Al Checco.

"IF LOST PLEASE RETURN TO WYATT EARP" (3F/B) The legend that Bobby Fleet said was engraved on the back of Andy's badge.

"IF YOU CAN FILL THE UNFORGIVING MINUTES" (224F/221B) First line of a poem Howard read just before he had to throw the last ball in a possible 300 game.

IMPRESSIONISTIC PAINTINGS (246F/245B) Howard bought paintings at a little out-of-the-way shop in Mt. Pilot. They ran $10, $15, $20 each. The "regular" paintings (clowns and apples) were only $7 each.

INDIAN (200F/197B) Mayberry had one Indian, Tom Strongbow.

INDIAN (246F/245B) Howard bought a six-foot Indian and put it on the right side of the entrance door to his living room. He bought the Indian to help transform his "old homestead" into a swinging bachelor pad.

INDIAN ELIXIR (87F/B) Colonel Harvey's "magic" potion, that happened to be eighty-five percent alcohol. He sold it as a tonic "to purge the body and lift the spirits; to put a light in the eye, a spring in a step, a lift in the voice and hope in the human heart." Aunt Bee bought two bottles, got drunk, and sang "Toot Toot Tootsie" at the piano. The elixir sold for a dollar a bottle.

INH-851 (156F/B) Newton Monroe's license plate number.

THE INSPECTOR 26th episode filmed and broadcast. Original broadcast date was April 10, 1961. It was written by Jack Elinson and Charles Stewart, and directed by Bob Sweeney. Regulars included Andy Griffith, Don Knotts, Ronny Howard, and Hal Smith as Otis. Guests included Jack Prince as Luke Rainer, Ray Lanier as Sam, Willis Bouchey as Mr. Brady, and Tod Andrews as Ralph Case, the Inspector.

INTERCONTINENTAL FLYER (84F/B) The bike Simon Winkler bought for his son Arnold, the "spoiled kid." It cost seventy dollars.

I

INTERCONTINENTAL NEWS (41F/39B) Joe Layton, the crook, pretended he worked for this photo agency.

"INTERNATIONAL DATELINE" (153F/B) One of the columns in the "Mayberry Gazette."

INTERSTATE PEST CONTROL (72F/71B) Nonexistent state agency Andy invented as an excuse to keep Freddy Fleet and His Band With A Beat in Mayberry long enough to convince Mayor Stoner to let the Mayberry Band go to the band festival.

INVENTORY (123F/122B) Counting job Andy and Barney had to do for the county. There were seven blankets and three desklamps on the property list, among other things.

INVISIBLE RAY (202F/199B) Andy said he would use an invisible ray to get back into the house after Arnold pretended that the blankets he and Opie used to cover the abandoned baby were "electronically-controlled" and that they threw off a "radioactive gas."

IR51957 (165F/169B) The license plate number of the government car driven by Agent Heathcote.

IRENE (246F/245B) The nurse Goober asked to Howard's swinging party. She couldn't come because she went into the operating room at five that afternoon.

IRIS (220F/B) The girl Arnold Bailey invited to his thirteenth birthday party.

IRON (24F/B) Dr. Benson felt that Barney needed iron. Barney wanted to know if he was "gonna make it."

IRRESISTIBLE ANDY 7th episode filmed and 5th episode broadcast. Original broadcast date was October 31, 1960. It was written by David Adler, and directed by Don Weiss. Regulars included Andy Griffith, Don Knotts, Ronny Howard, Frances Bavier, and Elinor Donahue as Ellie Walker. Guests included Harry Antrim as Fred Walker.

"IS THERE NO MERCY?" (111F/110B) Sign Bee and the women carried when they picketed the jail to protest the eviction of Mr. Frisby from his land.

"IS THIS DARLENE MASON'S NEXT CONQUEST?" (168F/B) The headline under the photo of Andy and Darlene Mason that ran in the "Mayberry Gazette." This picture aggravated Helen.

ITALIAN NATIONAL ANTHEM (241F/249B) According to Bee at the meeting of the Mayberry civic league that welcomed the Vincentes to Mayberry, the Italian national anthem was "O Solo Mio."

MR. IZAMOTO (135F/B) Owner/operator of the Mt. Pilot Judo Society, whose help Andy enlisted in getting Fred Plummer to leave Barney alone. Barney was a member of the society.

J86-449 (66F/64B) License plate number of Mr. McBeevee's truck.

"A J. C. PENNEY WINDOW" (71F/72B) When Floyd dressed up as a rich widower in a smoking jacket and an ascot to impress Madeline Grayson, Andy told him he looked good enough to be put in "a J. C. Penney window."

"J TO Z" (125F/124B) To keep Andy busy at the courthouse, Barney dropped the "J to Z" file cabinet drawer and Andy had to refile it.

JA-4128 (35F/B) License plate number of the Thunderbird convertible Elizabeth Crowley, the woman speeder, was driving when she was arrested by Andy.

JACK (172F/170B) He robbed the state mobile museum. His partner was Stella. They were caught when Warren shot their station wagon with the town cannon.

JACK (209F/210B) Charlie Lee's nephew. He went to the University of North Carolina, and mastered in psychology. When Bee wanted out of her partnership with Charlie, Jack bought her share of Aunt Bee's Canton Palace. His fortune after he bought in was "Today is your lucky day."

"JACK AND THE BEANSTALK" (115F/114B) Fairy tale Andy read to Otis to get him to go to sleep.

"JACK THE RIPPER" (108F/107B) Barney thought that Jack the Ripper might have read "Robin Hood."

JACKSON (82F/B) Andy Taylor's middle name.

BRIAN JACKSON (208F/212B) Mayberry sculptor. He charged the town $1,200 to sculpt a statue of Andy's and Bee's ancestor, Seth Taylor. Jackson was responsible for over ninety percent of the headstones used in Mayberry. Jackson's wife ran off with a traveling man.

J. HOWARD JACKSON (61F/B) Big shot publisher who got a speeding ticket from Andy and didn't show up for the trial. Andy went to his office and insisted he come back to Mayberry to stand before him as judge. He did, Andy fined him fifteen dollars, and Jackson was livid that Andy dragged him back for such a measly fine. Jackson then put his best investigative reporter, Jean Boswell, on Andy. He told her to get enough dirt on Andy to destroy him. She came on to Barney who, in a foolish moment of self-importance, blabbed to her about what he found wrong with the way Andy did his job. She wrote her article, and it was damning enough to have Andy brought up on charges. Barney explained himself at the trial in an impassioned defense of Andy, and the case was dropped. Barney learned yet another lesson about pride.

JIMMY JACKSON (137F/B) Little boy who wouldn't cross the street. Otis pulled him across. Jimmy fell and skinned his knee. His mother complained; they lived on that side of the street and Jimmy didn't have to cross!

MR. JACKSON (215F/B) Opie's football coach. He brought Flip Conroy to practice one day to take over as coach. Flip spent ten years with the Giants, and came back to Mayberry to work in his father's business.

MRS. JACKSON (137F/B) Jimmy's mother. She came into the courthouse to complain about Otis, who had dragged her son across the street. The boy fell and skinned his knee. The problem: the Jacksons lived on that side of the street and Otis didn't have to cross Jimmy.

RICK JACKSON (52F/B) Choir member who had to quit the choir because he had his adenoids and tonsils removed.

SHERIFF JACKSON (144F/B) President of the Sheriff's Association. He saw Gilly Walker's car inside the courthouse and assumed it was part of the traffic safety program.

JACKSONVILLE (184F/B) Hometown of Bee's niece, Martha, her husband Darryl, and their infant daughter, Evie Joy.

SGT. JACOBS (114F/113B) The state police officer who called Andy to tell him they were bringing the "prisoner of love" to the Mayberry jail.

JAILBREAK 50th episode filmed and broadcast. Original broadcast date was February 5, 1962. It was written by Harvey Bullock, and directed by Bob Sweeney. Regulars included Andy Griffith, Don Knotts, Ronny Howard, and Howard McNear. Guests included Ken Lynch, Allan Melvin, Fred Sherman, Frank Warren, Bob McQuain, Sally Mills, and Rita Kenaston.

JAKE (90F/B) Myrt Lesh's partner.

GILBERT JAMEL (150F/B) The producer of the fictitious "Sheriff Without A Gun" TV show. The show was really a ruse to rob the Mayberry Security Bank.

JESSE JAMES (108F/107B) Barney thought that Jesse James might have read "Robin Hood."

JAMS (50F/B) 30¢

JANUARY 21 (106F/B) One of the dates Barney resigned as deputy.

JASE (112F/111B) Jase told Andy that if they filled up Barney's sidecar with water they could take a bath in it.

JASON (10F/12B) (15F/B) (31F/B) (97F/101B) Hotel clerk at the Mayberry Hotel. In 15F/B, Jason checked in Wilbur Finch. In 97F/101B, Gomer was telling Jason a story about Bertie Blush. Wally got so disgusted with Gomer's talking that he fired him.

JOHNNY PAUL JASON (65F/67B) (77F/79B) (101F/96B) (108F/107B)(125F/124B) (129F/130B) (154F/B) (157F/B) (161F/160B) (181F/B) In 65F/67B, he told Opie that if you licked an indelible pencil you died in a minute-and-a-half. In 77F/79B, he told Opie that if you put a horse hair in stagnate water it would turn into a snake. In 101F/96B, Johnny Paul told Opie that if birds were touched, they would die. In 108F/107B, Johnny Paul was one of Opie's "merry men." He raided his mother's fruit and vegetable bin for Wary Willy the Hobo. In 125F/124B, it's mentioned he had a "lergic." Opie said that during April and May he wasn't allowed to breathe. In 129F/130B, Opie told Johnny Paul that the sermon was about Cain and Abel and "Don't be surprised if somebody gets killed." In 154F/B,

Opie stayed overnight at his house. In 157F/B, it's said that Johnny Paul had Chemistry Set #1. In 161F/160B, Bee called Johnny Paul's house when Opie wasn't home by six o'clock. This was the day Opie wrecked his bike. In 181F/B, he teased Opie about not knowing how to dance.

MR. JASON (166F/B) He fixed the handle on Bee's valise before they left on their trip to Hollywood. It broke before they boarded the bus. It wasn't said if Mr. Jason was related to Johnny Paul Jason.

MRS. JASON (108F/107B) Johnny Paul's mother. She called Andy to tell him that somebody had raided her fruit and vegetable bin.

"JASPER VS. KOWALSKI" (159F/B) Boxing match advertised by a sign posted at the carnival.

"JAYLENE NAOMI CONNORS" (74F/B) Naomi Connors' alias.

JEFFERSON COUNTY SEAT (85F/B) Wally went there for a week.

MRS. JEFFREYS (83F/B) Head of the Ladies League. She didn't approve of Rafe Hollister as soloist for the League-sponsored musicale.

JENKINS (27F/B) Next-door neighbor of Old Man Flint. Jenkins had sons.

AL JENKINS (211F/207B) One of Barney's co-workers on the Raleigh police force. Barney introduced Al to Andy as "one of our top men."

BUZZ JENKINS (77F/79B) Buzz was stealing chickens from Al's Poultry Headquarters. This necessitated a chicken stakeout by Barney until 4:00 A.M. one night.

ED JENKINS (178F/B) Mayberry insurance man (played by Jack Dodson before his Howard Sprague days) who handled the claim for Aunt Bee's "lost" brooch.

FRED JENKINS (41F/39B) Man who came to Mayberry claiming he was from the FBI and was there to give Andy an award for having the lowest crime rate in the United States. In reality, he and his partner were there to rob the Mayberry Security Bank. Andy discovered the ruse, however, when Jenkins allowed himself to be photographed with Andy for the local paper. FBI special agents never allowed themselves to be photographed. Andy then trapped the two men trying to open the vault.

LOU JENKINS (224F/221B) Member of the Emmett's Fix-It Shop bowling team. Lou had been bowling well, but prior to an important tournament he had to go to Atlanta on business, thus necessitating a replacement.

MARVIN JENKINS (223F/226B) Young man (played by Jack Nicholson) who was arrested and charged with the burglary of Brice's Department Store. Aunt Bee was a juror at his trial. He was found innocent after Andy made the connection with a lighter found at the scene and a young man who was *too* interested in Jenkins' guilt.

MAYOR JENKINS (5F/8B) Mayor of Mayberry before Mayor Pike. He attended Tom Silby's "funeral."

LUKE JENSEN (70F/68B) The "cow thief." He stole cows by putting shoes on them and walking them off the farms. Luke spent time in the Nashville county jail. Luke's dog's name was Mac.

JENSEN ORTHOPEDIC LOAFERS (74F/B) Company owned by Charlie O'Malley's father-in-law.

"THE JEROME SANGER SHOW" (167F/B) A favorite TV show of Opie's. He, Andy, and Bee watched it when they were in Hollywood.

JERRY (1F/B) Friend of Opie's. Opie remembered him in his prayers.

"JEWELRY WATCH REPAIR" (125F/124B) Sign on the front of Fred Sterling's jewelry store. The jewelry store was next to the antique shop.

JIM (11F/B) Prisoner Andy released from jail for the Christmas holiday.

"JIM APACHE, INDIAN SPY" (167F/B) A favorite TV show of Opie's. He, Andy, and Bee watched it when they were in Hollywood.

JIMMY (5F/8B) Friend of Opie's. Opie gave him a sock in the head, enjoyed it, and didn't charge him for it. Opie hit him because Jimmy made fun of Charlotte, Opie's girlfriend.

JIMMY (81F/B) The "loaded goat" owned by Sy Hudgins. Jimmy ate a case of dynamite and posed a problem for Andy and Barney.

"JINGLE BELLS" (3F/B) (11F/B) (36F/37B) In 3F/B, the song Barney played for Bobby Fleet on the harmonica. In 11F/B, the song Barney sang at the Christmas Eve party. In 35F/37B, the song Barney played for Melissa Stevens and her "Daddy" on the harmonica.

THE JINX 49th episode filmed and broadcast. Original broadcast date was January 29, 1962. It was written by Jack Elinson and Charles Stewart, and directed by Bob Sweeney. Regulars included Andy Griffith, Don Knotts, Frances Bavier, Ronny Howard, and Howard McNear. Guests included John Qualen as Henry Bennett, Clint Howard as Leon, Sherman Sanders, Sherwood Keith, and Frank Warren.

"JINXING RAY" (49F/B) Vibrations emitted by jinxes. According to Barney, the ray was discovered by Buzz Fluhart.

JL-327 License number of the squad car, visible in the following episodes: 2F/B, 4F/6B, 11F/B, 23F/B, 24F/B, 27F/B, 31F/B, 32F/B, 33F/34B, 39F/36B, 40F/38B, 46F/B, 47F/B, 50F/B, 53F/B, 54F/B, 60F/B, 61F/B, 62F/B, 68F/70B, 73F/70B, 74F/B, 76F/78B, 82F/B, 86F/B, 87F/B 89F/B, 97F/101B, 100F/99B, 103F/B, 110F/109B, 111F/110B, 113F/121B, 123F/122B, 128F/133B, 135F/B, 140F/B, 144F/B, 147F/B, 149F/B, 154F/B, 155F/B, 170F/171B, 173F/174B, 183F/182B, 196F/203B, 213F/B, 229F/228B, 237F/236B, and 247F/246B.

JOE (224F/221B) Goober hollered to him to turn up the air conditioning at the Mayberry Lanes. Joe was probably the owner of the bowling alley.

"JOE ORDINARY" (67F/65B) Barney told Andy that Andy was just was "Joe Ordinary" to Peggy McMillan.

JOEY (51F/B) (61F/B) (215F/B) Friend of Opie's. In 51F/B, he was one of the entrants at the Boy's Day competition. In 215F/B, Joey played on Opie's football team, coached by Flip Conroy.

JOHN (165F/169B) The stage name of the Taylors' chauffeur in Hollywood. His real name was Bob. Bee called him Bob.

JOHN (172F/170B) He set up the Mayberry Marching Band for the Founder's Day parade.

"JOHN HENRY" (41F/39B) Song Andy sang to Otis in the cell.

"JOHN JACOB JINGLEHEIMER SCHMITT" (127F/126B) The song Andy, Barney, Gomer, and the eleven boys sang around the campfire when they went "back to nature."

BILLY JOHNSON (51F/B) Boy who won first place in the fifty yard dash at the Boy's Day competition.

BONNIE JOHNSON (176F/B) She went to the class reunion. Barney remarked that she had "got hefty."

CHARLIE JOHNSON (231F/230B) The man who bought Andy's short-lived investment, the Laundercoin.

CLARA JOHNSON (33F/34B) (43F/B) (58F/B) (75F/B) (120F/119B) Bee's lady friend, played by Hope Summers, who, in later episodes, became Clara Edwards. In 33F/34B, Barney tried to sell her a vacuum cleaner. In 43F/B, it's said that she'd won the pickle competition at the county fair for eleven years in a row. In 58F/B, Clara encouraged Bee to date Fred Goss. She convinced Bee that she was in Andy's way, hampering his personal life. In 120F/119B, Clara convinced Bee to buy "bargain" meat at Diamond Jim's.

CLIFFORD JOHNSON (229F/228B) High school boy who played lead guitar in Opie's band, "The Sound Committee."

EARL JOHNSON (78F/76B) He broke his key off in his car the previous spring. He was never able to get it out.

FLUFFY JOHNSON (194F/B) Girl from the gas company who had her eye on Orville Portnoy, the night man at the bakery. She wore false nails and one day she shook her finger at Orville and a nail flew off. Then she cried and put a hanky to her eye and her eyelashes came off. Floyd offered this cautionary tale to Bee as a warning against her wearing a wig.

MISS JOHNSON (16F/20B) (17F/B) (71F/72B) In 16F/20B, Andy greeted her as she came out of the cell after Barney arrested the whole town. In 17F/B, she was mentioned as Opie's teacher. In 71F/72B, Opie brought Andy a message from Miss Johnson.

MR. JOHNSON (43F/B) Clara Johnson's late husband. He loved her award-winning pickles.

MRS. JOHNSON (72F/71B) Woman Andy greeted on Main Street.

OFFICER JOHNSON (30F/B) Eddie Brooks escaped from him. Johnson was a state police officer.

PETE JOHNSON (7F/5B) Andy told him he had "the dangest longest eyelashes" in order to put him on Ellie Walker's trail. Andy did it because he thought Ellie was after him.

ROSAMAE JOHNSON (216F/B) "Colonel Tim's Talent Time" amateur show launched her career.

WENDELL JOHNSON (72F/71B) Mrs. Johnson's (of 72F/71B) son.

THE JOHNSON MINE (32F/B) Abandoned mine on the outskirts of Mayberry. Opie almost got into trouble there when he went wandering after Aunt Bee forbade him to go to the courthouse after school, thinking the jail was a bad influence on him.

THE JOHNSON PLACE (145F/B) House Andy got called to because of a wild drunken party there. Otis was a participant.

JOHNSON'S SPORTING GOODS (171F/172B) Counterfeit bills turned up here in this episode.

MR. JOHNSTON (191F/192B) Emcee at the barbershop quartet competition.

JOKES FOR ALL OCCASIONS (216F/B) Book by the author Pepe that Howard Sprague bought to help him with his comedy routine.

CHESTER JONES (16F/20B) Jud Fletcher hollered at Chester. Barney arrested Jud for disturbing the peace.

GEORGE JONES (205F/B) Stranger who came to Mayberry to find investors for his project; he claimed he had a map that showed the location of the Ross Treasure. Howard, Goober, Helen, and Bee all invested $100 each—against Andy's advice. Later, Andy gave in and also invested. It turned out that Jones *was* a con man; he fled Mayberry with everyone's money. He was later caught in Florida.

MIKE JONES (241F/249B) (248F/247B) Sam's son. In 241F/249B, Mike played checkers with Papa Vincente. In 248F/247B, he was being harassed by the bully, Edgar Watson. Opie stepped in and helped Mike, causing Mike to develop a sort of "hero worship" for Opie.

MRS. JONES (139F/B) She loved babies and lived near Andy. Aunt Bee brought Andelina Wash, Briscoe Darling's granddaughter, over for Mrs. Jones to see.

SAM JONES (247F/246B) Gentleman farmer who sort of took over Andy's place in Mayberry at the end of the series. Sam ran for—and won—the position of head of city council. He ran at the suggestion of Howard Sprague, and at the urging of Andy and others.

LOUIS JORDAN (186F/187B) Man Andy suggested as a replacement for Goober at the filling station. Louis was supposed to go fishing with Goober, though, and so couldn't fill in for him at work.

JUANITA (28F/B) (35F/B) (36F/37B) (47F/B) (51F/B) (52F/B) (67F/65B) (102F/B) (249F/248B) One of Barney's periodic girlfriends. In 28F/B, her last name was given, Beazley. In this episode, she worked at the Junction Cafe, and its phone number was 142R. In 35F/B, Barney told Elizabeth Crowley that Juanita was another girl he dated. In 47F/B, Barney mentioned that he wanted to play two-handed post office with Juanita. In 51F/B, Barney took her to Mt. Pilot for Chinese food. They had the family dinner for one, and the bill was $2.75. In 52F/B, Barney sang the song "Juanita," when thinking of his waitress friend. In 67F/65B, Barney called her. In 102F/B, Juanita guessed that a rocket was coming through Mayberry when Barney called her to "not tell her" about the gold shipment coming through town. In 249F/248B, Goober was dating her. Juanita was going to Myer's Lake every night with Harold Fawcett to "discuss business," or so Goober thought.

"JUANITA'S POEM" (85F/B) The following poem was composed by Barney Fife and recited to Juanita:

> Juanita, lovely dear Juanit
> From your head down to your feet
> There's nothing half so sweet as
> Juanita, Juanita
> Lovely dear Juanit
> Oh, there are things of wonder

Of which men like to sing
There are pretty sunsets
And birds upon the wing
But of the joys of nature
None truly can compare with
Juanita, Juanita
She of beauty beyond compare
Juanita, Juanita
Lovely, dear Juanit

JUBELL (72F/71B) He wanted a haircut.

JUD (42F/B) (76F/78B) (109F/108B) (137F/B) (142F/141B) (192F/191B) In 42F/B, Jud left the barbershop to go tell everyone that Andy and Barney were going to a meeting of the Esquire Club. In 76F/78B, Jud teased Barney into ticketing the governor's car when it was parked in front of the Post Office. In 109F/108B, Jud, along with Mr. Latham, regaled a crowd with the story of how Barney pulled a gun on Mr. Meldrim, the banker. Also in that episode, Andy scolded Jud that it could have been him trapped in the Old Mine Cave collapse. In 137F/B, Jud was Deputy #2, deputized by Barney. In 142F/141B, Jud teased Andy about marrying Helen. In 192F/191B, Jud was a member of the Regal Order of the Golden Door to Good Fellowship, the Mayberry men's lodge.

JUDGEMENT DAY (3F/B) Bobby Fleet said he wanted to be out of the Diner by Judgement Day.

MR. JUDSON (185F/B) Helen wanted to fix up Mrs. Sprague with Mr. Judson.

"THE JUG" (11F/B) The Mayberry jail, according to Andy.

JUGHEAD PETERS AND HIS ARISTOCRATS (216F/B) "Colonel Tim's Talent Time" amateur show launched their career.

JUNCTION CAFE (28F/B) Popular truck stop. Juanita Beazley worked there. Its phone number was 142R.

JUNE (35F/B) Clarence Folk, the attorney, started umpiring ballgames every June.

JUNE 23, 1952 (110F/109B) The Saturday that the queen of the state Apricot Festival came to Mayberry. (In the real world, that date was a Monday.) Andy escorted her around town.

JUNIOR COLLEGE (36F/37B) School in Savannah that Melissa Stevens claimed she attended.

JUNIPER ROAD (187F/186B) About one-and-a-half miles from the lake, Willard Foster swerved on Juniper Road to avoid hitting a cow. He ditched his car and Goober had to tow him in.

JUSTICE OF THE PEACE (4F/6B) Andy let Barney act as justice to rule on a parking citation the deputy wrote the sheriff. Barney's ruling: Not guilty.

K

KANSAS (168F/B) (243F/242B) In 168F/B, it was mentioned that Darlene Mason grew up in Kansas, near White Water Creek. In 243F/242B, it was said that Helen went to grammar school in Kansas. She was state spelling bee champion in eighth grade.

"THE KANSAS CITY CHRONICLE" (244F/243B) The newspaper that ran the original photo of Helen Crump being arrested.

"KATZENJAMMER KIDS" (67F/65B) During a teasing session, an irate Barney told Andy that if he were twins he could be the Katzenjammer Kids.

MELINDA KEEFER (37F/40B) One of Barney's blind dates for Andy. She was from Detroit, she had fat knees, and she talked a lot.

"THE KEEPER OF THE DOOR" (192F/191B) Goober's job at the Regal Order of the Golden Door to Good Fellowship. The secret knock was two long knocks and three short knocks. The password was "Geronimo."

"THE KEEPER OF THE FLAME" (46F/B) Opie's job in his club, "The Wildcats." He had to bring the sacred candle to each meeting.

KEEPER OF THE FLAME 46th episode filmed and broadcast. Original broadcast date was January 8, 1962. It was written by Jack Elinson and Charles Stewart, and directed by Bob Sweeney. Regulars included Andy Griffith, Don Knotts, Ronny Howard, and Frances Bavier. Guests included Everett Sloane as Jubell Foster, Grace Lenard, Robert Gallagher, Terry Dickinson, Flip Mark, and Mark Rodney.

"THE KEEPER OF THE FLASHLIGHT" (46F/B) Andy's suggestion for a title change for Opie's role in his club, "The Wildcats," after they retired the "sacred" candle.

KELLY (191F/192B) A hobo. Kelly told Jeff Nelson, the escaped prisoner, that Andy always treated prisoners with respect. Jeff then went back and helped Andy win the barbershop quartet competition.

MRS. KELSEY (78F/76B) She had to go to Mt. Pilot. She gave Andy and Barney the job of taking in her laundry. It wasn't said if she was related to Old Man Kelsey.

OLD MAN KELSEY (133F/131B) Ernest T. Bass said the United States was bounded by Old Man Kelsey's woods, creek, and ocean.

"KEROSENE CUCUMBERS" (43F/B) The name Barney assigned to Aunt Bee's homemade pickles.

KESTER (31F/B) Member of the Mayberry Drum and Bugle Corp who quit the band because the other members wouldn't practice at his house.

HARVEY KESTER (179F/B) Mayberry's last famous person before Clarence Earp came to town. Harvey repaired Gloria Swanson's radio sets.

KETCHUP AND MUSTARD (23F/B) Andy used ketchup and mustard to dirty some dishes so Aunt Bee wouldn't feel unneeded when she went away for a while.

CHARLES KEYES (223F/226B) The first witness at the trial of Marvin Jenkins. He saw Jenkins leaving Brice's Department Store at 9:30 P.M. carrying a TV set.

KG62114 (187F/186B) Willard Foster's car phone number.

KIEGELHEIMER'S (212F/208B) The clothing store where Barney rented the double-breasted tuxedo he wore to the premiere of Teena Andrews' movie in Mayberry.

TILLY KINCAID (200F/197B) (203F/201B) Lady friend of Bee's and Clara's. Also, a snoop and gossip. In 200F/197B, it was mentioned that at the previous week's garden club meeting, Tilly gave a well-received review of *Roses Are The Backbone Of Your Garden*, by Mabel J. Mosley. The thrust of the book was "spare the insecticide, but do not spare the fertilizer." In 203F/201B, she was involved in the Mayberry Garden Club flower show.

"KING ARTHUR" (32F/B) Story Andy read to Opie in the courthouse after school.

THE KING ARTHUR PAGEANT (233F/231B) Howard wanted to go to the pageant and then to the Blue Rock Caverns in Morgantown on his and Millie's honeymoon.

THE KING OF ENGLAND (124F/123B) Barney figured Malcolm Merriweather must have cooked for the king because of how good his Cornish pastry tasted.

JEFF KINGSLEY (224F/221B) Jeff was mentioned as a possible bowling substitute for Lou Jenkins. Jeff was ruled out, though, because he had the flu.

RALPH KINGSLEY (171F/172B) One of the counterfeiters who hired Aunt Bee. Ralph interviewed Violet Rose Schumaker for the job. Ralph's partner was Arnold Finch.

THE KIT KAT CLUB (123F/122B) The club where Daphne wanted Andy and Barney to take them ("the fun girls") for a drink.

"KITTEN ON THE KEYS" (36F/37B) The song Barney offered to play for Melissa Stevens and her "Daddy" on the harmonica.

ALFRED KITTERLY (176F/B) He planned on attending the Class of '48 Mayberry Union High reunion. Andy remembered that he drove an Essex with "Hey Toots" on the side, and that once he blew up the chemistry class.

KIWANIS CLUB MEETING HALL (240F/B) Locale in Mayberry suggested—and ruled out—as a possible site for the US/USSR summit meeting eventually held at Andy's house.

KL-5-7486 (242F/241B) Roy Swanson's phone number.

KLEIN'S COFFEE SHOP (139F/B) Restaurant to which Mr. Winslow took his daughter, Halcyon, with the intention of arranging a relationship with Barney.

"KLEP, KLEP" (127F/126B) The sound the brush made on the side of the pestle when Floyd made hot lather. He always loved that sound and that was one of the reasons he didn't like automatic lather machines.

"KLEPTOMINERAC" (53F/B) The way Barney pronounced kleptomaniac.

"A KNUCKLE SANDWICH" (34F/33B) Sheldon the Bully threatened Opie with a knuckle sandwich if he didn't give him his milk money nickel.

JED KOONTZ (180F/B) The car Aunt Bee bought from Goober for $295 once belonged to Jed. Jed broke in the seats nicely; he weighed over 290 pounds. It wasn't said if Jed was related to Myra.

MYRA KOONTZ (117F/116B) Mayberry woman who worked at the lingerie shop. The story that was going around town about her had something to do with a guy from Chattanooga.

KOREA (29F/B) Sam Becker served his army stint in Korea. During his tour, he backed into a hen house and got spurred by a rooster.

KP (107F/127B) Gomer got twenty-eight weeks of KP from Sgt. Carter for, essentially, being Gomer: four weeks for being late, and six weeks for talking, and then later eight weeks for singing under a bucket, and ten more weeks for talking to Andy through the barrack's window.

ED KRUMPACHER (148F/B) Friend of Andy's who wanted to get Andy in an executive training program for a big industrial company. Ed was from St. Paul, Minnesota.

EVA KRYGER (187F/186B) Makeup woman on the Foster Furniture Polish commercial.

KS-321 (95F/B) License plate number of a car parked behind the courthouse.

WILLIS KUNDIFF (199F/196B) Bee told Goober about an accident Willis had that was similar to Goober's (they were both hit from behind). As of 199F/196B, Willis was still in traction at Mt. Pilot Hospital. Andy explained to Goober later that Willis was ninety-one years old.

KURRITUCK (62F/B) The town where Barney's cousin, Virgil, changed buses.

L

L73218 (112F/111B) The license plate number of the second truck Barney stopped at Checkpoint Chickie. He issued the driver a speed warning.

DORIS LACY (144F/B) Woman Bee thought called her. It wasn't Doris, though, it was Don Yelton.

LADIES AUXILIARY (28F/B) (162F/164B) Mayberry women's club. In 28F/B, it was stated that Bee had held a successful rummage sale for the Auxiliary and raised enough money to buy a PA for the school. In 162F/164B, they had run a charity bazaar for eighteen years when Warren came to town and arrested the ladies for gambling. He cited Article 156, Section 16. Warren deputized Gomer to arrest all the ladies, including Aunt Bee.

LADIES AUXILIARY BAZAAR (162F/164B) Yearly charity event. Bingo was the main draw and in 162F/164B, Warren felt that the ladies violated Mayberry gambling laws. He arrested them all, including Aunt Bee.

LADIES HISTORICAL SOCIETY OF SUMMITVILLE (216F/B) Organization that asked Clara Edwards to address one of their meetings after they heard Howard Sprague's jokes about her family on "Colonel Tim's Talent Time Show."

LADIES LEAGUE MUSICALE (83F/B) The musical event in which Barney wanted to sing. He lost out to Rafe Hollister.

"LADY BEAUTIFUL" (243F/242B) Magazine read by a lady under a dryer in the beauty parlor.

"LADY MAYBERRY" (138F/B) The central character in the Mayberry centennial pageant. For years, it had been played—very nicely—by Clara Edwards. In 138F/B, however, Clara had to be out of town during the pageant, so Bee tried out for the role. She got it as a last resort and was terrible. Clara returned before the show and was thrilled that Bee had the part, but when Clara recited the beautiful opening speech, Bee realized that Clara was definitely better in the part and relinquished the role to her. The role was renowned for that opening speech, which began: "Eventide. The gentle rustling of the leaves, the birds seeking out their nest. Oh, my happy valley! England, you're so far away."

THE LADY'S CLUB (5F/8B) Annabelle Silby belonged to the club.

"LADYBUG" (60F/B) The name of the horse that did very well at Hialeah for Bill Medwin, the bookie barber.

LADYFINGER (222F/225B) Millie Hutchinson offered a ladyfinger in lieu of a cream bun. She worked in Boysinger's Bakery.

LAKE CHARLES (129F/130B) Hometown of Ollie and Nora (Bee's sister and brother-in-law), and Nora's widow friend, Racine Tyler.

LAKE LOON (127F/126B) Web-footed, red-crested lake loon. Andy invented the bird and then imitated it in order to lead Barney back to camp without the deputy knowing he was being helped.

"LAKE PATROL" (110F/109B) Andy drove down to Myer's Lake to make sure all the lake cottages were boarded up.

MYRA LAMBERT (153F/B) Schoolmate of Opie's. She played a raindrop in the school play. Her appearance was duly noted in Opie's paper, "The Mayberry Sun."

LAMPS AND SHADES (222F/225B) Main Street business next to Myers' Real Estate Company.

LANCELOT (32F/B) Andy explained to Opie that Lancelot was the honest knight in "King Arthur."

"THE LAND OF RHYTHM AND PLEASURE" (74F/B) The land where Barney promised to take Big Maude Tyler, while dancing with her.

EDNA LARCH (166F/B) Edna asked Andy to call her second cousin in Colorado when the Taylors got to Hollywood. It wasn't said if Edna was related to Emma Larch, but in all likelihood Edna was Emma's mother.

EMMA LARCH (152F/B) She and Robert Gribbel decided to get married even though eleven years before he had written "Bobby Gribbel hates Emma Larch" in the cement outside Floyd's Barbershop. Bobby had gone with Emma ever since he broke off with Andrew Beazley's daughter.

MRS. LARCH (186F/187B) (194F/B) (231F/230B) In 186F/187B, she returned a blanket to Weaver's and bought two other things. Goober made a mess of the transaction while working for Weaver's, after Flora took his job at the filling station. In 194F/B, Mrs. Larch was at Clara's reception for Reverend Leighton. In 231F/230B, Andy gave her a ticket. She got mad because she was one of his Laundercoin customers and expected better treatment.

LARCHMONT COUNTY (240F/B) Locale suggested and ruled out as a possible site for the US/USSR summit meeting. The meeting was eventually held in Mayberry.

MRS. LARKES (117F/116B) Woman who discovered Barney hiding in the dresses in Weaver's Department Store. Barney was trying to crack Weaver's shoplifting problem.

LARRY (204F/202B) One of the two crooks who robbed a Mt. Pilot bank of $6,000. He and Fred hid out in the Carson shack.

JOE LARSON (10F/12B) Mayberry boy who was in the Army with Ed Sawyer, and who exposed Ed to the ways and people of Mayberry through the "Mayberry Gazette." Ed then adopted Mayberry as his own hometown, and came to Mayberry as the "stranger in town."

"LATE SHOW SAT. NIGHT" (4F/6B) Sign on the marquee of the Mayberry Theater. Later, the theater became known as the Grand.

MR. LATHAM (109F/108B) Mayberry man who, along with Jud, regaled a crowd with the story of how

Barney pulled a gun on Mr. Meldrim, the banker, as he opened his own bank.

LONNIE LATTIMER (168F/B) The columnist who wrote the "Longtitudes & Latitudes" travel column in the "Mayberry Gazette."

"LAUGH-A-MINUTE TAYLOR" (83F/B) The name Barney called Andy after Andy joked that flies would buzz around Barney's mouth because of all the honey and water the deputy used for his singing voice.

"THE LAUGHING CAVALIER" (211F/207B) Painting on the wall of Barney's room in Ma Parker's boarding house.

LAUNDERCOIN, INC. (231F/230B) The company in which Andy invested. He opened one of their laundromats on Main Street. There were already two in Mt. Pilot.

LAVINIA (92F/B) One of the potential "wives for Andy" that Barney sent over to Andy's house.

"LAW AND ORDER" (150F/B) The magazine that ran the article about Andy called "Sheriff Without A Gun." It began, "Even though Sheriff Andy Taylor doesn't carry a gun, Mayberry has one of the lowest crime rates in the country. And working with Sheriff Taylor is his most capable deputy, Barney Fice [sic]."

"LAW OFFICER'S MANUAL" (33F/34B) Bob Rogers found a system in the manual to reorganize Barney's bulletin board.

"LAW-ABIDING GOD-FEARING CITIZENS" (41F/39B) The Mayberry citizens, as described by by Andy.

LAWMAN BARNEY 73rd episode filmed and 70th episode broadcast. Original broadcast date was November 12, 1962. It was written and directed by Aaron Ruben. Regulars included Andy Griffith and Don Knotts. Guests included Orville Sherman, Norman Leavitt, Bob McQuain, and Allan Melvin as Neil.

"LAWN, TRASH, GARAGE, ASHES" (97F/101B) Opie's regular chores. He wrote them on his wrist so he wouldn't forget.

"ANDREW PAUL LAWSON" (71F/72B) The name Andy used when he posed as Floyd's son to convince Madeline Grayson that Floyd was a rich widower. The "Paul" came from Opie calling Andy "Paw" in front of Grayson.

BESSIE LAWSON (188F/B) The Mayberry cow mistakenly killed by an Indian in May 1762, an incident which sparked the Battle of Mayberry.

COLONEL CALEB "STONEWALL" LAWSON (188F/B) Ancestor of Floyd's, and a "hero" of the Battle of Mayberry.

DANIEL LAWSON (208F/212B) Ancestor of Floyd Lawson and Mayberry's first Indian agent. He started a trading post that grew to the township of Mayberry with a population of 1,800. Floyd wanted a statue of him erected in the town square instead of the one of Seth Taylor. He felt the $1,200 would be better spent on Lawson than Taylor.

FLOYD LAWSON Floyd Lawson was another of Mayberry's "children." He found wonderment in the simplest of day-to-day happenings. He was so naive, he thought that Bill Medwin, the bookie barber, was a nice addition to his business. He was always a gentleman, and the few times he did get angry he would sputter and pout like a spoiled prince. Everyone loved—and protected—Floyd. When Floyd died, part of the gentleness of Mayberry was lost forever. Floyd Lawson was one of Mayberry's treasures. (See additional entries beginning with the words "FLOYD" or "FLOYD'S")

MELBA LAWSON (29F/B) Floyd's wife. She had a walking stick that she used to prop open the cellar door when she brought up the preserves.

NORMAN LAWSON (15F/B) (49F/B) Floyd's son. In 15F/B, he played "Saximinia" for Wilbur Finch during what everyone thought was an audition. In 49F/B, he dropped a fly ball during a softball game after Henry Bennett touched it. Barney offered this as proof that Henry was, indeed, a jinx.

"LAWSON PICTURES, INC." (71F/72B) The nonexistent company Floyd used as a mailing name to attract rich widows.

"A LAWYER" (161F/160B) Floyd thought that Opie might grow up to be a lawyer.

"A LAWYER LETTER" (122F/121B) The letter Barney sent to the Miracle Salve Company from "Bernard P. Fife. Attorney at Law" as a response to their "blacklist" scare letter to Trey Bowden. Trey had sent back all the salve he couldn't sell.

JOE LAYTON (41F/39B) The crook who came to town with Fred Jenkins. He pretended he was a photographer for Intercontinental News.

"LEANIN' ON THE EVERLASTING ARMS" (117F/116B) Barney alleged that Ben Weaver only waved his arms during the singing of this hymn. He never sang the words, according to Barney.

"LEARN-A-MONTH" (145F/B) Monthly magazine Barney subscribed to; every month there was a new topic. Subjects included medicine, science, insect life, etc. In 145F/B, the month's topic was "Odd Facts Known By Few." The previous month, it had been "Psychology." The magazine sold for a quarter.

CHARLIE LEE (209F/210B) Head chef at the defunct Spareribs Tavern. He planned on going back to Pittsburgh and getting a job at Wong Soo's Canton Palace. He and Bee became partners, however, and opened Aunt Bee's Canton Palace in the Tavern's location. She invested $400 and then sold her share to Charlie's nephew, Jack.

ROBERT E. LEE (39F/36B) Frank Myers' great-great-grandfather posed with Lee.

LEFT SIDEBURN (10F/12B) Barney's. According to the deputy, Floyd always cut it too short.

A LEG OF LAMB (12F/10B) (45F/B) (92F/B) In 12F/10B, Otis hit his mother-in-law with a leg of lamb. In 45F/B, Jeff Pruitt ate a whole leg of lamb in Andy's kitchen. He called it a "light" dinner. In 92F/B, it was disclosed that leg of lamb was Andy's favorite dish.

THE LEGEND OF BARNEY FIFE 177th episode filmed and broadcast. Original broadcast date was January 17, 1966. It was written by Harvey Bullock, and directed by Alan Rafkin. Regulars included Andy Griffith, George Lindsey, Frances Bavier, and Howard McNear. Guests included Don Knotts as Barney Fife, Jack Burns as Warren Ferguson, Frank Cady as Farley Upchurch, Harry Holcomb as Warden Hix, and Ted White as Avery Noonan.

"THE LEGEND OF SLEEPY HOLLOW" (92F/B) The story Andy was reading (or trying to read) to

Opie when Barney sent over all the potential "wives for Andy."

MRS. LEGRANDE (231F/230B) One of Andy's Laundercoin customers. She asked him if her dress would shrink.

REVEREND LEIGHTON (194F/B) Single minister who came to Mayberry for a two-week stay. During his stay, Bee got talked into wearing a blonde wig by Bernice, the hairdresser. She wore it once to a reception for the Reverend at Clara's and then didn't know what to do; the Reverend had preached "Be Yourself" his first Sunday in town. Eventually, she told him about the wig and he wasn't the least bit upset. Leighton was offered a parish in Mt. Pilot but turned it down. Clara had eyes for the Reverend.

LEMON AND LIME SODA (246F/245B) One of the drinks Howard Sprague offered at his "swinging" party.

LEMON PIE (109F/108B) Andy guessed that Helen Crump made a lemon pie to bring to the town picnic.

LEMONADE STAND (54F/B) Opie's business endeavor in Art Crowley's vacant lot. He sold the lemonade for two cents a cup.

LENNY (122F/121B) One of the two operators of the Miracle Salve Company. He worked with an unnamed manager.

LEON (78F/76B) (79F/77B) (102F/B) (117F/116B) In all these episodes, Leon offered his peanut butter and jelly sandwich to either Andy or Barney.

BUZZY LEONARD (146F/B) Andy and Barney found a piece of Buzzy's car when searching for the "lucky letter" in the dump.

THE LEONARD BOY (161F/160B) He got mad at his brother, stole his car, drove it to the marsh, and set it on fire. It wasn't said if the Leonard boy was related to Buzzy Leonard. (See the entry ANDY'S BAD DAY)

HENRY LEONETTI (84F/B) Henry "Shopping Bag" Leonetti was wanted for grand larceny. He had a $4,000 reward on his head. Barney put up his wanted poster in the courthouse.

"LERGIC" (125F/124B) Opie thought that Aunt Bee had one because she was crying. She was crying because Barney told her that Andy and Helen were getting married.

LES (155F/B) Man from the highway department who called Andy to tell him to expand the 50 mph zone as far as Fancy Gap.

BERNARD LESH (90F/B) The probably nonexistent late husband of Myrt Lesh. She claimed she was selling her car to pay off his funeral expenses: she owed $140 to Pilot Pines Funeral Parlor. Barney was touched that his name was also Bernard.

MYRT LESH (90F/B) "Hubcaps Lesh." Old lady who ran a used car racket and sold Barney a 1954 Ford sedan that broke down on its first time out. (See the entry FORD SEDAN)

"LET NO HORSE GO THIRSTY" (88F/B) The legend on the David Mendlebright Memorial Horse Trough in the center of Mayberry.

LETTUCE (135F/B) (148F/B) (186F/187B) (203F/201B) 9¢.

DOUGLAS LEWIS (124F/123B) (215F/B) Young boy whose family moved to Raleigh, leaving Clara Edwards with an open two hours to give Opie piano lessons.

ERNIE LEWIS (242F/241B) Classmate of Goober's and Roy Swanson's at automobile trade school. He ate hot dogs every day. According to Roy, Ernie never made it; he owned a little gas station that pumped only 200 gallons of gas a day. (Goober pumped 80 to 90 gallons of gas a day.)

MRS. LEWIS (186F/187B) She called Andy to complain about the kids making noise. Andy suggested she take her nap at five thirty; the kid's would all be home by then.

THE LEWISES (124F/123B) (215F/B) Mayberry family who had Opie over for Sunday dinner. That left only Andy and Barney to feed, but Aunt Bee took to her bed because she said she was sick. It was really her resentment over Malcolm Merriweather's taking over of her household. In 215F/B, the Lewises were moving to Raleigh, so Clara Edwards wouldn't be teaching Douglas piano anymore. This gave her an open two hours for Opie.

LICORICE SEEDS (14F/B) Opie traded his cap pistol to Tommy Farrell for the seeds. Opie planned on trading them to Jerry Parker for his skates until Andy vetoed the idea.

LIEUTENANT (95F/B) The police officer who dropped off the prisoners at the Mayberry jail.

"LIEUTENANT" (114F/113B) The "prisoner of love" wondered if that was the title by which she should call Barney.

"LIFESAVER MAN" (119F/118B) The name Gomer called Andy after the sheriff "saved" Gomer when some rags started smoldering in Wally's filling station.

LIFFER'S (135F/B) Mt. Pilot department store. They had a storewide sale. Barney drove Thelma Lou there to pick up some toiletries.

LIGHTER (223F/226B) Andy found a lighter in Brice's Department Store. The lighter belonged to the real burglar, Granger. This clue allowed Andy to solve the break-in and exonerate Marvin Jenkins, who was suspected of the crime. Aunt Bee had somehow known all along that Jenkins was innocent.

LILLIAN (125F/124B) Barney didn't want Lillian to bring her meatballs to Andy and Helen's "engagement party" because he said they were one percent meat, ninety-nine percent breadcrumbs. She brought them anyway. At the Naylen's anniversary party, they found the meatballs in potted plants, between magazine covers, and in the fireplace. James Masefield went home with three in his mackinaw pocket. Barney wanted Lillian to bring rolls.

BILL LINDSAY (196F/203B) Adult education instructor. Andy, Helen, Goober, Howard, and Floyd took his history course at night.

JIM LINDSEY (3F/B) (31F/B) In 3F/B, Jim was a Mayberry boy with a talent for guitar playing who Andy had to repeatedly arrest for disturbing the peace. Orville Monroe, in particular, objected to Jim playing the guitar in front of his funeral parlor. When Bobby Fleet came to town, Andy finagled Jim a job with Bobby's Band with a Beat. The job went to Jim's head, though, and Bobby fired him, forcing Jim to go back to Mayberry in disgrace in 31F/B, even though he wouldn't admit to the townsfolk what had happened. Andy found out the truth, however, and came through for Jim again, getting him his job back with Bobby. Jim had a hit record sometime between 3F/B and 31F/B, "Rock and Roll Rosie from Raleigh."

LINDY LOU (60F/B) A horse that Sarah, the operator, thought was a girl after she overheard Bill Medwin, the bookie barber, betting horses on the phone.

"LINE UP FOR LOOT" (219F/B) Promotion run by Early Gilly at his gas station. The contest took business away from Goober, which spurred him to start his own contest, "Grab Bag for Cash."

THE LINGERIE SHOP (117F/116B) Main Street business where Myra Koontz worked.

MR. LINKE (247F/246B) Emmett made a campaign call on a Mr. Linke during his campaign for head of city council. (Andy Griffith's personal manager and the executive producer of "The Andy Griffith Show" was Richard O. Linke.)

BARBARA SUE LINSEY (20F/16B) Young woman who delivered peat moss to Andy's house after it was announced that the sheriff would be the judge of the Founder's Day beauty pageant. It wasn't said if Barbara Sue was related to Clara. She delivered the peat moss carrying a parasol. She was #5 in the pageant.

CLARA LINSEY (15F/B) One of the women who gossiped in the drugstore about the phony blonde streaks in Millie Parsons' hair. The other women there were Aunt Bee and Emma Brand. The ladies also discussed Rose Blake's trip to Raleigh to buy a new set of teeth.

LIQUOR CONTROL BOARD OF NEBRASKA (227F/222B) Emmett was a friend of its chairman.

LITERARY GUILD (200F/197B) Clara set up a speaking engagement for Bee with the guild during Aunt Bee's campaign for city council. She arranged for Lillian Hartzell to play the sax; Lillian's version of "Flight of the Bumblebee" really livened up a crowd.

"LITTLE BUDDY" (45F/B) The name Jeff Pruitt called Barney. Jeff was played by Alan Hale, who later went on to "Gilligan's Island" where he played the Skipper, calling Gilligan his "little buddy."

"LITTLE ORPHAN ANNIE" (100F/99B) Comic strip Andy read to Opie before they went to church.

"LITTLE PERSUADER" (150F/B) The name Barney called his gun.

"THE LITTLE PRINCESS" (138F/B) Church play in which Bee, as a young girl, played the part of Alice. She even had her name in the church bulletin, "News From The Altar." Reverend Dargood was in charge of the production.

"THE LIVES OF SHEP AND RALPH" (97F/101B) TV show. Andy, Opie, Bee, and Gomer watched it in Andy's living room the night Gomer became their "house guest."

LIVING ROOM GROUP (117F/116B) Furniture set sold by Weaver's Department Store for $299.

LIZARD (125F/124B) Another of Opie's unseen pets. It was unnamed and lived in a lizard house in the backyard.

THE LOADED GOAT 81st episode filmed and broadcast. Original broadcast date was January 28, 1963. It was written by Harvey Bullock, and directed by Bob Sweeney. Regulars included Andy Griffith, Don Knotts, Ronny Howard, and Hal Smith as Otis. Guests included Bing Russell, Burt Mustin, and Parley Baer as Mayor Stoner.

MR. LOCKRIDGE (244F/243B) Head of the Mayberry school board. He presided over the hearing that threatened to fire Helen Crump from her teaching job due to her past involvement with hoodlums. (See entries HARRY BROWN and AUGUST 3 & 4, 1959)

THE LODGE (42F/B) (246F/245B) In 42F/B, the lodge met on Friday nights. In 246F/245B, Howard had met Shirley there the previous fall. It wasn't told if this "lodge" was The Regal Order of the Golden Door to Good Fellowship.

THE LODGE 192nd episode filmed and 191st episode broadcast. Original broadcast date was September 19, 1966. It was written by Jim Parker and Arnold Margolin, and directed by Lee Phillips. Regulars included Andy Griffith, Jack Dodson, Frances Bavier, Howard McNear, Ronny Howard, and George Lindsey. Guests included Mabel Albertson as Mrs. Sprague, George Cisar as Cyrus Tankersley, Burt Mustin as Jud, Sam Edwards as Tom Bedlow, and Ralph Rose as Clete.

LOITERING (40F/38B) Violation #63. Barney arrested Dave the Hobo on this violation.

"LOITERING, ILLEGAL ASSEMBLY, AND TAMPERING WITH OFFICIAL EQUIPMENT" (112F/111B) Violations. Barney wanted to charge the wiseguys who disconnected his sidecar from his motorcycle with these crimes.

LONAS HILL AND DAVISON AT-TORNEYS (122F/121B) Mt. Pilot law firm in room 108 on the same floor and in the same building as the Miracle Salve Company.

"THE LONE RANGER" (73F/70B) The name Neil and Matt derogatorily called Barney.

"THE LONE RANGER'S HORSE SILVER" (73F/70B) The name Neil and Matt derogatorily called Barney.

"LONGITIUDES & LATITUDES" (168F/B) Travel column in the "Mayberry Gazette" written by Lonnie Lattimer. When Andy, Bee, and Opie went to Hollywood to see the filming of "Sheriff Without A Gun," Lonnie ran the following in his column: "That traveling trio, Andy, Opie, and Bee Taylor are still in Hollywood, California, the film capital of the world. The movie being made about Andy, 'Sheriff Without A Gun,'—based on the life of a sheriff in a small community—is going well. Hi there, Mr. Celebrity! Your columnist has learned from reliable sources that the Taylors have made a change in plans. They'll stay in Hollywood, California, another two days. Remember, you read it here first."

LOOK PAW, I'M DANCING 181st episode filmed and broadcast. Original broadcast date was February 14, 1966. It was written by Ben Starr, and directed by Lee Phillips. Regulars included Andy Griffith, Ronny Howard, Aneta Corsaut, Frances Bavier, George Lindsey, and Howard McNear. Guests included Ronda Jeter as Sharon Porter, and Richard Keith as Johnny Paul Jason.

"THE LOOP" (109F/108B) The name Barney assigned to the business district of Mayberry.

LOST AND FOUND 178th episode filmed and broadcast. Original broadcast date was January 24, 1966. It was written by John L. Greene and Paul David, and directed by Alan Rafkin. Regulars included Andy Griffith, Frances Bavier, Ronny Howard, Jack Burns, Hope Summers, and George Lindsey. Guests included Arthur Malet as the Vagrant, and Jack Dodson as Ed Jenkins, the insurance agent. This was Dodson's first appearance on the show.

LOST LOVER'S CAVE (109F/108B) Another name for the Old Mine Caves, so named because at one point two lovers got lost there and were rumored to be spending all of eternity looking for each other. Andy and Helen got trapped there and were "rescued" by Barney.

"LOTSA LUCK TO YOU AND YOURS" (77F/79B) One of the ways Gomer Pyle bid farewell to people, although the only time we actually heard him say it was in his first appearance on the show. This was in the episode called "Man In A Hurry" (77F/79B), and he said it once to Andy, and once to Malcolm "man in a hurry" Tucker. Also, at one point in that episode, Andy said it to Gomer. Gomer seemed to abandon it after this episode, and he didn't use it at all in "Return To Mayberry."

LOU (168F/B) The still photographer for the movie about Andy, "Sheriff Without A Gun." He took the still of Andy and Darlene Mason that ran on the front page of the "Mayberry Gazette."

LOU (192F/191B) A member of the Regal Order of the Golden Door to Good Fellowship, the Mayberry men's lodge.

LOU (202F/199B) Arnold's father. He didn't want to tell Arnold the facts of life. He wanted Andy to tell Opie so Opie could tell Arnold.

LOUISE (65F/67B) Aunt Bee's aunt. In 65F/67B, Bee went to visit Louise for three or four days.

LOUISE (214F/B) Goober's canary. Goober once had to put up a mirror for her because she got lonely.

"LOVE" (146F/B) Dirty magazine Andy found while searching for Barney's "lucky letter" in the Mayberry dump. Barney's name was on the address label. It was the January issue.

"LOVE LIFTED ME" (174F/173B) The hymn Clara Edwards planned to play one Sunday to take advantage of the fact that the song didn't have too many flats. The church organ was on its way out.

LOVER'S LEAP ROCK (97F/101B) (136F/B) In 97F/101B, Gomer told Jason a story about Bertie Blush. The incident involving Bertie took place near the rock. In 136F/B, Andy wanted to know if Barney took Phoebe Gilbert to Lover's Leap.

HAROLD LOVITT (210F/211B) Mayberry citizen who was beat up by the Ferguson girl. That fight was the last incident of bad blood in Mayberry until the Howard Sprague/Floyd Lawson fight over a rent increase in 210F/211B.

"LOW BLOOD SUGAR CONTENT" (123F/122B) (124F/123B) Why Barney had to eat before he got too hungry. If he went hungry too long he would get a headache and then he wouldn't be any good to anybody. In 124F/123B, he told Andy that his mother had the same problem.

LOWELL (180F/B) Man who worked for the Mayberry township. He was cutting branches in front of Andy's house and Bee's car was parked in his way. Even though she wasn't supposed to, she moved the car without a licensed driver next to her. She drove into a tree.

"LOWEST CRIME RATE IN THE U.S." (41F/39B) Fred Jenkins, the FBI man who was really a crook, claimed that Mayberry had the lowest crime rate in the country.

MYRNA LOY (58F/B) Wayne Devereaux had a picture of Myrna in a pocket of a garment he brought in to Fred Goss, the cleaner.

BEN LUCAS (137F/B) Andy delivered Ben his gun permit.

THE LUCK OF NEWTON MONROE 156th episode filmed and broadcast. Original broadcast date was April 12, 1965. It was written by Bill Idelson and Sam Bobrick, and directed by Coby Ruskin. Regulars included Andy Griffith, Don Knotts, George Lindsey, and Howard McNear. Guests included Don Rickles as Newton Monroe.

THE LUCKY LETTER 146th episode filmed and broadcast. Original broadcast date was January 25, 1965. It was written by Richard M. Powell, and directed by Theodore J. Flicker. Regulars included Andy Griffith, Don Knotts, Ronny Howard, Howard McNear, George Lindsey, and Betty Lynn.

"LUCKY PEPPERMINTS" (110F/109B) Pierson's Sweet Shop's free flashlight promotion. Gomer claimed it was fixed. (See entry PIERSON'S SWEET SHOP'S "LUCKY PEPPERMINT PROMOTION")

LUCY BERNETT'S DRY GOODS STORE (218F/B) Andy said there was more excitement at the courthouse than at Lucy's store. He was making the point that excitement was relative, that even if there *was* more excitement at the courthouse than at the dry goods store, he still didn't do the business Marshall Dillon did.

LUKE (145F/B) Otis' cellmate in the Mt. Pilot jail. Luke's mother was a nurse.

LUKEN'S STYLE SHOP (75F/B) Mayberry lady's shop. In its window was the bed jacket Aunt Bee wanted for her birthday.

LUMBAGO (38F/41B) One of Mr. Wheeler's many physical complaints.

LUNCH FOR ANDY (170F/171B) Chicken salad sandwich, sliced tomatoes, pickles, and blueberry muffins. Tommy told Opie what Andy's lunch consisted of after he saw Aunt Bee walking Main Street. Tommy transmitted the info to Opie via his walkie-talkie.

LUNCHES FOR THE TAYLORS (225F/224B) Andy said that normal lunches for the Taylor family were hamburgers, cheese sandwiches, and meatloaf.

LUTHER (97F/101B) (100F/99B) In 97F/101B, his car was running rough so he pulled up in front of Andy's house in the middle of the night to let Gomer, the "house guest," listen to the engine. In 100F/99B, Luther was a saxophonist in the Mayberry Band.

MAC (70F/68B) Luke Jensen's dog. Andy knew Luke was back in Mayberry when he saw Mac rummaging through Early Gilly's trash can.

"MACARONI SURPRISE" (125F/124B) Dish on the Diner menu.

MR. MCBEEVEE (66F/64B) Telephone lineman. He befriended Opie, who described him to Andy as a man who walked around in the treetops, wore a great big shiny silver hat, knew how to make smoke come out of his ears, had twelve extra hands, and jingled when he walked. Andy didn't believe him. Eventually he realized he had to have faith in Opie and it was then, after he decided to take Opie at his word, that he found out that Mr. McBeevee was real.

SHARON MCCALL (132F/128B) Opie's classmate and girlfriend, who had to take a back seat to Opie's temporary infatuation with Helen Crump.

VIOLA MACCONKLER (95F/B) From his perch on the courthouse roof, Gomer saw her sneak by the barn to have some snuff.

MACDONALD'S FLYING SCHOOL (243F/242B) The flying school where Aunt Bee took her flying lessons. It was owned and operated by Mr. MacDonald, and he gave demonstration flights for five dollars.

MCGINNIS (50F/B) He was working south of the state line.

MCGINNISS'S (91F/B) Opie used to go to his place and climb his apple trees.

SUE ANN MCGRATH (173F/174B) Girl who worked at the dime store. Helen suggested her as a date for Warren.

MR. MACGRUDER (188F/B) Opie talked to him about the Battle of Mayberry.

"THE MACHINE" (200F/197B) Floyd's name for the group of businessmen who backed Howard Sprague's bid for city council.

"MACHO" IN MAYBERRY (48F/B) When Ellen Brown, the manicurist, came to Mayberry, Barney said he'd be inclined to treat a girl like her "a little rough." He said he'd "rough her up a little bit." He said, "They expect it." This was an unprecedented lapse in taste by the writers of that episode, Jack Elinson and Charles Stewart.

JED MCINTYRE (134F/B) Man Barney offered as an example of men being able to live without women just fine. He had lived in a shack for twenty-five years, and he was always smiling and, as Andy reminded Barney, talking to himself.

MACKADOO (79F/77B) The name Andy assigned to the Quincys to get Aunt Bee to tell what she knew about them.

DOC MACKENZIE (24F/B) Early Mayberry doctor.

"A MACKEREL SWIMMING DOWN-STREAM" (202F/199B) The analogy Goober suggested Andy use to explain the facts of life to Opie.

JOE MCKNIGHT (10F/12B) Mayberry man who, at the time Ed Sawyer came to town, was 103 years old.

MRS. MACKNIGHT (99F/98B) Andy and Barney discussed her recent big weight loss.

M

OLD MAN MACKNIGHT (239F/238B) Andy's first boss. Andy ran the popcorn machine for him at the theater. His first time on the job he put too much popcorn in the machine and it wouldn't stop popping.

PEGGY MCMILLAN (64F/73B) (65F/67B) (67F/65B) In 64F/73B, Opie got jealous of Peggy when Andy paid a lot of attention to her. Andy gave Opie a talk about a man needing a woman and explained to him that someday he might get married again, and Opie finally understood it was nothing against him. Opie and Peggy then became blood brothers. In 65F/67B, she was the Mayberry nurse who took a shine to Andy when Aunt Bee had to leave town. She helped out cooking and cleaning, much to Andy's chagrin. Andy, with a little needling from Floyd, assumed Peggy wanted to snare him into marrying her. Andy began to avoid her but finally—perhaps mistakenly—realized she had no ulterior motives, and they remained friends. Peggy dissappeared after this season. In 67F/65B, Andy dated Peggy, who Barney called his "rich girlfriend."

THE MACON BUS (62F/B) Barney's cousin, Virgil, was supposed to come into Mayberry on the Macon bus. He ended up walking into town because he missed getting back on the bus when it stopped in Springville.

"MAD DOG" (50F/B) One of Barney's nicknames, according to Barney.

MADAME OLGA'S (230F/229B) Mayberry lady's clothing store. Clara bought a dress there that had been in the window.

MADGE (53F/B) Girlfriend of Sheldon Davis. He talked to her on the phone from Mayberry.

MAGGIE (89F/B) Mayberry woman who did housecleaning as a business. When Aunt Bee left town for a few days, she arranged for Maggie to come in that Tuesday and clean the house for Andy and Opie.

"MAGIC" (40F/38B) The subject of the book Barney was reading at the end of this episode.

MRS. MAGRUDER (78F/76B) She cleaned the Mayberry Security Bank. Barney said he was Mrs. Magruder's cousin when he went undercover dressed as a woman to test the defenses of the bank.

MAHOGANY (5F/8B) Tom Silby's premature coffin was made of mahogany.

MAIN AND GARDEN ROAD (247F/246B) The corner where Goober's filling station was located.

"MAIRZY DOATS" (31F/B) The song Barney offered to play for Bobby Fleet on the harmonica.

MALCOLM AT THE CROSSROADS 164th episode filmed and 162nd episode broadcast. Original broadcast date was September 27, 1965. It was written by Harvey Bullock, and directed by Gary Nelson. Regulars included Andy Griffith, George Lindsey, and Howard McNear. Guests included Bernard Fox as Malcolm Merriweather, Howard Morris as Ernest T. Bass, Dennis Bradshaw as Johnny, and Kenneth Butts as Arnie.

MALCOLM'S RESTAURANT BILL (124F/123B) "17 and 6 pence 3 farthings."

"MALFEASANCE" (148F/B) When Barney ran for sheriff against Andy, he came up with seventy-six documented cases of malfeasance, including: traffic was out of control and jaywalking was rampant; the office was not equipped with tear gas and submachine guns; and Andy carried a shovel and rake in his trunk. Also, Andy didn't carry a gun.

FLORA MALLERBY (182F/183B) (186F/187B) Waitress at the Diner. In 182F/183B, Goober was sweet on Flora but she liked Andy. She came on kind of strong and Andy had to work hard at steering her towards Goober. In 186F/187B, she was "Goober's Replacement" at Wally's when Goober went trout fishing. She did so well, Wally didn't want her to quit. Goober quit Wally's and let Flora keep his job, but then Andy tried to convince Flora that women belonged at home. She bought it. (See entry FLORA)

SHERIFF MALONEY (44F/B) Sheriff of Greendale, North Carolina. He resigned his post, which prompted the Greendale town council to offer the job to Barney.

MAN IN A HURRY 77th episode filmed and 79th episode broadcast. Original broadcast date was January 14, 1963. It was written by Jim Fritzell and Everett Greenbaum, and directed by Bob Sweeney. Regulars included Andy Griffith, Frances Bavier, Don Knotts, Ronny Howard, and Jim Nabors. Guests included Robert Emhardt as Malcolm Tucker, William Keene as the Pastor, and Norman Leavitt as Wally.

THE "MAN IN PRISON" SPEECH (79F/77B) Barney gave this speech ("no more carefree hours") to the boys after Steve Quincy broke a street lamp with an apple core and blamed Opie. It backfired, however, when Barney locked himself in a cell. Andy repeated the speech to Barney through the cell door. Barney got mad and said Andy should be in the funny papers: "Get you a wig and a dress and you're another Emmie Schmaltz."

MAN IN THE MIDDLE 134th episode filmed and broadcast. Original broadcast date was November 2, 1964. It was written by Gus Adrian and David Evans, and directed by Alan Rafkin. Regulars included Andy Griffith, Don Knotts, Betty Lynn, and Aneta Corsaut.

"THE MAN WITH THE GOLDEN ARM" (127F/126B) The ghost story Andy told around the campfire to the eleven boys when they all went "back to nature."

A MAN'S BEST FRIEND 170th episode filmed and 171st episode broadcast. Original broadcast date was November 29, 1965. It was written by Art Baer and Ben Joelson, and directed by Alan Rafkin. Regulars included Andy Griffith, Ronny Howard, George Lindsey, Frances Bavier, and Howard McNear. Guests included Michael Petit as Tommy.

MAN'S PURSE (136F/B) Opie found Parnell Rigsby's purse with fifty dollars in it while walking home from school. It became Opie's when Rigsby didn't appear for it within a week. (Barney recited the appropriate code for Opie: "If the rightful owner does not appear to claim said funds, finder same keeps same.") Rigsby did appear, however, and Andy figured that Opie wasn't going to turn over the money when he found out that Rigsby had been to the courthouse, had told Opie who he was, and Opie hadn't surrendered the money. Turned out that Opie had gone to return everything he'd bought, in order to get the money back to return it to Rigsby. Andy learned another lesson about trusting his son in this episode.

MANHATTAN SHOE COMPANY (15F/B) The company for which Wilbur Finch worked. On the day the Mayberry people "auditioned" for him (thinking he was a talent scout for the "Manhattan Showtime" TV show), he sold sixty-seven pairs of shoes, a company record. His boss was Mr. Simmons.

"MANHATTAN SHOWTIME" (15F/B) TV show. The Mayberry men thought that Wilbur Finch was a talent scout for the show.

THE MANHUNT 2nd episode filmed and broadcast. Original broadcast date was October 10, 1960. It was written by Jack Elinson and Charles Stewart, and directed by Don Weis. Regulars included Andy Griffith, Don Knotts, Ronny Howard, and Hal Smith as Otis. Guests included Cheerio Meredith as Emma Brand, Dick Elliot as Mayor Pike, Ken Lynch, Mike Steen, and Lillian Culver as Barney's mother, Mrs. Fife.

THE MANICURIST 48th episode filmed and broadcast. Original broadcast date was January 22, 1962. It was written by Jack Elinson and Charles Stewart, and directed by Bob Sweeney. Regulars included Andy Griffith, Don Knotts, and Howard McNear. Guests included Barbara Eden as Ellen Brown, the manicurist, and Dick Elliot as Mayor Pike. (See the entry "MACHO" IN MAYBERRY)

MAPLE ROAD (87F/B) Andy's house—number 332—was located on Maple Road in this episode. (See ANDY'S ADDRESS)

MAPLE STREET (137F/B) (153F/B) (161F/160B) (201F/204B) In 137F/B, the little boy, George, got his head stuck in a sewer on Maple Street. In 153F/B, Maple was one of the streets where Opie distributed copies of his paper, "The Mayberry Sun." In 161F/160B, Opie crashed his bike on Maple while riding no-hands to impress Sharon Porter. In 201F/204B, Andy lived at 14 Maple Street (See ANDY'S ADDRESS)

MARACAS (227F/222B) Myrtle brought Emmett, Andy, and Howard maracas from Mexico.

MARCH 15 (106F/B) One of the dates Barney resigned as deputy.

MARCH 17 (171F/172B) One of the dates given as Aunt Bee's birthday.

MARCH 3, 1951 (120F/119B) The date Ed (of Ed's Refrigeration) serviced Aunt Bee's "bargain" freezer.

THE MARCIER (168F/B) Hollywood restaurant where Andy and Darlene Mason ate on their date. The restaurant was Darlene's suggestion. She also suggested the escargot and Caesar salad.

JANE MARCUS (244F/243B) Helen Crump's dinner guest. The dinner caused Helen to run late for her date with Andy.

MARGARET (232F/233B) Elmo's wife.

MARIE (226F/223B) Attorney Lee Drake's maid.

"THE MARINE'S HYMN" (107F/127B) Song sung repeatedly by Gomer Pyle before he left for Camp Wilson. At one point during his induction into the Marines, Sgt. Carter made Gomer sing it with a bucket over his head.

MARION (246F/245B) The girl Howard asked to his swinging party. She turned him down.

MARLIN (243F/242B) Emmett Clark's big moment: he caught a 361-pound marlin in St. Petersburg.

MAROON TWO-DOOR (129F/130B) Ollie and Nora's car. Ollie got gas in Freeport on his way to Andy's. The car took 11.2 gallons and Ollie got fifteen miles to the gallon. The car's license plate number was AY-321.

"MARRIAGE LICENSES, BUILDING PERMITS, DOG LICENSES, SALES TAX PERMITS" (222F/225B) The legal documents Howard Sprague issued in his job as county clerk. There was a sign posted to that effect in his office.

SALLY MARSH (246F/245B) Girl Howard considered asking to his swinging party. Goober told him not to; Goober had already asked her and was turned down.

THE MARSH (161F/160B) It caught fire when the Leonard boy got mad at his brother, stole his car, drove it to the marsh, and set it on fire.

MARSHALL COUNTY (78F/76B) Barney read of a crime wave there: "A recent rash of burglaries in this community has the local sheriff's office greatly concerned. The sheriff attributes most of the robberies to the lack of security on the part of town merchants. Said Sheriff Wilson, 'We would have fewer robberies if folks showed less apathy'."

"MARSHALL DILLON" (73F/B) The name Neil and Matt derogatorily called Barney.

MARTHA (125F/124B) She said she'd bring a ham to Andy and Helen's "engagement" party.

MARTHA (184F/B) Bee's niece from Jacksonville. Her husband was Darryl, their daughter was Evie Joy. Martha called Bee and asked if they could leave Evie Joy with her while they went to Grace's for a wedding. Martha and Grace were sisters, and Andy's second cousins.

AUNT MARTHA (90F/B) Myrt Lesh claimed that the 1954 Ford sedan she wanted to sell had only been driven to her Aunt Martha's.

AUNT MARTHA (178F/B) (231F/230B) In 178F/B, it was stated that the brooch that Aunt Bee "lost" had been given to her by Aunt Martha. In 231F/230B, it was decided that Opie could stay with Aunt Martha if he ended up going to the University of North Carolina at Chapel Hill.

JIM MARTIN (187F/186B) Director for the Foster Furniture Polish commercial.

REVEREND MARTIN (153F/B) Opie ran a blurb in his paper, "The Mayberry Sun," that Andy thought the Reverend's sermons were "dry as dust." The Reverend read it before Andy could catch it and he hog-tied Andy into teaching Sunday school for "a month of Sundays."

MARTIN PHILLIPS COMPANY (184F/B) Company that sold pots and pans door-to-door. Bee made one of their salesmen feed Evie Joy her bottle. She bought things from him to keep him in the house.

MARTIN'S COTTAGES (186F/187B) Fishing area below Hansen's Hill where Goober went trout fishing.

MR. MARTINELLI (118F/117B) Main Street butcher. He swept his meat market out between 9:30 and 11:00 A.M. on Tuesdays and Thursdays. There was no parking in front of his store during those hours.

MARY (16F/20B) Andy greeted her as she came out of the cell after Barney arrested the whole town.

MARY (45F/B) Guest at Thelma Lou's "hen party." She opened the door for Andy, Barney, and Jeff Pruitt.

MARY (55F/B) She, along with Bee and Clara, made eighteen cakes for the church social.

MARY LEE (82F/B) One of Andy's and Barney's classmates at Mayberry Union High, Class of 1945. She served on the 18th Class Reunion Committee.

JAMES MASEFIELD (125F/124B) When he left the Naylen's anniversary party, three of Lillian's inedible meatballs were in his mackinaw pockets.

"THE MASKED SINGER" (116F/115B) (128F/133B) Leonard Blush. He got that name because when he sang he wore a mask to hide a skin condition. (See the entries LEONARD BLUSH and ELEANORA POULTICE)

DARLENE MASON (168F/B) Leading lady of the movie about Andy, "Sheriff Without A Gun." During the filming, she stayed at the Hollywood Marquee hotel. Andy was photographed with Darlene as a publicity move and the picture of the two of them made the front page of the "Mayberry Gazette." The headline read, "Is This Darlene Mason's Next Conquest?" Helen saw the picture, got mad, and Darlene had to call Helen to square things between her and Andy.

FRED MASON (52F/B) Choir member who had to quit the chorus because he worked nights and couldn't make practice.

HERB MASON (137F/B) Man from Hogarth Detectives who offered Andy a job with the firm. The job was in Raleigh and would have involved Andy leaving Mayberry. Barney was aghast: "Leave Mayberry?? Leave Mayberry??"

MRS. MASON (54F/B) (85F/B) Owner of Mason's Drugstore. In 85F/B, she made Barney an enlargement when he caught himself on the hidden camera during the "great filling station robbery." In 54F/B, she was one of Bert Miller's customers.

RALPH MASON (14F/B) Antique dealer who passed through Mayberry and stopped in Walker's Drugstore to buy a tin of pipe tobacco, which cost 25¢. While there, he offered Ellie $5 for an old copper washtub. Andy then assumed Mason was an easy touch and attempted to sell him the old cannon, which the town could not seem to get rid of. Mason bought it for $175—far more than it was worth—thanks in no small part to Andy's ridiculous history of the cannon. Andy repented in the end, though, and ended up taking $30 for the cannon instead of the original price. Turned out that Mason had had a customer for it all along, Milford Phillips, who bought it and donated it back to the town of Mayberry instead of the plaque he had originally planned on donating.

MASON'S DRUGSTORE (85F/B) Barney brought his film to Mrs. Mason's lab. She developed it right away for him. The picture she developed and blew up was one of Barney. He had been sure the picture would be of the culprit in "The Great Filling Station Robbery." (See the entry MRS. MASON)

MASON'S PICNIC (73F/70B) Yearly Mayberry event. Barney started the potato sack race with his pistol every year.

EDGAR J. MASTERS (112F/111B) Driver Barney stopped for doing 40 in a 35 mph zone. He issued him a warning. It wasn't said if he was related to John Masters.

JOHN MASTERS (52F/B) (83F/B) (88F/B) (116F/115B) (138F/B) Choir director and reservation clerk at the Mayberry Hotel. In 52F/B, he lived on Elm Street. In 83F/B, he was in charge of the Ladies League musicale. In 88F/B, a single room with a bath was $2.50 a night, without a bath $1.75. Room 27 was the farthest room in the back of the hotel. John usually ate his dinner at 8:00 P.M. In 116F/115B, he refused to let Barney sing the tenor solo in "Santa Lucia" after hearing Gomer sing. In 138F/B, he was in charge on the Mayberry Centennial Pageant.

PROFESSOR MATSUMATA (18F/B) The author of the book, *The Art Of Judo*. Barney read it in the courthouse. When Andy was told who the author was he asked, "He don't come from 'round here, does he?"

MATT (73F/70B) Farmer who, along with Neil, sold fruits and vegetables from the back of their truck. They both refused to move at Barney's command, and Andy was required to fabricate a story about Barney's fearsomeness in order to scare the guys into moving at Barney's orders.

BILL MATTHEWS (10F/12B) Lucy's brother. He wanted to beat up Ed Sawyer when Ed came on a little too strong to his sister.

LUCY MATTHEWS (10F/12B) Mayberry girl who Ed Sawyer, the "stranger in town," fell in love with from afar. He knew—among other things—that Lucy was class valedictorian, blue was her favorite color, she liked dancing and hot fudge sundaes, and that she was a Capricorn.

RUTHIE MATTHEWS (242F/241B) The girl Roy Swanson and Goober both liked when they were in auto trade school together. Roy married her.

MAUDE (23F/B) Bee's cousin Edgar's wife. She slept with the window open and got bursitis, necessitating Bee's trip to Mt. Pilot to help Edgar function.

MAUDIE (118F/117B) Naylor's wife. She threw a chicken at Naylor, so Andy charged them both with a "302": Disturbing the peace. Maudie was also charged with a "710": Assault with a deadly weapon (a chicken). This was the third time in a month. Naylor complained that all Maudie ever cooked was hogback. Andy fined them ten dollars or ten days in jail.

MAX (136F/B) Man in the sporting goods store who sold Opie a fishing rod.

"MAXIMUM SECURITY" (118F/117B) Cell keys in the desk drawer.

MR. MAXWELL (19F/B) Record producer from New York who came to Mayberry interested in making recordings of local folk songs. He looked for investors and this convinced Andy that he was a crook. He was legitimate, though, and he sold the record he made to National Records. The album was called "Music From Mayberry." (See entries "MUSIC FROM MAYBERRY" and NATIONAL RECORDS)

"MAY I HAVE THE NEXT DANCE?" (113F/112B) One of the phrases Andy taught Ernest T. Bass to say properly.

"MAY I HAVE THIS DANCE?" (113F/112B) One of the phrases Andy taught Ernest T. Bass to say properly.

MAY 1762 (188F/B) Date of the Battle of Mayberry.

MAY 16, 1959 (131F/129B) One of the dates given for Barney's start with the Mayberry sheriff's department. (See the entry BARNEY'S BEGINNINGS)

JOHN MAYBERRY (20F/16B) The role played by Floyd in the Founder's Day beauty pageant.

"MAYBERRY AFTER MIDNIGHT" (136F/B) (153F/B) One of the most popular columns in the "Mayberry Gazette." It was an innuendo-filled gossip column and, in 136F/B, it was stated that the column was written by sixteen-year-old Red Akins. In 153F/B, Opie used it as a model when editing his own paper, "The Mayberry Sun," only instead of hinting at certain things, Opie used actual names.

THE MAYBERRY BAND 72nd episode filmed and 71st episode broadcast. Original broadcast date was November 19, 1962. It was written by Jim Fritzell and Everett Greenbaum, and directed by Bob Sweeney. Regulars included Andy Griffith, Don Knotts, Ronny Howard, and Howard McNear. Guests included Thom Carney, Joseph Sirota, William Eben Stephens, Burt Mustin, Sherwood Keith, Norman Leavitt, Frank Levya, and Parley Baer as Mayor Stoner.

"THE MAYBERRY CHEF" (237F/236B) The name of Aunt Bee's cooking show. It was on daily on Channel 12 at 6:30 P.M.

THE MAYBERRY CHEF 237th episode filmed and 236th episode broadcast. Original broadcast date was January 1, 1968. It was written by the Emmy and Academy Award winning writer of "The Mary Tyler Moore Show" and "Terms of Endearment," James L. Brooks. It was directed by Lee Phillips. Regulars included Andy Griffith, Frances Bavier, Ronny Howard, and George Lindsey. Guests included Don Keefer as Carl Phillips, Jack Bannon as the Announcer, and Richard Poston as the Stage Manager.

"MAYBERRY CONFIDENTIAL" (244F/243B) Aunt Bee and Opie, in an attempt to elicit information from Helen about her arrest, told her some of their past indiscretions. Helen said their confessions sounded like "Mayberry Confidential" (previously called "Mayberry After Midnight"), a column in the "Mayberry Gazette."

MAYBERRY DRUM AND BUGLE CORP (31F/B) Part-time musical endeavor for Mayberry's men. They assembled for certain special events, which included the return to town of Jim Lindsey and the arrival of the Hollywood producer, Mr. Harmon.

MAYBERRY GARDEN CLUB (203F/201B) One of Mayberry's most important social clubs. Their annual flower competitions were often heated events.

"MAYBERRY: GATEWAY TO DANGER" (30F/B) The name Barney called the town after he unknowingly captured the escaped criminal, Eddie Brooks.

"THE MAYBERRY GAZETTE" (109F/108B) (153F/B) Mayberry's newspaper. It was a weekly. Four of its most read sections were "Washington Roundup," "International Dateline," "Social Security In Action," and "Mayberry After Midnight" (which later became known as "Mayberry Confidential").

MAYBERRY GIANTS (195F/193B) Ball team that was coached by Goober. Opie played on the team, and they lost to the Mt. Pilot Comets, 6-5. (See entries HOWARD'S DEFENSE OF ANDY and MAYBERRY GIANTS VS. MT. PILOT COMETS)

MAYBERRY GIANTS VS. MT. PILOT COMETS (195F/193B) Softball game umpired by Andy. He called Opie out on a key play (forcing a 6-5 loss to the Comets), and everyone hated him for it. Howard wrote an impassioned defense of Andy in the "Mayberry Gazette," and everyone's tune changed. Later, Helen developed a photo that showed Opie really had been safe. She tore up the photo. (See entry HOWARD'S DEFENSE OF ANDY)

MAYBERRY GOES HOLLYWOOD 13th episode filmed and broadcast. Original broadcast date was January 2, 1961. It was written by Benedict Freedman and John Fenton Murray, and directed by Bob Sweeney. Regulars included Andy Griffith, Don Knotts, Ronny Howard, and Frances Bavier. Guests included Howard McNear as Floyd Colby, Dick Elliot as Mayor Pike, Josie Lloyd as Juanita Pike, Jonathan Hole, and Dan Frazer.

MAYBERRY GOES BANKRUPT 39th episode filmed and 36th episode broadcast. It was written by Jack Elinson and Charles Stewart, and directed by Bob Sweeney. Regulars included Andy Griffith, Frances Bavier, and Ronny Howard. Guests included Dick Elliot as Mayor Pike, and Andy Clyde as Frank Myers.

MAYBERRY GOOD GOVERNMENT LEAGUE (195F/193B) Andy headed it.

THE MAYBERRY HOTEL (240F/B) The hotel was considered as a possible lodging site for the Russian visitors during the US/USSR summit meeting held in Mayberry. Barney mentioned that the Russians would be pleased with the hotel because the exterminators had been there the day before.

MAYBERRY ICE HOUSE (78F/76B) They didn't keep a night light on because it kept the watchman awake.

"MAYBERRY MERRY-GO-ROUND (36F/37B) Gossip column in the "Mayberry Gazette." This column announced that Barney had gotten engaged to Melissa Stevens.

THE MAYBERRY MINUTEMEN (86F/B) History troupe Andy helped Opie organize to spark his and his friends' interest in history, after Andy unwittingly gave Opie permission not to do his history homework. (This aggravated Opie's new teacher, Miss Crump.) The troupe's members were Opie, Whitey, Howard Pruitt, and Johnny Paul Jason. Their "fitness test" to qualify for membership was to learn all the dates Miss Crump gave them for homework.

"MAYBERRY MOTOR LODGE" (141F/142B) The name Barney called the jail when Andy tried to let Otis sleep past 8:00 A.M.

"MAYBERRY, MY MAYBERRY" (72F/71B) Song Barney played on his Andre Kostalanez Marchers cymbals.

MAYBERRY ON RECORD 19th episode filmed and broadcast. Original broadcast date was February 13, 1961. It was written by John Fenton Murray and Benedict Freedman, and directed by Gene Reynolds. Regulars included Andy Griffith, Don Knotts, Ronny Howard, Howard McNear, and Elinor Donahue. Guests included Hugh Marlowe as Mr. Maxwell, George Dunn, William Erwin, and the Country Boys.

"MAYBERRY PRIDE ICE CREAM" (234F/232B) The name Bradford Taylor suggested for Bee's ice cream. He wanted to market it.

MAYBERRY, R.F.D. 241st episode filmed and 249th episode broadcast. Original broadcast date was April 1, 1968. This episode was the last episode broadcast, and it set the stage for the next season's premiere of "Mayberry, R.F.D." It was written by Bob Ross, and directed by Peter Baldwin. Regulars included Andy Griffith, Frances Bavier, Aneta Corsaut, George Lindsey, Hope Summers, Jack Dodson, and Ken Berry as Sam Jones. Special guests included Gabrielle Tinti as Mario Vincente, Letitia Roman as Sophia Vincente, Bruno della Santina as Papa Vincente, Buddy Foster as Mike Jones, and Almira Sessions as Mrs. Fletcher.

THE MAYBERRY ROLLERS (224F/221B) Bowling team sponsored by Emmett's Fix-It Shop. Members were Andy, Goober, Emmett, and Lou Jenkins. In 224F/221B, Howard Sprague substituted for Lou and bowled a perfect 300 game.

"MAYBERRY RULES FOR A LONG HAPPY LIFE" (162F/164B) Andy explained them to Warren: "Don't play leap frog with elephants, don't pat a tiger unless its tail's wagging, and never, ever mess with the Ladies Auxiliary."

MAYBERRY SECURITY BANK (109F/108B) Mayberry's one and only bank. Mr. Meldrim was the manager and possibly the owner, and Jud (sort of) worked there as a guard.

"MAYBERRY SHERIFF RATED BEST IN STATE" (44F/B) "Mayberry Gazette" headline. For three years in a row, Mayberry County had the lowest crime rate in North Carolina.

"THE MAYBERRY SONG" (53F/B)

Mayberry'll shine tonight
Mayberry'll shine
When the moon comes up
And the sun goes down
Mayberry'll shine

"THE MAYBERRY SUN" (153F/B) Opie's newspaper. He and Howie Pruitt were the editors. It sold for four cents a copy, a penny to students.

MAYBERRY 397 (210F/211B) Howard Sprague's phone number.

MAYBERRY THEATER (4F/6B) Main Street theater, later called the Grand. It's marquee read, "Late Show Sat. Night."

MAYBERRY TOWN COUNCIL (13F/B) The council consisted of Andy, Mayor Pike, Floyd Colby, and Orville Monroe. They voted to allow Mr. Harmon to make his movie in Mayberry.

MAYBERRY TRANSFER COMPANY (239F/238B) Howard's first job was as a truck driver for this company. He quit after his first few days.

MAYBERRY UNION HIGH (82F/B) (104F/105B) In 82F/B, it was told that Andy and Barney both went to Mayberry Union High. In 104F/105B, Barney had its pennant on his boarding house room wall.

"THE MAYBERRY UNION HIGH THEME SONG" (82F/B)

"Mayberry Union High
Victory is yours well nigh
We'll hit the line for points everytime
The orange and blue will try, try, try, try
And when the victory's won
You'll be our favorite son
Proud waves your banner in the sky
Mayberry Union High"

MAYBERRY'S BEGINNINGS (138F/B) Mayberry was founded in 1864 and originally called "Happy Valley."

MAYBERRY'S BIGGEST INDUSTRY (162F/164B) Making patchwork quilts.

MAYBERRY'S ELEVATION (241F/249B) 671 feet above sea level.

MAYBERRY'S FIRST INDIAN AGENT (208F/212B) Daniel Lawson, ancestor of Floyd.

MAYBERRY'S POPULATION (208F/212B) (241F/249B) In 208F/212B, it was stated that Mayberry's first Indian agent, Daniel Lawson, started a trading post that grew to "a township of 1,800." Assuming that Mayberry reached township status at the beginning of the series, we can assume that Mayberry's population in 1960 was, in fact, 1,800. In 241F/249B, Mayberry's population—as given on a train depot sign (along with the town's elevation of 671 feet above sea level)—was 5,360. The population increase in eight short years was 3,560, a 300 percent growth rate.

MAYBERRY'S "SECRETS" (10F/12B) How to make turnip jam, possum pie, fried chicken and johnnycake. Andy jokingly called these recipes the town's "secrets" when most of the townspeople, including Barney, thought that Ed Sawyer, the "stranger in town," was actually a spy.

"MAYBERRY'S SHAME" (39F/36B) Frank Myers' house, according to all the members of the town council except Andy.

MAYBERRY'S TOWN CENTER (247F/246B) It was bounded by Main and Central, and Elm and Maple.

MAYOR'S COURT (35F/B) Court presided over by the mayor as judge, and called whenever necessary. It was usually convened when someone arrested by Andy refused to pay the imposed fine and insisted on a trial.

Elizabeth Crowley, the woman speeder, got a hearing before the mayor's court.

MBB624 (201F/204B) Dr. Thomas Peterson's license plate number.

"MEANDERING WITH MARGARET" (41F/39B) The name of the newspaper column that Margaret Williamson wrote for a newspaper in Raleigh.

"MEANER THAN A BEAR BACKED INTO A BEEHIVE" (2F/B) Andy, if he missed a meal, according to Aunt Bee.

MEATLOAF (240F/B) The US and USSR ambassadors ate Bee's meatloaf in Andy's kitchen late the night of the summit meeting.

MEATLOAF PLATE (182F/183B) The dish Andy and Goober ordered from Flora Mallerby at the Diner. Goober liked Flora but she was sweet on Andy. She brought Andy a giant serving and Goober a small one.

"MECHANICS MONTHLY" (106F/B) One of Gomer Pyle's magazine subscriptions. He picked up the magazine and a postcard at the Post Office and then made a U-turn on Main Street. Barney charged him with a "911," leading to the "Citizen's Arrest" of Barney by Gomer.

A MEDAL FOR OPIE 51st episode filmed and broadcast. Original broadcast date was February 12, 1962. It was written by David Adler, and directed by Bob Sweeney. Regulars included Andy Griffith, Ronny Howard, Don Knotts, and Frances Bavier. Guests included Bob McQuain, Ralph Leabow, Joan Carey, and Pat Coghlan.

MEDIUM RARE (74F/B) The way Barney took his hamburgers.

BILL MEDWIN (60F/B) The "bookie barber." Medwin rented space in Floyd's Barbershop ostensibly to use for barbering but, in reality, he used it as a bookie joint. Andy and Barney discovered his ruse and snared him. Barney dressed in drag to catch him. Medwin charged $1.50 for a facial and 80¢ for a shampoo. The shampoo price caused Barney to wonder what he'd charge to give a customer a bath.

MR. MELDRIM (78F/76B) (109F/108B) (150F/B) Owner (?) of the Mayberry Security Bank. In 109F/108B, he had an audit coming up and had to work on a Saturday. He also had a cold. When Barney saw him trying to get into the bank, a handkerchief over his face, the deputy assumed a robbery and so pulled a gun on him. The townsfolk tormented Barney unmercifully until he "rescued" Andy and Helen from the Old Mine Cave collapse.

MEMORIAL HORSE TROUGH (88F/B) Water trough in the center of Mayberry. It was in memory of the late David Mendlebright. The trough had a plaque that read "Let no horse go thirsty."

CORA MENDLEBRIGHT (77F/79B) Maude's sister. She lived in Mt. Pilot and she and Maude visited by phone every Sunday for three or four hours. Their call prevented Malcolm Tucker, the "man in a hurry," from using Andy's party line phone.

DAVID MENDLEBRIGHT (88F/B) Probably the dead husband of Barney's landlady, Maude Mendlebright. The Memorial Horse Trough in the center of town was in David's memory.

MRS. MAUDE MENDLEBRIGHT (77F/79B) (82F/B) (104F/105B) Owner and operator of the Mendlebright Park Apartments, and Barney's landlady. In 77F/79B, Maude and her sister in Mt. Pilot, Cora, visited by phone for three or four hours. They did this every Sunday. In 82F/B, she grew mushrooms in her cellar as a spare time business. Once, when Barney got a bad sunburn and couldn't raise his arms, Maude washed his hair. Andy and Barney saved her money by exposing her "beau," Mr. Fields, as a crook and a con artist.

MENDLEBRIGHT PARK APARTMENTS (104F/105B) Barney's home. It was owned and operated by Mrs. Maude Mendlebright, and some of her rules included "No children, no pets, no cooking." Also, she didn't permit any light bulb to be used larger than a forty watt. She usually had no vacancies. Maude evicted Barney for cooking in his room. Barney's rent was six dollars a week. (See floor plan of Barney's room included in this book)

THE MERCHANT OF MAYBERRY 54th episode filmed and broadcast. Original broadcast date was March 5, 1962. It was written by Leo Solomon and Ben Gershman, and directed by Bob Sweeney. Regulars included Andy Griffith, Don Knotts, Ronny Howard, and Frances Bavier. Guests included Sterling Holloway as Bert Miller, Will Wright as Ben Weaver, Sara Seegar, Mary Lansing, and Bob McQuain.

MERILEE (82F/B) Woman at the "class reunion" who told Ramona Wiley that Andy had a son.

MERLE (72F/71B) Member of the Mayberry Band. He was asked by Mayor Stoner to get different color balloons.

MERLE (120F/119B) He called Andy about a sign that had fallen again. Andy had told Barney to take care of it.

MATT MERLIS (68F/69B) (92F/B) In 68F/69B, Matt explained to Opie what "stood up" meant. In 92F/B, Opie said Matt was his "best friend." Opie and Matt got into a "rough house on the playground." Opie got filthy dirty and scraped his knee.

JAMES MERRIWEATHER (138F/B) The settler of Mayberry. Andy played his part in the Mayberry Centennial Pageant.

MALCOLM MERRIWEATHER (89F/B) (124F/123B) British gentleman's gentleman. In 89F/B, he had an accident while passing through Mayberry looking for Route 43. (Malcolm made Fletch Roberts drive into a pile of packing crates.) Les told Andy Malcolm did "thirty or forty dollars" worth of damage. He couldn't pay for the damages, so Andy gave him a job working in the Taylor household. Malcolm was Mayberry's first butler. He was from "Eckmondwight up Arbeshire way," and had worked as a valet and falconkeeper for Colonel Chumley. He had wanted to pay for his damages (which he said came to "14 pounds 10 shillings thrupence 3 farthings) on "the never never" (a little now, a little later). Malcolm knew how to make paper ladders and excellent Cornish pastry. He also made very nice "bubble-and-squeak." Opie especially enjoyed the faces Malcolm drew on his hard-boiled eggs. Malcolm called Bee a "regular bobbydazzler." In 124F/123B, Bee began to feel left out because of the efficient way in which Malcolm was running her household (on the pretext of giving her an unwanted rest), and so took to her bed. Malcolm realized what was happening, and pretended to get drunk on sherry. Barney called him "an English Otis." Andy recognized the ruse and they parted on good terms.

"MERRY CHRISTMAS FROM STATE PRISON" (11F/B) The legend Andy read on the card he received from the Hubacher brothers. He was wrong. The card actually read, "Greetings from State Prison."

"THE MERRY MADCAP OF MAYBERRY" (216F/B) The name Colonel Tim used to introduce Howard Sprague on his "Talent Time" amateur show.

MEXICAN FARMACIA (227F/222B) Myrtle bought some foot powder there during her, Bee's, and Clara's trip to Mexico.

MEXICO (227F/222B) (234F/232B) In 227F/222B, Bee, Clara, and Myrtle vacationed there. In 234F/232B, Bradford Taylor claimed he sold the copper mines which he had owned in Mexico.

MIAMI (47F/B) (68F/69B) In 47F/B, Ronald Bailey was on his way to Miami when he sideswiped Fletch Dillbeck in Mayberry. In 68F/69B, Peggy McMillan's friend, Don, was on his way to a pharmacy convention in Miami when he stopped to see Peggy.

FRED MICHAELS (221F/235B) Vice President in Charge of Regional Sales for northeast North Carolina for the Emblem Oil Company of El Paso, Texas. He wanted Goober, "the executive," to put in a third pump.

PAT MICHAELS (168F/B) Publicity man for the movie "Sheriff Without A Gun." He called Mayberry "Blueberry."

MID-MOUNTAIN FINANCE COMPANY (31F/B) The finance company that financed Jim Lindsey's red convertible. They repossessed it after he missed three payments.

MIDNIGHT (229F/228B) Opie came home at midnight the night his band, "The Sound Committee," played as Brenda Roachs' birthday party. The latest he had ever been out before that night was ten o'clock.

MIDNIGHT MADNESS (27F/B) Cologne sold at Walker's Drugstore. Ellie sprayed Andy with it, making him smell "like a gardenia blossom."

"MIDNIGHT SPECIAL" (31F/B) Song Andy and Jim Lindsey performed after supper at Andy's house.

"MIGHTY CASEY" (224F/221B) The poem Howard read just before he was scheduled to bowl his last ball in a possible 300 game.

"A MIGHTY FINE CHARACTER MEDAL" (4F/6B) Andy wanted to give Opie this medal for telling him who pushed the squad car in front of the fire plug.

MILDRED (113F/112B) Mrs. Wiley's maid.

MILES ROAD (129F/130B) Harry's Pond, the new trout pond, was located on Miles Road, two miles east from the courthouse.

THE MILL (28F/B) Lester Scoby couldn't get a job there.

BERT MILLER (54F/B) Peddler who sold door-to-door in Mayberry and its environs. Andy and Barney, in an attempt to alleviate Bert's aches and pains, helped him set up a little stall in Art Crowley's vacant lot on Main Street. This raised the ire of Ben Weaver, who repeatedly attempted to put Bert out of business. Andy escalated his assistance to Bert until it got out of hand, and Andy realized he was playing with Bert's life just to aggravate Ben. Eventually it worked out, though, and Andy was actually able to have Ben give Bert a salesman's job in Weaver's. Bert more often than not tried to discourage a customer from making a purchase.

JERRY MILLER (159F/B) Roby and Early's son, and the sultan and one-man band in the "Sultan's Favorite" carnival show. He was a size 38 banjo player and he came from Morgantown, West Virginia. Bee had once lived there and knew his family. When the carnival show closed up (in not-a-small way thanks to Andy), Bee forced Andy to give Jerry a job in the courthouse.

LEROY MILLER (231F/230B) State trooper who came to Mayberry with Inspector Rogers.

OFFICER MILLER (30F/B) State policeman from whom Eddie Brooks escaped.

MILLER'S POND (247F/246B) Unspecified locale. Harry was on his way there.

"MILLIE" (134F/B) The alias Thelma Lou invented for Helen on her blind date with Andy.

"MILLIE GRACE" (134F/B) The alias Barney invented for Helen after Thelma Lou called her Millie and Barney called her Grace. They were arranging a blind date with Helen for Andy.

ABIGAIL MILLIKEN (9F/7B) She was having a party and Miss Rosemary spent one afternoon baking pies for the party.

THE "MILLIONS FOR . . ." QUO-TATION (34F/33B) (196F/203B) (203F/196B) Quotation used three times in the series, twice differently, and twice attributed to different people. In 34F/33B, Andy, in a story to Opie about courage, used the quotation, "Millions for charity, but not one cent for tribute." In 196F/203B, Floyd read about Charles Coatsworth Pinckney, who said, "Millions for defense, but not one cent for tribute." In 203F/196B, Howard Sprague quoted Charles Coatsworth Paynton as having said, "Millions for defense, but not one cent for tribute." (See entries CHARLES COATSWORTH PAYNTON and CHARLES COATSWORTH PINCKNEY)

THE MILLSTONE FARM (112F/111B) Andy needed the squad car to go out there.

THE MILO BOYS (112F/111B) World War I vets of Mayberry.

MILTON (82F/B) Barney's middle name. But in 25F/B, he said his middle name was Oliver. And in 103F/B and 114F/113B, he said his middle initial was "P."

MR. MILTON (61F/B) The state's prosecutor who heard the case against Andy, who was brought up before him on malfeasance charges. The charges were orchestrated by J. Howard Jackson and Jean Boswell.

MIND OVER MATTER 199th episode filmed and 196th episode broadcast. Original broadcast date was October 31, 1966. It was written by Ron Friedman and Pat McCormick, and directed by Lee Phillips. Regulars included Andy Griffith, George Lindsey, Frances Bavier, Howard McNear, and Ronny Howard. Guests included George Selk as Dr. Bennett, and Sue Taylor as the Girl.

MISS MINGUS (99F/98B) Ernest T. Bass broke a street light in front of her house. Merlin Bracey called to tell Andy about it.

THE MINISTER (234F/232B) Unnamed cleric who pledged $100 to Bee's cousin, Bradford, who had a scheme for marketing Aunt Bee's homemade ice cream.

MINNIE (151F/B) The mother of Andy's "cousin," Gloria.

MIRACLE SALVE (122F/121B) The salve distributed by the Miracle Salve Company of Mt. Pilot. Opie and his friends tried to win a pony by selling the salve, which, according to its label, was good for "poison ivy, athlete's foot, prickly rash, complexion, and spring itch." When Trey Bowden sent his back, the company sent him a "blacklist" letter which frightened him. Barney then concocted a scheme with Gomer; he posed as U.T. Pendyke, D.V.M., and tried to convince the owners of the company that the salve cured the mange. The scheme backfired, and 946 jars of the salve were delivered to Opie Taylor, Sr. (Gomer). The salve cost thirty-five cents a jar. (See entry MOLLY HARKINS' MANGE CURE)

MIRACLE SALVE COMPANY (122F/121B) Salve company based in Mt. Pilot. It was owned and operated by Lenny and another unnamed man. They operated out of room 106 in an unnamed building. (See entry MIRACLE SALVE)

MIRACLE-SWEEP (33F/34B) The number one vacuum cleaner on the market and the machine Barney began selling door-to-door after he resigned the sheriff's department.

"MISS BEE TAYLOR FOR PRO-GRESSIVE GOVERNMENT" (200F/197B) Poster Opie made for Aunt Bee's campaign for city council.

"MISS CITY SLICKER" (37F/40B) The name Barney derogatorily called Karen Moore.

"MISS FRIED CHICKEN OF MAYBERRY" (103F/B) The name Andy bestowed on Aunt Bee after she served an especially tasty chicken dinner.

"MISS GADABOUT" (230F/229B) Aunt Bee, according to Clara Edwards, after Bee went out of town with Professor Hubert St. John.

"MISS GOTROCKS" (67F/65B) The name Barney called Peggy McMillan.

"MISS HELEN CRUMP BEING BROUGHT IN FOR ARRAIGNMENT IN CONNECTION WITH..." (244F/243B) Photo caption beneath the picture of Helen being arrested. Andy found the photo while looking for a history outline Helen had asked him to find.

"MISS LUNCHEON TRAY" (124F/123B) Title Andy said they should bestow upon Aunt Bee for the lunch she brought him and Barney. It consisted of "tuna fish sandwiches with little sweet gherkins cut into 'em, and chocolate brownies with walnuts in 'em."

"MISS MAYBERRY JUNIOR" (20F/16B) The title Andy and Floyd bestowed on Mary Wiggins in the barbershop after the Founder's Day beauty pageant. They "crowned" her using a towel and an upside-down hat.

"MISSY" (24F/B) Andy's nickname for Ellie Walker.

"MR. BIG" (40F/38B) Barney thought that Dave the Hobo might have been Mr. Big of the Capone gang.

"MR. BIG" (236F/237B) The name Emmett Clark sneeringly called his wife's brother, Ben Beecham.

MR. COOKIE BAR (93F/B) Snack Barney usually included when he brown-bagged his lunch.

"MR. FIXIT" (123F/122B) Barney, according to Barney. He was referring to his handling of supper, and then his bungling of getting rid of Skippy and Daphne.

"MR. FIXIT" (123F/122B) Barney, according to Barney. He was referring to his handling of supper, and then his bungling of getting rid of Skippy and Daphne.

"MR. INDEPENDENT" (104F/105B) Barney, according to Barney. He coined this self-description after Mrs. Mendlebright evicted him for breaking her rules.

"MR. INDEPENDENT WHEELS" (90F/B) Barney, according to Barney. This was in reference to his decision to buy his own car.

MR. McBEEVEE 66th episode filmed and 64th episode broadcast. Original broadcast date was October 1, 1962. It was written by Ray Allen Saffian and Harvey Bullock, and directed by Bob Sweeney. Regulars included Andy Griffith, Ronny Howard, Frances Bavier, and Don Knotts. Guests included Karl Swenson as Mr. McBeevee.

"MR. ROCKEFELLER" (136F/B) The name Andy called Opie after the $50 Opie found became his. Opie suggested saving $1 and spending the rest. Andy convinced him that saving $40 and spending $10 would be better.

"MR. MEDICO" (99F/98B) The name Ernest T. Bass called the doctor at the Army recruiting office.

"MISTER X" (178F/B) The man Warren hypothesized stole Aunt Bee's "lost" pin.

"MRS. PINKNEY VARIEGATED RED" (203F/201B) The rose variety that Aunt Bee cross-pollinated with an "Alma Swarthouse Sunset Pink" to create her "Deep Pink Ecstasy" rose.

SHERIFF MITCHELL (38F/41B) (169F/165B) (173F/174B) Mt. Pilot sheriff. In 38F/41B, Andy called him to inquire about Henry Wheeler. In 169F/165B, Andy called him to tell him that Warren would be alone the following day. In 173F/174B, Mitchell called Andy to tell him about a wreck on the highway.

MME. PHOEBE'S BEAUTY SALON (13F/B) The name the Mayberry Beauty Salon was changed to after the Hollywood movie was scheduled to be made in town.

MODEL A (67F/65B) The car Andy had when he was young. One summer he and Barney started out on a trip to New Orleans in the Model A. It burned out a bearing "about D-Queen Junction." Andy later sold the car for twelve dollars.

MRS. MOGRAH'S (96F/100B) Andy sent Opie there to eat grits and prunes. Andy sent him there because he had to go rescue Aunt Bee after she was kidnapped by Briscoe Darling.

MOHAMMED'S BIRTHDAY (17F/B) Holiday used by Lars Hansen—pretending he was a Moslem—as an excuse to buy the Morrison sisters' moonshine, which they called "Special Elixir," and which they wouldn't sell for anything but a holiday.

MOLE (10F/12B) William Buntley had one on his right ear and his mother used it to tell him apart from his twin brother, Robert.

MOLINE, CALIFORNIA (166F/B) Warren Ferguson's sister and brother-in-law lived there. They had four kids, and he was a Lion.

"DOC" MOLLOY (50F/B) He robbed the furniture company payroll. While being held in the Mayberry jail, Barney inadvertently let him escape.

MOLLY HARKINS MANGE CURE (122F/121B) Barney, posing as U.T. Pendyke, D.V.M., said that he had been using Molly Harkins' before he discovered that Miracle Salve cured the mange. (See entry MIRACLE SALVE)

MOM'S DINER (67F/65B) Mayberry diner that boasted home cooking.

MONROE (155F/B) Man from the highway department who called Andy to tell him to expand the 50 mph zone as far as Fancy Gap.

NEWTON MONROE (156F/B) Peddler who came to Mayberry. He sold junk out of his car trunk and was arrested by Andy. Newton's license plate number was INH-851. Some of the items he sold included a watch that told the temperature and sold for $8.98, the "Star of Peoria" ring, transistor radios, "fur" stoles for $13.25, and pineapple skinners for $2 each. Andy realized he was a no-luck schmuck, so he gave him a job as a sheriff's assistant (which he botched). As a last chance, Andy gave Newton the job of painting his porch. He ruined it and made a mess, but Andy finished it for him, letting Newton think he did it himself. His newly found confidence spurred him to go into the painting business. Newton was thirty-four years old in 156F/B.

ORVILLE MONROE (3F/B) (13F/B) (17F/B) In 13F/B, Orville was shown as the owner of the funeral parlor and also as a TV repairman. He changed his parlor's name to "Hollywood Funerals" when the Hollywood movie was to be made in Mayberry. In 17F/B, Barney suggested that Orville could be a deputy for the still raid he was planning.

THE MONROE DOCTRINE (196F/203B) One of the history topics discussed in the adult education course Andy and the others took.

MONROE NURSERY (220F/B) Mt. Pilot business. Bee woke Andy to tell him it burned down.

"THE MONSTER" (173F/174B) The name Helen assigned to Warren after he made a pass at her. He was sleepwalking after watching a love story on TV.

"THE MONSTER FROM MARS" (163F/161B) Movie that was playing in Mayberry. The monsters had four sets of teeth.

"THE MONSTER FROM OUT-OF-TOWN" (134F/B) The movie Andy, Helen, Barney, and Thelma Lou were supposed to go see during Andy's and Helen's blind date.

"THE MONSTER FROM THE MOON" (163F/161B) Movie that was playing in Mayberry. The monsters had three sets of teeth.

"THE MONSTER THAT ATE MINNESOTA" (175F/B) Movie Goober wanted to go see instead of attending the art show.

HARRIET MOODY (175F/B) She went to the same art class as Bee. Harriet was into plate painting. The class met on Wednesday evenings. There were ten students, including Bee and Harriet.

"THOMAS A. MOODY" (53F/B) The alias of Sheldon Davis, the "guest of honor."

THE MOON MEN INVADE VENUS ON GIANT BATS (173F/174B) Book Warren gave Goober to read.

"MOON MULLINS" (171F/172B) The comic strip Andy was reading when Bee made him turn to an ad in the "Help Wanted" section which she wanted to answer.

The ad was for a clerk at a printing store, and the business turned out to be a counterfeiting operation.

"THE MOON OF MANICURA" (83F/B) Song in Barney's repertoire.

EVAN MOORE (166F/B) Aunt Bee's cousin. He lived in Asheville, North Carolina.

KAREN MOORE (37F/40B) Thelma Lou's cousin from Arkansas. Thelma Lou and Barney fixed her up with Andy, who proceeded to make a fool of himself by being macho and treating her like dumb girl. Karen put him in his place, however, by beating him at the skeet shoot in front of everyone. She was a pro.

MOOSIE (77F/79B) Girl discussed by the two Mendlebright sisters on one of their Sunday afternoon phone visits.

MISS MORAN (110F/109B) Andy and Barney's fourth grade teacher.

MORAVIAN CHURCH BASEMENT (240F/B) Locale in Mayberry that Barney suggested as a possible site for the US/USSR summit meetng.

MOREHEAD CITY (60F/B) The city where Bill Medwin, the "bookie barber," had girlfriends, according to Sarah, the operator. She had overheard his horse-betting phone calls. A lot of the horses had girl's names.

MORELLI'S RESTAURANT (132F/128B) (155F/B) (207F/209B) (246F/245B) (249F/248B) Mayberry's most popular (and perhaps only) Italian restaurant. In 132F/128B, Barney took Thelma Lou to Morelli's for her previous birthday (they usually went Dutch). Barney told Andy that they'd let you take a bottle in there, and that they had red-checkered tablecloths. Barney and Thelma Lou had the deluxe special. (Barney also explained that you could hold it down to $1.85 if you didn't have the shrimp cocktail. They didn't.) They had minestrone, which was delicious, and, as the main dish, Pounded Steak a la Morelli. It was so good Barney sent his compliments to the chef. The cook looked up from his pounding and waved. They had candles and a gypsy violinist that night. The violinist played six or eight songs at Barney's table, so Barney slipped him a quarter. Those guys work on tips, he explained. In 155F/B, Barney didn't want to go there because on Monday the special was creamed chicken. In 207F/209B, Andy, Helen, Howard, and Alice Harper went there for supper. In 246F/245B, George proposed to Mrs. Sprague at Morelli's as they were finishing the rice pudding. In 249F/248B, Goober took Edith Gibson there for their computer-arranged date.

JESS MORGAN (69F/66B) Moonshiner arrested by Andy. He was being held in custody just when Roy Stoner was elected the new mayor. Andy let Jess go home for three days to harvest his crops, much against the wishes of Mayor Stoner. When Jess didn't come back to the jail on time, Stoner believed he was right in not trusting Jess. It turned out that Jess was trapped up a tree by a bear.

JIM MORGAN (85F/B) The young man falsely accused of the "Great Filling Station Robbery." He solved it by wiring the cash register to car batteries and catching Pothrow Henson.

MRS. MORGAN (69F/66B) Jess's wife. She came to get Jess out of jail.

MORGANTOWN (233F/231B) For his and Millie's honeymoon, Howard wanted to go there for the King Arthur pageant, and then on to the Blue Rock Caverns.

DETECTIVE MORLEY (95F/B) Law officer involved in the recapture of Doc and Tiny.

CLARABELLE MORRISON (17F/B) One of the two Morrison sisters. They ran a still and made what they called their "Special Elixir," which they sold for four dollars. They would only sell the moonshine for holidays, however.

JENNIFER MORRISON (17F/B) One of the two Morrison sisters. They ran a still and made what they called their "Special Elixir," which they sold for four dollars. They would only sell the it for holidays, however.

MORT (78F/76B) One of the crooks who tried to rob the Mayberry Security Bank. Howie was the other one.

MORT'S CLOTHING (30F/B) Main Street store.

THE MORTONSON'S (143F/B) Mayberry family. Barney tried to sell them the Simms' house.

HAROLD MOSLEY (213F/B) Promotion director for Bryant Publishing Company. He was assigned to promote Helen Crump's book, *Amusing Tales of Tiny Tots.*

MABEL J. MOSLEY (200F/197B) Author of *Roses Are the Backbone of Your Garden.* Tilly Kincaid reviewed the book at a meeting of the Mayberry Garden Club.

MOTORCYCLE AND SIDECAR (112F/111B) Barney's purchase at the war surplus auction in Mt. Pilot. It was model #RJ300.

MOTORCYCLE PLAQUE (112F/111B) In order to convince Barney to get rid of his motorcycle, Andy burned the following into a plaque (with Opie's woodburning set) and planted it in the bike: "First motorcycle to cross the Marne River Battle of Chateau Thierry . . . 6-12-18 Passenger, Blackjack Pershing. Driver Corporal Nate Jackson A. E. F." When Barney read the plaque, he said the motorcycle should be in the "Smith Brothers Institution."

MT. PILOT (23F/B) (38F/41B) (41F/39B) (51F/B) (54F/B) (68F/69B) (126F/125B) (132F/128B) (135F/B) (210F/211B) (222F/225B) (225F/224B) (226F/223B) (231F/230B) (236F/237B) (245F/244B) (246F/245B) Mayberry's sister city. In 23F/B, it was stated that Bee's cousin Edgar and his wife Maude lived there. In 38F/41B, Henry Wheeler worked there before coming to Mayberry. While there, he sponged off Mary Grady and her brother, Bill. In 41F/39B, we learned that the town had a new state police building. In 51F/B, Barney took Juanita there for Chinese food. The bill was $2.75. They had the family dinner for one. In 54F/B, it was reported that Jim Stevens had a store in Mt. Pilot. In 68F/69B, it was the town where Lydia Crosswaithe worked. In 126F/125B, it was revealed that Thelma Lou's dentist was in Mt. Pilot. It was twelve miles each way, Gomer drove her, and she bought him lunch. In 132F/128B, Barney wanted to take Juanita there for a drive-in movie. In 135F/B, Barney called it Mayberry's "sister city." This was the purported reason Barney gave for wearing his uniform on his day off. In 210F/211B, Goober drove there to see the French film, "La Vie Du Femme." Also in that episode, Floyd considered opening a two-chair barbershop there. In 222F/225B, it was said that Mt. Pilot was Millie Hutchins' hometown. In 225F/224B, it was mentioned that Emmett once had a fix-it shop there. In 226F/223B, Goober went there to buy a suit for the prior year's harvest ball. He was too late; all that was left was a size 46. In 231F/230B, Mt. Pilot was identified as the location of Bradbury Business College. It was also where Laundercoin, Inc. already had two coin launderies. In 236F/237B, Ben Beecham considered Mayberry and Mt. Pilot "virgin territory" for insurance sales. In 245F/244B, it was where Bernie the Furrier's store was located. In 246F/245B, it was where Mrs. Sprague and her new husband, George, would be living after they married. George had a business there. Also in that episode, Howard told about the little out-of-the-way shop there where he bought the impressionistic paintings. (See all specific entries mentioned in this entry)

"MT. PILOT BUGLE AND SUN" (213F/B) Mt. Pilot newspaper. Bryant Publishing ran a full-page ad in the paper for Helen Crump's new book, *Amusing Tales of Tiny Tots.*

MT. PILOT CIVIL SERVICE OFFICE (131F/129B) Andy went there to get the new deputy height and weight requirements, since deputies were now under Civil Service. They were five feet eight inches and 145 pounds, no exceptions.

MT. PILOT COMETS (195F/193B) Ball team that went up against the Mayberry Giants and beat them. It was coached by Mr. Carter.

MT. PILOT 4872 (249F/248B) Edith Gibson's phone number.

MT. PILOT HIGH SCHOOL (218F/B) (243F/242B) In 218F/B, it was stated that Andy threw a no-hitter against them; Mayberry lost, 10-0. In 243F/242B, Andy told the story of how he caught the winning touchdown pass against them in the fourth quarter, four seconds to go, fourth down. Andy was fourth string in. (See the entry "FOURTH QUARTER, FOUR SECONDS TO GO, FOURTH DOWN")

MT. PILOT HOSPITAL (199F/196B) Willis Kundiff was put in traction there after his auto accident.

MT. PILOT JUDO SOCIETY (135F/B) Club headed by Mr. Izamoto and based in Mt. Pilot. It was situated between Peggy's Beauty Salon and Williams Interiors and Furniture. The club gave out membership cards. Barney's read, "This is to certify that Mr. Bernard Fife is a member of the Mt. Pilot Judo Society." Andy enlisted Mr. Izamoto's help in getting Fred Plummer to leave Barney alone.

MT. PILOT MUNICIPAL COURT (223F/226B) The setting of Marvin Jenkins' trial. Aunt Bee was a juror.

"MT. PILOT TIMES" (174F/173B) Harlan Robinson ran this ad in the "Mt. Pilot Times" for his organ: "Sacrifice. Privately-owned organ, 2 manual, 19 pedal. Originally cost $3500, will sell for $2000." (See entry HARLAN ROBINSON)

MOUNTAIN FOLKLORE (121F/120B) Book Barney checked out of the library. He hoped to find something in the book that would help Andy stop Charlene Darling in her attempt at marrying the sheriff. Barney found this: "If a rider dressed in black riding east to west on a white horse in the light of a full moon passes a bridegroom,

he is cursed and the union is cursed." Also, "If you wear a ruby ring and ride an old horse, the horse'll go mad."

MOUNTAIN WEDDING 94th episode filmed and broadcast. Original broadcast date was April 29, 1963. It was written by Jim Fritzell and Everett Greenbaum, and directed by Bob Sweeney. Regulars included Andy Griffith and Don Knotts. Guests included Howard Morris as Ernest T. Bass, Denver Pyle as Briscoe Darling, The Dillards as the Darling Boys, Dub Taylor, and Hoke Howell.

MOUSETRAP (120F/119B) Gomer found a mousetrap and a golf ball while examining Aunt Bee's freezer.

A MOUSTACHE CUP WITH ROSES ON IT (111F/110B) The gift Mr. Frisby, the egg man, gave to Aunt Bee on the occasion of his going out of business.

MOZZARELLA (59F/B) Barney's favorite pizza.

MP-3791 (90F/B) License plate number of "Barney's first car."

BESS MUGGINS (11F/B) Sam Muggins' wife. She came to the jail to spend Christmas Eve with her husband (who was in for moonshining) after Ben Weaver refused to allow Andy to release Sam for Christmas.

BILLY MUGGINS (11F/B) Sam and Bess's son. He came to the courthouse for a Christmas Eve party after his father was arrested for moonshining.

EFFIE MUGGINS (11F/B) Sam and Bess's daughter. She came to the courthouse to spend Christmas Eve with her father after he was arrested for moonshining.

SAM MUGGINS (11F/B) Moonshiner brought in to the jail by Ben Weaver.

MULBERRY SQUEEZINGS (139F/B) Mr. Darling told Barney the jug he passed the deputy held mulberry squeezings. It was actually moonshine.

MULLIGAN'S STEW (108F/127B) The dish Wary Willy the Hobo was preparing when Opie and his "merry men" came upon him in the woods.

MR. MUNDT (129F/130B) Andy gave him a two-dollar parking ticket for parking in front of a fire hydrant. Ollie called him a "firebug."

MURILLOS (183F/182B) Head of the band of gypsies that came to Mayberry. La Farona was his mother, Sabella his sister, and Sylvio his "good friend." He sold Bee earrings and a shawl for $12.50 ($4.50 for the earrings and $8 for the shawl), and he sold Clara the same earrings. He listened to Station CQL out of Greenland for his "magical" weather prediction abilties. He sold Andy a short wave radio with no works inside.

MURPHY'S HOUSE OF THE NINE FLAVORS (105F/104B) Mayberry ice cream parlor. Barney brought Thelma Lou ice cream from the shop: West Indian Licorice Mocha Delight. It cost forty cents. He collected the money from Thelma Lou.

MUSHROOMS (82F/B) Barney's landlady, Maude Mendlebright, grew mushrooms in her cellar as a spare time business.

"MUSIC FROM MAYBERRY" (19F/B) The album of folk songs recorded in Mayberry by Mr. Maxwell. The record was bought and distributed by National Records.

"MUSIC TO SNIP BY" (19F/B) The song Andy and the Country Boys performed in Floyd's

Barbershop. It was an instrumental and probably had no real title.

MY FAIR ERNEST T. BASS 113th episode filmed and 112th episode broadcast. Original broadcast date was February 3, 1964. It was written by Jim Fritzell and Everett Greenbaum, and directed by Earl Bellamy. Regulars included Andy Griffith, Don Knotts, Frances Bavier, and Ronny Howard. Guests included Howard Morris as Ernest T. Bass, Doris Packer as Mrs. Wiley, and Jackie Joseph as Ramona Anchram.

"MY HOMETOWN" (189F/B) Song written by Bee Taylor and Clara Edwards as a tribute to their hometown, Mayberry. It was a gentle, slow ballad and the ladies were upset when rocker Keevy Hazleton changed it a little; he turned it into rock-and-roll. Eventually he listened to reason—and the complaining ladies—and performed the tune as a rock ballad. The lyrics are as follows:

> My Hometown
> Is the greatest place I know
> Where the neighbors I find
> Are gentle and kind
> And the living, easy and slow.
> My Hometown
> Is the only place to be
> Here the worries are small
> And the kids grow tall and strong
> And healthy and free
> It's my hometown
> My Hometown
> Mayberry, Mayberry.

"MY LITTLE GRAY HOME IN THE WEST" (63F/B) Song sung by Junior Hubacher during his stay in the Mayberry jail. It was a very touching moment.

"MY MOST UNFORGETTABLE CHARACTER" (218F/B) Essay Helen Crump assigned to her class. It had to be 500 words or more and she suggested it be someone they knew personally rather than an historical figure. Opie wrote about Arnold's father, Dr. Bailey; Arnold wrote about Andy.

MYER'S LAKE (34F/33B) (67F/65B) (225F/224B) (230F/229B) In 34F/33B, Andy took Opie to the lake and gave him a parable about courage. In 67F/65B,

Andy, Barney, Peggy McMillan, and Thelma Lou went to Myer's after they ate at Mom's Diner. Andy talked to a hawk. Then they all waded in the lake. Barney was at first too shy to take off his socks and shoes in front of Peggy and Thelma Lou, but Andy said it was OK: "Both the girls have brothers." In 225F/224B, Andy took Hollander and his friends there fishing. They went for bass, and Andy got four, Hollander, five. In 230F/229B, Bee went there with Professor Hubert St. John.

MYER'S REAL ESTATE COMPANY (222F/225B) Main Street business next to Spencer's Pipes and Tobaccos.

FRANK MYERS (39F/36B) Old man whose house was the worst in Mayberry. Frank didn't pay his property taxes for eight quarters and the city council voted to evict him. The job was given to Andy, who was the only member of the council to dissent. Andy invited Frank to stay with him and Aunt Bee. In going through Frank's "valuables," Andy discovered that Frank owned a one hundred-year-old bond from the town of Mayberry. The bond, which was now worth $349,119.27, suddenly became Frank's bargaining chip. He demanded payment from the town and began to go through mail-order catalogues looking for things to buy with his newly found fortune. But, of course, the town of Mayberry in no way could pay the bond off, so Andy arrived at an equitable solution: all the townsfolk would help fix up Frank's house and they would also write off all his back taxes. After all the work was done, however, it was discovered that the bond was bought with Confederate money and was therefore worthless. Andy convinced the townspeople to leave well enough alone, and Frank stayed in his newly decorated house. The production manager for this—and many other—episodes, was the real Frank E. Myers. (See the entry AIR CONDITIONER, NEW STOVE, COLOR TV, STEREO PHONOGRAPH)

MAYNARD MYERS (244F/243B) Old boyfriend of Helen Crump's. He used to write her love letters. Andy found the old letters while looking for a history outline for Helen. In 244F/243B, Helen told Andy that Maynard presently had six children.

MYRTLE (227F/222B) Bee and Clara's traveling companion to Mexico. Myrtle was a whiner and a complainer. She and Clara each paid for half their trip so Bee didn't have to choose which one to take with her.

N59558 (243F/242B) The number of the plane in which Bee took her flying lessons at MacDonald's Flying School. This was also the plane in which she soloed.

"NAB TO RAZISKY" (176F/B) N to R. The section of the fingerprint division to which Barney was promoted in the Raleigh police department. He got a salary of $95 a week and a $125 bonus at Christmas.

"NAIL POLISH AND EAU DE COLOGNE" (35F/B) When Aunt Bee took over as matron at the Mayberry jail for Elizabeth ("the woman speeder") Crowley, she sent Barney out for the cologne and nail polish.

"A NAKED SAVAGE" (120F/119B) Aunt Bee said Opie looked like one when he came down for breakfast on a hot day bare-chested. She wouldn't have it.

NASHVILLE (71F/72B) (112F/111B) In 71F/72B, Floyd said he had to go to Nashville to get away from Madeline Grayson, his lonely hearts club correspondent. She wrote him that she'd be coming to visit him on her way to her Palm Beach home. In 112F/111B, Mrs. Beggs' father took her sister, Tilly, to see a dentist in Nashville whose office was in the back of a store; "he warn't no good."

NASHVILLE BUS (48F/B) The bus Ellen Brown, the manicurist, took to Mayberry.

UNCLE NAT (81F/B) Otis's uncle. Otis thought that Jimmy, the "loaded goat," was his Uncle Nat.

NATE (29F/B) Mayberry man Barney drafted into the posse that went to Sam Becker's place. But Nate was late; he lost the keys to his car.

ALICE NATHAM (144F/B) A "sweet little old woman." Goober explained to her—on the phone—how to take the head off her car and clean the valves.

"NATION'S INDUSTRY" (221F/235B) Magazine Goober read after he bought Wally's Service Station and became an "executive."

"NATIONAL GEOGRAPHIC" (118F/117B) (153F/B) In 118F/117B, the magazine Andy read after Barney went on vacation. In 153F/B, the magazine Barney pretended to read while Fred Henry talked about the Widow Saunders. The article was about Africa. (See the entry THE WIDOW SAUNDERS)

NATIONAL GUARD ARMORY (112F/111B) Andy thought that Barney's "historical" motorcycle should be in the armory. They already had a cannon from the Civil War, and a jeep from World War II.

NATIONAL POTATO WEEK (17F/B) Holiday used by the Morrison sisters' customers as an excuse to buy the ladies' moonshine. The sisters would only sell their "Special Elixir" for "recognized" holidays.

NATIONAL RECORDS (19F/B) The Richmond record company that bought the album of Mayberry folk songs, "Music From Mayberry," from Mr. Maxwell. The royalty rate for Maxwell was 25¢ per record, for the investors 3¢ per record. (See the entry "MUSIC FROM MAYBERRY")

"NATIONAL STILL-SMASHING DAY" (17F/B) The day Andy and Barney broke up the Morrison sisters' still. Andy invented the day as an excuse to drink the moonshine that splashed on his face as Barney broke up the still.

NATURAL BRIDGE, VIRGINIA (115F/114B) Barney thought that Otis might have been going there with the money he saved from working a night job. He wasn't going anywhere, though, he was buying a car. (See the entry OTIS'S CAR)

THE NAVY (103F/B) Opie wanted to join the Navy after Andy raved about Opie's mistaken "all A's" report card. He had actually gotten an "F" in arithmetic. So, instead of joining the Navy, he ran away from home.

THE NAYLENS (125F/124B) At the Naylen's anniversary party, Lillian's meatballs were found in plants, magazines, and the fireplace. (See the entry LILLIAN)

NAYLOR (118F/117B) Maudie's husband. Maudie threw a chicken at Naylor, and Andy charged them both with a 302 (disturbing the peace). Naylor complained that all Maudie ever cooked was hogback. Andy fined them ten dollars or ten days in jail. (Andy needed a vacation at this point.) (See the entry MAUDIE)

NC-206 (131F/129B) License plate number of a car parked in front of Floyd's Barbershop.

RALPH NEAL (128F/133B) Con who escaped from the state prison and who came to Mayberry. He was five feet ten inches and 165 lbs.

"NEARLY TWENTY CENTS MORE" (237F/236B) Bee had to pay nearly twenty cents more per pound for pot roast because the new butcher refused to cut the fat off before weighing it. Mr. Harkinson always did.

"NEAT" (132F/128B) Barney's nickname for Juanita.

NECTARINE CRUSH (73F/70B) Soda from the cooler at Wally's Service Station. Floyd had already opened one when he realized that there was a new flavor in there he had been wanting to try, "Huckleberry Smash."

DR. NEELY (122F/121B) One of U. T. Pendyke's (Barney's) nonexistent associates. According to Pendyke, Neely would be interested in Miracle Salve as a mange cure.

MAVIS NEFF (213F/B) Girl who worked at the drugstore. She was kind of loose. Andy asked her out to spite Helen, who broke dates with Andy to work on her book. Andy took Mavis to Myer's Lake but it didn't work out. Harvey Bunker had to quit being scoutmaster after he dated Mavis. (See the entry HARVEY BUNKER)

"A NEGLIGEE WITH A BLACK NIGHTGOWN" (245F/244B) Andy suggested this to Emmett as an appropriate twenty-fifth anniversary gift for Emmett's wife, Martha.

NEIL (73F/70B) One of the farmers who sold produce from the back of a truck parked behind Dexter Street. His partner was Matt, and neither of them would move when

Barney ordered them to. (See entries MATT and DEXTER STREET)

"NEKOO YUTA AY CHOCHOONAY" (87F/B) Colonel Harvey claimed this was Shawnee sign language. He didn't translate it.

NELLY (86F/B) The name of Paul Revere's horse, according to Andy.

JEFF NELSON (191F/192B) Prisoner in for fighting, stealing chickens, and picking pockets. He was in for ten days. He was also a great tenor. When Howard Sprague couldn't sing in the barbershop quartet competition, Andy reluctantly agreed to use Jeff. Jeff escaped and came across the old hobo, Kelly, who remarked that Andy had always treated prisoners with respect. Jeff returned, sang, and they won the competition for the third year in a row, which allowed them to keep the trophy permanently in Mayberry.

SERGEANT NELSON (57F/B) Capitol City cop who showed Andy around their police department.

NELSON'S FUNERAL PARLOR (107F/127B) Mayberry funeral parlor. They put out a calender with the lyrics to the "Marine's Hymn" on it. That was how Gomer learned the words.

NELVIN (125F/124B) In order to insure privacy, Nelvin put up quarantine signs on his property that said he had cholera, yellow fever, and bubonic plague. He didn't want magazine subscriptions or his septic tank pumped out. Andy told him to get a "No Peddlers or Agents" sign, and to take down the quarantine signs.

NEURALGIA (201F/204B) (234F/232B) Clara Edwards suffered from it for many, many years. In 201F/204B, she regaled Floyd with details of where and how it hurt. In 234F/232B, she picked up her heating pad from Emmett's. She asked for it in a whisper. After all, there were men present.

"NEVER HIT YOUR GRANDMA WITH A GREAT BIG STICK" (94F/B) Song performed by the Darlings.

THE NEW DOCTOR 24th episode filmed and broadcast. Original broadcast date was March 27, 1961. It was written by Jack Elinson and Charles Stewart, and directed by Bob Sweeney. Regulars included Andy Griffith, Don Knotts, Ronny Howard, Frances Bavier, and Elinor Donahue. Guests included George Nader as Dr. Robert Benson.

A NEW DOCTOR IN TOWN 201st episode filmed and 204th episode broadcast. Original broadcast date was December 26, 1966. It was written by Ray Brenner and Barry E. Blitzer, and directed by Lee Phillips. Regulars included Andy Griffith, Frances Bavier, Ronny Howard, Aneta Corsaut, and Howard McNear. Guests included Hope Summers as Clara Edwards, William Christopher as Dr. Thomas Peterson, and Sari Price as Miss Oakley, Dr. Peterson's nurse. (Ironically, after playing a doctor here, William Christopher went on to play a priest—Father Mulcahy on "M*A*S*H," for the entire run of the series—rather than a doctor.)

"NEW FEATURE MAGAZINE" (188F/B) Magazine Goober read in the barbershop. He had taken it from Floyd's four months before, and then brought it back a month later.

THE NEW HOUSEKEEPER 1st episode filmed and broadcast. Original broadcast date was October 3, 1960. It was written by Jack Elinson and Charles Stewart, and directed by Sheldon Leonard. Regulars included Andy Griffith, Frances Bavier, Ronny Howard, and Don Knotts. Guests included Cheerio Meredith as Emma Brand, Frank Ferguson as Wilbur Pine (Rose's husband), and Mary Treen as Rose, Andy's resigning housekeeper.

NEW JERSEY (62F/B) Home state of Barney's cousin, Virgil.

"THE NEW MAYBERRY MINSTRELS" (116F/115B) The name Eleanora Poultice suggested for Andy, Barney, and Gomer when their choral "trio" went over so well at the concert. It was supposed to be a solo.

NEW ORLEANS (41F/39B) (67F/65B) (71F/72B) In 41F/39B, a busload of tourists passed through Mayberry from New Orleans. Floyd stopped the bus to show the tourists two famous lawmen, Barney and Andy. Floyd charged them two bits apiece to tour the courthouse. In 67F/65B, this story was told: one summer when they were young, Andy and Barney started out on a trip to New Orleans in Andy's Model A. It burned out a bearing "about D-Queen junction." Andy later sold the car for twelve dollars. Also in this episode, Peggy McMillan told Andy that she had been to New Orleans and Paris. In 71F/72B, Cliff Devereaux and his family went to New Orleans on a visit.

"NEW RIVER TRAIN" (83F/B) The song Rafe Hollister performed at the Ladies League musicale. Andy accompanied him on guitar.

NEW YORK (10F/12B) (100F/99B) (116F/115B) (226F/223B) In 10F/12B, New York was where Ed Sawyer originally came from. In 100F/99B, the visiting preacher, Dr. Breen, was from New York. In 116F/115B, John Masters got the arrangement of "Santa Lucia" from New York. In 226F/223B, when Lee Drake came looking for Andy, Goober told her he went to New York. (See all entries mentioned)

NEW YORK-CUT STEAK (153F/B) The Widow Saunders and the dishcloth salesman ate it at the Half Moon Roadhouse. (See the entry THE WIDOW SAUNDERS)

THE NEW YORK GIANTS (215F/B) Flip Conroy's team for ten years before he retired to Mayberry.

BRUCE NEWDELL (153F/B) Karen Folker was chasing Bruce when she fell down on the Elm Street playground.

"NEWS FROM THE ALTAR" (138F/B) The name of the church bulletin that printed Bee's name when she played the part of Alice in "The Little Prince."

"NICE" (105F/104B) The adjective Andy and Barney repeatedly used to describe Mary Grace Gossage in order to convince Gomer to take her to the chamber of commerce dance.

"NICE EVENIN' AIN'T IT?" (113F/112B) One of the phrases Andy taught Ernest T. Bass to say properly.

NICKEL (34F/33B) Opie's milk money cost a nickel. Sheldon the Bully took the nickel away from Opie every day, until Opie straightened him out.

NICOTINE (38F/31B) Mr. Wheeler's flower spray had too much nicotine for little flowers.

NINE (110F/109B) The number of blades on Opie's knife.

9:00 A.M. (18F/B) The time the Boones came to the courthouse every day for their "niceness" lessons from Andy.

NINE DOLLARS PER MONTH (236F/237B) The price Emmett wanted to charge Goober for the insurance policy Emmett tried to sell during his short-lived career as an insurance salesman. He worked for Martha's brother, Ben Beecham.

946 JARS (122F/121B) The number of jars of Miracle Salve that Barney had delivered to Andy in his failed attempt to help Opie out of a bind.

9-0-7 (88F/B) Violation against Briscoe Darling: dipping a hat in a horse trough. He dipped his hat in the David Mendlebright Memorial Horse Trough. (Briscoe's truck required eleven hatfuls of water when it overheated.)

9-1-1 (106F/B) The violation for which Barney wrote Gomer a ticket: making a U-turn. It bore a five-dollar fine.

9-1-2 (106F/B) Violation. Barney threatened to write Gomer a citation for this offense: insulting an officer's intelligence.

9:00 P.M. (68F/69B) The time Barney said they pulled in the sidewalks in Mayberry.

NINE PESOS (227F/222B) The amount Bee, Clara, and Myrtle tipped the bellboy when they got to their hotel in Mexico.

9-2-3 (106F/B) Unspecified violation for which Barney wrote Gomer a ticket.

1952 (137F/B) The year Andy started as sheriff of Mayberry. (See the entries THE SHERIFFS OF MAYBERRY and ANDY'S BEGINNINGS)

1948 (176F/B) The year Andy and Barney graduated from Mayberry Union High School. (See entry 1945)

1945 (82F/B) The year Andy and Barney graduated from Mayberry Union High School. (See entry 1948)

1960 (131F/129B) The year Barney met Thelma Lou. They met at Wilton Blair's funeral.

1931 (106F/B) The year Sheriff Pinckley arrested Tyler Branch's dad, Purcell, for disturbing the peace. Purcell drove down Main Street with the cutout open on his REO Flying Cloud.

1928 (91F/B) The year Barney was born.

1929 (139F/B) The year Barney was born.

$98.50 (223F/226B) Opie got a mail-order solicitation for commercial art lessons. Twelve lessons cost $98.50.

$97.00 (153F/B) The slipcovers the Widow Saunders bought cost ninety-seven dollars.

NINETY-THREE (238F/239B) The age at which Jarrod Hooper died.

NIP IT (IN THE BUD) (45F/B) (67F/65B) (76F/78B) (79F/77B) (106F/B) (112F/111B) In 45F/B, Barney wanted to "nip it" re: Jeff Pruitt's fascination with Thelma Lou. In 67F/65B, he suggested Andy's romance with the rich Peggy should be nipped. In 76F/78B, Barney gave the following speech to Chester after he caught him throwing a gum wrapper on the sidewalk: "You start with gum wrappers, and then it's paper bags, then newspapers, then tin cans, then rubbish. First thing you know Mayberry's up to here in litter! Now, litter brings slums, and slums bring crime. Is that what you want to see started here in Mayberry, a crime wave? Well, I don't. And I aim to nip it in the bud." In 79F/77B, Steve Quincy broke a street lamp with an apple core and blamed it on Opie. Barney then gave his famous "motorcycles and leather jackets" speech, of which this is the last part: "I say this calls for action and now! Nip it in the bud! First sign of youngsters going wrong, you've got to nip it in the bud. Nip it! You go read any book you want on the subject of child discipline and you'll find every one of them is in favor of bud nipping. There's only one way to take care of it." Andy then asked, "Nip it . . ?" And Barney replied, "In the bud!" In 106F/B, Barney shouted it at Otis when Otis was chanting, "Barney's in jail, Barney's in jail." Barney was locked up—at his own choosing—rather than pay the ticket Gomer gave him when Goober made a citizen's arrest for Barney's U-turn.

"NO COFFEE, TEA, OR PUNCH, THANK YOU" (113F/112B) One of the phrases Andy taught Ernest T. Bass to say properly.

"NO HANDS" (161F/160B) Opie was riding his bike no hands when he crashed it into a tree. He was trying to impress Sharon Porter.

"NOBODY LEAVES A WASHBASIN THE WAY YOU DO" (104F/105B) Mrs. Mendlebright's praise of Barney.

NOD (101F/96B) One of the three orphaned songbirds Opie adopted after he accidentally killed their mother with a slingshot. The other two birds were Wynken and Blynken.

NOOGATUCK (138F/B) The Indian chief Barney played in the Mayberry Centennial Pageant.

AVERY NOONAN (177F/B) Barney sent him to prison. When Barney returned to Mayberry for a visit, Warden Hix from the county work farm called Andy with the news that Noonan had escaped and was heading for Mayberry. Barney was, of course, afraid, Andy knew it, and Warren could not believe it. Andy ended up catching Noonan and making it look like Barney made the collar. Barney wanted to give the credit to Warren: "It's his town now, not mine." Barney was wrong, Mayberry would always be Barney's hometown.

CISSY NOONAN (114F/113B) Woman who wanted all white choir robes with black collars.

NORA (129F/130B) Bee's baby sister. She was married to Ollie and they had two children, Roger and Bruce. They came to visit Andy and Bee for a week. Nora tried to fix Andy up with her neighbor, Racine Tyler. (See mentioned entries)

NORBERT (146F/B) He ran over Barney's foot with a truck, of which the license plate number was GP-780. Barney gave him a citation for speeding, reckless driving, and failure to observe an officer.

NORMA'S BEAUTY SHOPPE (148F/B) Thelma Lou's hairdresser. The shop was on Main Street next to Ted's Pet Shop.

NORMAN (235F/234B) One of the guys who hung around the general store on St. Benedict's Island in the Caribbean.

"NORMAN FELDSPAR" (104F/105B) One of Mr. Fields' aliases.

NORMAN'S GROCETERIA (105F/104B) Mayberry grocery store. Andy related a story about a collie that had been shaved for the summer going up to Mrs. Speers in Norman's. Al Becker was also standing there.

NORRIS (242F/241B) Goober left Norris in charge of the filling station when he went to the auto show in Raleigh.

NORTH AVENUE (163F/161B) Street in Mayberry where the houses were "antebellum, early nineteenth century," according to Frank Smith.

NORTH CAROLINA STATE PRISON (11F/B) The home of the Hubacher brothers, thanks to Andy and Barney.

"NORTH SIDE OF TOWN" (236F/237B) The better section of Mayberry; the people with whom Martha Clark wanted to associate.

NORTH SLOPE (127F/126B) Barney went there to look for Opie after he was discovered to be missing from the "back to nature" camping trip. Barney got lost. (See the entry LAKE LOON)

"NORTHERN PART OF MOZAMBIQUE" (234F/232B) Bradford Taylor said Mayberry reminded him of the "northern part of Mozambique."

NOVEMBER (104F/105B) The month Barney first moved into Mrs. Mendlebright's boarding house.

"NOW IS THE MONTH OF MAY" (116F/115B) The song Barney rehearsed for Eleanora Poultice as part of his ongoing vocal training.

NUIT DE PARIS (69F/66B) "Paris Nights," Barney's cologne. It had Riviera rose petals in it. Andy and Opie both thought it smelled like paint.

NUTRITION MONEY (103F/B) The money Aunt Bee gave Opie every day for a midmorning snack at school.

NYLON TIRES (245F/244B) Goober offered Emmett a deal on nylon tires as a twenty-fifth wedding anniversary gift for Emmett's wife, Martha.

"O SOLO MIO" (241F/249B) Bee said this song was "the Italian national anthem," as she spoke at the meeting of the Mayberry Civic League that welcomed the Vincentes to Mayberry. (See the "VINCENTE" entries)

MISS OAKLEY (201F/204B) Dr. Thomas Peterson's nurse. She assisted in the removal of Opie's swollen tonsils.

OAKMONT ROAD, MT. PILOT (174F/173B) Harlan Robinson's address.

OFF TO HOLLYWOOD 166th episode filmed and broadcast. Original broadcast date was October 25, 1965. It was written by Bill Idelson and Sam Bobrick, and directed by Alan Rafkin. Regulars included Andy Griffith, Ronny Howard, Howard McNear, Frances Bavier, Aneta Corsaut, and George Lindsey. Guests included Jack Burns as Warren Ferguson, Maudie Prickett as Edna Larch, and Owen Bush as Mr. Jason.

"OFF WE GO INTO THE WILD BLUE YONDER" (243F/242B) The song Bee sang as she came downstairs after she started taking her flying lessons.

OFFICIAL STARTER (51F/B) Barney, at the yearly Boy's Day competition. He got to fire his pistol.

"OFFICIAL VERIFICATION" (33F/34B) Barney refused to remove a wanted poster from "his" bulletin board until he received "official verification," even though it was all over the papers that the criminal in question had been captured.

"OH, MY BARNEY" (41F/39B) Song written by Barney and sung to the tune of "Oh, My Darling."

In a jailhouse down in Dixie
Fightin' crime and riskin' life
Dwelled a sheriff and his buddy
Pistol Packin' Barney Fife
Oh my darin', oh my darin'
Oh my darin' Barney Fife
He's a deadly crime-stopper
What a copper Barney Fife
Then one day there come a-ridin'
Two bad men to rob a bank
But Fife was tricky, a dead-eye dicky
Now they're locked up in the tank

At this point Andy chimed in, making up the following:

Oh my Barney, Oh my Barney
Had a jail and couldn't lock it
Had a bullet for his pistol
Had to keep it in his pocket

"OH MY DARLING" (132F/128B) The song to which the students in Miss Crump's class danced.

OIL RAGS (119F/118B) Wally threw a cigar butt into a barrel of oil rags. They smoldered while Gomer slept. Andy woke Gomer, which Gomer saw as a great lifesaving move. Gomer then immediately professed to be eternally in Andy's debt, much to the sheriff's dismay. (See the entry "LIFESAVER MAN")

OKRA (73F/70B) 13¢ a pound as sold by Neil and Matt from the back of their truck.

"THE OLD COUNTRY" (69F/66B) London, England, according to Andy.

"THE OLD HOMESTEAD" (246F/245B) The name Howard called his and his mother's house.

"OLD LADY CRUMP" (86F/B) The name Opie used to describe Helen when she first took over his class.

OLD MAN MCCABE (240F/B) Mayberry man who owned a big house and lived there with his housekeeper. Barney used to play in his front yard. McCabe used to call Barney, "The Scamp." Barney would steal McCabe's apples, and play "Run, Sheep, Run," "Early, Early, Urchin Free," and "One, Two, Three Red Light" in McCabe's yard. Barney suggested McCabe's house as a possible site for the US/USSR summit meeting.

OLD MINE CAVES (109F/108B) Caves on the outskirts of Mayberry, near the site of the town picnic. Andy and Barney used to play in them when they were kids. Andy and Helen explored them during the town picnic, got caught in a rockslide, and were trapped in the caves. They were able to find a way out and hitched a ride back to town. When they heard on the radio that Barney had mobilized the entire town in a rescue operation, they went back to the caves and "re-trapped" themselves. They were later "rescued" by Barney. (See the entry "DEPUTY FIFE HERO IN CAVE RESCUE")

"OLD MR. TRANSPARENT" (125F/124B) The name Barney called Andy. The deputy thought that Andy was trying to hide his upcoming engagement to Helen.

OLD OAK TREE (13F/B) Centerpiece of the town of Mayberry. The townspeople wanted to cut it down when the Hollywood producer, Mr. Harmon, planned on making a movie in the town. Harmon was aghast and insisted they leave the tree alone.

OLD PEOPLE'S HOME (206F/B) Bee's sister, Ellen, took Bee to a handicraft exhibit at the home during Bee's visit.

"OLD PERSUADER" (110F/109B) The name Barney called his gun.

OLD PLANK BRIDGE (115F/114B) Otis drove through the railing and drowned, in Andy's and Barney's fictional eulogy of the drunk.

"OLD ROSCOE" (150F/B) The name Barney called his gun.

OLD SAM (198F/200B) Legendary—but real—giant silver carp that lived in Tucker's Lake. Everybody talked about hooking Old Sam but it was a beginner—Howard Sprague—who caught him. He donated Sam to the Raleigh Aquarium and everybody got mad; Sam was born and raised in Tucker's and that was where he belonged. Howard finally realized—thanks to Opie—that he had destroyed a tradition and so decided to put Sam back. Everyone was then happy.

"OLD TIGER FIFE" (212F/208B) Barney's nickname—according to Barney—when he dated Teena Andrews (nee Irene Flogg) in high school. (See the entries IRENE FLOGG and TEENA ANDREWS)

OLIVE (99F/98B) Waitress at the Diner. She was a widow with four children, and Andy and Barney both left her a quarter tip.

OLIVER (25F/B) In 25F/B, Barney's middle name. However, in 82F/B, his middle name was given as Milton. And, in 103F/B, 114F/113B, and 122F/121B, his middle initial was given as "P." (See the entries BARNEY'S MIDDLE NAME AND/OR INITIAL, MILTON, and "P")

OLIVER TWIST (202F/196B) The book which gave Arnold his knowledge of orphan asylums.

OLLIE (65F/67B) Man who called Floyd for a four o'clock appointment.

OLLIE (129F/130B) Aunt Bee's brother-in-law. He was married to Bee's baby sister, Nora. They had two children, Roger and Bruce, and they lived in Lake Charles. They came to visit Andy and Bee and caused quite a turmoil. Ollie tried to take over Andy's job, and did things such as play with the squad car's siren and the rifles. Andy hadn't seen Ollie for fifteen years.

CHARLIE O'MALLEY (74F/B) Mayberry man who owned a house which was used as a hideout by the "convicts at large." Charlie was in Detroit and the house was empty. The three lady convicts held Barney and Floyd as hostages. O'Malley's father-in-law was the founder of Jensen Orthopedic Loafers.

"ON HIS STOMACH" (207F/209B) How Howard Sprague slept.

"ONCE BIT, BEST FORGIT" (16F/20B) Barney used this saying to console himself after he realized he was wrong to arrest the whole town.

"ONCE BURNT IS A LESSON LEARNT" (16F/20B) Barney used this saying to console himself after he realized he was wrong to arrest the whole town.

1:00 A.M. (153F/B) The time the Widow Saunders got home from her date with the dishcloth salesman.

"ONE-AND-A-HALF BOYS PER SQUARE MILE" (5F/8B) The number of needy boys in Mayberry County.

1¢ (153F/B) The student rate for Opie's newspaper, "The Mayberry Sun."

$1.00 (58F/B) The amount Fred Goss charged to clean a suit.

$1.00 (133F/131B) Ernest T. Bass spent this amount to put gold leaf on his front tooth.

$1.00 (136F/B) Barney found a dollar once. He spent it all on a girl.

$1.50 (60F/B) The amount Bill Medwin, the bookie barber, charged for a facial.

$1.60 (38F/41B) The amount Mr. Wheeler charged Bee to spray her flowers.

$1.25 AN HOUR (161F/160B) Goober's wage at the filling station.

142 R (28F/B) Phone number of the Junction Cafe.

$100.00 (39F/36B) The face value of Frank Myers' 1861 Town of Mayberry bond.

$100.00 (234F/232B) The amount the Minister pledged to Aunt Bee's cousin Bradford's ice cream marketing scheme.

150 POUNDS (120F/119B) The weight of the side of beef that Bee bought from the discount butcher, Diamond Jim. It was tough. It cost her $133.50.

145 POUNDS (131F/129B) The weight required for Barney to remain a deputy. Bee helped him by feeding him a meal of pork chops, mashed potatoes, corn, rolls, and banana cream chocolate pie. Thelma Lou helped by bringing Barney a double rich vanilla malted with two raw eggs.

145,000 (225F/224B) The number of miles that were on Aunt Bee's convertible.

163 POUNDS (117F/116B) The weight of the "shoplifter" after she was caught wearing all the goods she stole from Weaver's Department Store.

162 YARDS (225F/224B) The length of the #4 hole on the Walnut Hills golf course.

$133.50 (120F/119B) The cost of the 150-pound side of beef Bee bought at Diamond Jim's.

132 POUNDS (117F/116B) Barney's weight.

103 YEARS OLD (10F/12B) The age of Joe McKnight when Ed Sawyer came to Mayberry.

120-125 POUNDS (51F/B) Barney's weight when he won the fifty-yard dash medal as a boy.

ONE MILE (40F/38B) The distance from Andy's house to Myer's Lake.

"ONE MISTAKE A BETTER CAKE" (16F/20B) Barney used this saying to console himself after he realized he was wrong to arrest the whole town.

115 (87F/B) Violation. Parking next to a hydrant.

1:00 P.M. (61F/B) The time of the malfeasance hearing against Andy.

177 MAIN STREET (171F/172B) The address of Hansen's Print Shop. They went out of business at that address. The two counterfeiters, Ralph Kingsley and Arnold Finch, opened a money factory at that address.

1:30 P.M. (3F/B) The time Bobby Fleet and his Band with a Beat arrived in Mayberry.

1000 (74F/B) Sally's prison number. She was one of the "convicts at large."

$1,000.00 (236F/237B) The amount of money Opie would receive at the age of twenty-one from an insurance policy Andy bought from Emmett.

"1,2,3 RED LIGHT" (240F/B) The game Barney used to play in Old Man McCabe's front yard.

ONE WEEK (161F/160B) The trial period Mr. Doakes allowed Opie and Billy Crenshaw. He hired them both for one week at his market. At the end of the week, Doakes chose Opie.

ONE-PUNCH OPIE 79th episode filmed and 77th episode broadcast. Original broadcast date was December 31, 1962. It was written by Harvey Bullock, and directed by Bob Sweeney. Regulars included Andy Griffith, Don Knotts, Ronny Howard, and Frances Bavier. Guests included Clint Howard as Leon, Stanley Farrar, Kim Tyler, Scott McCartor, and Richard Keith.

ONION (38F/41B) Mr. Wheeler asked to borrow one from Bee for a stew he was making.

ONIONS (73F/70B) 5¢ a bunch as sold by Neil and Matt from the back of their truck.

ONLY A ROSE 203rd episode filmed and 201st episode broadcast. Original broadcast date was December 5, 1966. It was written by Jim Parker and Arnold Margolin, and directed by Lee Phillips. Regulars included Andy Griffith, Frances Bavier, Ronny Howard, and Howard McNear. Guests included Hope Summers as Clara Edwards, Maxine Semon as Tillie, John Reilly as Billy, and Ruth Thom as Ella Carson.

"THE ONLY LAW WEST OF MT. PILOT" (109F/108B) The Mayberry sheriff, according to Barney.

PREACHER RAYMOND OPEL (139F/B) The Darlings' minister.

"OPERATION GOLD TRUCK" (102f/B) The name Barney assigned to the gold shipment that passed through Mayberry.

"OPERATION PICKLE SWITCH" (43F/B) Andy's and Barney's plan to put store pickles in Aunt Bee's jars, so they would be able to eat the pickles without suffering.

"OPERATOR FIFE" (115F/114B) The name Barney called himself when he staked out Otis's activities after the drunk bought a car.

OPIE AND HIS MERRY MEN 108th episode filmed and 107th episode broadcast. Original broadcast date was December 30, 1963. It was written by John Whedon, and directed by Dick Crenna. Regulars included Andy Griffith, Don Knotts, Frances Bavier, and Ronny Howard. Guests included Richard Keith as Johnny Paul Jason, Joey Scott as Howard Pruitt, Dennis Rush as Whitey, and Douglas Fowley as Wary Willy the Hobo.

OPIE AND MIKE 248th episode filmed and 247th episode broadcast. Original broadcast date was March 18, 1968. It was written by Douglas Tibbles and Bob Ross, and directed by Lee Phillips. Regulars included Andy Griffith, Frances Bavier, Ronny Howard, George Lindsey, Ken Berry as Sam Jones, and Buddy Foster as Mike Jones.

OPIE AND THE BULLY 34th episode filmed and 33rd episode broadcast. Original broadcast date was October 2, 1961. It was written by David Adler, and directed by Bob Sweeney. Regulars included Andy Griffith, Don Knotts, Ronny Howard, and Frances Bavier. Guests included Terry Dickinson as Sheldon the bully.

OPIE AND THE CARNIVAL 158th episode filmed and broadcast. Original broadcast date was April 26, 1965. It was written by Fred Freeman and Lawrence J. Cohen, and directed by Coby Ruskin. Regulars included Andy Griffith, Ronny Howard, George Lindsey, Frances Bavier, and Aneta Corsaut. Guests included Richard Keith as Johnny Paul Jason, Lewis Charles as Pete, and Billy Halop as Charlie.

OPIE AND THE SPOILED KID 84th episode filmed and broadcast. Original broadcast date was February 18, 1963. It was written by Jim Fritzell and Everett Greenbaum, and directed by Bob Sweeney. Regulars included Andy Griffith, Ronny Howard, and Don Knotts. Guests included Ronnie Dapo as Arnold Winkler, Harlan Warde as Simon Winkler, and Mary Lansing as Mrs. Tarbochs.

OPIE FINDS A BABY 202nd episode filmed and 199th episode broadcast. Original broadcast date was November 21, 1966. It was written by Stan Drebel and Sid Mandel, and directed by Lee Phillips. Regulars included Andy Griffith, Ronny Howard, Frances Bavier, George Lindsey, and Aneta Corsaut. Guests included Sheldon Golomb as Arnold Bailey, Jack Nicholson as Mr. Garland, Jamie Kelly as Mrs. Garland, and James McCallion as Lou. (This was Nicholson's first of two appearances on the show. The other was in 223F/226B, "Aunt Bee the Juror," as Marvin Jenkins.)

OPIE FLUNKS ARITHMETIC 157th episode filmed and broadcast. Original broadcast date was April 19, 1965. It was written by Richard Morgan, and directed by Coby Ruskin. Regulars included Andy Griffith, Don Knotts, Ronny Howard, Frances Bavier, and Aneta Corsaut. This episode was the last regular-season appearance of Don Knotts.

OPIE LOVES HELEN 132nd episode filmed and 128th episode broadcast. Original broadcast date was September 21, 1964. It was written by Bob Ross, and directed by Aaron Ruben. Regulars included Andy Griffith, Don Knotts, Frances Bavier, Ronny Howard, and Aneta Corsaut. Guests included Mary Lansing as Miss Primrose, Richard Keith as Johnny Paul Jason, Betsy Hale as Betty Ann, and Ronda Jeter as Sharon McCall. Group dances performed in this episode were staged by Jennie Gold.

OPIE STEPS UP IN CLASS 225th episode filmed and 224th episode broadcast. Original broadcast date was October 9, 1967. It was written by Joseph Bonaduce, and directed by Lee Phillips. Regulars included Andy Griffith, Frances Bavier, Ronny Howard, Paul Hartman, and Jack Dodson. Guests included Sandy Kenyon as George Hollander, Joyce Van Patten as Laura Hollander, Don Wyndham as Billy, Ivan Bonar as Mr. Breckinridge, Ward Ramsey as Mr. Glendon, Monty Margetts as the Maid, and Thom Carney as the Chauffeur.

"OPIE TAYLOR, SR." (122F/121B) Pose Gomer adopted when he and Barney went to the Miracle Salve Company to try and get Opie and his friends out of their trouble with the company.

OPIE THE BIRDMAN 101st episode filmed and 96th episode broadcast. Original broadcast date was September 30, 1963. It was written by Harvey Bullock, and directed by Dick Crenna. Regulars included Andy Griffith, Ronny Howard, Don Knotts, and Frances Bavier. (This was the epitome of "The Andy Griffith Show." The single best episode of all 249 episodes.)

OPIE'S ALLOWANCE (84F/B) Opie received a quarter per week for cleaning the garage, taking out the ashes, keeping the woodbox filled, and setting the table every night.

OPIE'S APTITUDE TEST (157F/B) Barney administered the following test to Opie after the boy got a "D" in arithmetic and everybody—except Helen—overreacted.

1. If you had a choice, what would you do? Read a book or build a boat?
2. If somebody were to present you with a gift, would you prefer an electric motor or a chemistry set?

Opie picked read a book and electric motor.

OPIE'S AUTOGRAPHS (165F/169B) While in Hollywood, Opie got the autographs of Audie Murphy, Tony Curtis, Doris Day, Rock Hudson, Kirk Douglas, Dean Martin, and Dave Schneider. Schneider was a necktie salesman. His sunglasses fooled the Taylors.

OPIE'S CHARITY 5th episode filmed and 8th episode broadcast. Original broadcast date was November 28, 1960. It was written by Arthur Stander, and directed by Don Weis. Regulars included Andy Griffith, Ronny Howard, and Frances Bavier. Guests included Stu Erwin as Tom Silby, and Lurene Tuttle as Annabelle Silby.

OPIE'S DRUGSTORE JOB 239th episode filmed and 238th episode broadcast. Original broadcast date was January 15, 1968. It was written by Kent Wilson, and directed by Lee Phillips. Regulars included Andy Griffith, Ronny Howard, Jack Dodson, and George Lindsey. Guests included Robert F. Simon as Mr. Crawford, Sheldon Collins (formerly Golomb) as Arnold Bailey, Diane Deininger as Mrs. Briggs, and Jim Begg as the Man.

OPIE'S FAVORITE PIE (32F/B) (103F/B) In 32F/B, apple. In 103F/B, butterscotch.

OPIE'S FIRST LOVE 220th episode filmed and broadcast. Original broadcast date was September 11, 1967. It was written by Ron Friedman and Pat McCormack, and directed by Lee Phillips. Regulars included Andy Griffith, Ronny Howard, Frances Bavier, and George Lindsey. Guests included Sheldon Golomb as Arnold Bailey.

OPIE'S FORTUNE 136th episode filmed and broadcast. Original broadcast date was November 16, 1964. It was written by Ben Joelson and Art Baer, and directed by Coby Ruskin. Regulars included Andy Griffith, Ronny Howard, Don Knotts, and Frances Bavier. Guests included Jon Lormer as Parnell Rigsby, Mary Jackson as Mrs. Rigsby, and Bill McLean as Mac, although on the air he was called "Max."

OPIE'S GIRLFRIEND 190th episode filmed and broadcast. Original broadcast date was September 12, 1966. It was written by Budd Grossman, and directed by Lee Philips. Regulars included Andy Griffith, Ronny Howard, Frances Bavier, Aneta Corsaut, George Lindsey, and Howard McNear. Guests included Mary Ann Durkin as Cynthia, and John Reilly as Billy.

OPIE'S GODFATHER (67F/65B) Barney Fife.

OPIE'S GROUP 229th episode filmed and 228th episode broadcast. Original broadcast date was November 6, 1967. It was written by Doug Tibbles, and directed by Lee Phillips. Regulars included Andy Griffith, Ronny Howard, Frances Bavier, George Lindsey, Paul Hartman, and Hope Summers. Guests included Sheldon Collins as Arnold, Jim Kidwell as Clifford, Joe Leitch as Wilson, Gary Chase as Jesse, and Kay Ann Kemper as "Joy," although the character name in the credits is probably incorrect. There was no "Joy" character in this episode, but there was a "Phoebe" for which no screen credit was given. It's likely that Kay Ann Kemper played Phoebe.

OPIE'S HOBO FRIEND 40th episode filmed and 38th episode broadcast. Original broadcast date was November 13, 1961. It was written by Harvey Bullock, and directed by Bob Sweeney. Regulars included Andy Griffith, Don Knotts, Frances Bavier, and Ronny Howard. Guests included Buddy Ebsen as David Browne, the hobo.

OPIE'S ILL-GOTTEN GAIN 103rd episode filmed and broadcast. Original broadcast date was November 18, 1963. It was written by John Whedon, and directed by Jeffrey Hayden. Regulars included Andy Griffith, Ronny Howard, Don Knotts, Frances Bavier, and Aneta Corsaut.

OPIE'S JOB 161st episode filmed and 160th episode broadcast. Original broadcast date was September 13, 1965. It was written by Art Baer and Ben Joelson, and directed by Larry Dobkin. Regulars included Andy Griffith, Frances Bavier, Ronny Howard, Howard NcNear, and George Lindsey. Guests included Ronda Jeter as Sharon, John Bangert as Billy, and Norris Goff as Mr. Doakes.

OPIE'S LETTER TO HELEN (132F/128B) Opie decided he was in love with Helen. So, along with his gift to her of nylon stockings—for which he paid 80¢: 74¢ in savings and 6¢ from cashing in three soda bottles—he also sent her this note:

> "Dear Miss Crump,
> XXXXXXXXXXXXXXXXXXXXXX
> Your friend, Opie."

There were twenty-three X's.

OPIE'S MOST UNFORGETTABLE CHARACTER 218th episode filmed and broadcast. Original broadcast date was April 3, 1967. It was written by Michael Morris and Seaman Jacobs,, and directed by Lee Phillips. Regulars included Andy Griffith, Ronny Howard, Frances Bavier, George Lindsey, Aneta Corsaut, and Jack Dodson. Guests included Sheldon Golomb as Arnold, and Joy Ellison as Betsy.

OPIE'S NEWSPAPER 153rd episode filmed and broadcast. Original broadcast date was March 22, 1965. It was written by Harvey Bullock, and directed by Coby Ruskin. Regulars included Andy Griffith, Ronny Howard, Frances Bavier, and Don Knotts. Guests included Dennis Rush as Howie Pruitt, Kelly Thordsen as Harold Grigsby, Vici Raaf as Sue Grigsby, Irene Tedrow as Mrs. Foster, William Keene as Reverend Martin, and Burt Mustin as Sam Benson.

OPIE'S PIANO LESSON 215th episode filmed and broadcast. Original broadcast date was March 13, 1967. It was written by Leo and Pauline Townsend, and directed by Lee Phillips. Regulars included Andy Griffith, Ronny Howard, Frances Bavier, and Hope Summers. Guests included Rockne Tarrington as Flip Conroy, Richard Bull as Mr. Jackson, Maudie Prickett as Mrs. Larch, Sheldon Golomb as Arnold, Chuck Campbell as Boy #3, Johnny Jenson as Tim, and Kirk Travis as Joey.

OPIE'S PROVISION BAG FOR GEORGE FOLEY (4F/6B) Opie packed George—the "runaway kid"—a bag containing sweet pickles, marshmallows, olives, bubble gum, and a peanut butter-and-sardine sandwich.

OPIE'S RIVAL 64th episode filmed and 73th episode broadcast. Original broadcast date was December 3, 1962. It was written by Sid Morse, and directed by Bob Sweeney. Regulars included Andy Griffith, Frances Bavier, and Ronny Howard. Guests included Joanna Moore as Peggy McMillan.

OPIE'S THREE WISHES (142F/141B) These are the wishes Opie wanted fulfilled by Count Iz Van Talecki:
1. A jacknife.
2. A "B" in arithmetic.
3. Helen could still be his teacher in the sixth grade.

All three came true.

OPIE'S WANT AD (239F/238B) Opie ran an ad that got him a job working for Mr. Crawford at the drugstore: "Wanted. Steady Job. After school and on Saturdays. I am nearly 14 years old, untrained but ambitious and willing to learn. Opie Taylor. 426." He wanted to earn enough money to buy a new electric guitar.

ORANGE AND BLUE (82F/B) Mayberry Union High School's colors.

ORANGE CRATES (104F/105B) Barney used the crates to make bookshelves after he moved out of Mrs. Mendlebright's boarding house and into the backroom of the courthouse.

ORANGE SODA (246F/245B) One of the drinks Howard Sprague offered at his "swinging" party.

ORANGES (29F/B) (54F/B) (84F/B) (133F/131B) In 29F/B, three pounds for 25¢. In 54F/B, and 133F/131B, 29¢ a dozen. In 84F/B, 19¢.

ORCHARD ROAD (228F/227B) The location of the abandoned Ferguson farm.

ORDINANCE 502 (32F/B) Being intoxicated in a public place. Andy ruled that Otis violated this law and sentenced him to a two-dollar fine or twenty-four hours in jail. Otis, of course, took the twenty-four hours.

OREGANO (206F/B) The secret ingredient in Goober's, Mrs. Sprague's, and Helen's Uncle Edward's special tomato sauce.

"OREGON TO NOVA SCOTIA" (43F/B) Barney gave away all of Aunt Bee's pickles to people he stopped on the road. He said they were scattered "from Oregon to Nova Scotia."

ORVILLE MONROE'S FUNERAL PARLOR (3F/B) Main Street business. Jim Lindsey played guitar in front of the parlor. Orville complained and Andy arrested Jim for disturbing the peace. Orville doubled as Mayberry's TV repairman.

OSCAR (1F/B) Opie's never-seen lizard.

OSGOOD (44F/B) Mayberry man who had an argument with Huey Welch over a spike fence Osgood built which was blocking the sun to Huey's chickens. Barney arrested them, and Andy solved the problem by suggesting Osgood put up a chicken wire fence.

JONATHAN T. OSGOOD (132F/128B) Author of the book, *Poems of Romance*.

OTIS SUES THE COUNTY 141st episode filmed and 142nd episode broadcast. Original broadcast date was December 28, 1964. It was written by Bob Ross, and directed by Howard Morris. Regulars included Andy Griffith, Don Knotts, Howard McNear, and Hal Smith. Guests included Jay Novello as Attorney Neil Bentley, and Bartlett Robinson as Mr. Roberts.

OTIS THE ARTIST 175th episode filmed and broadcast. Original broadcast date was January 3, 1966. It was written by Fred Freeman and Lawrence J. Cohen from a story by Bob Ross, and it was directed by Alan Rafkin. Regulars included Andy Griffith, Hal Smith as Otis, Frances Bavier, Ronny Howard, George Lindsey, and Jack Burns as Warren Ferguson.

OTIS THE DEPUTY 204th episode filmed and 202nd episode broadcast. Original broadcast date was December 12, 1966. It was written by Jim Parker and Arnold Margolin, and directed by Lee Phillips. Regulars included Andy Griffith, Jack Dodson, and Hal Smith as Otis. Guests included Charles Dierkop as Larry, and Joe Turkell as Fred.

OTIS'S BEGINNINGS (152F/B) On September 23, 1941, at 2:00 P.M., Otis Campbell was booked for intoxication at the Mayberry Garden Club flower show. The sentence was suspended because it was the defendant's first offense.

OTIS'S CAR (115F/114B) Otis took a night job to save the money to buy a car. Andy and Barney at first tried to guess what he was saving for—his own still? A suit of clothes? (No, he had a suit.) A fishing pole? Or maybe a trip to Natural Bridge, Virginia, or that alligator farm in Florida? No, he was buying a "hot rod." It's license plate number was AY-321.

OTIS'S DIRECTIONS TO RAFE HOLLISTER'S STILL (44F/B) "Go out Route 22 past Wainsboro, Medville, Thorndike, Hobson, through Virginia, Pennsylvania, Ohio, back through West Virginia, Kentucky, Tennessee, into Mayberry on Route 10, to Elm Street, 411 Elm Street." 411 Elm Street was Barney's address.

OTIS'S EULOGY (115F/114B) To dissuade Otis from driving drunk, Andy and Barney pretended to eulogize him while he was asleep in his cell. They invented a story that Otis drove down Two Mile Hill, around the curve, out on Old Plank Bridge, through the railing, and drowned. They then sang "We Shall Meet," threw water on Otis, and told him he was dreaming.

OTTO (118F/117B) Mayberry merchant. Andy assured him that his doorknob would be checked as usual even during Andy's vacation.

"OUTER MONGOLIA" (230F/229B) Subject of the next lecture at the Mayberry women's club, after Professor Hubert St. John's lecture on South America.

OUTGOING AIR MAIL SLOT (36F/37B) The slot Barney had to show Melissa Stevens at the Post Office when she came to town.

"OVER 8,000 FEET" (243F/242B) The height to which Aunt Bee flew in her first demonstration flight at MacDonald's Flying School.

"OVER EIGHT WEEKS" (183F/182B) Helen Crump said there hadn't been any rain in Mayberry for over eight weeks when the gypsies came to town.

P

"P." (103F/B) (122F/121B) In both of these episodes, Barney said his middle initial was "P." However, in 25F/B and 114F/113B, he said his middle name was Oliver. And in 82F/B, he said his middle name was Milton. (See entries BARNEY'S MIDDLE NAME AND/OR INITIAL," MILTON, and OLIVER)

ETHEL PAGE (116F/115B) Organist who used to perform at the Pot 'O Honey Restaurant. She still had the canary with her during these performances.

THE PAGEANT 138th episode filmed and broadcast. Original broadcast date was November 30, 1964. It was written by Harvey Bullock, and directed by Gene Nelson. Regulars included Andy Griffith, Don Knotts, Ronny Howard, and Frances Bavier. Guests included Barbara Perry as Doris Williams, Olan Soule as John Masters, Hope Summers as Clara Edwards, and James Brewer as Duane.

SHERIFF FRED PALEY (106F/B) Early sheriff of Mayberry. He was in office after Sheriff Pinckley and before Sheriff Dale Buckley. (See entry THE SHERIFFS OF MAYBERRY)

PALM BEACH (71F/72B) Madeline Grayson claimed she had a home there.

CATHERINE PALMER (64F/73B) Friend of Aunt Bee's. She wasn't feeling well and Aunt Bee brought her over something to eat.

DOUG PALMER (54F/B) Mrs. Palmer's husband.

LOUISE PALMER (100F/99B) (120F/119B) In 100F/99B, Andy borrowed a sewing machine from her so Bee and Clara could work on the band costumes. In 120F/119B, it was stated that Fred Pawlis worked for her.

MRS. DOUG PALMER (54F/B) (58F/B) In 54F/B, she was one of Bert Miller's customers. In 58F/B—according to Fred Goss, the drycleaner—she brought in suits with elderberry wine stains.

PALMERTON CAFE (155F/B) (159F/B) In 155F/B, Skippy and Daphne sped by it at 45 mph in a 20 mph zone. In 150F/B, it was shown as the cafe on the corners of Paymore and Rockford Streets.

CLIFF PAMALEE (191F/192B) The tenor Wally suggested to take Howard's place in the barbershop quartet. The problem with Cliff? He was hard of hearing and sang too loud.

PANAMA CANAL DAY (17F/B) Holiday used by the customers of the Morrison sisters as an excuse to buy the ladies' moonshine. The sisters would only sell their "Special Elixir" for recognized holidays and special ocassions.

PANCAKE EATING CONTEST (243F/242B) Goober won the contest at the county fair by eating fifty-seven pancakes.

PANSY (162F/164B) Daughter of Dick. When Dick's wife was arrested by Warren for playing bingo, Dick showed up for supper at Andy's house with Pansy.

PANSY (203F/201B) Blue ribbon category at the Mayberry Garden Club flower show.

PANSY DIVISION (203F/210B) First prize at the Mayberry Garden Club flower show went to Floyd Lawson. Second prize went to Ella Batkins. They were the only two entries.

PAPER LADDER (89F/B) (124F/123B) The toy Malcolm Merriweather made for Opie.

"A PAPERMILL IN CANADA" (234F/232B) According to Bradford Taylor, one of his many travel stops.

PARCEL POST WINDOW (36F/37B) Barney had to direct Melissa Stevens to the window when she first came to town. (See "STEVENS" entries and the entry OUTGOING AIR MAIL SLOT)

PARCHEESI (26F/B) One of the games Barney played against himself. He also played himself at checkers and cassino.

PARIS (6F/4B) (67F/65B) In 6F/4B, Andy mentioned that he had been there during the war. In 67F/65B, Peggy McMillan told Andy that she had been to New Orleans and Paris.

AGNES JEAN PARKER (211F/207B) Daughter of Ma Parker. She played up to Barney, leading him on, in order to get information from him as to where the police would be on stakeout for the supermarket robberies. Agnes Jean and her family were the perpetrators of the robberies. Barney called her "Ag."

BETTY PARKER (153F/B) Classmate of Opie's. Betty let Bobby Wilson carry her books. She also wrote sugar notes to Hector Stiles.

BETTY PARKER (217F/B) Sister of Tommy Parker. She worked at the Embassy Dance Hall in Siler City. Howard Sprague ended up falling for Betty when he became Tommy's "big brother." He started out simply driving her to work, but before long, he was hooked. Andy found out and made Howard realize that he was neglecting not only Tommy, but his own Civil Service exam preparations.

GILLY PARKER (58F/B) He brought in a pair of pants to Fred Goss, the drycleaner. It had a poker chip in its pocket.

HENNY PARKER (211F/207B) One of the Parker boys, and a crook.

JERRY PARKER (14F/B) Opie's friend. Opie planned on going to Jerry's and skating back; he wanted to trade his "licorice seeds" for Jerry's skates. It wasn't said if Jerry was related to Betty and Tommy Parker, the Parker family from Raleigh, or any of the other Parkers in Mayberry. Opie got the licorice seeds when he traded his cap pistol to Tommy Farrell.

JUDGE PARKER (47F/B) The judge who heard Ronald Bailey's case.

LEROY PARKER (211F/207B) One of the Parker boys, and a crook.

MA PARKER (211F/207B) Barney's landlady in Raleigh, and a crook.

TOMMY PARKER (217F/B) Howard became his "big brother." Tommy had a high IQ and lived alone with his sister, Betty. His parents traveled with a carnival ten months out of the year. Howard ended up falling for Betty. (See BETTY PARKER)

PARKER CREEK (200F/197B) (208F/212B) Creek on old Ranch Road, the main road from Raleigh to Mayberry. In 200F/197B, the ladies, led by Bee, wanted to build a new bridge over the creek, but Howard suggested building it on Baker Street. This would save $3,628, including $468 to repair the old bridge. In 208F/212B, Clara Edwards wanted to plant flowers on the railing of the bridge that ran over the creek with the $1,200 in the civic improvement committee's treasury.

THE PARKERS (211F/207B) The family Barney lived with in Raleigh. They had a boarding house. The Parkers were the ones behind a string of supermarket robberies in Raleigh. They were getting their information from Barney. He was naively telling the family exactly where the police would be on stakeout. Andy figured out the truth while he was in Raleigh visiting Barney, and he made Barney look like a hero. This saved Barney's job. The Parkers consisted of Ma, Leroy, Henny, and Agnes Jean.

MRS. PARKINS (237F/236B) Non-existent woman Andy told Aunt Bee he hired to do the cooking while Bee did her cooking show, "The Mayberry Chef."

PARKINSON'S FALLS (166F/B) Andy suggested he and the family go there with some of the $1,000 he received from Belmont Studios. Bee and Opie instead wanted to go to Hollywood.

OLD MAN PARMALEE (143F/B) Andy bought the Taylor house from Parmalee.

ESTELLE PARSONS (58F/B) Mayberry girl. Bee asked Andy if he was taking her to an unnamed Saturday night dance.

MILLIE PARSONS (15F/B) She put blonde streaks in her hair. Bee Taylor, Clara Linsey, and Emma Brand gossiped about her in the drugstore one afternoon.

PASSKEY (55F/B) One of the Gordon boys being held in the Mayberry jail used the metalcraft set given to him by Barney to make a passkey to break out of the cell.

THE PASTOR (224F/221B) Bee suggested him as a replacement bowler for Lou Jenkins. Andy turned the Reverend down because the boys on the team occasionally used profanity. Bee understood.

PATTERSON'S (110F/109B) Clothing store where Barney paid $3.95 for a new shirt. He bought it because he thought he was going to escort the queen of the state Apricot Festival around Mayberry on June 23, 1952. Andy took her instead. (See mentioned entries)

PATTY'S PLACE (230F/229B) Roadhouse cafe. Bee wanted to take Professor Hubert St. John there during her "swinger" charade.

PAUL REVERE HIGH SCHOOL (82F/B) School in Chicago. Mrs. Ralph Haines was "in debate" there.

FRED PAWLIS (120F/119B) He worked for Louise Palmer. Because he once helped Bee fix a clothesline, she wanted him to look at her broken freezer.

PAYMORE AND ROCKFORD STREETS (159F/B) School crossing corner. Andy assigned it to Jerry Miller.

CHARLES COATSWORTH PAYNTON (203F/196B) Historical figure to whom Howard Sprague attributed the quotation, "Millions for defense, but not one cent for tribute." (See CHARLES COATSWORTH PINCKNEY and THE 'MILLIONS FOR...' QUOTATION)

SAM PEABODY (5F/8B) Mayberry alderman who attended Tom Silby's funeral. Tom never liked Sam and was upset later when he heard that Sam had been to his funeral (Tom hadn't died, he'd run away from his wife). (See TOM SILBY)

PEABODY ROSE (38F/41B) Bee grew one and Mr. Wheeler complimented her on it.

PEACE OFFICER'S BOWLING TOURNAMENT (140F/B) The Mt. Pilot event that prevented Andy from seeing Helen on a Thursday night.

PEACHES (73F/70B) 13¢ a pound as sold by Neil and Matt from the back of their truck.

PEACHES (162F/164B) (192F/191B) (201F/204B) 10¢.

PEANUT BUTTER (65F/67B) While Aunt Bee was at her Aunt Louise's, Peggy McMillan made Opie a peanut butter sandwich for lunch.

PEANUT BUTTER AND BOLOGNA, PEANUT BUTTER AND LIVERWURST, PEANUT BUTTER AND PEANUT BUTTER (4F/6B) The variety of sandwiches Opie prepared for George ("the runaway kid") Foley's trip to Texas.

PEANUT BUTTER AND JELLY SANDWICH (78F/76B) (79F/77B) (102F/B) (117F/116B) Leon offered one to either Andy or Barney in each of these episodes.

PEARL (142F/141B) Woman Andy greeted on Main Street.

PEARS (148F/B) 25¢.

PEAS (162F/164B) 10¢.

"PEETON PLACE" (150F/B) The way Barney pronounced "Peyton Place."

PEGGY'S BEAUTY SALON (135F/B) Mt. Pilot business next to the Mt. Pilot Judo Society.

PENCIL (196F/203B) Opie gave Andy a pencil for his adult education night course in history. The pencil had Howie Forman's teeth marks on it.

MRS. ETHEL PENDLETON (244F/243B) (245F/244B) In 244F/243B, she was the head of the PTA and the sometime housekeeper of Andy and Opie. She instigated the hearing to remove Helen from the school system after it was discovered that Helen had been arrested. In 245F/244B, she stayed with Andy and Opie when Aunt Bee went out of town.

"U. T. PENDYKE, D.V.M." (122F/121B) Pose Barney adopted when he and Gomer went to the Miracle Salve Company in an attempt to get Opie and his friends out of their trouble with the company. He said his practice was "limited to small animals, dogs, cats, birds of all kinds and small sheep." He told the manager he tried the Miracle Salve on six animals and that on all six it cured their mange. He said he had previously been using Molly Harkins Mange Cure.

PENITENTIARY (50F/B) Book Barney read.

"A PENNY EARNED IS A PENNY TAXED" (120F/119B) Andy's response to Bee's assertion that "A penny saved is a penny earned." She used the maxim to defend buying sugar in a twenty-five-pound sack because it was more economical. She then spilled half the sugar on the table because the sack was too unwieldy to handle.

PEORIA (38F/41B) Bee's family moved there when she was eighteen.

PEPE (216F/B) Author of *Jokes For All Occasions*, the book Howard bought to help build up his comedy act.

THE PERFECT FEMALE 37th episode filmed and 40th episode broadcast. Original broadcast date was November 27, 1961. It was written by Jack Elinson and Charles Stewart, and directed by Bob Sweeney. Regulars included Andy Griffith, Don Knotts, Frances Bavier, and Betty Lynn. Guests included Gail Davis as Karen Moore.

PERFUME (11F/B) (245F/244B) In 11F/B, the gift from Ben Weaver to Ellie Walker at the Christmas Eve party held at the courthouse. In 245F/244B, Goober suggested perfume (or a smoked ham) as an anniversary gift for Martha Clark from her husband, Emmett.

DOYLE PERKINS (220F/B) (221F/235B) (225F/224B) Mayberry clothier. In 220F/B, he sold Opie a new suit for Arnold Bailey's thirteenth birthday party. In 221F/235B, Goober did a valve job on his car. In 225F/224B, he sold Andy a new suit.

MRS. PERKINS (229F/228B) Woman who wouldn't speak to Aunt Bee because of the volume of Opie's band's rehearsal. It wasn't said if Mrs. Perkins was related to Doyle Perkins.

OLD MR. PERKINS (105F/104B) (247F/246B) In 105F/104B, it was mentioned he always stood in the stag line at the chamber of commerce dances. It wasn't said if this was Doyle Perkins, the clothier. In 247F/246B, Andy and Howard went to see him to encourage him to vote for Sam for head of city council.

"PERSONAL" (11F/B) The note Hilda Mae put on all her cards to Barney.

PETE (184F/B) Friend of Opie's. He and Opie fed Evie Joy blueberries.

"PETE THE TRAMP" (40F/38B) The name Barney called Dave the Hobo.

BURLEY PETERS (72F/71B) Member of the Mayberry Band. He played the chair.

JENNIE PETERS (165F/169B) She got jealous that Bee was the sweepstakes winner on "Win or Lose."

MAGGIE PETERS (194F/B) She had a reception for the new Reverend Leighton.

MRS. PETERS (161F/160B) Mayberry woman who phoned the following order in to Mr. Doakes' market: loaf of bread, one pound of butter, and paper napkins.

PETERSON (140F/B) The Stokes County game warden who arrested Andy for fishing without a license. He took Andy and Helen to a Siler City justice of the peace and fined Andy twenty-five dollars. Andy called Goober to have Barney bring the money, and the story got twisted into a non-existent wedding ceremony for Helen and Andy.

PETERSON (176F/B) He came to the class reunion.

DETECTIVE PETERSON (211F/207B) One of Barney's co-workers on the Raleigh police force. Peterson told Barney that they were out of paper towels in the men's room.

LES PETERSON (17F/B) Rube Sloan thought that Les snitched on his still to Andy.

MRS. PETERSON (80F/B) She called Andy to tell him her cat, Fluffy, was on the roof. It wasn't said if she was related to Rafe Peterson.

RAFE PETERSON (35F/B) Mayberry attorney who was mentioned as possible counsel for Elizabeth Crowley, the woman speeder. He was ruled out when it was realized that he was selling aluminum siding instead of practicing law.

DR. THOMAS PETERSON (201F/204B) The "New Doctor in Town," a golf-playing doctor who took over Dr. Bennett's practice when he retired. The old-timers resisted this young whippersnapper until Andy (a little reluctantly, and with a push from Helen) allowed Peterson to remove Opie's swollen tonsils. When everything worked out fine, the townsfolk accepted the new doctor. Clara decided to let him take a look at her neuralgia, and Floyd thought he'd talk to him about his sinuses. His nurse was Miss Oakley.

"PETULLA ABONDOLA" (108F/107B) The body part that Opie said Wary Willy the Hobo fractured. Barney said it was in the brain. Willy claimed he had a bad leg, the result of a fracture he sustained while working as a fireman on the C B & Q Railroad.

"PETULLA OBLONGATA" (108F/107B) The body part that Wary Willy the Hobo claimed he fractured while employed as a railroad fireman.

"PHANTOM FIFE" (59F/B) The name Andy called Barney in reference to Barney's sneaking around to set up a party for Andy's and Mary's "engagement."

PHEASANT (127F/126B) Gomer called Barney on his claim that he could catch a pheasant with a handmade snare.

CHARLIE PHELPS (112F/111B) Charlie copied the sheriff's star off the squad car and painted it on Barney's motorcycle.

UNCLE PHIL (233F/231B) Millie Hutchins' uncle. Millie and Howard went to see Uncle Phil and Aunt Hannah in Wheeling when they decided to get married.

CARL PHILLIPS (237F/236B) Owner of Channel 12 in Siler City. He approached Aunt Bee to do a cooking show on his station. The show was called "The Mayberry Chef."

MILFORD PHILLIPS (14F/B) Milford planned on donating a plaque to take the place of the old cannon in the town square. He changed his plans, however, when Andy sold the cannon to the antique dealer, Ralph Mason, who then sold it to Milford. Milford, a former Mayberry resident, donated the cannon back to the town. (See entries CANNON and RALPH MASON)

PHILOMATHIAN LITERARY SOCIETY (82F/B) Mayberry Union High school organization. Andy was the group's secretary. They cut out current events and pasted them in a book. Barney was blackballed from the group by Jack Egbert.

PHOEBE (229F/228B) Young guest at Brenda Rhodes' birthday party. She was impressed with Opie because he was in a band.

DUNCAN PHYFE (25F/B) Ancestor of Barney's. Barney figured he was probably a carpenter. Barney researched Duncan's familial connections in his search for proof that he was related to a Revolutionary War hero, Nathan Tibbs. It turned out that Otis Campbell, not Barney, was related to Tibbs.

PICK (3F/B) Jim Lindsey bought one from a store in Winston-Salem, North Carolina.

PICKLE BOTTLING PLANT (210F/211B) Factory next door to Floyd's new barbershop in Mt. Pilot.

THE PICKLE FACTORY (9F/7B) When Barney resigned as deputy after a derogatory poem was written about him on the wall of the bank, he said he could always get a job as a brine tester at the pickle factory. (See THE BANK POEM)

THE PICKLE STORY 43rd episode filmed and broadcast. Original broadcast date was December 18, 1961. It was written by Harvey Bullock, and directed by Bob Sweeney. Regulars included Andy Griffith, Don Knotts, Frances Bavier, Ronny Howard, and Hope Summers. Guests included Lee Krieger, Stanley Farrar, and Warren Parker as the Judge. (See "DON KNOTT'S FAVORITE EPISODE")

"PICKUPS AND SPLASHES FROM FLOOR AND POOL" (153F/B) The title of Barney's one-time only newspaper column. It ran in the Central High School newspaper.

"PICNIC" (140F/B) The movie that Goober said starred Cary Grant. This was his excuse to do his Grant impression. ("Picnic" actually starred William Holden.)

PICNICS (74F/B) (76F/78B) (115F/114B) (120F/119B) (135F/B) (160F/163B) 29¢. It was never stated just what was included for the 29¢.

PIEDMONT HOTEL (167F/B) (168F/B) The hotel Andy, Bee, and Opie stayed at in Hollywood. They stayed in room 403. (See DARLENE MASON)

PIERCE COUNTY (53F/B) North Carolina county that threw out Sheldon Davis, aka Thomas A. Moody.

PIERRE (48F/B) Ellen Brown's former boss and, later, husband. She worked as a manicurist and left him to come to Mayberry. At the end of 48F/B, she went back with Pierre.

JESSE PIERSON (110F/109B) Owner of Pierson's Sweet Shop, a Mayberry candy store.

THE PIERSON PLACE (36F/37B) The house Gladys Stevens and her husband, George, rented when they came to Mayberry. It was on the Post Road.

PIERSON'S SWEET SHOP (110F/109B) Mayberry candy store. They ran a "Lucky Peppermints" promotion that Gomer claimed was fixed.

PIERSON'S SWEET SHOP'S "LUCKY PEPPERMINT PROMOTION" (110F/109B) You bought peppermints from the store. If you got one with a green center, you won a flashlight. If you got one with a pink center, you won a free peppermint. One Thursday Gomer bought ten mints, and all were white centers. Another time he bought twelve more and they, too, were all white. This led Gomer to believe the promo was fixed.

PIGS (135F/B) 37¢.

EARL PIKE (136F/B) He bought his son a new car. His son was fifty-seven years old.

JOSEPHINE PIKE (20F/16B) The mayor's daughter and #6 in the Founder's Day beauty pageant. It wasn't said if Josephine or the mayor were related to Earl or Nat Pike.

MAYOR PIKE (2F/B) (16F/20B) (41F/39B) (48F/B) In 2F/B, he was introduced as an early mayor of Mayberry. In 16F/20B, Barney arrested Pike on a Code 439: vagrancy and loitering. In 41F/39B, he was happy about Mayberry's "crime-free" record. In 48F/B, he shot three rabbits.

NAT PIKE (29F/B) Four-year-old friend of Opie's who told him that a penny hit by lightning was worth six cents. It wasn't said if Nat was related to the mayor, Josephine, or Earl Pike.

PILLOW (165F/169B) Andy brought Helen a pillow from Hollywood that had "Hollywood, California" on it. He put a strand of pearls inside. (She had been willing to settle for the pillow.)

PILOT PINES FUNERAL PARLOR (90F/B) Myrt Lesh claimed she owed the parlor $140 for her late husband Bernard's funeral expenses, and that's why she was selling her car, a 1954 Ford sedan. (See FORD SEDAN)

PIN (178F/B) Antique pin Aunt Bee claimed was lost. She collected the insurance on the pin and found it later.

SHERIFF PINCKLEY (106F/B) Early sheriff of Mayberry. He was sheriff during the 1930s. Andy and Barney found an old arrest record of Pinckley's from 1931. Purcell Branch (Tyler's dad) was arrested on a misdeameanor: disturbing the peace. He drove down Main Street with the cutout open on REO Flying Cloud.

CHARLES COATSWORTH PINCKNEY (196F/203B) Historical figure Floyd read about. Pinckney said "Millions for defense, but not one cent for tribute." (See CHARLES COATSWORTH PAYNTON and THE 'MILLIONS FOR. . .' QUOTATION)

WILBUR PINE (1F/B) Andy's first housekeeper, Rose, married Wilbur, leaving Andy alone with Opie. This brought Aunt Bee into the Taylor household and began the history of our favorite show.

PINE AND MAIN (99F/98B) Andy and Barney waited for Ernest T. Bass at this intersection.

PINEAPPLE SKINNER (156F/B) Barney bought one for Thelma Lou from Newton Monroe.

PINK ELEPHANT (115F/114B) Otis's cellmate.

PINK LADY COSMETICS (231F/230B) Classified ad read by Andy.

PINK TOWELS (35F/B) When Elizabeth Crowley decided to fight her speeding fine and stay overnight at the Mayberry jail, Andy sent Barney out for pink towels.

PIZZA PLACE (168F/B) The Hollywood restaurant where Bee and Opie ate the night Andy had a date with Darlene Mason.

"PLAN A" (178F/B) Insurance plan Ed Jenkins wanted to sell Andy.

PLANTING MARIJUANA (29F/B) Barney thought that Sam Becker was planting cannabis because he worked in his fields late at night. Actually, he worked at night because he was too busy during the day taking care of his pregnant wife to do any work in the fields.

A PLAQUE FOR MAYBERRY 25th episode filmed and broadcast. Original broadcast date was April 3, 1961. It was written by Leo Solomon and Ben Gershman, and directed by Bob Sweeney. Regulars included Andy

Griffith, Don Knotts, Ronny Howard, and Hal Smith as Otis Campbell. Guests included Dick Elliot as Mayor Pike, Burt Mustin as Jud, Dorothy Neumann, Isabel Randolph, Carol Veazie, Joseph Crehan, and Joseph Hamilton.

CLYDE PLAUNT (222F/225B) Mt. Pilot man and former boyfriend (at least in his own eyes) of Millie Hutchins. He gave Howard a hard time when Howard started dating Millie.

"PLAY CHECKERS, TALK, GRUNT" (210F/211B) Opie's description of the activities of the boys who hung around Floyd's Barbershop.

MARY PLEASANCE (141F/142B) Notary public at the bank. She went to Great Dismal Swamp to hunt black bear with Dixie Bell Edwards. Because she was out of town, Otis had to go to Mt. Pilot to get his accident form notarized.

"PLEASE TAKE CARE OF MY BABY" (202F/196B) The note pinned to the abandoned Garland baby that Opie and Arnold found on the courthouse steps.

FRED PLUMMER (135F/B) Grocery clerk hired by Mr. Foley to work in the market. Barney told him three times not to sweep trash into the street. The fourth time Barney wrote him a ticket: "Time: 12:00, Location: Main St., Traffic: Clear." It was a four-dollar fine. Plummer told Barney if he ever caught him out of uniform, he'd beat him up. Andy found out and dressed the judo expert, Mr. Izamoto, in Barney's suit so he could beat up Plummer without Barney losing his pride. Plummer believed it was Barney and he left the deputy alone after that. Plummer weighed 200 pounds.

PERRY PLUMMER (191F/192B) The best tenor who auditioned as a replacement for Howard Sprague in the barbershop quartet. It wasn't said if Perry was related to Fred.

PLUMS (73F/70B) 8¢ a pound as sold by Neil and Matt from the back of their truck.

POCKETWATCH (38F/41B) (74F/B) (123F/122B) (246F/245B) How Andy told time.

POEMS OF ROMANCE (132F/128B) Book by T. Jonathan Osgood. Barney selected a poem from it for Opie to read to his "girl," who just happened to be Helen. The poem: "When you and I are far apart, I no longer live. My heart is bursting from within with all my love to give. Lovesick as I am . . ." Opie read it to Helen on the phone.

SHERIFF POINDEXTER (152F/B) Sheriff during the "case of the punch in the nose." He straightened it out. The case took place in 1946. (See CHARLIE FOLEY)

POLICE AUCTION (142F/141B) Mt. Pilot auction. Barney and Goober went together and Goober bought a role of copper tubing. He paid thirty cents for it and could have gotten it anywhere for sixteen. Barney bought a box from some gypsies that contained instructions on how to contact the dead Count Iz Van Talecki.

POLICE EMERGENCY COMMITTEE (232F/233B) When Andy got sick, Goober formed this committee. It was made up of Goober, Emmett, and Howard.

"THE POLICE GAZETTE" (26F/B) Magazine Andy once subscribed to, but cancelled when Barney joined the Mayberry sheriff's department. He

explained to Inspector Case that the magazine had a lot of girly pictures in it and Barney, "he ain't never been married."

POLICE OFFICER'S QUALIFYING (146F/B) The shooting test Barney had to pass every year. It was at the Mt. Pilot pistol range. In 146F/B, Barney was afraid of failing because he didn't pass on a "lucky letter" chain letter. He passed.

POLITICS (196F/203B) One of the subjects Goober pontificated about to Aunt Bee during his "beard" stage.

POLITICS BEGIN AT HOME 200th episode filmed and 197th episode broadcast. Original broadcast date was November 7, 1966. It was written by Fred S. Fox, and directed by Lee Phillips. Regulars included Andy Griffith, Ronny Howard, Howard McNear, Frances Bavier, Jack Dodson, and George Lindsey. Guests included Hope Summers as Clara Edwards, Ruth Thom as Ella, and Maxine Semon as Tillie Kincaid.

MRS. POLK (113F/112B) Guest at Mrs. Wiley's singles dance on the night Ernest T. Bass crashed the party. Mrs. Polk handled the rock Ernest T. threw through the window, much to the disgust of Barney, who had wanted to fingerprint the stone.

MABEL POLLACK (216F/B) Woman who called Bee to complain about Howard Sprague's comedy routine on "Colonel Tim's Talent Time Show." He made gentle fun of Mayberry. (See HOWARD'S COMEDY ROUTINE)

FRANKLIN POMEROY (7F/5B) (16F/20B) In 7F/5B, Andy told him he had a cute nose in order to put him on the trail of Ellie Walker. Andy believed Ellie was after him. Franklin worked at the Mayberry Security Bank. In 16F/20B, Barney arrested Franklin with the rest of the town when Andy was out of town.

"POMP AND CIRCUMSTANCE" (72F/71B) The song Barney played on his Andre Kostalanez Marchers cymbals.

A PONY (122F/121B) Opie and his friends tried to win one by selling Miracle Salve.

PORK CHOPS AND FRIED APPLE RINGS (4F/6B) George Foley's mother was preparing this supper the night George realized he didn't want to run away from home.

PORK ROAST (148F/B) (196F/203B) In 148F/B, 27¢ a pound. In 196F/203B, 47¢ a pound.

ALPHA PORTER (231F/230B) She dropped off her laundry at the courthouse. She was Sharon's mother.

MRS. PORTER (108F/107B) Whitey's mother. She called Andy to tell him her ham was missing.

SHARON PORTER (133F/131B) (161F/160B) (181F/B) (231F/230B) In 133F/131B, she answered the question Helen asked Ernest T. Bass. In 161F/160B, Opie was sweet on Sharon and crashed into a tree while trying to impress her by riding no-hands. In 181F/B, Opie told how he danced with her at the church social and "stomped" all over her feet. He did better with her at the school party. In 231F/230B, it was stated that she was the daughter of Alpha Porter.

TROOPER PORTER (2F/B) State police officer who came to Mayberry with Captain Barker to assist in the "manhunt." Porter got the map of Mayberry County for Barker.

WHITEY PORTER (108F/107B) One of Opie's "merry men." He stole a ham from his mother for Wary Willy the Hobo. It was not said if he was related to Alpha or Sharon Porter.

PORTLAND, OREGON (43F/B) The hometown of one of the travelers to whom Barney gave a quart of Aunt Bee's "kerosene" pickles.

ORVILLE PORTNOY (194F/B) Night man at the bakery. Fluffy Johnson from the gas company had her eye on him. (See FLUFFY JOHNSON)

POST ROAD (36F/37B) (55F/B) In 36F/37B, the road where the Old Pierson Place was located. In 55F/B, Andy had to serve some papers to someone out on the Post Road.

POT 'O HONEY RESTAURANT (116F/115B) Restaurant where Ethel Page used to sing on Sunday afternoons. She still had the canary with her during these performances.

POTATO SACK RACE (73F/70B) Barney started it every year at the Mason's picnic with his pistol.

POTATO SALAD (240F/B) The US and USSR ambassadors ate it late at night in Bee's kitchen during their summit meeting at Andy's house.

POTATOES (29F/B) (54F/B) (91F/B) (183F/182B) In 29F/B, ten pounds for 49¢. In 54F/B, ten pounds for 29¢. In 91F/B, 29¢. In 183F/182B, a ten pound bag for 39¢.

POTTER'S CAVE (213F/B) Goober brought strangers to Helen's house after her book was published, telling them that seeing Helen was "more exciting than Potter's Cave or watching the high school being sandblasted."

ELEANORA POULTICE (116F/115B) (138F/B) Barney's voice teacher. The sign in front of her house read, "Eleanora Poultice Singing Dancing Piano." Eleanora actually taught the legendary Leonard Blush, and two years after she met him Leonard sang "The Star-Spangled Banner" at the county insecticide convention. Eleanora rehearsed Barney in "Now is the Month of May," and she insisted that he sing the solo in "Santa Lucia" at the choir recital. In 138F/B, she also gave Barney speech training.

POUNDED STEAK A LA MORELLI (132F/128B) The main dish of the deluxe special at Morelli's. It came with minestrone and sold for $1.85.

"POW, POW, POW" (17F/B) Barney's description of what he did when he found an illegal still. He went at them with an axe.

THE POWELL PLACE (59F/B) Mary Simpson had to go out there. Someone had a cold.

THE PREAMBLE (103F/B) Barney attempted to recite it in this episode but botched it. The scene was very similar to the "police rules" recitation scene in 6F/4B.

PRESERVING JARS (75F/B) Andy bought Aunt Bee twenty-four jars for her birthday. She had wanted a bed jacket.

THE PRESIDENT (2F/B) Andy admitted to Opie that the President was probably more important than himself. He allowed that the Queen of England was likewise a bit more important than the Mayberry sheriff.

ELVIS PRESLEY (3F/B) As described by Andy, "That fella' we see every now and then on television, shakin' and screamin' kinda like somebody's beatin' his dog."

"PRICE-SPIRALING" (210F/211B) Floyd accused Howard of this dastardly deed when Howard tried to raise the rent on Floyd's Barbershop after buying the building from the Robinson family.

MISS PRIMROSE (132F/128B) Clerk at the lady's shop who helped Opie pick out a gift for Helen (only she didn't know it was for Helen.) Miss Primrose suggested handkerchiefs and Opie picked one but then changed his mind because it was only 50¢ and he had 74¢ to spend. He decided on stockings for 80¢ and had to go drink three bottles of pop to make up the 6¢.

"A PRINCE" (71F/72B) The name Floyd called Andy after the sheriff got him out of trouble with Madeline Grayson.

PRINCESS GRACE (245F/244B) She had a coat almost like the one Bernie the Furrier showed Emmett.

THE PRINCIPAL (32F/B) He called Aunt Bee to complain about Opie handcuffing Ralph Baker to the flagpole during lunch.

PRISONER OF LOVE 114th episode filmed and 113th episode broadcast. Original broadcast date was February 10, 1964. It was written by Harvey Bullock, and directed by Earl Bellamy. Regulars included Andy Griffith, Don Knotts, and Frances Bavier. Guests included Susan Oliver as the "prisoner of love," and James Seay.

"THE PRISONER OF LOVE" (114F/113B) Beautiful unnamed woman prisoner who was held in the Mayberry jail. Andy and Barney both fell in love with her because of her seductive ways, but she was all hype. She was arrested on suspected grand larceny; she was a jewel thief. She had an unnamed, never-seen partner.

RALPH PRITCHARD (52F/B) First tenor who had to leave the choir. He was on the road two out of three weeks.

JEFF PRITCHETT (7F/5B) Andy said he would swear in Jeff as a temporary deputy because Barney would not be available because he was taking Ellie to the town picnic. This was a ruse to get Barney to break his date with Ellie.

THE PROPRIETOR (235F/234B) The owner of the general store on St. Benedict's Island in the Caribbean.

ARNOLD PRUITT (181F/B) Goober suggested that Arnold at the record store could suggest some good dance records for Opie to use to learn how to dance.

FREDDY PRUITT (51F/B) Boy who won third place in the fifty-yard dash. It wasn't said if Freddy was related to Arnold, Jeff, Roy, and/or Howie Pruitt.

HOWIE PRUITT (108F/107B) (153F/B) (154F/B) In 108F/107B, Howie was one of Opie's "merry men." He stole half of a turkey from his mother to bring to Wary Willy the Hobo. In 153F/B, he was co-editor, with Opie, of their school newspaper, "The Mayberry Sun." It wasn't said if Roy and Howie were brothers. In 154F/B, Helen Crump said that Howie was becoming a "real monster."

JEFF PRUITT (45F/B) Mayberry farmer who came into town to find a wife. Barney wanted to help but changed his tune when Jeff picked Thelma Lou. Andy solved the problem by showing Jeff what living in town would be like; he dressed him up in a too-tight suit, made him eat little finger sandwiches for supper, and told him he'd have to work in a shoe store. Jeff returned to his neighbor, Bertha. It wasn't mentioned whether Jeff was related to Arnold, Howie and/or Roy Pruitt. (See BERTHA)

MRS. PRUITT (108F/107B) Howie's mother. She called Andy to tell him her turkey was missing.

ROY PRUITT (5F/8B) Little boy who donated five cents to the Underprivileged Children's Charity Drive. It was the second lowest amount give. The lowest was three cents, given by Opie Taylor. Roy, however, was one of the underprivileged children.

PSYCHIC PHENOMENA (142F/141B) The book Barney read after he got involved with the occult.

PSYCHOLOGICAL ASPECTS OF THE LAW (113F/112B) Book Barney got from the library. On the day Ernest T. crashed Mrs. Wiley's singles party, Barney had the book for five more days.

PTA FUND (244F/243B) School fund under the control of Mrs. Pendleton.

PTA MEETING (140F/B) Meeting that prevented Helen from seeing Andy on a Friday night.

"PUDDINTANE" (50F/B) One of Barney's nicknames, according to Barney.

PUMPKIN PIE A LA MODE (238F/239B) Andy's favorite dessert. Aunt Bee prepared it as a bribe for Andy's deciding vote on the choir robe/church repair question.

PUNCH SUPREME (163F/161B) Andy's specialty. It conisted of orange sherbert, tomato juice, root beer, and molasses.

MAYOR PURDY (44F/B) The mayor of Greendale, North Carolina.

MRS. PURDY (47F/B) Opie broke her backdoor window with a baseball. Andy made him pay for it, much to the surprise of Ronald Bailey.

PURPLE (231F/230B) Emmett's shirt turned purple when he washed it with his colored clothing at Andy's Laundercoin.

"THE PURPLE AVENGER" (221F/235B) One of Goober's favorite comics. It was all about the Grunch People.

PURSE (245F/244B) Andy suggested a purse as an anniversary gift for Martha Clark from her husband, Emmett.

MR. PURVIS (173F/174B) He climbed a tree to get away from his wife. Mrs. Purvis called Andy to get him down.

MRS. PURVIS (91F/B) (173F/174B) In 91F/B, she called Andy to have him get her cat out of the tree. In 173F/174B, she called Andy to have him get Mr. Purvis out of the tree.

"PUSSYCAT" (68F/69B) The name Barney called Thelma Lou.

PX LIBRARY ON STATEN ISLAND (29F/B) Barney was stationed there when he was in the Army. He was second-in-command of over 3,000 books. He didn't like to talk about it.

GOMER PYLE Yet another of Mayberry's "children." Simple almost to the point of idiocy, Gomer possessed a good-heartedness and a genuine sensitivity that fit right in with the warmth and ease of Mayberry. Gomer, literally, couldn't hurt a fly. Most of Gomer's predicaments came from his overly naive view of the world and Andy's quandry in trying to set things right. Unbelievably, in "Man in a Hurry" (77F/79B), Andy told Malcolm Tucker that Gomer was saving for medical school; he wanted to be a doctor! After one season, Gomer left town and joined the Marines, where Sgt. Carter had to take over dealing with Gomer's unique ways. Gomer missed Mayberry and likewise was missed by the townsfolk. He was spoken of often. (See additional entries beginning with the word "GOMER" or "GOMER'S," and see the Jim Nabors interview in this book)

GOOBER PYLE (137F/B) Gomer's cousin. In 137F/B, he was Deputy #1, as deputized by Barney. Goober was almost, but not quite, as naive as Gomer. He seemed to be a little brighter, too. Unlike Gomer, who seemed mentally dull, Goober instead was more childlike. He eventually bought Wally's Service Station and settled into a long, quiet life in Mayberry. He was a graduate of auto trade school, and enjoyed comic books and room painting. (See additional entries beginning with the word "GOOBER" and "GOOBER'S")

COLONEL GOOBER PYLE (188F/B) Officer of the North Carolina 7th Cavalry. Goober's ancestor and a "hero" of the Battle of Mayberry.

MAJOR GENERAL LUCIUS PYLE (107F/127B) Gomer Pyle's Marine role model. To help Gomer acclimate into the Marines, Andy led Sgt. Carter to believe that Gomer was the general's son.

QUAIL (118F/117B) An escaped prisoner said he was hunting quail. Quail were out of season. That clue, plus the fact that he was wearing prison shoes, tipped Andy off. The sheriff got him.

"QUE SERA SERA" (19F/B) Song Barney offered to play on the harmonica for Mr. Maxwell, the record producer.

"THE QUEEN" (71F/72B) Aunt Bee's role in "Six Who Pass While the Lentils Boil" when she was in Sunday school.

THE QUEEN OF ENGLAND (2F/B) One of the two people (the other being the President) that Andy admitted to Opie might be more important than himself.

THE QUEEN OF THE STATE APRICOT FESTIVAL (110F/109B) Girl who came to Mayberry on a promotional tour on June 23, 1952. Andy escorted her to the furniture factory, to Beaver Dam, and then for a snack at the Diner. Barney was upset because he had planned on taking her. Barney had paid $3.95 at Patterson's for a new shirt.

QUEENIE (118F/117B) Mrs. Croute's cat. Queenie got stuck up a tree.

THE QUICK DRAW (30F/B) (32F/B) (37F/40B) (110F/109B) In 32F/B, Barney tried to teach Opie the move in the courthouse after school. In 37F/40B and 110F/109B, he shot his gun off in the holster while attempting to demonstrate his famous move.

QUIET SAM 29th episode filmed and broadcast. Original broadcast date was May 1, 1961. It was written by Jim Fritzell and Everett Greenbaum, and directed by Bob

Sweeney. Regulars included Andy Griffith, Don Knotts, Frances Bavier, Howard McNear, and Hal Smith. Guests included William Schallert as Sam Becker.

STEVE QUINCY (79F/77B) A bully from Richmond who moved to Mayberry with his family and rented a house on Grove Street owned by Charlie. Steve was nine, his mother was married once before to someone in the service, and his father sold farm implements. Before they moved to Mayberry, Mrs. Quincy had had an operation on her foot. Steve tormented Opie, who finally stood up to him. (See NIP IT (IN THE BUD))

THE QUINCYS (79F/77B) Family who moved to Mayberry from Richmond. Their son was Steve, a nine-year-old bully. To get Aunt Bee to tell what she knew about the family, Andy made up a story that they were from Tennessee, they had no children, the husband was in insurance, and their last name was Mackadoo.

R

R & M GRAIN ELEVATORS (67F/65B) Firm in Raleigh owned by Peggy McMillan's father.

"R.I.P. THOMAS SILBY 'A FINE MAN AND A DEAR HUSBAND' 1908-1958" (5F/8B) The legend on Tom Silby's premature tombstone.

R24-871 (52F/B) The license plate number of Jeff Pruitt's truck.

"THE RABBIT" (51F/B) Barney's nickname, according to Barney, after he won the fifty yard dash as a kid.

"A RACETRACK IN AFRICA" (234F/232B) One of Bradford Taylor's travel stops, according to Bradford Taylor.

RADIOACTIVE POISON GAS (202F/199B) Arnold said that the "electronically-controlled" blankets he and Opie used to cover the abandoned Garland baby threw off radioactive poison gas.

RAFE HOLLISTER SINGS 83rd episode filmed and broadcast. Original broadcast date was February 11, 1963. It was written by Harvey Bullock, and directed by Charles Irving. Regulars included Andy Griffith, Don Knotts, and Ronny Howard. Guests included Jack Prince as Rafe Hollister, Olan Soule as John Masters, Parley Baer as Mayor Stoner, Kay Stewart as Mrs. Jeffreys, Isabel Randolph as Mrs. Hollister, and Ohola Nesmith as Mrs. Dennis.

"A RAINDROP" (153F/B) Myra Lambert's role in the school play.

LUKE RAINER (26F/B) Mayberry farmer who took shots at people because he was afraid someone would report his still. Inspector Ralph Case wanted to use tear gas and riot equipment to get Luke, but Andy just walked up to Luke's door—right through the gunfire (knowing Luke would never hurt him)—and arrested him, scolding him for acting like a young'un as he took him back to the car.

RALEIGH (52F/B) (54F/B) (104F/105B) (105F/104B) (119F/118B) (236F/237B) The capital of North Carolina. In 52F/B, the new "wanted" posters came from Raleigh. In 54F/B, Andy called Raleigh to get some merchandise on consignment for Bert Miller. In 104F/105B, Mrs. Mendlebright and Mr. Fields planned on buying a house there after they were married. In 105F/104B, Mary Grace Gossage was headed there when she stopped to see Thelma Lou in Mayberry. In 119F/118B, it was told the Arcade was one of the attractions in town. In 236F/237B, Emmett went there to take a one week insurance training course.

RALEIGH AQUARIUM (198F/200B) Howard donated the legendary silver carp, Old Sam, to the aquarium. They put him in a tank that read "Silver Carp Caught In Mayberry, North Carolina. Donated By Howard Sprague."

When he realized that he had destroyed a tradition, he asked for Sam's return and released him back into Tucker's Lake. (See "OLD SAM")

RALEIGH BANK ROBBERY (228F/227B) It was committed by Eddie Blake.

RALEIGH PHILARMONIC (229F/228B) Emmett once heard them play.

RALEIGH SECURITY BANK (247F/246B) Herb Bradshaw resigned as head of Mayberry's city council to become head teller at this Raleigh bank.

RALEIGH YMCA (119F/118B) (240F/B) In 119F/118B, Barney and Virgil stayed there on their vacation. In 240F/B, Barney lived there after moving away from Mayberry.

RALPH (31F/B) (72F/71B) Member of the Mayberry Drum and Bugle Corp. In 31F/B, his assignment was to hold the banner with Charlie. In 72F/71B, he moved to use balloons at the Apricot Festival.

RALPH (200F/197B) Mayberry councilman. He had to move out of town, which necessitated his resignation from the council. This started the battle between Howard Sprague and Bee Taylor for the seat.

RALPH (220F/B) Boy at Arnold Bailey's thirteenth birthday party.

RANCH ROAD (200F/197B) Street where Parker Creek was located.

RAPI (227F/222B) A Spanish shawl. Bee sent Opie one from Mexico.

MAX RASMUSIN (84F/B) Max "The Tongue" Rasmusin was wanted for grand theft auto. He had a $1500 reward on his head. Barney put up his "wanted" poster in the courthouse.

RAYBURN (176F/B) He came to the class reunion.

RAZOR BLADES (54F/B) Andy's purchase from Bert Miller, the peddler.

RD-757 (60F/B) (74F/B) In 60F/B, the license plate number of the car the horse bettors drove into Mayberry when they came to see Bill Medwin, the bookie barber. In 74F/B, the plate number of Floyd Lawson's car.

RED (31F/B) The color of Jim Lindsey's car. It was financed by the Mid-Mountain Finance Company and was repossessed after Jim got three payments behind.

RED AND PURPLE (210F/211B) The color of the ceramic tile in the bathroom of Floyd's Barbershop.

RED FORD CONVERTIBLE (226F/223B) Attorney Lee Drake's car.

RED, WHITE, AND BLUE SLEEVE GARTER (39F/36B) One of Frank Myers' valuables.

THE REEF AT NAGTIN (160F/163B) Restaurant John Canfield took Bee to on their first date. She had the fish platter with butter sauce, he had the pounded steak, and they both had lace cornbread.

"THE REGAL ORDER OF THE GOLDEN DOOR TO GOOD FELLOWSHIP" (192F/191B) Mayberry's lodge for men. Goober was Keeper of the Door (the password was "Geronimo"), and Andy was Voting Proctor. The lodge had twenty-seven members. The secret knock was two long knocks and three short knocks. Andy sponsored Howard Sprague for membership, but Mrs. Sprague didn't like the idea. She told Goober a made-up story about Howard having a gambling problem like his father. Goober blackballed Howard but the truth came out, Goober withdrew the blackball, and Howard became a member.

REGIS (102F/B) Crazy Mayberry man who lived in the woods. On the day the gold shipment was to pass through Mayberry, Regis came to town carrying a sign that read, "Down With The Gold Standard, Vote For The Single Tax."

"A REGULAR BOBBYDAZZLER" (124F/123B) The name Malcolm Merriweather called Aunt Bee, meaning it as a compliment.

THE REHABILITATION OF OTIS 145th episode filmed and broadcast. Original broadcast date was January 18, 1965. It was written by Fred Freeman and Lawrence J. Cohen, and directed by Peter Baldwin. Regulars included Andy Griffith, Don Knotts, Howard McNear, and Hal Smith as Otis. Guests included Frank Cady as Luke.

"RELIABLE BARNEY FIFE" (1F/B) (2F/B) In 1F/B, Barney asserted that he wanted to be known as "Reliable Barney Fife." In 2F/B, he described himself using that adjective, so he apparently felt he had achieved "reliability."

"RENAISSANCE" (243F/242B) The word Opie asked for help in spelling.

"A RENDEZVOUS WITH DESTINY" (44F/B) Barney said he had one after he was offered the sheriff's job in Greendale, North Carolina.

RENEE (212F/208B) Secretary in the Raleigh police department.

REO FLYING CLOUD (106F/B) Purcell Branch's car. In 1931, when he drove down Main Street with the cutout open on the car, Sheriff Pinckley arrested him for disturbing the peace.

RESIGNATION DATES (106F/B) The dates Barney resigned the deputy's position: January 21, February 7, and March 15.

THE RETURN OF BARNEY FIFE 176th episode filmed and broadcast. Original broadcast date was January 10, 1966. It was written by Bill Idelson and Sam Bobrick, and directed by Alan Rafkin. Regulars included Andy Griffith, Ronny Howard, Frances Bavier, and Aneta Corsaut. Guests included Don Knotts as Barney Fife, Betty Lynn as Thelma Lou, Barbara Perry as Floss, Burt Mustin as Mr. Crowley, Alberta Nelson as Nettie Albright, Ted Jordan as Gerald, Virginia Sale as Woman #1, and Edna M. Holland as Woman #2.

THE RETURN OF MALCOM MERRIWEATHER 124th episode filmed and 123rd episode broadcast. Original broadcast date was April 20, 1964. It was written by Harvey Bullock, and directed by Coby Ruskin. Regulars included Andy Griffith, Don Knotts, Ronny Howard, and Frances Bavier. Guests included Bernard Fox as Malcolm Merriweather.

REX BENSON AND THE SING-SONGERS (187F/186B) The vocal group who starred on "The Rex Benson Show."

"THE REX BENSON SHOW" (187F/186B) TV show watched by the Taylors. It was sponsored by Foster's Furniture Polish.

RFD #1 BANNERTOWN (136F/B) Parnell Rigsby's address.

RHEUMATISM (10F/12B) Floyd had it. It acted up every December.

RHINESTONE BUTTONS (58F/B) Aunt Bee's blue print had twenty-three.

RHUBARB PIE (119F/118B) Aunt Bee made one for Andy to have after his boiled dinner and cribbage game at the firehouse.

RHYTHM GUITAR (229F/228B) Opie's position, on an acoustic guitar, in his band, "The Sound Committee."

RIB ROAST (223F/226B) (237F/236B) In 223F/226B, Bee made one for supper for the Monday and Tuesday she had to serve on the jury. In 237F/236B, Bee made one on her cooking show, "The Mayberry Chef."

RICE PUDDING (246F/245B) George and Mrs. Sprague were finishing their pudding at Morelli's when George proposed to Howard's mother.

"RIFLE FIFE" (157F/B) The name Barney claimed he was called in high school because of his "bullet" football passes.

RIGHT EAR (10F/12B) The ear on which William Buntley had a mole. The mole enabled his mother to tell him apart from his twin brother, Robert. The "stranger in town," Ed Sawyer, knew that.

"RIGHT IN HIS HIP POCKET" (126F/125B) Where Barney told Gomer he had Thelma Lou. Gomer repeated this to Thelma Lou and this caused Barney and Thelma Lou's relationship to go "phfftt."

MRS. RIGSBY (136F/B) Parnell's wife. Andy and Barney told her that they had found Parnell's purse.

PARNELL RIGSBY (136F/B) The owner of the black purse with the fifty dollars in it that Opie found on his way home from school. He lived at RFD #1 in Bannertown. He ran a lost and found ad: "Lost. Vicinity of Mayberry. A black leather change purse with $50 in it. If found please contact Parnell Rigsby, RFD #1, Bannertown."

OLD MAN RIMSHAW (98F/97B) Owner of the Rimshaw Place, a house on the outskirts of Mayberry that was reputed to be haunted. It was said that Rimshaw put chains on his hired man and then did away with him with an axe.

THE RIMSHAW HOUSE (98F/97B) Also known as the Rimshaw Place and reputed to be haunted. In reality, the "ghosts" were actually Otis Campbell and Big Jack Anderson. They ran a still in the basement of the house. It was originally owned by Old Man Rimshaw but was later abandoned. The rumor went that Rimshaw put chains on his hired man and then did away with him using the axe that still hung on the inside of the door leading to the cellar.

"A RIOT OF COLOR" 196F/203B The phrase Aunt Bee used to describe an old beau of hers who had "brown hair and blue eyes; his beard came out red."

"RIP VAN WINKLE" (117F/116B) The name Barney called Asa Breeny because he slept while on the job as night watchman at Weaver's Department Store.

MRS. RITTER (120F/119B) Woman who called Bee for an unspecified chat.

THE RIVALS 91st episode filmed and broadcast. Original broadcast date was April 8, 1963. It was written by Harvey Bullock, and directed by Bob Sweeney. Regulars included Andy Griffith, Ronny Howard, Don

Knotts, and Betty Lynn. Guests included Ronda Jeter as Karen Burgess.

RIVER ROAD (50F/B) The road on which the Half Moon Trailer Park was located.

RIVIERA ROSE PETALS (69F/66B) Barney claimed they were in his cologne, "Nuit de Paris." Andy and Opie both thought the cologne smelled like paint.

RJ300 (112F/111B) The model number of the war surplus motorcycle and sidecar Barney bought at the war surplus auction in Mt. Pilot. He bought it to carry fire-fighting equipment, guns and ammunition, another deputy for raids, and for going back and forth to the store.

BRENDA ROACH (229F/228B) Opie's band, "The Sound Committee," played at her birthday party.

MRS. ROACH (229F/228B) She called to book Opie's band, "The Sound Committee," for her daughter Brenda's birthday party. The party was on a Saturday at seven o'clock and the pay was five dollars per man.

THE ROADSIDE RESTAURANT (155F/B) Thelma Lou suggested eating there but Barney nixed the idea because the coffee was extra and they only gave you one roll per person.

ROANOKE, NORTH CAROLINA (52F/B) The choir finals were held there.

ROAST BEEF DINNER (238F/239B) Aunt Bee made one in an attempt to bribe Andy into voting for the choir robes over the repair of the church. Roast beef was one of Andy's favorites.

ROAST BEEF ON RYE (65F/67B) Sandwich Peggy McMillan prepared for Andy when Bee was out of town at her Aunt Louise's.

"ROBE OFFENDING" (35F/B) Andy fined Elizabeth Crowley, the woman speeder, thirty dollars for this crime.

"ROBE-DIGNITY OFFENDING" (3F/B) The crime committed by Bobby Fleet that prompted Andy to raise his fine to seventy dollars.

THE ROBERT E. LEE NATURAL BRIDGE (94F/B) An oak tree that fell across a creek.

DOC ROBERTS (232F/233B) Mayberry physician. Andy went to see him when he had the flu.

DR. ROBERTS (214F/B) Veterinarian. Arnold Bailey once had a cat that didn't eat for three days. He brought him to Dr. Roberts.

FLETCH ROBERTS (89F/B) (164F/162B) Man at the Depot. In 89F/B, Fletch drove into a pile of packing crates, thanks to Malcolm Merriweather's disruption of traffic. In 164F/162B, he needed a bookkeeper. Floyd suggested Malcolm for the job.

MR. ROBERTS (141F/142B) The county's head attorney. He came to Mayberry to hear Otis's negligence claim.

DALE ROBERTSON (166F/B) Helen's landlady wanted Andy to get her a picture of Robertson when the Taylors were in Hollywood.

MRS. ROBERTSON (165F/169B) She got jealous when Bee won prizes on "Win Or Lose."

ROBIN HOOD (108F/107B) The character Opie pretended to be with his "merry men": Johnny Paul Jason, Howie Pruitt, and Whitey. When playing in the woods, they came across Wary Willy the Hobo, who convinced them he was in need of food. They stole food from their mothers for Willy, using the Robin Hood story as a model.

HARLAN ROBINSON (174F/173B) Mt. Pilot man who wanted to sell his organ to build a new barn. He ran an ad in the "Mt. Pilot Times" offering it for $2,000. All Souls Church wanted to buy the organ but they only had $1,200 in the treasury. Andy got some of the local businessmen to pledge the balance. Nobody came through, though, and Andy had to return the organ. Clara was heartbroken and insisted on going with Andy to return the instrument. While at Robinson's she sang "Some Enchanted Evening" to him and he was so taken by her that he agreed to wait for the balance of the money. Harlan lived on Oakmont Road in Mt. Pilot.

THE ROBINSON FAMILY (210F/211B) Mayberry family that moved to California. They owned the building in which Floyd's Barbershop was located for "twenty or thirty" years. In 210F/211B, they put the building up for sale through Harry Walker Real Estate Company of Mayberry.

ROCK (82F/B) Barney owned one that had been his father's.

"THE ROCK" (55F/B) Andy's house, according to Otis, after Andy turned his house into a prison. He turned Otis over to Aunt Bee. She was his temporary warden.

"THE ROCK" (95F/B) The Mayberry jail, according to Barney. It had two rules: "Obey all rules, and don't write on the walls."

"ROCK AND ROLL ROSIE FROM RALEIGH" (31F/B) Jim Lindsey's first and only record hit. It wasn't said if "Rosie" was recorded with Bobby Fleet and his Band with a Beat, or if it was a solo project of Jim's.

"ROCK HUDSON MOVIES" (22F/B) Andy suggested Rock's movies to Barney as a how-to guide to romance.

"ROD" (110F/109B) The name Barney called his gun.

MRS. RODENBACH (78F/76B) Woman under the dryer when Barney kicked his way through the bank vault wall into the beauty parlor. Barney greeted her. She was not surprised that Barney was wearing a dress.

RODNEY (232F/233B) He took care of the filling station while Goober headed the police emergency committee during Andy's bout with the flu.

ROGER (129F/139B) Ollie and Nora's son.

BOB ROGERS (33F/34B) Lawyer from the North Carolina state's attorney's office. He was sent to Mayberry to see law enforcement in action. Barney assumed that Rogers was his replacement. Rogers seemed to be able to do everything better than Barney but it turned out his knowledge was all "book learning." Barney resigned to sell vacuum cleaners door-to-door. Rogers reminded Andy of the "Green River ordinance," which required a peddler's license for door-to-door sales. In the end, Rogers realized his rigidness and Barney realized that Andy had no intention of letting his deputy go. Rogers was sent to Mayberry by Andy's friend, Ralph Baker. The license plate number of the car he drove was DC-269.

GINGER ROGERS (227F/222B) On their trip to Mexico, Myrtle told the leader of the mariachi band that Clara Edwards was Ginger.

INSPECTOR ROGERS (231F/230B) Head of the state bureau of investigation. He visited Andy at the courthouse.

"ROLL OUT THE BARREL" (31F/B) The song Barney offered to play on his harmonica for Bobby Fleet.

ROLLERSKATES (11F/B) Ben Weaver's gift to Opie at the Christmas Eve party in the courthouse.

"ROMEENA" (113F/112B) (133F/131B) (164F/162B) In 113F/112B, "Romeena" is the name Ernest T. Bass called Ramona Anchram. In 133F/131B, she turned down Ernest T.'s marriage proposal, and in 164F/162B, Ernest T. Bass had to earn twelve dollars so he could buy a tent and lantern for his honeymoon with Romeena.

CEASAR ROMERO (167F/B) His house number in Hollywood was 505. Andy, Opie, and Bee saw it on their trip.

ROOM 209 (10F/12B) The room in the Mayberry Hotel where Wilbur Hennessey got drunk and fell out the window.

ROOM 216 (10F/12B) The room in the Mayberry Hotel which had just been painted green at the time that Ed Sawyer, the "stranger in town," checked in.

ROOSTER (29F/B) Sam Becker got spurred by one when he backed into a henhouse in Korea.

"ROSCOE" (110F/109B) The name Barney called his gun.

ROSE (1F/B) Andy and Opie's housekeeper before Aunt Bee came to live with them. Apparently, Rose came to work for Andy right after Andy's wife died. Rose left Andy to marry Wilbur Pine.

"ROSEMARIE" (150F/B) Mayberry stage production. Barney played the Nelson Eddy part. The "Mayberry Gazette" said Barney gave a "stellar performance."

ROSEMARY (92F/B) One of the potential "wives for Andy" Barney sent to Andy's house.

MISS ROSEMARY (9F/7B) Seamstress. Barney walked her to church every Sunday. She wore a different color shirtwaist every week. Rosemary was unbelievably shy and it took Andy's finaglings to get Barney to admit he wanted to court her. She was never seen again after this episode.

MRS. ROSENBACH (84F/B) Arnold Winkler, the "spoiled kid," knocked her over while riding his bicycle on Main Street. All her groceries spilled onto the sidewalk. She had been talking with Edith Blessing about Mrs. Tarbochs. Andy and Barney helped her with her groceries.

ROSES ARE THE BACKBONE OF YOUR GARDEN (200F/197B) Book by Mabel J. Mosley. It was reviewed by Tillie Kincaid at a meeting of the Mayberry Garden Club.

"ROSES OF PICCARDY" (36F/37B) The song Barney offered to play on his harmonica for Melissa Stevens and her "Daddy".

CHARLIE ROSS (14F/B) Junk dealer. Barney told Andy that Charlie would take the old cannon off the green if the town payed him fifteen dollars.

THE ROSS TREASURE (205F/B) Legendary treasure, rumored to be $100,000 worth of gold. It was supposed to have been stolen from a Union troop train during the Civil War by Ross's Raiders. People in Mayberry had been searching for it for years. The stranger,

George Jones, came to town, claiming to be the great-nephew of one of the descendants of the raiders. He said he had a map. He bilked Bee, Helen, Goober, Howard, and Andy. He fled to Florida and was caught.

ROSS'S RAIDERS (205F/B) They weren't on either side during the Civil War. They just went around stealing. They took $100,000 worth of gold from a Union troop train and buried it on the outskirts of Mayberry. George Jones had a map that said the treasure was buried near Hopkins Creek.

MISS ROUNDTREE (159F/B) One of the women who insisted that Andy shut down the "goochie-hoochie" show at the carnival.

ROUTE 88 (204F/202B) Road just before Franklin Junction. The crooks, Larry and Fred, could have cut off route 88 after their Mt. Pilot bank robbery.

ROUTE 43 (89F/B) (95F/B) In 89F/B, it was the road Malcolm Merriweather was looking for when he slammed into Andy's car. In 95F/B, it was said that the road was five miles from the county line.

ROUTE 31 (101F/96B) Two men were hurt in an accident on Route 31 that involved a two-ton trailer and a pickup truck.

"ROW, ROW, ROW YOUR BOAT" (111F/110B) The song Barney attempted to get the protesting women to sing as they blocked the county's bulldozer at Frisby's farm.

ROY'S LAUNDRY SERVICE (55F/B) The laundry service that did some of Aunt Bee's wash. They promised laundry back by Wednesday.

RUBY (41F/39B) Barney's birthstone. Barney said rubies would be O.K. to set in his "crime free" medal.

RUBY CREEK, NORTH CAROLINA (167F/B) On Bus #6 in Hollywood, the man sitting behind Andy was from Ruby Creek.

"RUDOLPH RABBIT" (237F/236B) Cartoon show aired opposite "The Mayberry Chef," Aunt Bee's cooking show, every day at six-thirty. Goober was upset because he'd have to miss Rudolph to watch Aunt Bee. Rudolph happened to be on Venus.

RUDY (174F/173B) Mayberry businessman who pledged $150 for the new church organ and then backed out of the debt.

RULE 8, SECTION B (29F/B) Parking too close to a hydrant.

RUM CAKE (222F/225B) Millie Hutchins offered a rum cake in lieu of a cream bun.

THE RUMOR 125th episode filmed and 124th episode broadcast. Original broadcast date was April 27, 1964. It was written by Jim Fritzell and Everett Greenbaum, and directed by Coby Ruskin. Regulars included Andy Griffith, Don Knotts, Ronny Howard, Frances Bavier, Aneta Corsaut, Betty Lynn, Howard McNear, and Jim Nabors. Guests included Ronda Jeter as Ethel, Molly Dodd, Mary Lansing, William Newell, and Ronny Howard's father, Rance Howard.

"RUMPELSTILTSKIN" (115F/114B) Fairy tale Andy had read in the past to Otis to get him to go to sleep. In 115F/114B, he read him "Jack and the Beanstalk."

"RUN, SHEEP, RUN" (240F/B) The game Barney used to play in Old Man McCabe's front yard.

RUNAWAY KID   4th episode filmed and 6th episode broadcast. Original broadcast date was November 7, 1960. It was written by Arthur Stander, and directed by Don Weis. Regulars included Andy Griffith, Don Knotts, Frances Bavier, and Ronny Howard. Guests included Dennis Holmes, Donald Losby, and Pat Rosson as George Foley.

RUNAWAY NOTE (1F/B) When Opie decided to leave home as a protest against Aunt Bee's arrival, Andy offered to write the following note for him: "Dear Paw: I am running away from home and you will never see me again." This made Opie decide to stay home.

"THE RUNAWAY TRAIL" (4F/6B) The road Andy said George Foley was on.

TRACY RUPERT (14F/B) He scratched his initials in the old cannon with a nail. Andy told the antique dealer, Ralph Mason, that the initials were really Teddy Roosevelt's.

MR. RUSKIN (240F/B) Russian interpreter who participated in the US/USSR summit meeting held at Andy's house.

RUTH (162F/164B) Wife of Harlan, mother of Corlis. Ruth was arrested by Warren with the Ladies Auxiliary. Harlan showed up at Andy's house for supper with Corlis.

"RUSTLING CATTLE" (244F/243B) The occupation of one of Bee's great-uncles, according to Bee's mother.

SABELLA (183F/182B) Gypsy. Sister of Murillos, daughter of La Farona. She often danced as Murillos sang and Sylvio (their friend) played the guitar. Sabella was an expert with the crystal ball, and often told fortunes (at three dollars a shot). She once told Goober he would one day be a rich millionaire.

MR. SABLE (237F/236B) The announcer for Channel 12 in Siler City. He introduced Aunt Bee's cooking show, "The Mayberry Chef."

"SAFETY PROCEDURES ON COUNTRY ROADS" (68F/70B) Special report written by Barney. It had a jingle: "Walk on the left side after dark or you'll wind up playing the harp." Investigator Upchurch remembered Barney had written the report and was impressed with it. Barney then cancelled his plans to give Upchurch "the big freeze." (See mentioned entries)

GEORGE SAFFERLY (10F/12B) Mayberry man who owned a service station which he later sold to Ed Sawyer. It was never verified that Safferly's later became Wally's, but it's likely.

ST. BENEDICT'S ISLAND (235F/234B) The island in the Caribbean where Howard moved to start his "new life." He became disillusioned in a short time and moved back to Mayberry. He realized that his pot of gold was in Mayberry.

PROFESSOR HUBERT ST. JOHN (230F//229B) Guest lecturer for the Mayberry woman's club and author of *I Know South America*. He fell for Bee, not because of her, but because she was a dead ringer for his dead wife, Ethel Montgomery St. John. Ethel had been dead ten years when St. John came to Mayberry. When Bee discovered that Ethel had been a homebody, she dressed up like a swinger to rid herself of St. John and to stop feeling like "a ghost."

JONATHAN ST. JOHN (230F/229B) Son of Hubert and the late Ethel St. John. Hubert called Jonathan to tell him that Bee was a carbon copy of Ethel.

ETHEL MONTGOMERY ST. JOHN (230F/229B) The late wife of author Hubert St. John. Bee was her twin and that was why he was so smitten with her.

ST. LOUIS WORLD'S FAIR 1906 (39F/36B) Frank Myers had a brass medallion from this fair. It was one of his "valuables."

ST. PETERSBURG (243F/242B) The town where Emmett landed his 361-pound marlin.

SALAD AND ROAST BEEF (161F/160B) Supper at the Taylor's the night Opie wrecked his bike trying to impress Sharon Porter.

"SALINE SOLUTION: 2 CC IN THE GLUTEUS MAXIMUS" (24F/B) The injection Dr. Benson gave Harvey Willick because of Harvey's hypochondriacal insistence on some kind of shot. Ellie Walker thought this was hilarious. Andy felt left out.

SALLY (74F/B) The third "convict at large." Her prison number was 1000.

SALLY (91F/B) Nonexistent girl Barney pretended he was talking to in an attempt to make Thelma Lou jealous.

SALT-AND-PEPPER SUIT (135F/B) Barney's suit. Old Man Goss lost it while he had it for drycleaning. It was mistakenly sent to a guy named Fitz in

Siler City. Goss found it but Barney refused to wear it because Fred Plummer had threatened to beat him up if he ever caught him out of uniform. Andy helped out by dressing up the judo expert, Mr. Izamoto, in the suit. Izamoto beat up Plummer while posing as Barney. Barney had bought the suit just for dancing; it was perfect for "the dip." (See FRED PLUMMER and MR. IZAMOTO)

SAM (12F/10B) When Barney got sweet-talked into signing the "Ellie for council" petition, Sam called him a "weak-kneed, chicken-livered, yellow-streaked turncoat."

SAM (48F/B) He caught six trout.

SAM (50F/B) Floyd's dog.

SAM (174F/173B) Mayberry businessman who pledged $150 for the new church organ. He later backed out of the pledge.

SAM BECKER'S DRUGSTORE PURCHASES (29F/B) Absorbent cotton, antiseptics, vitamins, tranquilizers, and swab sticks.

SAM FOR TOWN COUNCIL 247th episode filmed and 246th episode broadcast. Original broadcast date was March 11, 1968. It was written by Dick Bensfield and Perry Grant, and directed byLee Phillips. Regulars included Andy Griffith, Ken Berry, Jack Dodson, Aneta Corsaut, Paul Hartman, George Lindsey, Ronny Howard, and Frances Bavier. Guests included Gil Lamb as Lou, Don Sturdy as Harry, Penny Kunard as Mrs. Farley, Dick Johnstone as Mr. Calvin, Mary Lou Taylor as Mrs. Barton, and Roy Engel as Mr. Perkins (Engel's character was erroneously listed in the credits as "Mrs. Engel").

"SAM'S THE BEST, THE HECK WITH THE REST" (247F/246B) The slogan suggested by Goober for Sam's campaign for head of city council.

"SAME OLD COURTHOUSE, SAME OLD DESK, SAME CHAIR" (176F/B) The litany Barney recited—almost in awe—when he returned to Mayberry for a class reunion.

"TAYLOR SANDERS" 213F/B) The name Roger Bryant called Andy.

"SANDY" (213F/B) The name Roger Bryant called Andy.

SANTA CLAUS (11F/B) Barney played Santa at the Christmas Eve party held in the courthouse. He was the skinniest Santa to ever visit Mayberry.

"SANTA LUCIA" (104F/105B) (116F/115B) In 104F/105B, the song Barney sang to Thelma Lou while he entertained her in his new "pad": the backroom of the courthouse. In 116F/115B, it was the song the choir planned on performing at the recital. Barney was scheduled to sing the tenor solo. After John Masters, the director, heard Gomer singing it while changing a tire, he insisted on having Gomer do the solo instead of Barney. Barney was crushed, so Gomer feigned laryngitis so Barney could sing. When Barney found out he was faking, he refused to do the solo. Andy solved the problem by bringing both Barney and Gomer out of the ranks at the moment of the solo, turning it into a trio.

SARAH (2F/B) (10F/12B) (125F/124B) Never-seen telephone operator first mentioned in 2F/B. In 10F/12B, Ed Sawyer, the "stranger in town," knew that Sarah took a pinch of snuff now and then. In 125F/124B, she promised to bring a turkey to Andy's and Helen's "engagement party." There were scores of other episodes in which various townsfolk talked to Sarah.

SATURDAY NIGHT SOCIAL (24F/B) Weekly Mayberry event. Everybody went.

AL SAUNDERS (167F/B) The assistant director of "Sheriff Without A Gun."

BOB SAUNDERS (187F/186B) Assistant director on the Foster Furniture Polish commercial.

THE WIDOW SAUNDERS (153F/B) Mayberry widow and the subject of a discussion initiated by Fred Henry at Mr. Foley's market. It seemed that the widow was seen at the Half Moon Roadhouse with a dishcloth salesman. They ate New York-cut steak; the salesman was six feet tall, and he drove a fast-back wire-wheeled coupe. They got in at 1:00 A.M. The widow's late husband, Wilbur, left her $6,500 in insurance money, and she had recently spent $97 on new slipcovers. (See mentioned entries)

WILBUR SAUNDERS (153F/B) Late husband of the Widow Saunders. He left her $6,500 in insurance money. (See THE WIDOW SAUNDERS)

SAUSAGE (91F/B) (120F/119B) (133F/131B) (135F/B) 59¢ a pound.

SAVANNAH (36F/37B) The town where George Stevens claimed he had a cotton mill. Also, the town where Melissa Stevens said she attended junior college.

THE "SAVE THE SCOBY HOUSE FUND" (28F/B) Fund started by Andy and Barney. They held a rummage sale to raise money. After Ben Weaver relented on his foreclosure proceedings, the "Save the Scoby House Fund" was donated to the school library fund.

SUELER SAWLEY (95F/B) Gomer saw her walking Main Street from his perch on the courthouse roof.

ED SAWYER (10F/12B) The "stranger in town" who "adopted" Mayberry after serving in the Army with resident Joe Larson and reading Larson's copies of the "Mayberry Gazette." Ed put everybody off by coming on too strong and knowing everything about them. Eventually, though, with the help of Andy, Ed was accepted, bought George Safferly's service station and, ironically, was never seen or heard from again. Ed was originally from New York and had no family of his own. Ed was sweet on Lucy Matthews.

"SAXIMINIA" (15F/B) The song Floyd's son, Norman, played on the sax for Wilbur Finch.

"SAY HELLO TO TONTO" (3F/B) Bobby Fleet's farewell to Andy as he and the band left Mayberry.

SAYBERTOWN (138F/B) The town where Clara Edwards' sister lived. The sister got ill and called Clara away from her role as Lady Mayberry in the centennial pageant. (See "LADY MAYBERRY")

SAZERAC (67F/65B) New Orleans drink Peggy McMillan ordered at the restaurant in Raleigh the night Andy took her to dinner. Andy had a draft beer.

"THE SCAMP" (240F/B) The name Old Man McCabe called Barney when Barney played in his front yard as a boy.

MR. SCHLUMMER (143F/B) (166F/B) Mayberry realtor. In 143F/B, he collected five percent on his deals. This convinced Barney to go into the real estate business. In 166F/B, Goober told him about Andy's $1,000 check for the "Sheriff Without A Gun" story.

EMMIE SCHMALTZ (79F/77B) After Andy teased Barney about his "man in prison" speech to the boys (which culminated in the deputy locking himself in cell #2), Barney got mad and said Andy should be in the funny papers: "Get you a wig and a dress and you're another Emmie Schmaltz."

DAVE SCHNEIDER (165F/169B) Necktie salesman who wore sunglasses. While the Taylors were in Hollywood, the sunglasses fooled them into asking for Dave's autograph.

SCHOOL PARTY (181F/B) Social gathering which usually served as an excuse for the boys to horse around and play practical jokes on the girls. The pranks included hand buzzers, rubber snakes, and spiders. Helen Crump turned it into a dance, Opie was destroyed because he couldn't, and Andy had to gently "force" him to attend. After Opie saw Andy dancing with Helen, Opie danced with Sharon Porter and a splendid time was had by all.

SCHOOL TREASURY (197F/198B) At the time of the "senior play," there was only thirty-eight dollars in the treasury.

SEYMOUR SCHRECK (139F/B) Author of *Twenty Scientific Tricks A Boy Can Do At Home* and *Fun In The Garage On A Rainy Day*.

ELEANOR SCHROEDER (144F/B) She called Bee to tell her about Gilly Walker's car being in the courthouse.

VIOLET ROSE SCHUMAKER (171F/172B) Woman who worked at the coal company and who interviewed for the secretary job that Aunt Bee eventually got. The counterfeiters, Kingsley and Finch, hired Bee over Violet Rose.

BENJAMIN SCHUSTER (84F/B) Alias "Benjy Schoos," alias "Benny Shoot." He had a $3,000 reward on him. Barney put up his wanted poster in the courthouse.

MR. SCHWUMP (113F/112B) (123F/122B) (133F/131B) (210F/211B) In 113F/112B, he was the Mayberry man who tried to stop the rampage of Ernest T. Bass at Mrs. Wiley's house. Schwump handled the rock Ernest T. pitched through Mrs. Wiley's window, much to Barney's disgust: after it was touched he couldn't send it to the "boys at the lab" for fingerprinting. In 123F/122B, Andy didn't want to stand in the stag line at the dance with Mr. Schwump after Helen and Thelma Lou refused to go with him and Barney. In 133F/131B, Andy talked to him in front of the courthouse. In 210F/211B, he read the paper in the courthouse after Floyd vacated the barbershop.

SCIENTIFIC INTRODUCTIONS, INC. (249F/248B) Computer dating service founded by Dr. Edith Gibson. Her associate was Mr. Franklin.

HELEN SCOBY (28F/B) Lester's wife. She took in ironing to earn extra money.

LESTER SCOBY (28F/B) He and his wife lived in a house owned by Ben Weaver. Ben held the mortgage, which was $52.50 a month. Lester missed one payment and Ben demanded the whole balance: $780. He really wanted the property to build a warehouse. Andy stalled, but then he called Ben's bluff by demanding that the Scobys move and by treating them terribly. Ben then softened and even gave Lester a job at his store. Ben built his warehouse closer to town.

MARY SCOBY (28F/B) Lester and Helen's daughter.

"SCOOP FIFE" (153F/B) Barney's nickname, according to Barney, when he wrote his short-lived newspaper column, "Pickups and Splashes from Floor and Pool," at Central High.

S D - 5 6 1 (187F/186B) (195F/193B) In 187F/186B, Willard Foster's license plate number. In 195F/193B, the plate number of the car under which Goober was working.

SEBASTIAN (235F/234B) Young boy Howard met on St. Benedict's Island in the Caribbean.

SECOND CLASS SCOUT (67F/65B) Barney and Andy both achieved this in the same month.

SECOND-IN-COMMAND (29F/B) Barney's rank when he was in the Army. He was stationed at the PX library on Staten Island. He was second-in-command of over 3,000 books. Barney said, "I'd rather not talk about it."

SECOND TENOR (5F/8B) Tom Silby's place in the lodge choir before he "died."

SECRET AGENT F-45 (173F/174B) Warren was a sleepwalker and said that if he saw Agent F-45 on TV, he'd become him.

"THE SECRET PLACE" (35F/B) Secret fishing spot of Barney's. He caught a frog there the day he, Andy, Opie, and Floyd caught Elizabeth Crowley, the "woman speeder."

SECTION 17B, ARTICLE 4 (73F/70B) The law that stated that street vending was not permitted anywhere in Mayberry. Barney had a hard time enforcing the statute against Neil and Matt, the farmers who sold produce from a truck parked behind Dexter Street.

"SEEK AND YE SHALL FIND" (174F/173B) The sermon theme on the Sunday after Harlan Robinson agreed to wait for his money so All Souls Church could immediately take possession of his organ.

SENIOR CITIZEN LODGE (166F/B) Floyd suggested Andy stay there when they got to Hollywood.

THE SENIOR PLAY (197F/198B) Play put on once a year by the senior class of the high school. In 197F/198B, Helen Crump was the director, and she met with opposition from Mr. Hampton, the principal, over her plans to include (oh no!) the Frug. She changed the dance numbers to the Charleston, and he saw his error and let the show go on. (See MR. HAMPTON)

THE SENIOR PLAY 197th episode filmed and 198th episode broadcast. Original broadcast date was November 14, 1966. It was written by Sid Morse, and directed by Lee Phillips. Regulars included Andy Griffith, Aneta Corsaut, George Lindsey, Jack Dodson, and Howard McNear. Guests included Leon Ames as Mr. Hampton,

Chuck Brummit as Homer, Cynthia Hull as Estelle, and Mary Jackson as Miss Vogel.

SEPTEMBER 14, 1908 (8F/9B) The day Jedediah Wakefield was admitted to the hospital after his mule, Emmie, bit him on the behind.

SEPTEMBER 23, 1941, 2:00 P.M. (152F/B) Otis Campbell's first arrest for intoxication.

A SEPTIC TANK (90F/B) Before Barney bought his first car, his last big buy had been a septic tank for his parent's anniversary. When Barney told Andy about the purchase Andy said, "You're a fine son, Barn."

SERGEANT (114F/113B) The "prisoner of love" wondered if she should call Barney "sergeant."

THE SERMON FOR TODAY 100th episode filmed and 99th episode broadcast. Original broadcast date was October 21, 1963. It was written by John Whedon, and directed by Dick Crenna. Regulars included Andy Griffith, Don Knotts, Frances Bavier, Ronny Howard, Jim Nabors, and Hope Summers. Guests included William Keene as Reverend Tucker, David Lewis, Forrest Lewis, Roy Engel, and Joe Hamilton.

SETH TAYLOR DAY (208F/212B) Annual holiday in Mayberry to honor Andy's ancestor, Seth.

7:00 A.M. (38F/41B) Breakfast at the Taylor's.

7:00 A.M. TO 7:00 P.M. (102F/B) The hours of Wally's filling station.

"THE SEVEN DEADLY SINS" (226F/223B) The sermon the week of 226F/223B. Next week was "Gluttony."

$7.00 (120F/119B) The charge to replace a fuse in Andy's refrigerator. The job was done by an unnamed "man from Mt. Pilot."

$7.50 (210F/211B) The compromise Floyd and Howard agreed to regarding the rent increase Howard wanted after he bought the building in which Floyd's Barbershop was located. Floyd went up $7.50; Howard went down $7.50.

785 (106F/B) Violation: false alarm. Barney gave Gomer a ticket on this violation when he reported a crime at Wally's Service Station to urge Barney back to work as deputy.

7458 (2F/B) The number under the mug shot of the escaped prisoner, Dirksen.

$780.00 (28F/B) The balance due on Lester Scoby's mortgage.

SEVEN STITCHES (113F/112B) Hoggette Winslow needed seven stitches after Ernest T. Bass split her head open with his date-request rock.

7-10 (118F/117B) Assault with a deadly weapon. Andy charged Maudie and Naylor with a 7-10 when Maudie threw a chicken at Naylor.

SEVEN WINTERS (119F/118B) Gomer gave Andy enough wood to last seven winters.

SEVEN YEARS (203F/201B) Clara won the rose competition at the Mayberry Garden Club flower show for seven years in a row.

SEVENTEEN (82F/B) The age at which Barney could reach into a milk bottle and take out an egg.

SEVENTEEN (139F/B) The age Briscoe Darling's wife was when he married her. Briscoe was thirty. He was her second husband; her first got run over by a team of hogs.

1762 (188F/B) Year of the Battle of Mayberry.

$70.00 (3F/B) (210F/211B) In 3F/B, the amount to which Andy raised Bobby Fleet's fine for "robe-dignity offending." In 210F/211B, Mr. Coefield's first rent offer to Howard Sprague for Floyd's Barbershop.

"78" (80F/B) The number of the Raleigh bus that Luke Comstock took to Mayberry.

"75" (102F/B) The number of the gold truck that passed through Mayberry.

"THE 75¢ RULE" (84F/B) The rule Arnold Winkler said applied to little boys: they got a seventy-five cents allowance for no work. Andy turned down Opie's request for enactment of that particular rule.

75¢ AN HOUR (161F/160B) The amount Mr. Doakes paid for the delivery boy job at his market.

$75.00 (31F/B) (210F/211B) In 31F/B, the amount of money Jim Lindsey ended up owing around Mayberry after running up tabs all over town. In 210F/211B, Mr. Coefield's final rent offer to Howard Sprague for Floyd's Barbershop.

74¢ (132F/128B) The cash Opie had to spend on a gift for Helen: he bought her stockings. He had 74¢, the stockings were 80¢, so he had to go drink three bottles of pop and cash in the bottles to make up the difference.

SEVENTY MILES PER HOUR (35F/B) The speed at which Elizabeth Crowley, the woman speeder, was driving when she tried to speed through Mayberry.

BEN SEWELL (17F/B) Moonshiner who ran a still at Cowsill Flat on Hash Road. He sold moon for three dollars. He was arrested by Andy and Barney after the Morrison sisters snitched on him.

SEWING BASKET (11F/B) Christmas gift from Ben Weaver to Aunt Bee.

SHABOB'S (206F/B) Armenian restaurant in Raleigh. Bee's sister, Ellen, took Bee there for dinner. They wrapped everything in grape leaves at Shabob's.

"THE SHADOW" (119F/188B) The name Andy called Gomer due to Gomer's constant attention to Andy and the Taylor family. (Gomer was trying to repay Andy for "saving his life.")

"SHADY GROVE" (121F/120B) The song Charlene Darling sang after her marriage to Andy was cancelled.

SHAMPOOER (219F/B) Automatic wash-and-dry shampooer with patented foam-free rinse control. Floyd planned on buying it with the nonexistent $200 prize he won in Goober's "Grab Bag for Cash" contest.

DR. AMIEL SHARLOCK (202F/204B) Doctor who Howard quoted as saying that criminals could be returned to society. Howard tried some of Dr. Sharlock's techniques on the bank robber, Fred. Fred punched him.

SHARON (116F/115B) Girl in the choir. John Masters told her she came in a little too early.

SHAVING CREAM (210F/211B) Andy wanted to eat shaving cream when he was a kid, according to Floyd. He thought it was ice cream.

SHAWL (183F/182B) Murillos, the gypsy leader, sold Aunt Bee a shawl he claimed was once worn by Princess Teronoya. He charged her eight dollars.

"SHAZAM!" (85F/B) (95F/B) (98F/97B) (102F/B) (107F/127B) (109F/108B) (119F/118B) (126F/125B) (127F/126B) This was Gomer Pyle's—by way of "Captain Marvel"—all-purpose expletive and expression of surprise and wonderment. Throughout the run of the series, we find Gomer Pyle using "Shazam!" exactly seventeen times, with the first one in the episode called "The Great Filling Station Robbery" (85F/B) and the last (broadcast order, that is) in the pilot for his own series, "Gomer Pyle, U.S.M.C." (107F/127B). Gomer's first use of the word came as Barney showed him the surveillance camera that would end up taking Barney's own picture. The following schedule (in filmed order) gives the "Shazam!" per episode count:

"The Great Filling Station Robbery" (85F/B): two
"The Big House" (95F/B): one
"The Haunted House" (98F/97B): two
"A Black Day For Mayberry" (102F/B): three
"Gomer Pyle, U.S.M.C." (107F/127B): two
"Barney And The Cave Rescue" (109F/108B): one
"Andy Saves Gomer" (119F/118B): three
"Barney And Thelma Lou, Phffft" (126F/125B): one
"Back To Nature" (127F/126B): two

In addition, Gomer Pyle also did one "Shazam!" in the TV-movie, "Return To Mayberry."

"SHE'LL BE COMIN' ROUND THE MOUNTAIN" (29F/B) Song the people of Mayberry sang to Sam Becker after his son, Andy, was born.

SHELDON THE BULLY (34F/33B) The "bully" of "Opie and the Bully." He stopped Opie every morning on his way to school and extorted Opie's milk nickel, which forced Opie to finagle extra nickels from Andy, Barney, and Aunt Bee. Andy found out, told Opie a fable about himself being afraid of the bully, Hodie Snitch, and gave Opie the courage to stand up to Sheldon. Opie fought him and came into the courthouse triumphant. (See HODIE SNITCH)

SHERIFF BARNEY 44th episode filmed and broadcast. Original broadcast date was December 25, 1961. It was written by Leo Solomon and Ben Gershman, and directed by Bob Sweeney. Regulars included Andy Griffith, Don Knotts, Frances Bavier, and Hal Smith as Otis. Guests included Dabbs Greer and Ralph Dumke.

"SHERIFF MATT DILLON" (87F/B) Aunt Bee called Andy "Matt Dillon" when she got drunk on Colonel Harvey's Indian Elixir.

"THE SHERIFF RULES" (6F/4B) Barney futilely attempted to memorize the first rule: "An officer of the law shall enforce the law and order without regard to personal welfare and safety."

"SHERIFF TAYLOR TAKES HOLLY-WOOD BY STORM" (168F/B) Caption under the photo of Andy and Darlene Mason that ran in the "Mayberry Gazette."

"SHERIFF TRAILER" (141F/142B) The name Barney called Andy when Barney got drunk. He also sang "Sweet Adeline" with Otis.

"SHERIFF WITHOUT A GUN" (150F/B) (166F/B) (168F/B) In 150F/B, the article about Andy that ran in the magazine, "Law and Order." From the piece: "Quiet, unassuming, friendly, likable: all these adjectives truly describe Mayberry's Sheriff Andy Taylor." Andy said he didn't carry a gun because he didn't want people to fear a gun; he wanted them to respect him. The truth, according to

Aunt Bee, was that the gun made Andy feel too heavy on one side. In 166F/B, it was the movie of the same name made about Andy by Belmont Picture Studio. In 168F/B, it was said that Darlene Mason starred in the picture and that the publicity man for the movie was Pat Michaels.

SHERIFF'S DUTIES (109F/108B) Barney delineated these duties to Gomer on the occasion of Gomer being deputized, so Andy and Barney could go to the town picnic: "Communications, patrol coverage, watchin' out for stolen autos, and of course cooperating with state and federal officials to provide for the common defense, assure domestic tranquility, and maintain law and order in the entire area."

SHERIFF'S SAFETY CONFERENCE (144F/B) Conference held in Mt. Pilot. Andy allowed Goober to stay in the courthouse when he went to the conference. Goober then took Gilly Walker's car apart in the building.

THE SHERIFFS OF MAYBERRY (106F/B) (152F/B) In order: Sheriff Pinckley, Sheriff Fred Paley, Sheriff Dale Buckley, Sheriff Andy Taylor. In 106F/B, it was mentioned that Sheriff Poindexter was sheriff in 1946, but it wasn't said where in the order his term ran.

"SHERLOCK HOLMES" (178F/B) The name Andy called Warren when the deputy began his investigation into the mysterious "loss" of Aunt Bee's pin.

SHIMMERING ROSE (27F/B) Powder sold at Walker's Drugstore.

"SHIPPING INTERESTS" (36F/37B) George Stevens claimed he had shipping interests, along with his cotton mill in Savannah.

SHIRLEY (246F/245B) The girl Howard Sprague asked to his "swinging" party. She turned him down. She didn't remember she met him at the lodge the previous fall. She was leaving for Detroit.

HENRY SHOAT (128F/133B) The man from whom Barney got his bloodhound. The dog's name was Blue.

SHOOTING GALLERY PRIZES (158F/B) At the carnival, the shooting gallery offered the following: a genuine Swiss watch, a genuine bonehandled carving set from the Orient, a hairdryer, a fishing pole, a jacknife, a genuine ceramic pelican, a napkin holder with a log cabin on it, stuffed animals, an electric razor, and a thermometer.

THE SHOPLIFTERS 117th episode filmed and 116th episode broadcast. Original broadcast date was March 2, 1964. It was written by Bill Idelson and Sam Bobrick, and directed by Coby Ruskin. Regulars included Andy Griffith, Don Knotts, Frances Bavier, and Ronny Howard. Guests included Tol Avery as Ben Weaver, Charles P. Thompson as Asa Breeny, Lurene Tuttle as the Shoplifter, Clint Howard (Ronny's brother) as Leon, Jewel Rose, Elizabeth Harrower, and Mary Lansing.

SHORT-HAIRED MINK COAT (245F/244B) The coat Bernie the Furrier offered to Emmett for a hundred dollars.

SHORTY (144F/B) He couldn't stay in the courthouse for Andy, but he was still able to take care of the school crossing.

SHOVEL (121F/120B) Part of the sheriff department's "official equipment," according to Barney.

SHRIMP AND DUCK (225F/224B) The lunch Aunt Bee made when Opie invited Billy Hollander.

THE SHRINER CLUB (160F/163B) Bee and John Canfield went dancing there for two hours after they had dinner at the Reef at Nagtin. (See THE REEF AT NAGTIN and JOHN CANFIELD)

SICK LEAVE (129F/130B) Ollie had some coming, so he decided to stay at Andy's for a longer visit.

"SIDECAR EXPRESS" (112F/111B) Riding in Barney's new motorcycle's sidecar, according to Barney.

"SIGMUND FROOD" (133F/131B) According to Barney, he discovered "mother love."

SIGNS, OMENS, PORTENTS, AND CHARMS TO WARD OFF BAD LUCK (49F/B) The book Barney read in an attempt to ward off the bad effects of Henry "The Jinx" Bennett's presence. He learned to rub a redhead's head, and he also learned the following chants: "Come fish come/come fish come/Sam's at the gate with a frosted cape/come, fish, come"; and, "Fly away buzzard/fly away crow/Way down south where the winds don't blow/Rub your nose and give two winks/And save us from this awful jinx." The book originally belonged to Barney's grandmother. He also learned the incantation, "Winkum, thinkum, Nodimus rex/Protect us all from the man with the hex."

ANNABELLE SILBY (5F/8B) Mayberry woman whose husband left her because of her nagging. Annabelle was so proud, she couldn't admit he left her. She told everyone in town he died while out of town and even went so far as to have a funeral. Annabelle was chairperson of the underprivileged children's charity drive when her "late" husband, Tom, came back to town. (See TOM SILBY)

TOM SILBY (5F/8B) Husband of Annabelle Silby. Tom was a drinking man who left his wife because of her nagging. Annabelle wouldn't admit that her husband left her, so she told everyone that he was run over by a taxicab on a business trip to Charlottesville.

SILER CITY (135F/B) (225F/224B) (236F/237B) (237F/236B) In 135F/B, Siler City was the hometown of the man named "Fitz," who mistakenly received Barney's salt-and-pepper suit. In 225F/224B, Andy promised he'd drive Helen to Siler City, so Aunt Bee had to drive Opie to the Hollanders. She was going to a flower show in the direction of Walnut Hills anyway. In 236F/237B, Ben Beecham said that Siler City was "virgin territory" for insurance sales. In 237F/236B, Siler City was where Channel 12 was located.

"SILO RENTALS" (161F/160B) Sign on a storefront window on Main Street.

"THE SILVER HERRINGBONES" (246F/245B) Rock group that was a favorite of Howard Sprague's. Howard played one of their recordings at his "swinging" party.

ED SIMKINS (33F/34B) Grace's husband. Andy got a call from Grace that Ed had just given her what-for. This incident was predicted in Bob Rogers' "Crime Pattern in Mayberry" chart.

GRACE SIMKINS (33F/34B) Ed's wife. Ed gave her what-for.

MR. SIMMONS (15F/B) Wilbur Finch's boss at the Manhattan Shoe Company.

MR. SIMMONS (203F/201B) Head of the Simmons Seed Catalogue Company. He hosted the flower competition of the Mayberry Garden Club and also acted as judge.

MR. SIMMONS (208F/212B) Mayberry citizen who was the great-great-grandson of Winston Simmons. Mr. Simmons was the one who informed Bee and Andy of Winston's and Seth Taylor's checkered past. He told them on the day the statue of Seth was scheduled to be unveiled in the town square. (See SETH TAYLOR)

STEWART SIMMONS (60F/B) Resident of Triplett, North Carolina. Andy went to see him.

SIMMONS SEED CATALOGUE (203F/201B) The "Bible" of the Mayberry Garden Club. The winner of the rose competition was photographed with his or her winning flower, and the picture was used on the front cover of the catalogue.

JACKIE SIMMS (195F/193B) A member of the Mayberry Giants.

MARIE SIMMS (42F/B) The biggest blabbermouth in Mayberry. She called Bee the morning after Andy and Barney went to the meeting of the Esquire Club. Barney was waiting for the acceptance call.

THE SIMMS (143F/B) Lila and her husband. They considered buying Andy's house but got turned off when Opie told them about the noisy plumbing, the crack in the ceiling, and the leaky roof.

FRED SIMPSON (220F/B) Conceited boy who asked Opie's "first love," Mary Alice Carter, to Arnold Bailey's thirteenth birthday party after Opie had asked her. She had already agreed to go with Opie but stood him up for Fred. At the party Fred ignored her, preferring to dance with other girls and comb his hair. It wasn't said if Fred was related to either Mary or Walt Simpson.

MARY SIMPSON (56F/B) (59F/B) The county nurse. She was an early girlfriend of Andy's. In 56F/B, she eventually inoculated—with Andy's help—the reluctant Rafe Hollister with a tetanus shot. In 59F/B, Andy tried to court her but Barney kept getting in the way. When Andy told him he wanted to be alone with her, Barney assumed they were going to get married. This episode was very similar to 68F/69B, "Barney Mends A Broken Heart," and 125F/124B, "The Rumor." Mary didn't seem to have any memorable traits other than being able to make pizza at home. It wasn't said if she was related to Walt Simpson.

WALT SIMPSON (214F/B) Mayberry dairyman who drove his route in a horse-drawn wagon, which was pulled by his old friend, Dolly. When Walt went to visit his brother for four or five days, Opie took over caring for Dolly. Walt worked for Dogwood Dairy Farms. It wasn't said if he was related to Mary Simpson, the county nurse.

FRANK SINATRA (35F/B) Elizabeth Crowley told Barney he looked like Frank. Barney believed her.

A SINGER IN TOWN 189th episode filmed and broadcast. Original broadcast date was April 11, 1966. It was written by Stan Dreben and Howard Merrill, and directed by Alan Rafkin. Regulars included Andy Griffith, Frances Bavier, Ronny Howard, Howard McNear, George Lindsey, and Hope Summers. Guests included Jesse Pearson as Keevy Hazleton, Byron Foulger as The Clerk, Edgar Hess as the Stage Manager, Tom D'Andrea as Bill Stone, and Joel Redlin as Ferdie.

SIR WALTER RALEIGH LANDING DAY (17F/B) Holiday used by the customers of the Morrison sisters as an excuse to buy their moonshine. The sisters would only sell their "Special Elixir" for "recognized" holidays.

SIRLOIN STEAK (120F/119B) 99¢ a pound at Foley's Market; 89¢ a pound at Diamond Jim's, the discount butcher.

6¢ (29F/B) The amount a penny hit by lightning was worth, according to Nat Pike.

SIX CHILDREN (244F/243B) The number of kids Maynard Myers, an old beau of Helen's, eventually had.

SIX DOLLARS A WEEK (104F/105B) The rent Barney paid to live in Mrs. Mendlebright's boarding house.

SIX FEET (153F/B) The height of the dishcloth salesman the Widow Saunders dated.

SIX HOURS (210F/211B) The amount of time it took to ride to Mt. Pilot on a bicycle. (A very slow pace, as Mt. Pilot was only twelve miles away.)

600 SANDWICHES (4F/6B) The provisions Andy figured George Foley, the "runaway kid," would need to get to Texas.

SIX MONTHS (246F/245B) The length of time George and Mrs. Sprague went together before George proposed.

6-0-3 (87F/B) Violation: Selling without a license.

6:00 P.M. (236F/237B) (245F/244B) In 236F/237B, the time by which Emmett was usually home from work. In 245F/244B, the time Flora Mallerby got off of work. She worked at the Diner.

SIX PEOPLE (202F/196B) The number of people who called Aunt Bee to complain about Opie. He had asked them if they wanted a baby. He was trying to find a home for the abandoned Garland baby that he and Arnold had found on the courthouse steps.

6:30 P.M. (237F/236B) The time slot of Aunt Bee's cooking show, "The Mayberry Chef."

$6,500.00 (153F/B) The amount of insurance money Wilbur Saunders left his wife when he died. (See the "SAUNDERS" entries)

6-12 (67F/65B) Barney was called out on one. He said it was "an official code: two three's and two six's."

"SIX WHO PASS WHILE THE LENTILS BOIL" (71F/72B) The name of the play Aunt Bee did when she was a young girl in Sunday school. She played the queen.

SIXTEEN YEARS (114F/113B) The length of time Tyla Lee Vernon's husband courted her before he proposed.

$60.00 (35F/B) The total fine Andy imposed on Elizabeth Crowley, the woman speeder: $10 for speeding; $10 for contempt; $10 for contempt again; and $30 for robe offending.

63 (40F/38B) Violation: loitering. Barney arrested Dave the Hobo on a 63.

$65.00 (210F/211B) The new rent expense Howard wanted to impose on Floyd's Barbershop after he bought the building. Floyd's rent had been $50 for quite awhile. The $65.00 would have given Howard a five percent return on his money. Floyd refused to pay and vacated the building.

"THE SKATER'S WALTZ" (100F/99B) The song Andy led the Mayberry Band in at rehearsal.

SKIBALL (119F/118B) Barney and his cousin, Virgil, played four games at the Raleigh Arcade.

OSCAR SKINNER (62F/B) Proprietor of the Feed and Grain Store. Otis had an appointment with Oscar for a job on the day Virgil filed the cell keys smooth.

SKIPPY (68F/69B) (155F/B) In 68F/69B, she was introduced as one of the "fun girls" from Mt. Pilot. When Andy and Peggy had a fight, Barney arranged for Andy and him to meet Skippy and Daphne at the Tip-Top Cafe, twelve miles away in Mt. Pilot. In 155F/B, she got arrested for speeding through Mayberry; she and Daphne arrested themselves.

SKUNK (109F/108B) Goober had one as a pet. He ended up keeping it after he tracked it into a cave and it "anointed" him. It didn't have a name.

"THE SKYLINE OF MILWAUKEE, WISCONSIN" (39F/36B) Frank Myers had a commemorative spoon with the skyline on it. It was one of his "valuables."

JIM SLATER (174F/173B) Mayberry businessman who pledged $150 for the new church organ. He later backed out of the pledge.

VIOLA SLATT (99F/98B) The "biggest gossip in town," according to Barney.

"A SLIGHT OVERBITE" (65F/67B) Floyd said Peggy McMillan had one.

"SLIM" (74F/B) The name Big Maude Tyler called Barney.

SLIPCOVERS (153F/B) The Widow Saunders bought new slipcovers with some of the $6,500 insurance money her husband, Wilbur, left her.

RUBE SLOAN (17F/B) Moonshiner arrested by Andy and Barney after the Morrison sisters snitched on him.

"SMALL TOWN ADMINISTRATION" (61F/B) Jean Boswell, the reporter who posed as a college student to write a smear story on Andy, told Barney that she was writing her thesis on "small town administration."

SARAH SMEDLEY (178F/B) One of the Smedley sisters. Sarah came down with the flu and couldn't run the cookie booth at the bazaar. Clara called Bee and asked her to fill in running the booth and baking the twenty-six dozen cookies needed. Bee had run the booth the previous three years.

THE SMEDLEY SISTERS (167F/B) Mayberry ladies. While in Hollywood, Bee wrote a letter to one of the sisters.

FRANK SMITH (163F/161B) A Ph.D. from the Raleigh school board who came to Mayberry to work with Helen on a project. Andy got jealous of all the time Helen spent with Frank.

HANNAH SMITH (99F/98B) Lou's wife. Ernest T. Bass broke two panels in their greenhouse.

JACK SMITH (165F/169B) Forty-four-year-old emcee of the Hollywood game show, "Win Or Lose." Bee was the sweepstakes winner on the show. (See "WIN OR LOSE")

CAPTAIN JOHN SMITH (196F/203B) An early settler Andy mentioned during a discussion of American history in his night class.

LOU SMITH (99F/98B) Ernest T. Bass broke two panels in his greenhouse.

"THE SMITH BROTHERS INSTITUTION" (112F/111B) The museum where Barney thought his motorcycle should be placed after he read the phony "motorcycle plaque" Andy had placed on the bike.

SMOKED HAM (245F/244B) Goober suggested a smoked ham (and perfume) to Emmett as an anniversary gift for Martha.

OZZIE SNAKE (216F/B) "Colonel Tim's Talent Time Amateur Show" launched Ozzie's career.

SNACK BAR (73F/70B) Main Street restaurant. Barney sometimes ate lunch there.

SNAPDRAGON (203F/201B) A blue ribbon category at the Mayberry Garden Club flower show.

THE SNAPPY LUNCH (9F/7B) Mayberry eatery Andy suggested for lunch.

BOOJUM SNARK (64F/73B) According to Andy, the name of the Spirit of Fire.

SNEADLEY'S (231F/230B) Department store where Emmett bought a shirt for $3.95.

HODIE SNITCH (34F/33B) Bully from Andy's past. Andy told Opie about Hodie's refusal to let Andy fish a certain spot at Myer's Lake. He used the story to show Opie the meaning of courage. Hodie Snitch was more than likely fictitious, made up by Andy to use as an example.

SNOW VALLEY WHITE (203F/201B) Clara's white rose. She entered it every year in the Mayberry Garden Club flower competition.

SNOWSHOES (4F/6B) The critical piece of equipment that George Foley, the "runaway kid," realized he'd need to get to Texas.

SNUFF (10F/12B) Sarah, the operator, took a pinch now and then.

MR. SNYDER (101F/96B) Andy told Barney that Snyder was coming to the courthouse to do some work.

MRS. SNYDER (89F/B) (101F/96B) Andy's next-door neighbor. In 89F/B, Aunt Bee told Andy that if he needed anything when she was away, Mrs. Snyder was right next door. In 101F/96B, when Andy came home from work and found the dead songbird Opie had killed with his slingshot, he thought that Mrs. Snyder's cat had killed the bird. Mrs. Snyder was probably married to Mr. Snyder, also mentioned in this episode.

"SOCIAL SECURITY IN ACTION" (153F/B) One of the columns in the "Mayberry Gazette."

SOCKS (54F/B) Barney's purchase from Bert Miller, the peddler.

THE SOFTBALL TEAM (222F/225B) Ladies ball club. Goober dated certain members of the team.

SOLID GOLD (41F/39B) Barney wanted his "crime-free" medal made of gold.

SOMBREROS (227F/222B) Bee brought Emmett, Howard, and Andy sombreros from Mexico.

"SOME ENCHANTED EVENING" (174F/173B) Clara Edwards' rendering of this song to Harlan Robinson caused him to decide to wait for the money that the All Souls Church owed him for his organ.

MR. SOMERSET (93F/B) State inspector who came to Mayberry to turn down all of Barney's requests for more funds. He was crusty and cold until he saw the eleven "dogs, dogs, dogs" Barney had out back. Turned out he was a dog lover and approved all the funds requests.

"SOMETHING ABOUT BLONDES" (192F/191B) Movie at the show. Howard said it was "a wild one."

THE SONG FESTERS 116th episode filmed and 115th episode broadcast. Original broadcast date was February 24, 1964. It was written by Jim Fritzell and Everett Greenbaum, and directed by Earl Bellamy. Regulars included Andy Griffith, Don Knotts, Frances Bavier, and Jim Nabors. Guests included Olan Soule as John Masters, Reta Shaw as Eleanora Poultice, and Andy's then real-life wife, Barbara Griffith. The choral music for the show was supervised by Ric Ricardi.

SONGBIRD (101F/96B) Opie killed a mother songbird with his slingshot.

SOREGHUM MOLASSES (76F/78B) 20¢.

THE SOUND COMMITTEE (229F/228B) Opie's rock-and-roll band. It consisted of Clifford Johnson on lead guitar, Opie on rhythm acoustic, Wilson Brown on rhythm guitar, and Jessie Clayton on drums.

"SOURWOOD MOUNTAIN" (37F/40B) The song Andy and Karen Moore sang when Karen came to Mayberry.

THE SOUTH SIDE (39F/36B) Area of Mayberry where Frank Myers always did his fishing.

SOUTHERN BUS LINES (65F/67B) (166F/B) In 65F/67B, the bus Bee took when she went to see her Aunt Louise. In 166F/B, the bus Andy, Bee, and Opie took to the airport for their Hollywood trip.

"THE SPACE PHANTOM" (221F/235B) Comic book Opie brought Goober.

"THE SPACE RACE" (196F/203B) One of the subjects discussed by Goober during his "beard" stage. His victim was Aunt Bee.

SPANISH SHAWLS (227F/222B) Aunt Bee had one draped on the piano. Also, Bee sent Opie one from Mexico. It was called a rapi.

SPARERIBS TAVERN (209F/210B) Main Street restaurant owned by Mr. Hendricks that went out of business. Aunt Bee opened Aunt Bee's Canton Palace with Charlie Lee as her partner in the same location.

"SPECIAL AWARD FOR LEARNING" (133F/131B) The diploma Andy made up for Ernest T. Bass.

"SPECIAL ELIXIR" (17F/B) The Morrison sisters' moonshine.

MRS. SPEERS (105F/104B) A shaved collie came up to Mrs. Speers in Norman's Groceteria. Al Becker was standing there.

SPENCER'S PIPES AND TOBACCOS (222F/225B) Main Street tobacconist next to the theater.

"SPERANEOUS COMBUSTION" (162F/164B) The reason Warren gave Goober a ticket. Goober had some oily rags in a drum and Warren said they could start a fire. Goober told Andy that Warren said the fire would start by "speraneous combustion."

"THE SPIDERMAN" (221F/235B) Comic book Opie brought Goober.

ART SPIEGEL (166F/B) The man from Belmont Picture Studio who signed the $1,000 check sent to

Andy for the rights to use his "Sheriff Without A Gun" story.

SPINACH (32F/B) Aunt Bee wanted Opie to plant two rows of spinach alongside the garage.

THE SPIRITS (64F/73B) Fire, water, and air. Their names, according to Andy, were Boojum Snark (fire), Brillen Trant (water), and Grovely Barch (air).

"SPIT ON MY FINGER AND HOPE TO CROW" (244F/243B) The phrase Goober used to assure someone of his silence.

SPOON (39F/36B) One of Frank Myers' "valuables." It had the skyline of Milwaukee, Wisconsin on it.

LOUISE SPOONER (231F/230B) Lady friend of Aunt Bee's from Hartford. Bee gave her son, Willis, a collegiate dictionary.

WILLIS SPOONER (231F/230B) Louise's son. He lived in Hartford with his mother. He had his adenoids removed, and he was going to a small college in Connecticut with low requirements. Bee gave him a collegiate dictionary.

SPORT (97F/101B) Gomer once had a dog named Sport.

"SPORT" (161F/160B) The name Andy called Opie as the boy went through his one week trial period at Mr. Doakes' Market.

SPOT (170F/171B) (175F/B) In 170F/171B, Goober's "talking dog." He talked, thanks to the walkie-talkie Tommy planted under his collar. Goober planned on making it big with Spot, leaving Mayberry and going to "Chicago, New York, Hollywood, Raleigh." In 175F/B, Spot was Otis Campbell's imaginary dog.

HOWARD SPRAGUE (218F/B) Mayberry's "nerd." He was a quiet, neat man who lived with his widowed mother until she remarried towards the end of the series. He was a mama's boy. In one episode, Opie told Andy that Howard threw a baseball like Aunt Bee. But Howard was a gentle, good soul, and none of the rougher guys of Mayberry ever teased or made fun of Howard. In 218F/B, he reorganized the entire Mayberry sewer system. (See additional entries beginning with the word "HOWARD" or "HOWARD'S")

MRS. SPRAGUE (185F/B) (192F/191B) Howard's mother. She had her boy by her apron strings, and it wasn't until she got married and left town that Howard began to live a normal life. In 185F/B, she objected to Howard's date with Irene Fairchild, and so played sick. Helen insisted Andy talk with her. He did and convinced her she shouldn't devote her life to Howard, that she should have a social life. She agreed and started going out with Andy, Helen, Howard, and Irene. In 192F/191B, she told Goober a made-up story about Howard having a gambling problem so that Goober would blackball Howard at the lodge.

DOC SPRING (224F/221B) Goober suggested him as a substitute bowler for Lou Jenkins. Doc couldn't bowl, however, because Kathy Hawkins was "due any minute."

"THE SPRING OF 1938" (29F/B) This was when Andy flunked Miss Webster's biology class.

SPRING STREET (23F/B) Street where somebody knocked over a stop sign.

SPRINGVILLE (62F/B) The Macon bus that Barney's cousin, Virgil, took to Mayberry made a freshen-up stop in Springville. Virgil missed getting back on the bus.

"SQUIRT" (36F/37B) The name Glady's Stevens called Barney when Andy attempted to marry her and the deputy.

STAGE 40 (167F/B) The stage at Belmont Pictures where "Sheriff Without A Gun" was filmed.

"STALKING" (73F/70B) Barney's #1 job, according to Barney.

STAMP MACHINE (36F/37B) Barney had to show Melissa Stevens where it was when she first came to Mayberry.

STANDARD OUTFIT (131F/129B) At the Civil Service height and weigh-in, Barney was allowed to wear a "standard outfit": "Uniform (pants and shirt), no shoes, identification tag and chain." Because they didn't specify the type of chain, Andy equipped Barney with an extra heavy tow chain under his shirt and it gave Barney the extra weight he needed to qualify and remain as deputy.

ALICE STAPLETON (58F/B) Mayberry girl. Bee asked Andy if he was taking her to an unnamed dance on Saturday night.

"THE STAR OF PEORIA" (156F/B) The ring Newton Monroe tried to sell Barney for Thelma Lou.

STARBRIGHT MOTEL (166F/B) Goober suggested Andy stay there when the Taylors got to Hollywood. The motel gave guests a free newspaper every day.

"STARS AND STRIPES FOREVER" (72F/71B) Song #12 in the Mayberry Band's repertoire.

"THE STAR-SPANGLED BANNER" (116F/115B) Two years after Eleanora Poultice met Leonard Blush, he sang the "Star-Spangled Banner" at the opening of the county insecticide convention. Eleanora was especially proud of this.

STATE MOBILE MUSEUM (172F/170B) Traveling museum that was brought to Mayberry for the Founder's Day parade. Jack and Stella stole it, and Warren caught them by shooting their station wagon with the town square cannon.

STATE PENAL COMMISSION (11F/B) State board that recommended the "honor system" for prisoners, according to Andy.

STATE POLICE BUILDING (41F/39B) New building in Mt. Pilot that Barney threw up to Andy as an example of what Mayberry's jail should have been like.

STATE PRISON (128F/133B) Ralph Neal escaped from there.

STATE SPELLING BEE CHAMPION (243F/242B) Helen Crump, when she was in the eighth grade in Kansas.

STATEN ISLAND (29F/B) The PX library was on Staten Island. Barney was stationed there while in the Army. (See SECOND-IN-COMMAND)

STATION CQL (183F/182B) Radio station out of Greenland that broadcast worldwide weather reports. Murillos, the gypsy leader, listened to CQL for his "magic" weather-making and weather prediction abilities.

STATION KNC (212F/208B) The TV station that interviewed Barney and Teena Andrews at the premiere of her movie.

THE STATUE 208th episode filmed and 212th episode broadcast. Original broadcast date was February 20, 1967. It was written by Fred S. Fox, and directed by Lee Phillips. Regulars included Andy Griffith, Frances Bavier, George Lindsey, Hope Summers, Jack Dodson, and Howard McNear. Guests included Dale McKennon as Brian Jackson, the sculptor, and George Cisar as Cyrus Tankersley.

STEAK (34F/33B) Barney went and got one for Opie's eye after Opie had his fight with Sheldon the Bully.

"STEAK SANDWICH TIME" (134F/B) Barney promised Thelma Lou no more specials at the Diner when they made up after "the big bomb." It would be "steak sandwich time" all the way. (See THE BIG BOMB)

STELLA (172F/170B) One of the crooks that robbed the state mobile museum. Her partner was Jack.

FRED STERLING (125F/124B) Owner of the Main Street jewelry store—assumed to be called "Sterling's Jewelers"—where Helen bought her niece a charm bracelet for her graduation. Fred promised he'd shorten the bracelet by Friday. Barney saw Andy and Helen kiss in the store as he watched through the front window, immediately assumed they were getting engaged, and went out and started "The Rumor."

JELSICK STERN (99F/98B) Rival of Ernest T. Bass. Girls hung around Jelsick because he wore a uniform.

STEVE (4F/6B) Opie played cowboys with Steve and Tommy on Main Street. Opie had a duel with Steve. Later, Steve, Opie, and Tommy pushed Andy's squad car in front of a fire plug.

BERT STEVENS (112F/111B) One of the World War I vets in Mayberry.

FRED STEVENS (51F/B) Young boy who entered the Boy's Day competition. He entered the fifty-yard dash and the high hurdles.

GEORGE STEVENS (36F/37B) Glady's husband. They came to Mayberry and Gladys (aka Melissa) seduced Barney into proposing to her. She then hit him with a breach of promise suit. Andy called their bluff and revealed their ruse. They rented the Old Pierson Place on the Post Road.

GLADYS STEVENS (36F/37B) Melissa Stevens.

JIM STEVENS (54F/B) He owned a store in Mt. Pilot. Andy planned on selling Bert Miller's leftover merchandise to Jim.

MELISSA STEVENS (36F/37B) The alias Gladys Stevens used when she and her husband, George, came to Mayberry to rook someone (in this case, Barney) into proposing to Melissa with the intent of starting a "scare" breach of promise suit. She and her husband rented the Old Pierson Place on the Post Road.

HECTOR STILES (153F/B) Classmate of Opie's. Betty Parker wrote Hector "sugar notes."

STOCKINGS (132F/128B) Opie's rather adult gift to Helen. They cost him eighty cents.

STOKES COUNTY (140F/B) The locale of Mayberry and Myer's Lake.

BILL STONE (189F/B) Keevy Hazleton's manager and traveling companion.

MABEL STONER (75F/B) The mayor's wife. She was never seen.

MAYOR ROY STONER (69F/66B) (75F/B) (76F/78B) (83F/B) Mayberry's "stuffed-shirt" mayor. In 69F/66B, Stoner was elected mayor of Mayberry. In 75F/B, Stoner bought the bed jacket Bee had wanted for her birthday. Andy got it by selling the mayor his fishing pole. In 76F/78B, the mayor's first name was given as Roy. In 83F/B, Stoner did not want Rafe Hollister to perform in the Ladies League musicale.

STOOPBALL (132F/128B) Sharon McCall invited Opie over her house to play stoopball.

"THE STORY OF NOAH" (238F/239B) The story the Reverend Tucker used to explain the tilting of All Souls Church.

STRANGER IN TOWN 10th episode filmed and 12th episode broadcast. Original broadcast date was December 26, 1960. It was written by Arthur Stander, and directed by Don Weis. Regulars included Andy Griffith, Don Knotts, and Ronny Howard. Guests included William Lanteau, Walter Baldwin, George Dunn, William Erwin, Sara Seegar, Phil Chambers, Marlene Willis, and Pat Colby.

STRAWBERRY (234F/232B) Homemade ice cream flavor that won Bee first prize at the county fair.

STRAWBERRY FESTIVAL (206F/B) Bee's sister, Ellen, invited Bee to stay in Raleigh for the festival but Bee came home to take care of Andy.

STRAWBERRY ICE CREAM (47F/B) Homemade ice cream Bee made when Ronald Bailey had dinner with the Taylors while he was held over in Mayberry.

CHIEF STRONGBOW (188F/B) Tom Strongbow's ancestor and a "hero" of the Victory of Tucahoosee Creek, which the townspeople called the Battle of Mayberry. (See THE BATTLE OF MAYBERRY)

TOM STRONGBOW (188F/B) Mayberry Indian. Opie talked to him about the Battle of Mayberry, which Tom and his people called the Victory of Tucahoosee Creek. Tom's address was Box 222, R.R. #3, Mayberry. (See THE BATTLE OF MAYBERRY)

"A STUDENT OF HUMANITY" (125F/124B) Barney claimed he was a student of humanity because he interpreted Andy's and Helen's jewelry store kiss as proof of their pending engagement. Barney said Andy wouldn't kiss anybody in public unless he was carried away by a "transport of motion."

STUDENT SPECIAL (196F/203B) The name of the notebook Aunt Bee bought Andy for his adult education class in history.

STUFFED WHALE (5F/8B) A carnival fellow who once passed through Mayberry had one on display.

"SUBTLE BARNEY FIFE" (37F/40B) Barney, according to Barney, as he attempted to fix up Andy and Thelma Lou's cousin, Karen Moore. Andy said Barney was "as subtle as a pig squealin' for his supper."

"SUCH A LOVELY CAMPUS" (231F/230B) Yale, according to Aunt Bee.

SUE (215F/B) Lady friend of Bee's. She came over to inquire about Opie's piano lessons.

SUGAR (133F/131B) (162F/164B) (183F/182B) (196F/203B) (237F/236B) In 133F/131B and 162F/164B, 54¢. In 183F/182B, 196F/203B, and 237F/236B, 45¢.

"SUGAR NOTES" (153F/B) Betty Parker wrote them to Hector Stiles.

"SUGARPLUM" (45F/B) The name Jeff Pruitt called Thelma Lou.

"THE SULTAN'S FAVORITE" (159F/B) The carnival show that came to Mayberry. Jerry Miller was the one-man band. When the show closed because of complaints from some of the local women, Jerry was out of work. Andy gave him a job. Miss Edwards was among the complainers; she said the show was a "gucci-hucci dance."

JIM SUMMERS (7F/5B) He ran the meat market and was always cold. Andy picked up a hot water bottle for Jim at Walker's Drugstore.

SUNDAY SCHOOL (153F/B) Andy taught it for three years.

PHIL SUNKEL (72F/71B) A member of the Freddy Fleet band. Barney got his "cool chickie-baby" talk from Phil.

SUNNY JIM BARS (77F/79B) The candy bars Barney wanted to buy for Thelma Lou with the fifty cents he asked to borrow from Andy.

SUPER BARGAIN MARKET (211F/207B) Eleventh store robbed in Raleigh during the string of supermarket robberies which Andy solved while visting Barney. He gave Barney the credit.

SUPER FREEZE (120F/119B) The freezer Andy bought Bee so she'd have a place to store the 150 pound side of beef she bought at Diamond Jim's.

SUPPER (123F/122B) Barney suggested the following to Andy for supper: "Two chili-sized burgers with chopped onions, ketchup, piccalilli and mustard, side of french fries, slab of rhubarb pie, and a chocolate malt." He planned on getting it "to go" from the Diner. Andy said that meal would lay on his stomach. Barney said the Diner's food stayed hot—hours after you ate it.

SUPPOSE ANDY GETS SICK 232nd episode filmed and 233rd episode broadcast. Original broadcast date was December 11, 1967. It was written by Jack Raymond, and directed by Peter Baldwin. Regulars included Andy Griffith, Ronny Howard, Frances Bavier, Jack Dodson, George Lindsey, and Paul Hartman. Guests included Vince Barnett as Elmo, Charles Thompson as Doc Roberts, Anthony Jochim as Harvey, and Hollis Morrison as Alvin.

SUPREME COURT JUSTICE (229F/228B) Opie's original career goal before he decided to be a rock-and-roller.

DARLENE SWANSON (20F/16B) Nineteen-year-old daughter of Henrietta Swanson, who was voted "Young Lady Most Likely To Become Charming" at Miss Wellington's School for Girls. Her mother brought her to Andy's to borrow a cup of sugar after it was announced that Andy would judge the Mayberry Founder's Day beauty pageant.

GLORIA SWANSON (179F/B) Harvey Kester gained fame in Mayberry as her radio repairman.

HENRIETTA SWANSON (20F/16B) Woman who brought her nineteen-year-old daughter, Darlene, to Andy's house after it was announced that Andy would judge the Founder's Day beauty pageant. She came on the pretext of borrowing a cup of sugar.

ROY SWANSON (242F/241B) Classmate of Goober's at auto trade school. Goober ran into Roy at the auto show in Raleigh. Roy pretended he was a Senior Vice

President in Charge of Engineering for Amalgamated Motors. Goober began to pretend he was bigger than he actually was, and he picked up the tab at the Golden Palace, an expense he could in no way afford. He told Roy he had a chain of gas stations. The truth came out, however—via Opie—and Goober left the auto show feeling like a failure. They stopped for gas on the way home and found Roy working under a car, covered with grease. Goober didn't confront him, not wanting to embarrass an old friend. Roy's phone number was KL-5-7486. (See THE GOLDEN PALACE)

SWEDISH (222F/225B) Goober wanted to learn to speak Swedish because he once had a customer at the service station who spoke the language.

SWEET BRIAR NORMAL SCHOOL (203F/201B) Bee Taylor's and Clara Edward's high school. They were on the same basketball team; Bee was the backbone of the team but Clara was the best dribbler.

SWEET BRIAR NORMAL SCHOOL THEME SONG (203F/201B)

"Sweet Briar, oh Sweet Briar
Where hearts are young and gay
Sweet Briar, oh Sweet Briar
Forever and a day"
(Repeat)

JACK SWEET (82F/B) Classmate of Andy's and Barney's. At the class reunion, Barney mistook Ralph Haines for Jack.

SWEET CIDER (104F/105B) Barney got drunk on it after it turned hard. He then expressed his true feelings to Mrs. Mendlebright. Barney was a sloppy, emotional drunk.

SWEETPEAS (45F/B) The flowers Jeff Pruitt brought Thelma Lou.

HERBERT SWINDELL (146F/B) Andy and Barney found a love letter of Herbert's while searching for Barney's "lucky letter" in the Mayberry dump.

SWISS CHEESE SANDWICHES (246F/245B) The delicacy Howard offered the guests at his "swinging" party.

"SYLVIA" (128F/133B) The song Leonard Blush performed on his radio show.

SYLVIO (183F/182B) Gypsy. Friend of Sabella, La Farona, and Murillos. He played the guitar. He was incorrectly identified in the original episode's credits as "Grecos." (He was played by Jamie Farr, Corporal Klinger of "M*A*S*H" fame.)

THE "SYMBOL" SPEECH (135F/B) To bolster Barney's courage, Andy explained that he and Barney were symbols of the law and that their uniforms didn't really mean anything. Barney repeated the speech to Fred Plummer and Fred backed down from wanting to beat Barney up, but not because of the speech. Mr. Izamoto had already beaten him up—dressed in Barney's suit.

SYRUP (54F/B) (122F/121B) 27¢ a pint.

T

LUKE TAFT (105F/104B) Mayberry man who wore "black-and-white two tone shoes—wing tips, perforated tops—white shoelaces." Luke hit the sauce.

"TAIL-GUNNER" (101F/96B) Barney's best slingshot trick.

"TAILOR TAYLOR" (231F/230B) The name Andy said he'd be called if he answered the classified ad for Hong Kong suits.

TAILS (65F/67B) In Andy's and Opie's coin toss to determine whether they ate chicken or pot roast, tails was chicken.

"TAILSPIN TOMMY" (177F/B) Tommy's side-kick was Skeets Gallagher. Skeets was Barney's idol.

TALBOTT (3F/B) Mayberry postmaster. Andy convinced him that he had "quality criminals" on his bulletin board: "Train robbers, counterfeiters, smugglers, not to even mention foreign spies."

"TAMPERING UNLAWFULLY WITH A MOTOR VEHICLE" (4F/6B) The citation Barney wrote Andy. Andy attempted to push Barney's car in front of a fire plug.

TAMPICO TAMALE CONTEST (227F/222B) Bee won it. Her prize was a trip to Mexico.

CYRUS TANKERSLEY (192F/191B) (198F/200B) (208F/212B) (221F/235B) Mayberry citizen and the head of the Mayberry chamber of commerce. In 192F/191B, he was a member of the Regal Order of the Golden Door to Good Fellowship. He was the lodge president. In 198F/200B, he fished for Old Sam at Tucker's Lake. In 208F/212B, Bee and Clara invited Cyrus to view the completed statue of Seth Taylor. Cyrus was also one of Goober's frequent checker partners. In 221F/235B, Goober went to see Cyrus about borrowing the $2,000 he needed to buy Wally's Service Station. In this episode, Cyrus worked in a bank.

TAPE RECORDER 228th episode filmed and 227th episode broadcast. Original broadcast date was October 20, 1967. It was written by Michael Morris and Seamon Jacobs, and directed by Lee Phillips. Regulars included Andy Griffith, Ronny Howard, George Lindsey, and Frances Bavier. Guests included Herbie Faye as Eddie Blake, Sheldon Collins as Arnold Bailey, Jerome Guardino as Myles Bentley, and Troy Melton as the State Trooper.

ARTHUR TARBOCHS (84F/B) He wanted to move out of Mayberry with his wife because people talked about other people too much.

MRS. TARBOCHS (84F/B) Woman Andy and Barney greeted on Main Street. Barney remarked that she was getting gray for her age, and Andy explained that she was having trouble with Arthur, her husband. Arthur wanted

to move them out of Mayberry because people talked about other people too much.

TATE WARREN'S STORE (5F/8B) Store used as a border for one of the five sections Annabelle Silby divided Mayberry into for fund-raising purposes. The entire section ran "From Grover's Place over to Banner Street around Cornwall's Gas Station up to Tate Warren's store."

"TATTLETALE" (50F/B) A name Barney said he was never called.

A TAXICAB (5F/8B) Annabelle Silby told everyone that her husband, Tom, was run over and killed by a cab in Charlottesville.

ANDY TAYLOR The soul of Mayberry. Andy Taylor personified Mayberry; he was the living incarnation of the town. He was honest (except for a lapse in "Andy, the Horse Trader"), fair, patient, and was possessed with enviable common sense. He tried to be a good father but in many cases Opie taught him what trust was all about. He was very respectful to Aunt Bee, and he believed in work, family, and his town. His best friend was Barney. Andy always had trouble with women, and it wasn't until he met Helen Crump that he felt truly comfortable around the ladies. He never talked about his first wife or what made him a widower at such an early age. He accepted that tragedy the way he accepted all the other problems that came with life. He was television's last truly good man. He was a man of character and integrity. At the end of the series, he and Helen moved away from Mayberry. This betrayal from a man who told Sharon Duspaine that Mayberry was all that he ever wanted did not make sense. The town was never the same again. Until, that is, he and Helen moved back in 1985, and Andy once again became Mayberry's sheriff. The glory of Mayberry was reborn in April of 1985... forever. (See additional entries beginning with the word "ANDY" or "ANDY'S")

BEE TAYLOR The heart of Mayberry. Everyone's mother, grandmother, and aunt. A sincere, hard-working, compassionate woman who spent her life raising other people's children. The cleanliness of her kitchen was legendary. She was a heavy woman who moved around like a sixteen-year-old whippet-thin ballerina. When she first came to the Taylor household in "The New Housekeeper," Opie didn't like her. I personally thought he was nuts. How he could want Rose over Aunt Bee I could never understand. But as we all know, he came around before the end of that episode and was a devoted, obedient great-nephew from then on. Aunt Bee loved Andy and Opie more than she loved herself. She was slightly naive, but also wise and intuitive. Aunt Bee could almost read minds. Even though she wasn't born or raised in Mayberry, she never left town. Aunt Bee was the maternal spirit of Mayberry, the perfect mother, and almost everyone's best friend. Her death—sometime between 1971 and 1986—tore a hole in the fabric of the town. Fittingly, she was buried in her only real hometown, Mayberry. (See additional entries beginning with the words "AUNT BEE," "AUNT BEE'S," "BEE" or "BEE'S")

BRADFORD J. TAYLOR (234F/232B) Aunt Bee's cousin. Their fathers were brothers. At the time of 234F/232B, Bee hadn't heard from him for two years. Bee grew up with Bradford in West Virginia. Last she heard he'd sold his copper mines in Mexico, but he still owned a plantation in Brazil and a 41,000-acre sheep ranch in

Australia. Bee hadn't seen him since she was in her twenties. Bradford was supposedly the financial advisor to the crown prince of Denmark. Bee found out in 234F/232B that everything Bradford had ever told her in his letters, including all of the above, was completely untrue.

COLONEL CARLTON TAYLOR (188F/B) Andy's ancestor. He fought in the Battle of Mayberry.

OPIE TAYLOR The spirit and promise of Mayberry. A bright, spirited kid who grew up right. Andy did a good job with Opie, and sometimes even Andy didn't believe it. In "Opie's Fortune," Andy really believed that Opie was going to keep the money he found, even after the boy met Parnell Rigsby, the rightful owner. In "Opie's Charity" Andy really believed that Opie didn't want to donate to the underprivileged children's fund because he was cheap, when really he was saving to buy his poor girlfriend, Charlotte, a coat. Andy always ended up apologizing and realizing that Opie was a *good kid*. For some strange reason, this surprised Andy. Not me, though. I knew all along that Opie was the kind of kid you could always take at his word. Even when he wanted to be a rock-and-roller, he was an homogenized rocker, so clean-cut you couldn't help but know that he wouldn't throw his future away for sex, drugs, and rock-and-roll. Aunt Bee was aghast, but Andy, in this case, took the right tack: let Opie learn for himself. When Bee asked Clara to talk to Opie, Andy was upset; Clara did a good job, however, and the boys learned a lesson about priorities. Opie stayed in town with Aunt Bee after Andy and Helen moved away. He eventually became editor and publisher (and owner?) of the Mayberry newspaper, the renamed "County Courier Express." (See additional entries beginning with the word "OPIE" or "OPIE'S")

SETH TAYLOR (208F/212B) Great-great-grandfather of Bee Taylor. Seth built the first sawmill in Mayberry, organized the first Mayberry chamber of commerce, gave some of his personal land to the city, and lent some of his own money to the town during the Crisis of 1874. Along with Winston Simmons, the industrialist, Seth Taylor maneuvered to have the railroad placed in Mt. Pilot, bypassing Mayberry. Taylor and Simmons bought and sold land in the counties around Mt. Pilot and made a fortune. Mr. Simmons, the descendant of Winston Simmons, told Andy and Bee that his great-great-grandfather Winston and Seth were "two of the biggest swindlers this part of the country's ever known." Bee—upon hearing this news—was at first totally destroyed, but after realizing that Seth's wheelings and dealings made Mayberry what it was, she decided to go ahead with the dedication and erect the statue of Seth in the town square anyway.

"TAYLOR, PYLE AND FIFE" (116F/115B) The name Eleanora Poultice suggested for Andy, Barney, and Gomer after their vocal "trio" went over so well at the concert. It was supposed to be a solo. She decided against the name because she said it sounded to much like "Peter, Pyle and Mary."

"TAYLOR SANDERS" (213F/B) The name Roger Bryant called Andy.

TAYLORS IN HOLLYWOOD 167th episode filmed and broadcast. Original broadcast date was November 1, 1965. It was written by Bill Idelson and Sam Bobrick, and directed by Alan Rafkin. Regulars included Andy Griffith, Frances Bavier, and Ronny Howard. Guests included Gavin McCleod as Bryan Bender, Hayden Rourke as A.J. Considine, June Vincent as the Actress, Eddie Quillan as the Bellhop, Ross Elliot as Al, Robert Nichols as the Relief Bus Driver, Herb Vigran as the Gateman, and Yvonne Lime as the Stewardess. The Airline Sequence was furnished by TWA.

"TAYLORTOWN" (188F/B) According to Andy, Mayberry was almost called Taylortown in honor of his ancestor, Colonel Carlton Taylor.

"A TED WEEMS RECORD" (69F/66B) "Real dreamy stuff," according to Barney. He wanted to bring one to Juanita.

TED'S PET SHOP (148F/B) Mayberry Main Street business next to Norma's Beauty Shoppe.

ROSE TEMPLE (90F/B) Her clergyman nephew had a 1959 Ford for sale.

TEMPTING TOUCH (27F/B) Powder sold at Walker's Drugstore.

TEN (196F/203B) The number of history students in the adult education course Andy and the others took.

#10 (43F/B) The Preacher's wife's jar number at the county fair pickle competition. It wasn't said if this was Reverend Tucker's wife.

10¢ (183F/182B) The cost of soft drinks at Wally's Service Station.

TEN COUPLES (113F/112B) The number of couples that were at the fictitious party Barney set up in order to show Ernest T. Bass how to enter a room.

$10.00 (31F/B) (109F/108B) In 31F/B, Barney lent Jim Lindsey ten dollars. In 109F/108B, Barney gave Opie the same amount to go buy all the copies of the "Mayberry Gazette" he could find. It had the story of his "heroic" rescue in it.

$10.00 A DAY (225F/224B) The cost of Camp Winoke.

$10.00 A MONTH (235F/234B) The rent for Howard's cottage on St. Benedict's Island in the Caribbean.

$10.00 IN THREE DAYS (119F/118B) The amount of money Barney and his cousin, Virgil, spent in Raleigh during their vacation.

10:00 O'CLOCK (229F/228B) The latest Opie had ever been out before he came home at midnight the night his band, "The Sound Committee," played at Brenda Roach's birthday party.

10:31 A.M. (53F/B) The time the tour of the merchant's stores began for the "guest of honor."

10:30 P.M. (36F/37B) The time Barney went to bed on the night he had dinner with Melissa Stevens and her "Daddy."

$10,000.00 (39F/36B) The amount in the Mayberry treasury when Frank Myers demanded payment on his 1861 bond. (Actually, there was a little over $10,000.)

10,000 HEAD OF LONGHORN (234F/232B) Bradford Taylor claimed he was ready to ship 10,000 head.

10 to 1 (60F/B) The final odds on the horse, Apple Dumpling.

A "10-12" (78F/76B) A bank robbery.

TEN YEARS (118F/117B) In 1964, Barney had been on the Mayberry force ten years. (See BARNEY'S BEGINNINGS)

PRINCESS TERONOYA (183F/182B) Murillos, the gypsy leader, sold Aunt Bee a shawl he claimed was owned by Princess Teronoya. The story went that every five years the princess would light the sacred incense so that the gods would smile kindly on the gypsy kingdom. She ran off when she was eighteen; in effect, she only wore the shawl three times. That was why it looked so new. Murillos charged Aunt Bee eight dollars for the shawl.

"TEX" (4F/6B) George Foley's nickname.

"TEX" (66F/64B) Andy's cowboy nickname for Opie.

"TEXARKANA IN THE MORNING" (189F/B) Million-selling record of Keevy Hazleton's that was a personal favorite of both Clara Edwards and Aunt Bee.

TEXAS (4F/6B) The "runaway kid," George Foley, was considering running away to Texas.

"THANK YOU FOR THE DANCE" (113F/112B) One of the phrases Andy taught Ernest T. Bass to say properly.

"THAT LONESOME ROAD" (83F/B) Song in Rafe Hollister's repertoire. He performed it at the Ladies League musicale.

THATCHER'S WOODS (30F/B) Wooded area outside of Mayberry where Eddie Brooks abandoned his stolen car. When Andy was young, he spent more time in Thatcher's Woods than in school. Thatcher's Woods was three miles from the courthouse.

THE THEATER OF MAYBERRY (50F/B) The Grand. It was on Main Street.

THELMA LOU The only girl Barney ever loved. She and Barney always knew they would someday get married, but Barney packed up and moved out of Mayberry in a vain search for a big time law enforcement career. Thelma Lou also moved out of town soon after. Barney saw her again at a class reunion and was sure that the sparks would reignite. When he found out she had married (some guy no one knew), he was totally destroyed. He realized that Thelma Lou had truly been the only girl for him. But it was too late. He had let her get away. He took solace that night in a blonde from high school, Nettie Albright. Thelma Lou was a pleasant, quiet girl who was really quite lovely. She worked hard at keeping Barney's ego intact, realizing that his childish spirit was a very fragile thing indeed. A lesser woman would not have been so supportive. Barney—who never got over Thelma Lou—realized his lifelong dream on April 13, 1985. He and Thelma Lou were married in Mayberry, with Andy and Helen attending. He then settled into a quiet Mayberry life as Thelma Lou's husband and, yes, Andy Taylor's deputy.

THELMA LOU'S DENTIST (126F/125B) He was in Mt. Pilot. Gomer took her there, and she bought him lunch: sausages, three eggs, and six flapjacks. It set her back seventy cents.

THELMA LOU'S PHONE NUMBER (59F/B) (68F/69B) (117F/116B) In 59F/B and 68F/69B, "247." In 117F/116B, "596."

THEME SONG TO "THE ANDY GRIFFITH SHOW" "The Fishin' Hole." (See lyrics under "THE FISHIN' HOLE")

"THERAPETIC" (68F/69B) The way Barney pronounced "therapeutic." He said talking things out was "therapetic."

"THERE IS A TIME" (139F/B) Song performed by the Darlings, with Charlene singing and Andy playing along.

"THE THINKER" (196F/203B) (245F/244B) In 196F/203B, Andy said Goober looked like Rodin's "The Thinker" when he came back from his hunting trip wearing a beard. In 245F/244B, Goober sat like "The Thinker" in Emmett's repair shop.

"THE THIRD DEGREE" (111F/110B) Interrogation technique Barney tried on Otis to get him to tell where he was getting his moonshine. It consisted of Barney kicking a chair under Otis, slapping his own hand with a ruler, and shining a gooseneck lamp in Otis's eyes. The lamp drooped.

THIRD TUESDAY EVERY MONTH (116F/115B) The day that Leonard Blush's radio show was broadacst on Station YLRB in Mt. Pilot.

THIRTEEN (238F/239B) The number of blue choir robes Bee and Clara wanted to buy with the $500 willed to All Souls Church.

"A THIRTEEN-INCH, ONE BLUE-EYED, PART-OF-HIS-TAIL-FIN-MISSING FISH" (40F/38B) Dave the Hobo claimed he heard this fish jumping in Myers Lake. He used this as an excuse not to trim Andy's hedges.

THIRTY (139F/B) The age at which Briscoe Darling married his wife. She was seventeen. He was her second husband; her first had been run over by a team of hogs.

35¢ (122F/121B) The cost of a jar of Miracle Salve.

34,000 to 1 (224F/221B) The odds against bowling a perfect 300.

THIRTY HOURS (31F/B) The amount of rehearsal time Jim Lindsey missed when he quit Bobby Fleet's band.

THIRTY PERCENT (228F/227B) Eddie Blake offered his lawyer thirty percent of the take from the Raleigh bank robbery if he could get Eddie off.

THIRTY PERCENT OFF (120F/119B) The discount Bee claimed Clara could have gotten for Andy on a new freezer.

$37.00 (223F/226B) The cost of the short art course. Opie got the solicitation after turning down the more expensive course for $98.50.

$37.50 (238F/239B) The cost of the blue choir robes Bee and Clara wanted to buy with the $500 willed to All Souls Church.

THIRTY-SIX (94F/B) The number of panes of glass in the three windows of Briscoe Darling's cabin. (See entry ERNEST T. BASS)

30,000 (208F/212B) Population of Mt. Pilot.

THE THOMPSON BOY (178F/B) The Taylors' paperboy. He had been in the Taylor house when Aunt Bee discovered that her pin was missing. Andy refused to consider him a suspect and Warren reluctantly agreed to rule him out.

SALLY THOMS (153F/B) Classmate of Opie's. Opie revealed in his paper, "The Mayberry Sun," that Sally did not have naturally curly hair.

EDNA THOPE (82F/B) Classmate of Andy's and Barney's. Andy said Mrs. Ralph Haines reminded him of Edna. Edna was "in debate" at Mayberry Union High.

NEVIN THORPE (216F/B) One-man band on "Colonel Tim's Talent Time." He performed the "Blue Danube Waltz."

"THOSE ENDEARING YOUNG CHARMS" (83F/B) The song Andy, Barney, and Rafe Hollister sang in the courthouse.

THOSE GOSSIPIN' MEN 15th episode filmed and broadcast. Original broadcast date was January 16, 1961. It was written by Jack Elinson and Charles Stewart, and directed by Bob Sweeney. Regulars included Andy Griffith, Don Knotts, Frances Bavier, Ronny Howard, and Howard McNear. Guests included Jack Finch as Wilbur Finch, Cheerio Meredith as Emma Brand, Jonathan Hole, Mary Treen, Phil Chambers, Harry Antrim, and Sara Seegar.

3 (112F/111B) The new house number Opie burned into the Taylor house. Previously, in 50F/B, Andy's address had been given as 24 Elm Street, in 87F/B, 332 Maple Road, and in 201F/204B, as 14 Maple Street.

THREE (31F/B) (51F/B) (122F/121B) In 31F/B, Jim Lindsey had three guitars. He was also three payments behind on his car payments to the Mid-Mountain Finance Company. They repossessed his car. In 51F/B, it was the number of times Barney asked for a raise. In 122F/121B, it was the number of jars of Miracle Salve Andy bought from Opie.

"THE THREE BELLS" (116F/115B) The name Eleanora Poultice suggested for Andy, Barney, and Gomer after their vocal "trio" went over so well at the concert. It was supposed to be a solo.

3¢ (5F/8B) (153F/B) In 5F/8B, the amount Opie gave to the Underprivileged Children's Charity Drive. It was the lowest amount given. In 153F/B, the cost of Opie's newspaper, "The Mayberry Sun."

$3.00 (183F/182B) The amount Sabella charged Goober to tell him he was destined to be a rich millionaire.

$3.95 (110F/109B) (231F/230B) In 110F/109B, the amount Barney paid for a new shirt at Patterson's. He bought it on the day he thought he was going to escort the queen of the state Apricot Festival around Mayberry. Andy took her instead. Barney held a grudge for decades. In 231F/230B, $3.95 was the cost of Emmett's shirt. He had bought it at Sneadley's. It turned purple when he washed it with his coloreds at Andy's Laundercoin.

$3.75 (125F/124B) The amount Floyd said he donated to Andy's and Helen's "engagement party." He really gave $2.00 cash. Andy owed him $1.75 for a haircut, but Floyd said he wasn't going to charge him.

3:45 P.M. (40F/38B) The time the train stopped for water.

340 HORSEPOWER (236F/237B) The size of the engine of Ben Beecham's car.

THREE HOUR SERVICE (50F/B) Goss the tailor's claim.

$349,119.27 (39F/36B) The amount Frank Myers' 1861 Town of Mayberry bond was worth in 1961. It was later discovered to be worthless since it had been bought with Confederate money. Harlan Fergus at the Security Bank figured out what the bond could have been worth.

361 POUNDS (243F/242B) The weight of the marlin Emmett once landed in St. Petersburg.

THREE INCHES (238F/239B) The flooding of the church lowered the building an extra three inches. Instead of lowering it five inches, it lowered it "a total of eight."

THREE MILES (105F/104B) The distance from Thelma Lou's house to the chamber of commerce dance.

397 (210F/211B) Howard Sprague's phone number.

3-0-2 (118F/117B) Disturbing the peace. Andy charged Maudie and Naylor with this violation.

3-1-7 (88F/B) Violation against Briscoe Darling: occupancy of private property without permission of the owner.

3:00 P.M. (32F/B) (37F/40B) In 32F/B, the time Opie got out of school. In 37F/40B, it was the time Barney arranged for Andy to meet Karen Moore at the coffee shop.

371-J (77F/79B) Goober's phone number.

THREE SHOTS (2F/B) The number of shots Barney was to fire during the "manhunt" if he saw the escaped prisoner.

363 (187F/186B) Phone number at Wally's filling station.

332 MAPLE ROAD (87F/B) Andy's address in this episode. (See ANDY'S ADDRESS)

3,000 BOOKS (29F/B) Barney was second-in-command of over 3,000 books at the PX library on Staten Island. Barney said he'd "rather not talk about it."

$3,000.00 (245F/244B) The original retail price of the ranch mink coat Bernie the Furrier showed Emmett. Emmett's price was $1,800.

$3,600.43 (104F/105B) The money Mrs. Mendlebright withdrew from the bank as her share of the down payment on the house she and Mr. Fields planned on buying.

3,628.00 (200F/197B) The amount Mayberry would save by building the new bridge across Parker Creek on Baker Street instead of on Ranch Road.

"A THREE-TIME LOSER DOING TWENTY YEARS" (30F/B) Eddie Brooks.

THREE TROUT, TWO PERCH (35F/B) Floyd's catch at Myer's Lake. The fishing trip included Andy, Barney, Floyd, and Opie.

323 (64F/73B) Peggy McMillan's house number.

THREE WEEKS (196F/203B) The length of Goober's hunting trip.

THREE WISHES FOR OPIE 142nd episode filmed and 141st episode broadcast. Original broadcast date was December 21, 1964. It was written by Richard M. Powell, and directed by Howard Morris. Regulars included Andy Griffith, Don Knotts, Ronny Howard, Howard McNear, George Lindsey, and Aneta Corsaut. Guests included Burt Mustin as Jud.

THREE YEARS (105F/104B) (153F/B) In 105F/104B, it had been three years since Mary Grace Gossage had visited Mayberry. In 153F/B, three years was the length of time Andy taught Sunday school in Mayberry.

THREE'S A CROWD 59th episode filmed and broadcast. Original broadcast date was April 9, 1962. It was written by Jack Elinson and Charles Stewart, and directed by

Bob Sweeney. Regulars included Andy Griffith, Don Knotts, Frances Bavier, and Betty Lynn. Guests included Sue Ann Langdon as Mary Simpson the County Nurse.

THUNDER (29F/B) Otis Campbell was afraid of thunder.

THUNDERBIRD CONVERTIBLE (35F/B) Elizabeth ("the woman speeder") Crowley's car. She was driving it the day she was stopped by Andy and Barney for speeding.

"THURSDAY NIGHTS AT EIGHT" (42F/B) When the Esquire Club held their meetings.

FARLEY THURSTON (154F/B) The Taylors' butter and egg man after Orville Hendricks dropped them as customers. Hendricks was upset about the alleged romance between himself and Aunt Bee.

NATHAN TIBBS (25F/B) Revolutionary War hero and Otis Campbell's kin. When it was discovered that Otis was a direct descendant of Nathan, he was awarded a plaque which he very graciously (and soberly) turned over to the town of Mayberry.

"TICO TICO" (83F/B) Song in Barney's repertoire.

"TIGER" (3F/B) The name Andy called Barney.

"TIGER" (135F/B) The name Andy called Barney after Fred Plummer backed down from his confrontation with the deputy.

TIGER LIL (60F/B) A horse Sarah thought was a girl after she "overheard" Bill Medwin's horse-betting phone calls.

"TIGHTLIPS BARNEY" (102F/B) Barney promised he wouldn't say anything about the gold shipment that would be coming through Mayberry. He said he was a "tightlips."

"TILLER OF SOIL, FELLER OF TREES" (96F/100B) Briscoe Darling's self-description. He was trying to convince Aunt Bee to marry him.

TILLY (112F/111B) Mrs. Beggs' sister. She was a tall woman with long teeth due to a gum condition. In school they called her "The Beaver."

MRS. TILMAN (40F/38B) Her pie was stolen by Dave the Hobo.

TIM (215F/B) One of the boys on Opie's football team.

COLONEL TIM (216F/B) Host of "Colonel Tim's Talent Time" amateur show broadcast out of WASG in Raleigh.

TIMMY (23F/B) Friend of Opie's. He helped Opie make his bed when Aunt Bee was off visiting her cousin, Edgar, in Mt. Pilot.

TIN INKBLOT (119F/118B) Barney bought one at the Raleigh Arcade.

TINFOIL BALL (78F/76B) Asa Breeny had a big one.

TINY (95F/B) One of the crooks brought to the Mayberry jail. The other was Doc.

"TIPTOE THROUGH THE TULIPS" (31F/B) The song Barney offered to play for Bobby Fleet on the harmonica.

TIP-TOP CAFE (68F/69B) Club twelve miles away from Mayberry in Mt. Pilot. Barney arranged to meet Skippy and Daphne there after Andy and Peggy McMillan had a big fight.

TOD (129F/130B) Andy's second cousin and Opie's uncle. He was a wiper on an oil tanker and he'd been to Hong Kong, Singapore, London, and Paris. He didn't want to come to America, though. Andy said it had something to do with a girl in Cleveland.

TOLEDO (74F/B) The old Cascade Club was located in Toledo.

THE TOMAHAWKS (42F/B) Club formed by Opie, who also acted as its president. Its oath was: "As a Tomahawk I solemnly swear to be fair and square at all times." The oath was recited while facing the rising sun.

TOMATOES (135F/B) (148F/B) (161F/160B) (162F/164B) (183F/182B) In 135F/B, 10¢. In 148F/B, 161F/160B, and 162F/164B, 25¢. In 183F/182B, they were 43¢ a pound during the dry spell, which the townsfolk believed was caused by "the gypsy curse." The price went as high as 54¢ a pound during this spell. The 43¢ a pound tomatoes were imported from Mexico.

TOMMY (1F/B) Friend of Opie's. Opie remembered him in his prayers.

TOMMY (4F/6B) Boy Opie played cowboys with, along with Steve, on Main Street outside the courthouse. Tommy, Steve, and Opie pushed Andy's squad car in front of a fire plug.

TOMMY (170F/171B) New kid who came to Mayberry and had to be taught a lesson. Tommy's father was the chief accountant at the new shoe factory. Tommy was a good kid with a cruel streak. It was his idea to plant a walkie-talkie under the collar of Goober's dog, Spot, which led the naive Goober to believe the dog could talk. Andy found out and taught Tommy a lesson. Tommy was looking forward to owning a horse but, as he told Opie, his father was looking for the best price. Andy told Tommy a man came by wanting to sell a horse real cheap, but he couldn't remember the man's name. He told Tommy not to worry; he'd told the dog the man's name. Tommy got the message.

"TOMMY GUNS, TEAR GAS, LOUDSPEAKERS, SPOTLIGHTS" (2F/B) The equipment Captain Barker requested for his men during the "manhunt."

TONIC WITH A BEER CHASER (5F/8B) Tom Silby 's drink.

"TOOT TOOT TOOTSIE" (87F/B) The song Bee played and sang after she got drunk on Colonel Harvey's Indian Elixir.

THE TORNADO OF '55 (219F/B) Storm that hit Mayberry in 1955. Goober said that when Floyd found out that his $200 prize in Goober's contest was a mistake, his reaction would be like that storm.

"TOW SACK FULL OF LOVE" (139F/B) One of the songs in the Darlings' repertoire.

TOWER OF PISA (238F/239B) Aunt Bee offered the tower as a protest to Howard. He wanted to use the money willed to the church to fix the tilting of the church building. Bee and Clara wanted to buy choir robes.

TOWN COUNCIL (39F/36B) Mayberry town body which consisted of at least Mayor Pike, Harlan Fergus, and Andy Taylor. They voted to evict Frank Myers for not paying his property taxes for eight quarters. Andy didn't agree, and took Frank into his home.

TOWN HALL (52F/B) Choir practice was normally held there.

TOWN PICNIC (109F/108B) Yearly Mayberry social event.

"TOYS GAMES HOBBIES MODELS" (136F/B) The sign on the toy store window where Opie bought his fishing pole.

JOHN TRACY (217F/B) High school principal who talked to Howard Sprague about his potential "big brother" relationship with Tommy Parker.

BRILLEN TRANT (64F/73B) According to Andy, the Spirit of Water.

TRAVELING LAUNDRY KIT (227F/222B) The gift Myrtle gave Bee after Bee won the trip to Mexico.

TRAVERS (66F/64B) The phone dispatcher Mr. McBeevee spoke to on the telephone pole.

TREASURY DEPARTMENT (102F/B) Two men from the department came to Mayberry to tell Andy about the gold shipment that would be coming through town.

"TREES" (216F/B) Song sung "beautifully" (according to Bee) by a boy soprano on "Colonel Tim's Talent Time" amateur show.

"TRESPASSSING FORBIDDEN" (32F/B) Sign on the abandoned Johnson Mine.

A TRIP TO MEXICO 227th episode filmed and 222nd episode broadcast. Original broadcast date was September 25, 1967. It was written by Perry Grant and Richard Bensfield, and directed by Lee Phillips. Regulars included Andy Griffith, Aneta Corsaut, Paul Hartman, Frances Bavier, Jack Dodson, and Ronnie Howard. Guests included Hope Summers as Clara Edwards, Ruth Thoms as Myrtle, Vince Barnett as Elmo, Jose Gonzalez-Gonzalez as the Shopkeeper, Anthony Jochim as Harvey, Manuel Martin as the Violinist, Eddie Carroll as the Airport Clerk, and Natividad Vacio as the Hotel Clerk.

TRIPLETT (60F/B) Stewart Simmons lived there.

TROMBONE (72F/71B) Floyd's instrument in the Mayberry Band.

TROPICAL WORSTED (139F/B) The suit the Darlings bought for Opie at Weaver's Department Store.

MABEL TROTTA (238F/239B) Soprano in Mayberry's church choir. Bee and Clara had to warn her not to make her singing a solo.

TROUBLESOME CREEK (196F/203B) Goober and Shorty Watson went fishing there.

TROUT (69F/66B) The fish Barney put in the desk drawer to hide it from Mayor Stoner. The mayor found it anyway.

TRUCK TIRE CUFFLINKS (226F/223B) Goober wore them to the Harvest Ball.

TRUCKER'S CAFE (224F/221B) Mt. Pilot cafe and the sponsor of a league bowling team that competed with Emmett's Fix-It Shop of Mayberry.

"TRUE BLUE DETECTIVE MAGAZINE" (104F/105B) Barney had bound issues dating back to 1959. Some of its stories were "I Married A Fink," "How It Feels To Pull The Switch," and "I Picked A Pocket And Paid." (See "Barney's Room" floor plan for their location in his room)

LAMAR TRUNDLE (220F/B) When Andy was young, a girl he liked cancelled their date to go out with Lamar instead. Andy went to the party anyway and had a good time. He told Opie this story after Mary Alice Carter broke her date with Opie to go with Fred Simpson. Lamar may have been fictitious, like Hodie Snitch.

CHARLOTTE TUCKER (77F/79B) Girl discussed by the Mendlebright sisters on one of their Sunday phone visits. She was not related to Malcolm Tucker. She married a lens grinding man from Hutchinson, Kansas.

REVEREND HOBART M. TUCKER (100F/99B) (111F/110B) (135F/B) (238F/239B) All Souls Church preacher and a personal friend of Andy's and other Mayberry citizens. In 100F/99B, Reverend Tucker invited Reverend Breen to visit Mayberry. In 111F/110B, Bee suggested Otis talk to Reverend Tucker regarding his drinking. In 135F/B, he gave the sermon "Dice Are Loaded Against The Evil-Doer." In 238F/239B, he was a member of the finance committee.

MALCOLM TUCKER (77F/79B) The "man in a hurry." His car broke down on his way to Charlotte two miles outside of Mayberry, and he was forced to stay over while Goober fixed his car. Throughout the visit he was a nervous wreck, and couldn't wait to get out of town, but finally the magic of Mayberry won him over and at the end of the show he had fallen asleep in a rocker, a whole apple skin dangling from his hand. Andy had asked him if he could cut the skin off an apple and he at first wouldn't even try. The tranquil spirit of Mayberry finally gave him the steadiness to do the job. (See the Jim Nabors interview in the appendix section of this book)

MYRA TUCKER (165F/169B) Bee's lady friend. Myra got fed up with Bee's constant talking about the sweepstakes prizes she had won on "Win Or Lose."

TUCKER ENTERPRISES (77F/79B) Malcolm Tucker's business.

TUCKER'S LAKE (198F/200B) The home of Old Sam.

TUESDAY NIGHT (126F/125B) Barney and Thelma Lou's standing date. They would have cashew fudge and watch "that doctor show." After he and Thelma Lou made up over her flirting with Gomer, they both agreed that Tuesday night henceforth would be unbreakable; three days notice would be required to cancel.

TUNA SALAD (237F/236B) The dish Andy prepared for supper one of the nights Aunt Bee did her cooking show, "The Mayberry Chef."

TURKEY (108F/107B) Howie Pruitt brought Wary Willy the Hobo half a turkey. Howie stole it from his mother.

TURKEY WITH ORANGE DRESSING (11F/B) One of Aunt Bee's specialties. She made it for at least two Christmases, one of them the Christmas Eve party held in the courthouse in 11F/B.

TURNER'S GRADE (112F/111B) Hill on Highway 6 on outskirts of Mayberry. Even though the speed limit was thirty-five, Andy always gave the truckers an extra five to get over the grade. Much to Andy's chagrin, Barney set up "Checkpoint Chickie" on the grade and issued eleven speed warnings from his new motorcycle.

"TUSCORORA" (40F/38B) The magic word Dave the Hobo used to steal gumballs.

LAMAR TUTTLE (152F/B) Floyd's cousin. Otis got in a fight with LaMar.

TV OR NOT TV 150th episode filmed and broadcast. Original broadcast date was March 1, 1965. It was written by Ben Joelson and Art Baer, and directed by Coby Ruskin. Regulars included Andy Griffith, Don Knotts, Ronny Howard, Frances Bavier, Howard McNear, and George Lindsey. Guests included George Ives as Allen Harvey, Warren Parker as Mr. Meldrim, Charles Thompson as Asa Breeny, Barbara Stuart as Pat Blake, and as Special Guest, Gavin McCleod as Gilbert Jamel.

"TWEAKY" (82F/B) Barney's high school nickname.

TWELVE (238F/239B) The number of women in the Mayberry church choir.

#12 (72F/71B) "Stars & Stripes Forever" in the Mayberry Band's repertoire.

$12.00 (67F/65B) The price for which Andy sold his old Model A after it burned out a bearing "about D-Queen junction" on Andy's and Barney's trip to New Orleans one summer.

$1,200.00 (174F/173B) (208F/212B) In 174F/173B, the money in the All Souls Church treasury. They wanted to buy Harlan Robinson's organ, but they were $800 short. In 208F/212B, the amount the civic improvement committee had in their treasury, and the amount Brian Jackson the sculpto, charged them to make the statue of Seth Taylor.

"TWELVE MILES EACH WAY" (126F/125B) Mayberry to Mt. Pilot.

"TWELVE OR FIFTEEN" (243F/242B) The number of pancakes Goober ate as a "normal" portion.

25 ¢ (196/203B) Cost of a pound of apples.

"$20.00 OR TWENTY-FOUR HOURS IN JAIL" (3F/B) The fine Andy imposed on Bobby Fleet for overtime parking. He then raised it to seventy dollars for "robe-dignity offending."

TWENTY-EIGHT YEARS (210F/211B) In 210F/211B, the length of time Floyd had been in business in his barbershop on Main Street.

$25.00 (35F/B) The amount Andy was willing to settle for of the sixty-dollar fine he imposed on Elizabeth Crowley, the woman speeder.

$25.00 A MONTH (39F/36B) Harlan Fergus suggested paying off Frank Myers bond at twenty-five dollars a month.

TWENTY-FIVE MINUTES (237F/236B) The length of time it took to drive to Siler City from Mayberry.

$25,000.00 (228F/227B) The amount of money stolen in the Raleigh bank robbery.

25-23 (37F/40B) The final score in the skeetshooting competition. Karen Moore beat Andy.

TWENTY-FIVE YEARS (54F/B) In 54F/B, the length of time Ben Weaver said he'd been in business in Mayberry.

24 ELM STREET (50F/B) Andy's address. (See ANDY'S ADDRESS)

TWENTY-ONE (236F/237B) Andy bought an insurance policy from Emmett for Opie. At the age of twenty-one, Opie would receive $1,000.

A "21 JEWEL WATCH WITH A PURE GOLD BAND" (53F/B) Barney tried to sell this to Sheldon Davis in an attempt to ferret him out as a crook. The "pure gold band" looked like a gold-plated Twist-O-Flex watchband.

"TWENTY-ONE OR TWENTY-TWO" (75F/B) Bee's age, according to Bee.

"TWENTY OR THIRTY YEARS" (210F/211B) The Robinson family owned the building in which Floyd's barbershop was located for twenty or thirty years. The building was on Main Street. The Robinson's moved to California and put the building up for sale.

TWENTY SCIENTIFIC TRICKS A BOY CAN DO AT HOME (139F/B) Book by Seymour Schreck, author of *Fun In the Garage On a Rainy Day*. From the book, Opie learned how to put an egg in a bottle and how to make a wishbone unbreakable.

TWENTY-SEVEN YEARS (106F/B) In 1963, Otis Campbell celebrated twenty-seven years of drinking. He started in 1936.

TWENTY-THREE (58F/B) The number of rhinestone buttons on Bee's blue print dress.

20/20 (2F/B) (30F/B) Barney's eyesight.

TWILIGHT BLUSH (27F/B) Powder sold at Walker's Drugstore. Andy jokingly picked this powder because of his complexion.

"THE TWILIGHT ZONE" (106F/B) Otis thought he was in the zone when he came into the Mayberry jail and found Barney locked in a cell.

"TWINKLETOES TIME" (123F/122B) Dance time, according to Barney.

TWO BITS (41F/39B) The amount Floyd charged the New Orleans tourists to tour the courthouse and see Andy and Barney.

"TWO CHAIRS NO WAITING" (60F/B) The sign Floyd put up after he took Bill Medwin, the bookie barber, into the barbershop.

$2.40 (244F/243B) The amount Goober collected for the PTA fund.

$2.75 (51F/B) The bill the night Barney took Juanita to Mt. Pilot for Chinese. They had the family dinner for one.

$2.16 (31F/B) The amount Jim Lindsey spent at Walker's Drugstore. He told Ellie to charge it.

$2.20 (5F/8B) The money Opie saved up in his piggy bank to buy his girlfriend, Charlotte, a coat.

"$2.00 OR TWENTY-FOUR HOURS" (32F/B) The fine Andy imposed on Otis for being in violation of Ordinance 502: Being intoxicated in a public place. Otis took the twenty-four hours.

"$2.00 OR TWO DAYS IN JAIL" (11F/B) The fine levied on Ben Weaver by Andy. He stole the bench from in front of the courthouse. Ellie Walker paid Ben's fine.

TWO DOZEN (75F/B) The quantity of preserving jars Andy bought Bee for her birthday.

"TWO ESCAPED CONVICTS" (129F/130B) Andy told Ollie that two cons were on their way to Mayberry. Ollie got scared and left Andy's house. Fast.

247 (59F/B) (68F/69B) Thelma Lou's phone number.

242 (47F/B) (51F/B) The Diner phone number, where Juanita could be reached.

200 ACRES (225F/224B) The size of Camp Winoke.

$200.00 (228/227B) The cost of Eddie Baker's suit.

$200.00 A MONTH (231F/230B) Andy's earnings if his Laundercoin took off.

$299.00 (117F/116B) The price of the living room group sold at Weaver's Department Store.

267 SQUARE MILES (5F/8B) The size of Mayberry County.

200 YEARS (210F/211B) According to Andy, the length of time Mayberry's been small.

"TWO IN LOVE" (222F/225B) Movie with Ed Olson and Viola Kern. Howard took Millie to see it. It played Monday through Wednesday. Millie described it as a "three handkerchief picture."

"TWO LADS AND A SHERIFF" (116F/115B) The name Eleanora Poultice suggested for Andy, Barney and Gomer after their vocal "trio" went over so well at the concert. It was supposed to be a solo.

TWO MILE HILL (115F/114B) The hill Otis drove down in the fictional eulogy recited by Andy and Barney.

2-0-4 (111F/110B) "Bribery, collusion, tampering with and/or intimidation of a material witness." The violation Barney suggested they arrest Mr. Frisby on after he refused to leave his land.

2-1-5 (106F/B) Unnamed violation for which Barney gave Gomer a ticket.

TWO PAGES (153F/B) The size of Opie's newspaper, "The Mayberry Sun."

TWO ROWS (32F/B) Aunt Bee wanted Opie to plant two rows of spinach alongside the garage.

26043 (2F/B) The number on the escaped prisoner Dirksen's back.

"TWO SLICES OF APPLE PIE BETWEEN TWO PIECES OF APPLE PIE AND A SLAB OF APPLE PIE FOR DESSERT" (34F/33B) Aunt Bee said Opie would prefer this for lunch.

THE "TWO STEP" (67F/65B) The only dance Andy could do.

TWO SUGARS (37F/40B) The way Barney took his coffee. (See BARNEY'S COFFEE)

$2,000.00 (221D/235B) Amount Goober needed to make a down payment on Wally's Service Station.

2389 (168F/B) Helen Crump's phone number.

TWO WEEKS (238F/239B) The length of time Howard ran the water on the side of the church in order to correct its tilt.

TWO YEARS (36F/37B) The length of time Melissa Stevens said she attended junior college in Savannah.

MR. TWYFORD (163F/161B) Frank Smith's superior. He waited for the results on the Watkins Grading Manual.

TX-4 (170F/171B) Opie's call code with Tommy as they used walkie-talkies.

"ANNABELLE TYLER" (74F/B) One of Big Maude Tyler's aliases.

BARBIE TYLER (103F/B) Classmate of Opie's. Opie said she was "teacher's pet." Andy suggested that she might have been teacher's pet because she got good marks.

BIG MAUDE TYLER (74F/B) One of the "convicts at large." Big Maude was the leader of the cons. Her aliases were Clarisse Tyler, Maude Clarisse Tyler, Anabelle Tyler, and Ralph Henderson. She was five feet six, had dark hair, and weighed 175 pounds. Her prison number was 8216.

"CLARISSE TYLER" One of Big Maude Tyler's aliases.

"MAUDE CLARISSE TYLER" (74F/B) One of Big Maude Tyler's aliases.

RACINE TYLER (129F/130B) Widow friend of Bee's sister, Nora. Nora insisted Racine would be a perfect match for Andy. Racine was left $4,000 when her husband died. She lived in Lake Charles. Her husband owned Tyler Bakery. She was also left a three-year-old truck with original paint. Racine's phone number was 439-7123.

TYLER BAKERY (129F/130B) The business of Racine Tyler's husband. When he died, he left her a $4,000 insurance policy and a three-year-old truck with original paint.

U

"THE UMBRELLA MAN" (83F/B) Song in Barney's repertoire.

"UNCLE HENRY" (38F/41B) The name Andy called Henry Wheeler in order to call his bluff regarding his threatened marriage to Aunt Bee.

UNDERPRIVILEGED CHILDREN'S CHARITY DRIVE (5F/8B) Program headed by Annabelle Silby to raise money for the needy children of Mayberry. (See ANNABELLE SILBY)

"UNIT ONE" (2F/B) The squad car, according to Barney.

UNIVERSITY OF NORTH CAROLINA AT CHAPEL HILL (231F/230B) Opie's college, if Andy couldn't come up with the $15,000 it cost to go to a private school. UNC was half that.

UP IN BARNEY'S ROOM 104th episode filmed and 105th episode broadcast. Original broadcast date was December 2, 1963. It was written by Jim Fritzell and Everett Greenbaum, and directed by Jeffrey Hayden.

Regulars included Andy Griffith, Don Knotts, and Betty Lynn. Guests included Enid Markey as Mrs. Mendlebright, and J. Pat O'Malley as Mr. Fields.

FARLEY UPCHURCH (177F/B) (188F/B) In 177F/B, he was the editor of the "Mayberry Gazette." He came to the courthouse for a list of those who had attended the class reunion. Andy and Warren talked Farley into running a picture of Barney. In 188F/B, it was said he was also the publisher of the "Gazette." He sponsored an essay competition to celebrate the fiftieth anniversary of the newspaper. The theme was the Battle of Mayberry, and first prize was a gold medal and publication on the front page of the anniversary edition of the paper. Opie won. (See THE BATTLE OF MAYBERRY)

WILLIAM UPCHURCH (68F/70B) Investigator from the state special investigation section called to Mayberry to look into the rash of cow thefts.

"US FIFE'S IS WIRY" (24F/B) (106F/B) Barney's self-description.

US/USSR SUMMIT MEETING (240F/B) The meeting Barney arranged at Andy's house when given the job of setting up the accomodations. North Carolina was halfway between Florida, where the Russian ambassador was, and Washington, where the American ambassador was. The meeting at first started out badly, but later, during an impromptu meeting in Aunt Bee's kitchen late at night, the two ambassadors came to agreements on some key points. Barney was praised. The participants included the Russian ambassador, Mr. Vasilievich, and Mr. Clifford, the "distinguished representative" of the United States. (See mentioned entries)

VACUUM CLEANER (225F/224B) Emmett was fixing Aunt Bee's while the boys discussed Camp Winoke.

THE "VALUABLES" OF FRANK MYERS (39F/36B) A brass medallion from the St. Louis World's Fair of 1906, a spoon with the skyline of Milwaukee, Wisconsin on it, a genuine whalebone napkin ring, a buttonhook, a red, white, and blue sleeve garter, and a bond issued by the town of Mayberry in 1861.

COUNT IZ VAN TALECKI (142F/141B) The dead spirit Barney claimed to contact after he bought a box that Barney was sure had been owned by gypsies. The summoning procedure involved lighting a "genie"-shaped lamp and reciting the following: "I call upon you O Count Talecki to impart your mystical powers to earthly things. I ask you, whose presence hovers over us eternally, to invest these cards with your very spirit." Talecki was over 200 years old and Barney claimed that the count told him of Andy's and Helen's inevitable marriage.

CHARLIE VARNEY (115F/114B) Otis went to Charlie's house with a bottle of red-eye. Thinking he was going to drive home drunk, Andy and Barney went to arrest Otis. It turned out he'd sold the car to Charlie and wasn't going to drive anymore.

MR. VASILIEVICH (240F/B) Russian ambassador who participated in the US/USSR summit meeting held at Andy's house. (See US/USSR SUMMIT MEETING)

VEB-368 (54F/B) The license plate number of Joe Waters' truck.

"VENICE" (189F/B) Song. Aunt Bee's and Clara Edwards' attempted musical follow-up to their hit, "My Hometown." The opening lyrics were "If you like polo, golf or tennis, there is no place like Venice."

VERDY (140F/B) Wally's married daughter.

TYLA LEE VERNON (114F/113B) Her husband courted her for sixteen years before proposing. They lived in a "little yellow house two up from the corner." Barney told their story to the "prisoner of love."

MRS. VICKERS (81F/B) She thought that the dynamite blasts for the new underpass were Yankee cannons.

THE VICTORY OF TUCAHOOSEE CREEK (188F/B) The name the Indians used for the Battle of Mayberry. (See THE BATTLE OF MAYBERRY and TOM STRONGBOW)

"LA VIE DU FEMME" (210F/211B) French film. Goober drove to Mt. Pilot to see it. He reviewed it for Andy while they were both sitting on the bench in front of Floyd's Barbershop. He said those French sure knew how to have a good time, staying up late and drinking champagne. Goober was impressed.

QUEEN VINCENTA (183F/182B) Murillos, the gypsy leader, sold Aunt Bee and Clara earrings he said were once owned by Queen Vincenta. He claimed Aunt Bee was the "living image" of the queen.

MARIO VINCENTE (241F/249B) Italian man Sam Jones met while he was in the Army. Sam asked Mario to come to the States and work for him on his farm. Mario came but he brought his father, Papa Vincente, and his sister, Sophia. "Families stay together," he explained.

PAPA VINCENTE (241F/249B) Mario's and Sophia's father. He came with his children to the United States to live and work on Sam Jones' farm. Mike Jones attempted to teach him how to play checkers.

SOPHIA VINCENTE (241F/249B) Sister of Mario, daughter of Papa Vincente. She came with her father and brother to the U.S. to live and work on Sam Jones' farm. She was a very good cook; Sam's cook, Mrs. Fletcher, quit when Sophia took over the kitchen.

VIRGIL (62F/B) (119F/118B) Barney's cousin—on his mother's side—from New Jersey. He came to Mayberry to visit Barney and was hired by Andy. Barney persuaded Andy to give the boy a job, but he quickly fouled up everything and anything he touched. Virgil was a jinx. Andy realized, however, that Virgil was nervous and high-strung, and that when left alone could do beautiful carving work. Virgil's escapades included knocking a roast onto Andy's lap, backing the squad car into Andy's garage, breaking the bookcase glass with a broom, and filing the cell keys smooth. In 119F/118B, Virgil and Barney went to Raleigh for a one week vacation.

VIRGINIA LEE (20F/16B) Floyd's niece. She was entered in the Mayberry Founder's Day beauty pageant. Floyd wanted Andy, who was acting as judge, to pick Virginia Lee.

A VISIT TO BARNEY FIFE 211th episode filmed and 207th episode broadcast. Original broadcast date was January 16, 1967. It was written by Bill Idelson and Sam Bobrick, and directed by Lee Phillips. Regulars included Andy Griffith. Guests included Don Knotts as Barney Fife, Richard Chambers as Henny Parker, Betty Kean as Ma Parker, Richard X. Slattery as Captain Dewhurst, Margaret Teele as Agnes Jean Parker, Gene Rutherford as Leroy Parker, Robert Ball as Oldfield, Luana Anders as Miss Clark, Peter Madsen as Peterson, and Charles Horvath as Jenkins.

VITAMINS (237F/236B) Opie felt it was necessary to take vitamins when Andy took over the cooking during Aunt Bee's stint as "The Mayberry Chef."

VND-323 (50F/B) The license plate number of Doc Molloy's girlfriend's car.

MISS VOGEL (197F/198B) Home economics teacher. She made the costumes for the senior play.

"THE VOICE OF MT. PILOT" (128F/133B) Station WMPD, the radio station that carried Leonard Blush.

MRS. VONRODER (132F/128B) One of Andy's and Barney's teachers. They called her "The Beast of the Fourth Floor." They put ink in her thermos, a tack on her chair, and a garter snake in her desk drawer.

VOTING PROCTOR (192F/191B) Andy's job at the Regal Order of the Golden Door to Good Fellowship, the Mayberry men's lodge.

VT-772 (36F/37B) (69F/66B) In 36F/37B, the license plate number of Melissa Stevens' car. Her real name was Gladys. In 69F/66B, the license plate number of Mayor Stoner's car.

CISSY WAINWRIGHT (58F/B) Mayberry girl. Bee asked Andy if he was taking her to an unnamed Saturday night dance.

"A WAITRESS AND A REGISTERED NURSE" (105F/104B) At least two of Barney's previous dates.

F. WAKEFIELD (75F/B) Owner of F. Wakefield Beauty Salon. She was never seen.

JEDEDIAH WAKEFIELD (8F/9B) Ancestor of Josh Wakefield and his father. He was admitted to the hospital on September 14, 1908 after his mule, Emmie, bit him on the behind.

JOSH WAKEFIELD (8F/9B) Young man—a member of the feuding Wakefield family—who wanted to marry Hannah Carter. The Wakefields had been fueding with the Carters for eighty-seven years. Andy brought the feud to a head and eventually the two lovers were married.

MR. WAKEFIELD (8F/9B) Josh's father. He didn't want Josh to marry Hannah Carter. Hannah's father, Mr. Carter, had been carrying on the Wakefield/Carter feud, which had started eighty-seven years before. Andy brought things to a head by forcing them to hold a decisive duel; both of them ran away.

SONYA WALACHAKA (169F/165B) Twelve-year-old girl from Warsaw, Poland, who correctly predicted an avalanche in that town.

DR. WALKER (184F/B) He was the author of *From the Cradle to Junior College*. Bee read his book to learn how to take care of her grandniece, Evie Joy.

EARLY WALKER (70F/68B) Andy and Barney discovered Luke Jensen was back in town when they saw his dog, Mac, rummaging through Early Walker's trash can.

ELLIE WALKER (6F/4B) (7F/5B) (20F/16B) Fred's niece. In 6F/4B, she came to Mayberry to help her uncle in his drugstore. She had her pharmacy degree and became a romantic interest for Andy. In 7F/5B, she got mad at Andy for thinking that she wanted to marry him. In 20F/16B, Bee entered her (against her wishes) in the Mayberry Founder's Day beauty pageant. She was contestant #7. (See the Elinor Donahue interview in the appendix section of this book)

FRED WALKER (6F/4B) (7F/5B) Ellie's uncle and the owner of Walker's Drugstore. In 7F/5B, he urged Andy to ask Ellie to the town picnic.

GILLY WALKER (144F/B) He constantly complained to Goober about his carburetor. This carping forced Goober to dismantle Gilly's car in the courthouse. Gilly always drove fast.

HARRY WALKER (210F/211B) Real estate man who owned his own realty company. He handled the sale of the building in which Floyd's Barbershop was located. (The building was owned by the Robinson family. They lived in California.) As Harry showed the building to Howard Sprague, he punched the wall to show its strength and put his fist right through it.

TROOPER WALKER (2F/B) State police trooper under Captain Barker who came to Mayberry to aid in the "manhunt." Walker got the map markers for Barker and he also handed out the pictures of the prisoner.

WALKING STICK (29F/B) Melba Lawson used one to prop open the cellar door when she brought up the preserves.

WALLPAPER (153F/B) Mrs. Foster's chicken tasted like it.

WALLY (140F/B) Goober's boss.

WALLY (191F/192B) A member of the Mayberry Barbershop Quartet.

WALLY'S SERVICE STATION (102F/B) It was open 7:00 A.M. to 7:00 P.M.

WALNUT HILLS (225F/224B) Wealthy section of Mayberry County. Its residents sent their kids to Camp Winoke.

WALNUT HILLS GOLF COURSE (225F/224B) Frequent golf spot of George Hollander and his friends. The #4 hole was 162 yards.

THE WALRAVENS (200F/197B) Mayberry family that lived on Elm Street. When Bee used the beautification of Elm Street as a campaign issue in her bid for city council, Tillie Kincaid remarked, "If the Walravens would paint their house, it would certainly help.

ISAAC WALTON (64F/73B) According to Andy, "when it comes to fishing, he's the man that wrote the book." Opie wanted to bet that Isaac wasn't better than his Paw.

"WANDERING SPIDER" (129F/130B) The name Nora called Andy as she told Racine Tyler about him. Nora thought Andy had been single too long.

WANT ADS (161F/160B) (171F/172B) In 161F/160B, after Opie gave up his grocery store job to Billy Crenshaw, Andy ran the following want ad: "Wanted: eleven-year-old boy for part-time work after school and Saturdays. Must be bright, ambitious, and have a broken bicycle. Call Sheriff Taylor." In 171F/172B, the want ad Aunt Bee decided to answer was on page seven, third from the bottom. It read: "Wanted Female: Easy part-time work afternoons. Apply in person, 177 Main Street." The ad was run by Ralph Kingsley and Arnold Finch, two counterfeiters. Bee got the job.

WAR SURPLUS AUCTION (112F/111B) Auction in Mt. Pilot where Barney bought his motorcycle and sidecar, #RJ300. (See #RJ3OO)

MISS WARNER (86F/B) Opie's former teacher. Helen Crump took her place.

A WARNING FROM WARREN 169th episode filmed and 165th episode broadcast. Original broadcast date was October 15, 1965. It was written by Fred Freeman, and Lawrence J. Cohen, and directed by Alan Rafkin. Regulars included Andy Griffith, Aneta Corsaut, George Lindsey, and Howard McNear. Guests included Jack Burns as Warren Ferguson, and Charles Smith as the Counterman.

WARREN (144F/B) Andy told him he'd take care of it when he got back from the safety conference. Who Warren was or what "it" was, was not specified.

WARREN'S HANGOVER CURE FOR OTIS (175F/B) Sassafrass root, soreghum molasses, a raw egg, and hot sauce. Otis liked it.

WARY WILLY THE HOBO (108F/107B) The hobo "Opie and His Merry Men" met him in Crouch's Woods by Myer's Lake. Willy convinced the boys to put the Robin Hood story to work, and the boys then raided their mothers' larders to bring food to Willy. Andy eventually exposed Willy for what he was by offering him all sorts of jobs. Needless to say, Willy turned every job down, and then ran away. (See "PETULLA ABONDOLA")

WASG (216F/B) TV station in Raleigh that broadcast "Colonel Tim's Talent Time" amateur show. (The call letters were a jumbled acronym for "The Andy Griffith Show.")

CHARLENE DARLING WASH see CHARLENE DARLING

DUDLEY J. WASH (88F/B) (94F/B) (121F/120B) Mountain man and the husband of Charlene Darling. Dud was also known as Dudley A. Wash. In 88F/B, he was a private first class and he returned to Mayberry to marry Charlene. In 94F/B, Andy had to arrange a "preacher wedding" between Dud and Charlene to satisfy Ernest T. Bass, who insisted that justice of the peace weddings didn't count. Ernest T. also wanted to marry Charlene. In 121F/120B, Dud liked to sit up in the hills with his buddy, Hasty Buford, "drinking hard cider and punching each other in the arm and hollerin' 'flinch'." Charlene divorced Dud for grinning at Idele Bushy at preaching, and for disappearing for a week to hunt foxes with Hasty.

RAY WASHING (41F/39B) Mayberry jeweler. Mayor Pike told Ray to get started on Andy's and Barney's "crime-free" medals. Andy didn't like the idea. Barney told Ray he wanted a solid gold medal without diamonds, but rubies were alright (they were his birthstone).

WASHINGTON, D.C. (35F/B) (240F/B) In 35F/B, it was said that Washington was the hometown of Elizabeth Crowley, the woman speeder. In 240F/B, the American ambassador was there when Barney arranged the US/USSR summit meeting to be held in Mayberry.

"WASHINGTON ROUNDUP" (153F/B) One of the columns in the "Mayberry Gazette."

"WATCH OUT FOR THE RED BARON" (243F/242B) Opie yelled this to Aunt Bee as she headed off for her demonstration flying lesson.

JOE WATERS (45F/B) (54F/B) In 45F/B, he parked in a no parking zone. Barney tried to bluster him into moving but it took a stern look from Andy to make him move. In 54F/B, Joe drove a truck into town. It's license plate number was VEB-368.

BILL WATKINS (191F/192B) Tenor who auditioned to replace Howard Sprague for the barbershop quartet competition.

FRANK WATKINS (17F/B) He was mentioned by Rube Sloan to Andy as a possible snitch on Rube's still.

"THE WATKINS GRADING MANUAL" (163F/161B) The project Frank Smith worked on with Helen Crump. It was the reason Smith came to Mayberry. (See "EMBRYONIC MEGALOPOLIS")

COLONEL WATSON (107F/127B) The commanding officer of the Marine battalion stationed at Camp Wilson.

EDGAR WATSON (248F/247B) Bully. He harassed Mike Jones until Opie stepped in to help. Edgar was fifteen-and-a-half years old and thirty pounds heavier than Mike.

EMMA WATSON (61F/B) A chronic jaywalker, according to Barney. (See EMMA BRAND)

DEPUTY JOE WATSON (144F/B) He came to Mayberry with Sheriff Jackson.

SHORTY WATSON (196F/203B) He owned a grocery store in Mayberry, was the shortest of all the Watsons, and went fishing with Goober at Troublesome Creek. It wasn't said if Shorty was related to Emma.

WAWYER RIVER (198F/200B) Goober was so happy that Howard Sprague put Old Sam back into Tucker's Lake that he promised to take Howard "up Wawyer River."

WAXPAPER (121F/120B) 23¢.

"WE DEFY THE MAFIA!" (41F/39B) The slogan Barney yelled in a moment of exuberance just before Mayberry was awarded the FBI's "crime-free" medal.

"WE SHALL MEET" (115F/114B) The song Andy and Barney sang at Otis's phony "eulogy."

"WE SHALL NOT BE MOVED" (111F/110B) The song Bee and the women sang at Frisby's farm when the bulldozer came to knock it down.

"WE'RE BROTHERS TOGETHER" (5F/8B) The song the lodge brothers sang at Tom Silby's "funeral."

"THE WEATHER" (113F/112B) Specifically, the rain. Ramona Anchram's one and only topic of conversation.

BEN WEAVER (11F/B) (54F/B) (186F/187B) In 11F/B, he was an elderly curmudgeon of Mayberry who owned Weaver's Department Store. In 11F/B, he brought in Sam for moonshining with the complaint that his store sold spirits and he didn't want moonshiners taking his business. In 54F/B, Ben was upset that Bert Miller opened a stand in Art Crowley's vacant lot. Ben was also upset that Bert had had Andy's and Barney's assistance. In 186F/187B, he hired Goober as a salesman after Goober quit Wally's Service Station. (See mentioned entries)

WEAVER'S DEPARTMENT STORE (117F/116B) (139F/B) (171F/172B) In 117F/116B, it was the store owned by Ben Weaver and plagued by "The Shoplifters." To crack the case, Barney dressed up as a mannequin in Weaver's sporting goods department. Among the items sold in Weaver's was a beer can opener with an umbrella on it. In 139F/B, the Darlings bought Opie a suit at Weaver's. It was tropical worsted. In 171F/172B, a phony ten dollar bill showed up at Weaver's. Andy made good for it out of his own pocket. (See mentioned entries)

"WEB-FOOTED RED-CRESTED LAKE LOON" (127F/126B) The bird Andy invented and imitated in order to lead Barney back to camp without Barney knowing he was being helped.

DR. WEBSTER (122F/121B) One of U.T. Pendyke's (Barney's) fictitious associates. Dr. Webster would be interested in the Miracle Salve mange cure, according to Dr. Pendyke.

MISS WEBSTER (29F/B) She taught the biology class that Andy flunked in the spring of 1938.

THE WEDDING 246th episode filmed and 245th episode broadcast. Original broadcast date was March 4, 1968. It was written by Joseph Bonaduce, and directed by Lee Phillips. Regulars included Andy Griffith, Jack Dodson, Aneta Corsaut, George Lindsey, and Paul Hartman. Guests included Mabel Albertson as Mrs. Sprague, Iggie Wolfington as Mr. Watkins, and Terri Garr as The Girl.

WEDDING BELLS FOR AUNT BEE 58th episode filmed and broadcast. Original broadcast date was April 2, 1962. It was written by Jack Elinson and Charles Stewart, and directed by Bob Sweeny. Regulars included Andy Griffith, Ronny Howard, Frances Bavier, Hope Summers, and Hal Smith. Guests included Fred Sherman as Fred Goss, the Drycleaner.

WEDNESDAY AT 3:00 P.M. (136F/B) At this time, the fifty dollars Opie found would be his if no one claimed the funds. (See MAN'S PURSE and PARNELL RIGSBY)

THE WEENIE-BURGER (67F/65B) Restaurant. Andy took Peggy McMillan there.

WEENIES AND BEANS (65F/67B) The meal Andy prepared for supper when Aunt Bee was staying at her Aunt Louise's.

WEENIES AND ROOT BEER (108F/107B) Lunch in the woods for "Opie and His Merry Men" the day they ran into Wary Willy the Hobo.

HUEY WELCH (44F/B) Mayberry man who had a fight with Osgood over a spike fence Osgood built on their mutual property line. Huey's laying hens weren't getting enough sun. (See OSGOOD)

"WELCOME BACK CLASS OF '48" (176F/B) The sign Andy hung for the class reunion. However, in 82F/B, it was said that Andy and Barney were graduates of the Class of 1945.

"WELCOME HOME MAYBERRY JET SET" (227F/222B) Sign that welcomed home Bee, Clara, and Myrtle from their trip to Mexico.

"WELCOME SWEET SPRINGTIME" (52F/B) The song the Mayberry Choir sang at the choir finals in Roanoke. It was number 14A.

"WELCOME TO MAYBERRY, THE FRIENDLY TOWN" (48F/B) Sign on the outskirts of Mayberry.

WELFARE DEPARTMENT (202F/199B) The agency Andy threatened to call regarding Mr. and Mrs. Garland, the parents of the abandoned baby boy found by Arnold and Opie on the courthouse steps.

MISS WELLINGTON (20F/16B) Darlene Swanson's etiquette teacher and the founder of Miss Wellington's School for Girls.

MISS WELLINGTON'S SCHOOL FOR GIRLS (20F/16B) The charm school Darlene Swanson attended. While there, she was voted "Young Lady Most Likely To Become Charming." The school was in Raleigh.

WENDELL (235F/234B) One of his dogs started barking as Andy, Goober, Howard, and Emmett drank a pop at the filling station the night Howard returned from his "new life" in the Caribbean.

WES (235F/234B) One of the guys who hung around the general store on St. Benedict's Island in the Caribbean. Howard Sprague met him during his "new life."

WEST INDIAN LICORICE MOCHA DELIGHT (105F/104B) Ice cream flavor Barney brought Thelma Lou from Murphy's House of the Nine Flavors. It cost forty cents, and Barney made Thelma Lou pay.

WEST VIRGINIA (234F/232B) The state where Bee and her cousin, Bradford, grew up.

WESTWOOD FEDERAL PRISON (118F/117B) Penitentiary over 400 miles from Mayberry. An escaped prisoner from there was caught just twenty miles outside of Mayberry and was held in the Mayberry jail. Barney initiated "maximum security": cell keys in the drawer.

"WET SHOES IN THE SUNSET" (139F/B) A new song the Darlings learned.

"WHAT A TOWN IS DEPENDS ON THE PEOPLE" (222F/225B) Quotation by Millie Hutchins regarding Mayberry. This was really the unspoken (until this episode) creed of the show.

"WHAT I WOULD DO IF I HAD A TOOL CHEST" (158F/B) Essay written by Opie for his English class as a hint to Andy.

WHAT IT'S LIKE TO BE THE SON OF A SHERIFF (213F/B) The title of Opie's "book," which he decided to write after seeing the success of Helen's book, *Amusing Tales of Tiny Tots*. He had to ask Andy how to spell "bloodthirsty" for the book.

"WHAT'S YOUR HURRY?" (100F/99B) Sermon topic. It was given by the visiting preacher, Dr. Harrison Breen, in Mayberry's All Souls Church.

WHEELER, GOLDBRICK see "GOLD-BRICK WHEELER"

HENRY WHEELER (38F/41B) Traveling handyman who came to Mayberry and ended up staying with—and sponging off—Aunt Bee and Andy. At first, they were generous and good-hearted. Andy, however, got a little suspicious because Wheeler continually made excuses to get out of the work he had promised to do. Andy called a sheriff friend of his and found out that Wheeler was a con man. Andy called Wheeler's bluff and told him he expected him to marry Aunt Bee. He left and Aunt Bee never learned the truth. (A similar situation happened to Aunt Bee with her old beau, Roger Hanover, in 130F/132B.)

WHEELING (233F/231B) Millie Hutchins' hometown. She and Howard planned on getting married there before the plans fell though.

"WHEN THE SAINTS GO MARCHING IN" (105F/104B) The song Freddy Fleet and his Band with a Beat were playing when Andy, Barney, Helen, and Thelma Lou arrived at the chamber of commerce dance.

THE "WHIPLASH TEST" (199F/196B) After Goober got rear-ended, Floyd gave Goober this test: put your fists on your chest and try to make your elbows touch over your head. (Actually, it's physically impossible.) Goober's inability to perform this feat convinced him—and Floyd—that he was much more seriously injured than he had originally thought.

WHITE WATER CREEK (168F/B) Kansas locale near where Darlene Mason grew up.

WHITEY (86F/B) Opie's friend and a member of the history troupe, "The Mayberry Minutemen."

GERALD WHITFIELD (176F/B) Thelma Lou's husband. He was a foreman on a wrecking crew. They lived in Jacksonville. When Barney moved to Raleigh, Thelma Lou left Mayberry one month later. At the time of the class reunion in 176F/B, Thelma Lou had only been married six weeks. Their marriage lasted a brief sixteen months.

CYRUS WHITLEY (231F/230B) Graduate of Howard Sprague's alma mater, Bradbury Business College. At the time of 231F/230B, he was serving five years for embezzlement.

MRS. WICKS (25F/B) One of the ladies of the Women's Historical Society who came to Mayberry with the news that someone in town was a direct descendant of a Revolutionary War hero, Nathan Tibbs. It was Otis Campbell. Barney was convinced that it wasn't Otis, but himself instead. (See DUNCAN PHYFE)

A WIFE FOR ANDY 92nd episode filmed and broadcast. Original broadcast date was April 15, 1963. It was written by Aaron Ruben, and directed by Bob Sweeney. Regulars included Andy Griffith, Ronny Howard, Don Knotts, Aneta Corsaut, Betty Lynn, and Frances Bavier. Guests included Barbara Perry, Janet Waldo, Rachel Ames, and Janet Stewart.

MARY WIGGINS (20F/16B) First-grader and Opie's girl friend. Opie thought she should have been named the winner of the Mayberry Founder's Day beauty pageant. Andy and Floyd agreed and crowned her "Miss Mayberry Junior" in the barbershop with a towel and a hat. (See "MISS MAYBERRY JUNIOR")

"WILD BILL FIFE" (16F/20B) The nickname the Mayberry guys hung on Barney after he arrested the whole town.

"A WILDCAT" (218F/B) Andy told Opie that the first dollar he ever put in his piggy bank he earned by catching a wildcat barehanded. Aunt Bee cleared up the story by explaining to Opie that what he caught was a "wild cat" that was sick. The county had put a dollar bounty on all wild cats turned in. The cat Andy caught was so sick he just put his head down on Andy's shoulder and went to sleep. Andy tried to slant the story to give Opie material to use in his "Most Unforgettable Character" essay.

THE WILDCATS (46F/B) The club Opie and his friends started in Jubell Foster's barn. Opie's job was "Keeper of the Flame"; he had to bring the candle to each meeting. Also, all doings of the club had to remain secret or the teller would be struck down by the "Curse of the Claw."

MRS. WILEY (113F/112B) Mayberry social leader who had Saturday night singles' socials at her house. Ernest T. Bass broke her window in 113F/112B. He was searching for a woman.

RAMONA WILEY (82F/B) Classmate of Andy's and Barney's. It wasn't said if or how she was related to Mrs. Wiley. She signed Barney's yearbook with the note, "Barney beloved: The tears on my pillow bespeak the pain that is in my heart. Always, Ramona." She married Harry Bectoris.

"WILL YOU HELP US?" (86F/B) (136F/B) In 86F/B, Barney asked Andy if he'd help him and the boys start a history club. In 136F/B, Barney asked Andy if he'd help him and Opie build an erector set bridge.

HOWIE WILLIAMS (143F/B) Mr. Williams' son. Opie wanted to sell him his bike for $5.00. Andy revealed that the coaster brake slipped, the chain broke, and the inner tubes were worn. Opie then cut the price to $4.00, but Howie nixed the deal.

MR. WILLIAMS (143F/B) Owner of the house that Andy liked. Barney tried to arrange a sale. Barney said he could put Andy in the house for $3,500. He could get $24,000 for Andy's house, pick up Williams' house for $27,500, and get a mortgage at the bank for the balance.

SHERIFF WILLIAMS (145F/B) Mt. Pilot law officer. Andy called him looking for Otis.

WILLIAMS INTERIORS AND FURNITURES (135F/B) Mt. Pilot business next to the Mt. Pilot Judo Society.

MARGARET WILLIAMSON (41F/39B) Reporter for a newspaper in the state capital. She wrote a column called "Meandering With Margaret." She came to Mayberry to cover the ceremony awarding Mayberry the "crime-free" award. She was aghast to hear that Andy had killed a "Mr. Carp," who, in reality, was a fish.

HARVEY WILLICK (24F/B) Mayberry hypochondriac who insisted Dr. Benson give him an injection. The doctor obliged with a "saline solution—two cc—in the gluteus maximus." This cracked up Ellie Walker.

"WILLOUGHBY VS. PERKINS" (44F/B) Court case cited by Barney regarding the fight Osgood and Huey Welch had over the spike fence Osgood built on their mutual property line. The fence prevented Huey's laying hens from getting enough sun.

WILLOW AVENUE (153F/B) One of the streets in Mayberry where Opie delivered copies of his paper, "The Mayberry Sun."

"WILLOW BRANCHES AND WHITTLING KNIVES" (121F/120B) The weapons Dud Wash wanted to battle Andy with in their "fight" over Charlene Darling.

WILLOW CREEK ROAD (83F/B) The road where Rafe and Martha Hollister lived.

WILLOW LANE (69F/66B) Sort of a local lover's lane by the duck pond. Barney wanted to take Juanita there. In 91F/B, Barney wanted to take Thelma Lou to the duck pond and park. When Andy asked if they were going to have a "smooching party," Barney replied, "Que sera sera."

WILLOW STREET (44F/B) A quiet street in Mayberry.

WILLY JACK (97F/101B) His brakes screeched. Andy wrote him a ticket.

WILMINGTON (107F/127B) The day Gomer was to report to Camp Wilson to start Marine boot camp, Andy had an errand in Wilmington, so he drove Gomer to the camp. It's likely that Andy made up the errand just to make sure that Gomer got there all right.

• **BOBBY WILSON** (153F/B) Classmate of Opie's. Betty Parker let Bobby carry her books home.

MR. WILSON (165F/169B) He had a noisy fan belt.

MR. WILSON (205F/B) He sold the con man, George Jones, a one-way ticket to Miami.

SHERIFF WILSON (78F/76B) (191F/192B) In 78F/76B, he was the sheriff of Marshall County. In 191F/192B, he was the sheriff of Mt. Pilot. Andy never liked him and didn't want to lose to him in the barbershop quartet competition. He didn't.

TOM WILSON (42F/B) A member of the Esquire Club. Andy and Barney were introduced to him at one of the Club's meetings. In golf, he shot in the low eighties.

TROOPER WILSON (2F/B) State police trooper under Captain Barker who came to Mayberry to aid in the "manhunt." Wilson was the trooper with the rifle that had the telescopic sight.

WILSON VS. THORPE'S PHARMACY (6F/4B) Court case that took place in Mt. Corey in 1952. Barney thought the case might have been useful in their attempt to force Ellie Walker to sell Emma Brand her pills. Wilson wanted to buy arsenic to kill rats. The court ruled that he had the right to buy it. Wilson bought the arsenic on Tuesday, May 4, and was buried Friday, May 7. Barney remarked that it was a "terrible way to go, that arsenic. Must smart."

THE WILSONS (28F/B) They had an old lawn mower Andy figured they could get for the "Save the Scoby House Fund" rummage sale.

"WIN OR LOSE" (165F/169B) Hollywood TV show. While visiting Hollywood, Bee was the sweepstakes winner on the show. She won a refrigerator, a washing machine, a TV, a dishwasher, an ice crusher, a garbage disposal, a dryer, and a genuine ranch mink. The value of the prizes was $4,850. The tax on the prizes was $1,138.72. Bee sold everything to Weaver's Department Store except the TV and the garbage disposal. Her winning answer was "cinnamon with custard filling." While on the show, Bee said hello to Clara, Myra, Johnny Paul, Helen, Jud, Otis, Floyd, and Goober. The host of the show was Jack Smith.

ARNOLD WINKLER (84F/B) The "spoiled kid" who taught Opie how to talk back, get out of his chores, and throw a tantrum by crying and holding his breath. His father, Simon Winkler, bought him a new Intercontinental Flyer for seventy dollars, which Arnold rode on the streets of Mayberry. After the boy ignored Barney's first warning, Andy impounded the bike. When Simon came to retrieve it, Opie got a chance to see the "real" Arnold, and—more importantly—so did Simon. Andy let Simon use the woodshed to "explain" things to Arnold.

SIMON WINKLER (84F/B) Arnold's father. After he realized he had spoiled Arnold, he took the boy out to the woodshed behind the courthouse.

HALCYON LORETTA WINSLOW (139F/B) Her father saw Barney's picture in the paper when the deputy won four free haircuts at the church raffle. He then wanted to fix Barney up with Halcyon. Barney said she was "the ugliest girl you ever saw in your life." Barney said her father saw "civil servant, unmarried," and he was only thirty at the time. Her father made Barney a great offer: one-third interest in a prune-pitting operation, full use of the company car, interest in the family home, and a beautiful hillside plot in Mt. Pilot Cemetery. The old man arranged a meeting between Halcyon and Barney over an American cheese sandwich and a "guerney" (either Barney's word for "gherkin"

pickle, or for a "Guernsey"—a glass of milk) at Klein's Coffee Shop. Barney said Halcyon was "Beasto Maristo." Barney paid for the sandwich to wipe out any obligation. Halcyon went East to a finishing school. As of 139F/B, she was still ugly, single, and pitting prunes.

HOG WINSLOW (113F/112B) Father of Hoggette.

HOGGETTE WINSLOW (113F/112B) Hog Winslow's daughter. Ernest T. Bass tried courting her but it didn't work out. Barney remarked that her first name was pretty and Ernest T. told him it was French. Ernest T. hit her in the head with his "date-request rock"—she needed seven stitches. Hoggette decided to marry the taxidermist "what sewed up her head."

PREACHER WINSLOW (121F/120B) Clergyman who was scheduled to marry Andy and Charlene Darling.

WINSTON-SALEM, NORTH CAROLINA (3F/B) Jim Lindsey bought a new pick from a store there.

WINTERGREEN MINTS (161F/160B) The candy Andy gave Floyd and Goober.

AB WINTERS (224/221B) Mayberry man Goober suggested as a substitute bowler for Lou Jenkins. Ab couldn't bowl, however, because he played basketball Tuesdays and Thursdays and he had gone to a poker game the night before. His wife wouldn't let him out again. (Ab was a bit of a wimp.)

DOC WINTERS (29F/B) Early Mayberry doctor. His being out of town forced Andy to help Sam Becker's wife, Lily, deliver her baby.

EMMIE WINTERS (224F/221B) Ab's wife. She wouldn't let him bowl because she felt he was out too much. She seems to have been a bit domineering.

WMPD (128F/133B) "The Voice of Mt. Pilot." The station that broadcast Leonard Blush. (See LEONARD BLUSH and ELEANORA POULTICE)

WOMAN'S SKEETSHOOTING CHAMPION OF ARKANSAS (37F/40B) Thelma Lou's cousin, Karen Moore.

"WOMAN'S STUFF" (12F/10B) Andy aggravated Ellie Walker by describing the following as "woman's stuff" (he felt Ellie should have been doing these things instead of running for city council): "Going shopping, looking in windows, trying on hats, eating them little bitty sandwiches, and gossiping."

WOMEN'S BRIDGE CLUB (208F/212B) They met at the Mayberry town hall. This forced the civic improvement committee to hold their meeting in the courthouse.

WOMEN'S CLUB SIGN (230F/229B) "Mayberry Women's Club Presents Professor Hubert St. John, Author of *I Know South America*."

WOMEN'S HISTORICAL SOCIETY (25F/B) Organization that discovered that someone in Mayberry was the direct descendant of Revolutionary War hero, Nathan Tibbs. It was Otis Campbell. (See DUNCAN PHYFE and NATHAN TIBBS)

WONG SOO'S CANTON PALACE (209F/210B) Restaurant in Pittsburgh where Charlie figured he could get a job after the Sparerib Tavern closed in Mayberry.

WOODBURNING SET (112F/111B) One of Opie's birthday presents. He used it to burn a number on their house, much to Andy's dismay. Andy later used the set to burn a phony legend on a board. He used the legend to convince Barney to donate his motorcycle to the National Guard Armory. (See MOTORCYCLE PLAQUE)

"A WOODEN COWBOY AND A WOODEN DOG" (62F/B) The two carvings made by Barney's cousin, Virgil. These made Andy realize that Virgil had inner talents that needed to be brought out.

WOODS WAY (44F/B) A quiet street in Mayberry.

WOOLEN BATHROBE (245F/244B) The gift Emmett originally bought for Martha for their twenty-fifth anniversary. He returned it for a fur coat.

"WORDS THAT START WITH 'S'" (112F/111B) Barney discovered that if you rode into the wind with your mouth open and put your tongue on the roof of your mouth, it was impossible to pronounce words that started with "S." He realized this while riding his new motorcycle.

"THE WORKS" (22F/B) At Floyd's Barbershop. They consisted of "shave, haircut, witch hazel, eau de cologne, and toilet water."

WORLD WAR I VETS IN MAYBERRY (112F/111B) Al, Bert Stevens, and the Milo boys.

"THE WORST HOUSE IN TOWN" (39F/36B) Frank Myers' house, according to the Mayberry town council.

WP754 (234F/232B) Train number. Bradford Taylor snuck into Mayberry on this train.

A WRISTWATCH (131F/129B) For Barney's fifth anniversary as a deputy, Andy, Thelma Lou, Floyd, and Aunt Bee chipped in and bought Barney a stainless steel waterproof wristwatch. They had the back engraved "5."

"WYATT EARP" (16F/20B) (73F/70B) In 16F/20B, the name the Mayberry guys hung on Barney after he arrested the whole town. In 73F/70B, the name Neil and Matt derogatorily called Barney.

WYATT EARP 179th episode filmed and broadcast. Original broadcast date was January 31, 1966. It was written by Jack Elinson, and directed by Alan Rafkin. Regulars included Andy Griffith, Ronny Howard, Howard McNear, George Burns, and George Lindsey. Guests included Pat Hingle as Fred Gibson, Richard Jury as Clarence Earp, and Richard Keith as Johnny Paul Jason.

WYNKEN (101F/96B) One of the three orphaned songbirds Opie adopted after he accidentally killed their mother with his slingshot. (See BLYNKEN, NOD, and the intoduction to this book)

WYOMING (4F/6B) The "runaway kid," George Foley, was considering running away to Wyoming.

WZAZ (237F/236B) The call letters of Channel 12 in Siler City.

X2Y (170F/171B) Tommy's call code on the walkie-talkie. He talked to Opie.

YANCEY (68F/69B) Town in which the Gigolo Club was located.

YE OLDE BOOK SHOP (171F/172B) Main Street business.

YEARBOOK ENTRY: ANDY TAYLOR (82F/B) "Andrew Jackson Taylor; Second Vice President, 4H; Secretary, Philomathian Literary Society." Andy explained to Barney that the Philomathian Literary Society cut out current events and pasted them in a book. Jack Egbert blackballed Barney from the society.

YEARBOOK ENTRY: BARNEY FIFE (82F/B) "Bernard Milton Fife; Board of Directors, Tin Foil Drive; Hall Monitor; Volley Ball Court Maintenance Crew; Spanish Club."

YELLOW WAX BEANS (135F/B) Two pounds for 35¢.

DON YELTON (144F/B) He called Andy to tell him that there was something on Andy's desk with his name on it.

YLRB (116F/115B) Radio station in Mt. Pilot that broadcast Leonard Blush's radio show on the third Tuesday every month. (See LEONARD BLUSH and ELEANORA POULTICE)

THE YMCA (119F/118B) Raleigh club where Barney and his cousin, Virgil, stayed on their vacation.

"YOU PEOPLE ARE LIVING IN ANOTHER WORLD!" (77F/79B) Malcolm Tucker's exasperated exclamation after experiencing Mayberry's rather pronounced "casualness."

"YOU'RE THE CATS" (22F/B) Barney always wished he could say this to Thelma Lou.

"YOUNG LADY MOST LIKELY TO BECOME CHARMING" (20F/16B) Darlene Swanson. She was voted this at Miss Wellington's School for Girls in Raleigh.

YOUNG PEOPLE'S MEETING (206F/B) Howard called Andy about it, Goober screwed up the message, and Andy ended up eating three spaghetti dinners.

"THE YOUNG SWINGERS" (229F/228B) The name Andy suggested to Opie for his rock group. The name the guys finally agreed on was "The Sound Committee."

DOC ZACH (55F/B) When Andy had a tussle bringing in the Gordon boys, he stopped at Doc Zach's to get bandaged up.

ZONE DETECTION SYSTEM (211F/207B) The plan the Raleigh detectives devised to solve the string of supermarket robberies. Barney explained the system to the family committing the robberies. (See "PARKER" family entries)

A MAYBERRY MISCELLANY

Following is an alphabetical listing of some miscellaneous tidbits of information about Mayberry, our hometown, and also about the real-world people who helped bring Mayberry into our lives. (Special thanks must go to Richard Kelly for the inclusion of the unfilmed script, "The Wandering Minstrel," in his definitive look at the production of "The Andy Griffith Show," *The Andy Griffith Show*, published by John F. Blair.)

ANDY GRIFFITH'S FAVORITE EPI-SODE: "Barney's First Car" (90F/B). Don Knotts gave this information on "The Andy Griffith Show Silver Anniversary Special" broadcast on October 3, 1985, on cable station WTBS. The special celebrated the show's twenty-fifth anniversary on the air. The first broadcast of "The Andy Griffith Show" was on October 3, 1960.

ANDY'S APPEARANCE RECORD Andy Griffith/Andy Taylor was the only character to appear in every single episode of "The Andy Griffith Show." Every other character, at one point or another, had an episode (or more) off. Andy has the record of being the most ubiquitous Mayberryite we know.

ANDY'S MAGIC BOOK Andy had at least one book on magic in his bookcase. This information was given in a Post Toasties cornflakes commercial run sometime during the first three or four seasons of the show.

"CHRISTMAS IN MAYBERRY" Talked-about TV-movie. Watch for the second edition of *Mayberry, My Hometown* for all the info on "Christmas in Mayberry!"

"COCOON" Director Ron Howard's touching fable about aliens and senior citizens.

"DANNY MEETS ANDY GRIFFITH" Actually, the very first "Andy Griffith Show" episode. (See "The Danny Thomas Show")

"THE DANNY THOMAS SHOW" The genealogical father of "The Andy Griffith Show." The pilot for "Andy" was an episode of "The Danny Thomas Show" called "Danny Meets Andy Griffith." Danny Thomas—like Elizabeth Crowley, the woman speeder—zoomed through Mayberry and was snagged by our sheriff. This was the beginning of it all.

"DIARY OF A PERFECT MURDER" Made-for-TV movie broadcast on NBC March 21, 1986. It starred Andy Griffith as attorney Benjamin Matlock for the defense. This movie was the pilot for an NBC series called "Matlock" starring Andy, which premiered Saturday, September 20, 1986, at 10:00 P.M. on NBC. It then moved to its regular time slot, Tuesdays at 8:00 P.M.

DON KNOTTS' FAVORITE EPISODE: "The Pickle Story" (43F/B). Don Knotts gave this information on "The Andy Griffith Show Silver Anniversary Special," broadcast on October 3, 1985, on cable station WTBS. The special celebrated "The Andy Griffith Show"'s twenty-fifth anniversary on the air. The first broadcast of "The Andy Griffith Show" was on October 3, 1960.

DUNCAN, OKLAHOMA Ron Howard's birthplace.

FORTY ACRES, CULVER CITY, CALIFORNIA The locale where the exterior shots for "The Andy Griffith Show" were shot.

GEORGE LINDSEY'S FAVORITE EPI-SODE: "Dinner at Eight" (206F/B). Don Knotts gave this information on "The Andy Griffith Show Silver Anniversary Special" broadcast on October 3, 1985, on cable station WTBS. The special celebrated "The Andy Griffith Show"'s twenty-fifth anniversary on the air. The first broadcast of "The Andy Griffith Show" was on October 3, 1960.

"GOMER PYLE, U.S.M.C." The only other spin-off of "The Andy Griffith Show." It ran from September 25, 1964, to September 19, 1969. There were 150 episodes—black-and-white and color—and it ran on CBS in five different time slots: Friday/9:30; Friday/9:00; Wednesday/9:30; Friday/8:30; and Wednesday/8:00. It starred Jim Nabors as Gomer Pyle, and—as on "Mayberry, R.F.D."—there was much crossing over from "The Andy Griffith Show." Other cast members included Frank Sutton (now deceased) as Sgt. Vince Carter, and Ronnie Schell as Duke Slater. Crossover actors (in roughly the order of their guest appearances) included the following:

Allan Melvin	Ronny Howard
Elizabeth MacRae	Susan Oliver
Karl Swensen	Douglas Fowley
Ellen Corby	Peter Hobbs
Gavin MacLeod	Herbie Faye
Larry Hovis	Ron Reiner
Jean Carson	Arthur Batanides
Don Rickles	Hope Summers
Patty Regan	Jay Novello
Byron Morrow	Elizabeth MacRae
Ken Lynch	Milton Frome
Ruta Lee	Jesse White
Robert Emhardt	Frances Bavier
Dabbs Greer	Tol Avery
Al Checco	Jane Dulo
William Christopher	Maudie Prickett
Willis Bouchey	Burt Mustin
George Lindsey	Jackie Joseph
Charles Aidman	Trevor Bardette
Jamie Farr	Denver Pyle
Enid Markey	Jerry Van Dyke
Herb Vigran	Sheldon Leonard
Parley Baer	Hal Smith
Joyce Jameson	Lewis Charles
Andy Griffith	

"Gomer" was produced by "Andy" alumni Sheldon Leonard and Aaron Ruben and was syndicated by Viacom. There were three Mayberry-related "Gomer Pyle" episodes: the first was "A Visit from Cousin Goober," which is self-explanatory; the second was "Opie Joins the Marines," in which Andy and Ronny Howard both appeared; and the third was "A Visit from Aunt Bee," in which Aunt Bee came to Camp Henderson to blast Sgt. Carter for belittling Gomer on a radio program which she just happened to hear.

"GRAND THEFT AUTO" Ron Howard's first directorial attempt. He also starred in and co-wrote the film with his father, Rance Howard.

"GUNG HO" Director Ron Howard's comedy about the culture shock that occurs when Japanese auto workers take over a Philadelphia car plant.

"HAPPY DAYS" Ron Howard's successful sitcom after "The Andy Griffith Show."

"HEADMASTER" Aaron Ruben-produced CBS series starring Andy Griffith. This was Andy's first venture back into weekly TV after leaving "The Andy Griffith Show." It was cancelled after thirteen episodes.

"HEE HAW" George "Goober" Lindsey has been a regular on "Hee Haw" since "Mayberry R.F.D." went off the air.

THE HORN The Santa Monica nightclub where Andy Griffith saw Jim Nabors perform. This prompted Andy to offer Jim a job. (See the Jim Nabors interview in this book)

JASPER, ALABAMA George Lindsey's birthplace.

JIM NABORS' FAVORITE EPISODE: "Citizen's Arrest" (106F/B). Don Knotts gave this information on "The Andy Griffith Show Silver Anniversary Special" broadcast on October 3, 1985, on cable station WTBS. Jim Nabors gave this information to the author in the interview section of this book. The special celebrated the "The Andy Griffith Show"'s twenty-fifth anniversary on the air. The first broadcast of "The Andy Griffith Show" was on October 3, 1960.

RICHARD O. LINKE Andy Griffith's friend, manager, and partner for over twenty-five years.

MACADAMIA NUTS Jim Nabors owns and operates a macadamia nut farm in Maui, Hawaii.

"MAYBERRY, R.F.D." The sequel to "The Andy Griffith Show." It ran on CBS from September 23, 1968, to September 6, 1971. There were seventy-eight episodes, all in color, and it ran on Monday nights from 9:00-9:30. The show starred Ken Berry as Sam Jones, Frances Bavier as Aunt Bee Taylor (although she left the show in 1970), Arlene Golonka as Millie Swanson, George Lindsey as Goober Pyle, Jack Dodson as Howard Sprague, Paul Hartman as Emmett Clark, and Buddy Foster as Mike Jones. Andy Griffith was the producer of "Mayberry, R.F.D.," and Metromedia was the syndication company that handled the show. A number of the "Mayberry, R.F.D." episodes were similar in theme to episodes of "The Andy Griffith Show." The most notable are as follows:

"Andy Griffith Show"/"Mayberry, R.F.D."

Opie's Newspaper/The Copy Machine
Aunt Bee and the Lecturer/Aunt Bee's
    Cruise
Helen the Authoress/Howard the Poet
Aunt Bee Takes A Job/Millie the Secretary
Wyatt Earp/Palm Springs Cowboy
Only a Rose/The Mynah Bird
Aunt Bee the Crusader/The Mayberry Road
The Pageant/The Mayberry Float
Aunt Bee's Crowning Glory/Hair
A Warning From Warren/Millie's Dream

Floyd the Gay Deceiver/Goober the
    Housekeeper
Big Brothers/Howard the Dream Spinner
Barney and the Cave Rescue/Goober the
    Hero
The Wedding/Howard the Swinger
Aunt Bee Learns to Drive/Mike's Car

(Also, there was actually an episode called "The New Housekeeper"!) A number of actors, writers and directors crossed over from "The Andy Griffith Show" to "Mayberry, R.F.D." Among them were (roughly in order of their appearance:)

ACTORS:
Hope Summers
Douglas Fowley
Mary Lansing
Ruta Lee

WRITERS:
Dick Bensfield & Perry Grant
Joseph Bonaduce
Bob Ross
Charles Stewart

Two other interesting things happened in "Mayberry, R.F.D." worth noting: First, of course, was the marriage of Andy Taylor to Helen Crump. They then moved away to Cleveland, Ohio, where Andy spent twenty years working as a postal inspector. The second momentous event was the birth of Andy and Helen's son, Andy Jr., whom we have never seen. In "Return to Mayberry," he wasn't even mentioned, although by that time he was almost eighteen years old. Andy Taylor, Jr. was born in the "Mayberry, R.F.D." episode entitled "Andy's Baby." It was written by Roswell Rogers and the plot revolved around a conflict between Emmett, Goober, and Howard. They all wanted to be the godfather of Andy Jr.

MAYBERRY'S ZIP CODE Mayberry's Zip Code was 27599. We learned this from a segment on "Return to Mayberry" broadcast on WTBS's "Good News" program. The segment was called "Re-Taylored." It was run on a Sunday prior to the NBC broadcast of "Return."

MOLINE, ILLINOIS Ken Berry's birthplace.

MORGANTOWN, WEST VIRGINIA Don Knotts's birthplace.

MT. AIRY, NORTH CAROLINA Andy —father of Mayberry—Griffith's birthplace.

NBC The network that broadcast "Return to Mayberry." The movie was up against the miniseries "Dream West" with Richard Chamberlain, and the James Bond movie "The Man with the Golden Gun." It blew them both out of the water. "Return" pulled a 34.6 Nielsen rating and a gigantic 53 share. This means that more than 28.3 million households—over 55 million people—returned to Mayberry on Sunday, April 13, 1986. The show ran at 9:00 P.M. EST and was the second highest rated show of the week. Out of seventy-one prime time programs run that week, only "The Cosby Show" was able to outpace Andy and his gang.

"THE NEW ANDY GRIFFITH SHOW" The retitled "Headmaster." It, too, was a failure for Andy Griffith and was cancelled after thirteen episodes.

"NO TIME FOR SERGEANTS" Pre-Mayberry Andy Griffith movie, with Andy starring as Will Stockdale. It was originally done on broadway and was a huge success when brought to the screen. Don Knotts also appeared in the film.

"OPIE GOES TO WASHINGTON" Fictitious movie Ron Howard thought about making. He revealed this in an interview with the "New York Daily News."

"OPIE SCORES" Fictitious movie Ron Howard thought about making after he saw how much money "Deep Throat" made. He revealed this in an interview with the "New York Daily News."

ROANOKE ISLAND, NORTH CAROLINA Andy Griffith has a home there.

"SPLASH" Director Ron Howard's fish tale. Man meets mermaid and true love swims instead of sinks.

SYLACAUGA, ALABAMA Jim Nabors's birthplace.

TED TURNER Owner of WTBS, the "Superstation," one of the strongest advocates of the Mayberry experience and a broadcaster of the reruns since the early seventies.

27599 Mayberry's Zip Code.

VIACOM The syndication company that controls sales and distribution of "The Andy Griffith Show" tapes. According to a recent "Variety," the reruns are sold—for those stations interested in taking them on—for cash. Currently, between eighty and a hundred markets are broadcasting "The Andy Griffith Show" reruns. For instance, in my area—served by Storer cable—we were able to watch Andy and his gang four times a day at one point!

"THE WANDERING MINSTREL" An unfilmed "Andy Griffith Show" episode written by Harvey Bullock and Ray Saffian Allen. The only place any information has ever appeared about this script has been in Richard Kelly's masterful book, *The Andy Griffith Show*. What is fascinating about this script for the fan is the abundance of new characters—many of whom seem to have been related to other residents of Mayberry, but who never appeared in any episode other than this one. For the record, here is a compilation of Mayberry data from "The Wandering Minstrel."

AUNT BEE'S DIET In this episode, Aunt Bee actually admitted she was on a diet. Peggy offered her a candy and she replied "Gracious no. They're delicious, but I have to think of my diet." She ate them anyway.

BERT Store owner who sold soda from a cooler in front of his store.

PEGGY CARTWRIGHT Andy's girlfriend.

LYLE FENTON Mayberry postal clerk. He would give Wally money for stamps. He usually took the money out of his own pocket.

RUSTY FINCH One of the children who greeted Wally Jordan on his return to Mayberry. Wally remembered Rusty had wanted a bike for his birthday.

GEORGE Owner of a Mayberry clothing store. He was a no-nonsense businessman. He gave Wally Jordan a job, but eventually realized that perhaps Wally's carefree ways were better—for everyone.

WALLY JORDAN The "wandering minstrel." A guitar-playing pied piper who would travel the countryside, playing the guitar and supplying the local kids with lollipops. When Wally visited Mayberry, Andy thought he'd do a good thing and get him a regular job. It didn't work out, though. Wally—the perfect free spirit—became quick with his tongue and plainly unhappy. Everyone—including Andy—realized that Wally didn't belong behind a counter in a store and at the end of the episode he took to the road with his new guitar and rejuvenated spirit.

LILA-BELLE Wally Jordan's beat-up old guitar. After receiving a new one from the Mayberry Music Store, he gave Lila to George, who was astonished to learn he could play "Home on the Range" on it.

MAYBERRY MUSIC STORE Mayberry business that hired Wally as their "advertising manager." They gave him a new guitar and he agreed to display the back of it when he wasn't playing it. The back was painted "Shop at The Mayberry Music Store."

MUDVILLE Town Wally pretended he was in to tease the Mayberry children.

GINNY PARKER One of the children who greeted Wally Jordan on his return to Mayberry. Wally remembered that Ginny had a black cat, and he predicted—correctly—that the cat would have six kittens. Wally told Ginny she'd have to stop calling the cat "Walter."

SNUFFY PIERSON One of the children who greeted Wally Jordan on his return to Mayberry. Wally remembered Snuffy never got to school on time.

POKEY CORNERS Town Wally pretended he was in to tease the Mayberry children.

DENNY SARGENT One of the children who greeted Wally Jordan on his return to Mayberry. Wally remembered Denny had lost a tooth.

WIDOW SCULLY A friend of Wally's. He stopped by to see her on his return to Mayberry. She suffered "with her sciatic."

WALTER Ginny Parker's female cat. After Walter had six kittens, Wally Jordan reminded Ginny she'd have to stop calling the cat "Walter."

"WHAT IT WAS WAS FOOTBALL" Monologue written and performed by Andy Griffith in his early "pre-Andy Taylor" days. This piece was recorded on an album by Andy and also performed—among other places—on "The Ed Sullivan Show."

"WHAT MAYBERRY MEANS TO ME" Poem recited by George "Goober" Lindsey at the conclusion of his nightclub stand-up comedy routine.

WTBS The Superstation, broadcasting out of Atlanta, Georgia by satellite to cable stations all over the country. WTBS has shown reruns of "The Andy Griffith Show" continuously since the early seventies. The station is owned by Ted Turner, a firm believer in the Mayberry experience. The reruns of the show consistently win their time slot for Ted.

Mayberry
My Hometown

Part III
Going Home to Mayberry:
A Look at the "Return"

"You know,
you people that live in the small towns,
you really got it made."

Barney Fife
"The Return Of Barney Fife"

RETURNING TO MAYBERRY
THE STORY OF THE ULTIMATE REUNION

A look at the two-hour NBC TV-movie
"Return to Mayberry"
broadcast Sunday, April 13, 1986, at 9:00 P.M.

I wasn't sure how I felt about a "Return to Mayberry."

Initially I had the same kind of reaction to announcements for the show that I did before I saw the first "Star Trek" movie: excitement and trepidation. Will they be able to pull it off? Will this return to Mayberry shatter old dreams and memories? Or will the magic be recreated now—twenty-five years later—with all of the sparkle and romance of the early days? The whole problem with returning to Mayberry for the fan is that most of us have never left. We call Mayberry our home and we visit it all the time.

THE PRELIMINARIES

Production on the movie started early Monday morning, February 10, 1986, and just about everyone was there. The cast included Andy Griffith, Don Knotts, Ron Howard, Jack Dodson, Aneta Corsaut, Betty Lynn, Jim Nabors, George Lindsey, Hal Smith, Denver Pyle, Maggie Peterson, The Dillards, and Howard Morris. The script was by Harvey Bullock and Everett Greenbaum, and the director was Bob Sweeney.

Two "regular" members of the cast were not included in the script: Elinor Donahue and Ken Berry. Howard McNear, Paul Hartman, and Hope Summers had all died some years before, and Frances Bavier was reported to be too ill to appear.

The advance word was staggering. This was big news that had a big interest. Here's a list of the broadcasts and print media which I saw, a veritable flood of pre-"Return" hoopla spread over three months:

ANDY ON LETTERMAN
("Late Night With David Letterman," NBC)

ANDY ON "HOUR MAGAZINE"
(Hosted by Gary Collins)

"THE SECOND TIME AROUND":
MAYBERRY ON "20/20"
(Barbara Walters & Dick Schaap, Feb. 20, 1986)

CNN'S "SHOWBIZ TODAY":
A VISIT TO MAYBERRY (2 Parts)
(Jim Thomas, Lee Leonard & Liz Wickersham,
Feb. 20-21, 1986)

WTBS'S "GOOD NEWS": "RE-TAYLORED"

(Liz Wickersham & Chuck Roberts)

"TIME" IN MAYBERRY
(*Time* magazine's "Back to the Time Warp")

"THE ENQUIRER" LOOKS AT DON KNOTTS
(David Wright)

"THE STAR" VISITS MAYBERRY
(Paul Vandenberg)

"ET" "RTM"
("Entertainment Tonight" with Mary Hart &
Dick Shoemaker, Mar. 5, 1986)

"LOOK WHAT HAPPENED TO
THE BOY NEXT DOOR":
"20/20" VISITS RON HOWARD
(Barbara Walters, Mar. 27, 1986)

"PM MAGAZINE" HOSTS A "MAYBERRY REUNION"
(Syndicated TV show)

"IN MAYBERRY, YOU CAN GO HOME AGAIN":
"TV GUIDE" VISITS MAYBERRY
(Betty Goodwin, Mar. 27, 1986)

"PEOPLE MAGAZINE" GOES HOME TO MAYBERRY
(Jane Hall, "Going Home to Mayberry," Apr. 14, 1986)

ANDY, BARNEY, AND GOMER VISIT
BRYANT & JANE
("Today" show appearance, April 11, 1986)

"SHOWBIZ TODAY": A TALK WITH ANDY GRIFFITH
(Cheryl Washington, CNN)

NBC ran a number of different spots promoting "Return to Mayberry," and the most common one was a short piece done in rhyme: "Andy Griffith's back. Opie's back, and Barney, too. With Gomer and Goober and Thelma Lou. They're all back for all new laughs in America's hometown. And they'll shoot the works when they 'Return to Mayberry.' A World Premiere movie tomorrow."

Even "Saturday Night Live" acknowledged our hometown. In the "Weekend Update" segment of the April 12, 1986 show, "anchorman" Dennis Miller said the following:

"Tomorrow night NBC will present 'Return to Mayberry,' a made-for-TV movie that pays a visit to present-day Mayberry and all of its delightful citizens. Boy, hard to believe that Gomer and Goober are still pumpin' gas, huh? These two guys made Heckyl and Jeckyl look like brain surgeons."

A NEW CHAPTER

What was it like to "Return to Mayberry"? It was like going home. A radically changed home, perhaps, but home nonetheless.

There were strangers living in the Taylor house and sitting on the Taylor front porch. Main Street, Mayberry, was almost unrecognizable, and the coziness of the town center had been replaced with a wide two-lane street that had a flagpole smack dab in the center.

Otis would never again let himself in and out of the Mayberry jail, and even though the window on the shop read "Emmett's Fix-it Shop," someone else was running that, too.

The newspaper's name had been changed, as well as the squad car's license plate number.

Barney had been away for twenty years, living all that time—if you can believe it—in the Raleigh YMCA.

And most importantly, our Aunt Bee was dead.

But everyone returned to Mayberry, and that's really all that counts.

The show got a whopping 53 share in the Nielsens. That means that almost half of the TV sets in America returned to Mayberry on Sunday, April 13, 1986. The only show that beat it nationally was "The Cosby Show."

So, what else did we learn about our hometown from "Return To Mayberry?"

A lot. The show brought back the entire history of our hometown, some details of which were sleeping in the backroom of our minds. And there certainly have been changes in the past twenty years. But a lot has stayed the same. First, the changes.

Andy has moved back to Mayberry with the idea of running for sheriff again. Since he stayed with Opie, we know that he sold the Taylor house when he moved out of state. (I would have liked to have seen Opie stay in that house with his wife, but Opie instead chose a big old rambling hounddog of a house on the outskirts of Mayberry that overlooked fields and gamboling horses.) Opie married a girl named Eunice. Who was Eunice and where did she come from? We're never told, although it's possible that she was a native of Mayberry.

Otis is sober and driving his own ice cream truck, but we're never told what happened with his wife, Rita. We don't know if Rita's still alive.

Gomer came back to Mayberry after the Marines and became partners in the G & G Service Station with his cousin Goober, who appears to have never left.

Howard is still county clerk, still single, and gone totally gray. During the film, he decides to dye his hair in an attempt at snaring Rose, the young Mt. Pilot librarian he happens to fancy. Despite the advance clips, however (especially the ones that show Howard and Rose at the wedding reception), we are never shown Rose during the movie. Likewise the scenes where Gomer sings "Because" at Barney and Thelma Lou's wedding: those scenes were simply eliminated.

But probably the saddest development was the disclosure of the death of Aunt Bee. Sometime between the end of "Mayberry, RFD," and "Return To Mayberry" Aunt Bee went to that great Mayberry in the sky. Despite her having been born in West Virginia, Bee Taylor was buried in

Mayberry, a fitting final resting spot for one of Mayberry's proudest citizens. It's likely that Andy and Helen came back to Mayberry for the funeral, although we don't know if Opie was running the paper at the time of her death. Even if he was, it's unlikely that he would have written her obituary.

There were a couple of problems with the plot of "Return To Mayberry." Originally, I think the "Mayberry Monster" was supposed to have been the doing of the other candidate for sheriff, Ben Woods. The way the movie ended up, though, it seemed as though it was all Wally Butler's doing. The movie made it seem as though Butler wanted only to stimulate tourist interest in the monster, thus increasing business at his restaurant and new sixteen-unit motel. (In fact, the article in "Time" magazine actually said that the monster was planted by another "sheriff-hopeful.") I think a scene where Butler and Woods discussed the race and then ended it off with a wink or some other kind of indication that they were in cahoots would have clarified a weak point in the script. The final version of the movie didn't really give enough motive to Butler. The old "Andy Griffith Show" way would have been for Woods to promise something to Butler, either in the form of a zoning favor or a tax break if he got elected, thereby motivating Butler to discredit Barney and get Woods elected. But I'd bet that that was in the script originally, and that the editing room kind of confused things. The plot as I have laid it out is quintessential Bullock-Greenbaum. Nonetheless, as it appeared, the film still entertained and showed us Mayberry today, and we are all the better for its appearance.

FINAL NOTE

I'd like to use these last few lines to offer a personal thank you to Andy Griffith.

Andy has given us a place and a time that has a magic, a charm, and a beauty that will never die.

"Return to Mayberry" was not *War and Peace*, nor was it ever meant to be.

But the truth is that there is value and, yes, importance in the simple honest things of day-to-day life, and the town of Mayberry is one of the countless little hometowns that dot all of America, where people are born, grow up, work, die, and are buried—all within two miles of their father's and their grandfathers' birthplaces.

We should all be thankful such places exist, and we should all be thankful that there are people like Andy Griffith (and everyone who worked with him) who feel a need to show the rest of us just what real living is all about.

After all, what can you show me from this fast-paced, hi tech, brave new world that can compare with sitting on Andy's front porch around eight on a Mayberry spring evening, sipping a lemonade and listening to the crickets?

Search for your spiritual hometown, and when you find it, embrace it and revel in it.

I know I've found mine.

186

"RETURN TO MAYBERRY" ENTRIES

"ACTING SHERIFF" Since Sheriff Patterson had died, Barney had been acting sheriff of Mayberry.

ANDY'S CANDIDACY FOR SHERIFF After Andy heard that Barney was running for sheriff, he cancelled his own plans to run. As he put it, "Barney hasn't had too many high spots these last years. Everybody deserves one. This may be his big one. I won't stand in his way." Opie tried to convince Andy to run: "Everybody here in town—they remember you and they like you." He told Andy he was "the most qualified man for the job," but he couldn't convince him to run against his former deputy.

ANDY'S SPEECH At Barney and Thelma Lou's wedding reception, Andy made the following speech:

"You know, there's a feeling around here that these two were always meant to be married. And I guess just like it was always in the cards for Helen and me to come home. And for Barney to be my deputy again. But not everybody's moving in. Opie and his little family will be leaving for a big new job out of state."
Eunice: "If you like, Barney, we'll leave our crib for you two!"
Barney: "Well, what in the world would we want with a . . . ."
Andy: But I wouldn't be surprised at all if someday they'll be coming back. Yeah, there's something about Mayberry and Mayberry folk that never leaves you. No matter where life takes you, you always carry in your heart the memories of old times and old friends. So, here's to all of us. Old friends!"

AUNT BEE'S LAST WORDS When Andy went to put flowers on Aunt Bee's grave, he heard her voice in his memories. In the most touching and sad scene of the movie, we hear Aunt Bee say the following:

"You know, Andy, all I ever wanted was for you and Opie to be good citizens and to treat people right. And I know you will. You two boys are the button on the cap of kindness. Oh, and remember: one green vegetable every day. One hot meal. Six glasses of water. And it's asleep before midnight that's important."

We do indeed miss that wonderful lady.

BARNEY AND THELMA LOU'S BEST MAN Andy Taylor. He almost got the wedding ring stuck on his finger during the ceremony.

BARNEY'S ELECTION SIGN "Vote Fife for Sheriff." They were everywhere.

BARNEY'S SPEECH At Barney's election rally, he made the following speech:

"I wanna thank you all for coming. Thank you. Tomorrow you're gonna vote for the new sheriff of Mayberry. Now, what qualities do you want in your next sheriff? How about a man who's had fifteen years of service right here in this town? And background? How about a man who's a native born-and-bred Mayberrian? A man who's a firm and fair friend to one and all, man and woman, child, rich and poor, young and old irregardless. So tomorrow, when you go into that booth and close the curtain, I'm asking you—and I found out only five minutes ago that he's willing to be sheriff—I'm asking you to write in the name Andy Taylor. Because that's exactly what I'm gonna do."

Andy won the election and Barney once again became his deputy.

"THE BASTION OF DEFENSE" The name Wally Butler called Barney. He also told him he liked "the cut of [his] jib."

BEN WOODS' SIGN "Vote for Ben Woods Sheriff."

"THE BINGHAMPTON POST" New York state newspaper that offered a job to Opie. Opie accepted the job and left Mayberry. As Opie put it: "Bigger paper, bigger town, more responsibility, more money."

BRISCOE'S THIRD BORN Charlene.

BUICK Andy Taylor's car. It's license number was 790-VTQ, and as Andy arrived in Mayberry it was "lurching." It needed a new carburetor. Andy adjusted it and it ran well enough to get him around for a few days. The carburetor finally gave out just as Andy was driving Opie's wife, Eunice, to the hospital to deliver her and Opie's son. Andy delivered the baby in the back seat of the Buick.

OLD MAN SAM BURROWS He lived up by Myer's Lake. He was missing some chickens. (They were stolen by Ernest T.)

BURSITIS Barney had a touch in his left shoulder.

WALLY BUTLER Young man who bought the old Mayberry restaurant, "The Shanghai Garden," and converted it to a Continental menu, changing the name to "Butler's Pantry & Inn." He also put up a sixteen-unit motel in Mayberry. It was Butler who masterminded the "Mayberry Monster" scam. He figured it would bring tourists to Mayberry and, as a result, to his restaurant and motel. Butler gave Ernest T. Bass an old frock coat he had worn in college in a show. His name was in it. Andy read the name and figured out that the monster was Butler's doing. It wasn't said if Butler was Mayberry born. Based on the ending of "Return to Mayberry," it seemed likely that he would be moving away.

BUTLER'S CRIMES After Andy caught Wally Butler and Ernest T., he detailed Butler's offenses: the scam with the dragon was a misdemeanor, being in the shed was trespassing, and persuading Ernest T. to steal the chickens and dogs was probably—in Mayberry—considered grand theft.

BUTLER'S PANTRY & INN The former Shanghai Garden restaurant. Wally Butler bought it and changed the menu to Continental.

CARDINAL TRAILS BUS STOP The bus stop where Andy picked up Helen upon her arrival in Mayberry.

CHANNEL 10 Siler City TV station. Lloyd Fox was one of their reporters. Ralph was either a camerman or a soundman.

CHICKEN AND DUMPLINGS Charlene Darling and her family brought Barney and Thelma Lou a dish of chicken and dumplings for their reception, assuring the sheriff that the chicken "was one of ours."

"CHICKEN THIEVDERS" Ernest T. was very proud of the "professionalism" of his family: "My daddy was a chicken thievder, my granddaddy was a chicken thievder. They was the best in this part of the state."

CLEVELAND, OHIO Andy and Helen had been living there for the twenty years prior to their return to Mayberry. They had an apartment and Andy worked as a postal inspector.

CONTINENTAL The new menu at Butler's Pantry & Inn.

"THE COUNTY COURIER EXPRESS" The Mayberry newspaper, successor to the "Mayberry Gazette." Opie Taylor was publisher and editor, but it's unclear whether he owned it. At one point, he referred to his position as a "job." It's likely that whoever bought the "Mayberry Gazette" changed its name and hired Opie to run it when he came back home after college. In addition to home delivery, the "Courier Express" was sold from boxes scattered throughout Mayberry. Howard Sprague worked part-time for Opie as a photographer.

COURTHOUSE LAYOUT We don't know if there were any major changes made in the courthouse over the past twenty-five years since all we saw of it during "Return to Mayberry" was the corner of the building with Andy's desk in it. We never got to see the cells.

CUBAN SUNSET The hair color Howard used to dye his hair. It turned his hair red.

"CURSE OF THE FIFE" Barney's quick temper.

"THE CUT OF YOUR JIB" Wally Butler liked Barney's.

"THE DOGGONES" When Gomer and Goober first saw Andy Taylor pull into their garage after twenty years, Goober greeted him with "Well, doggone!" Gomer then countered with "Double doggone." Goober topped him with "Double double doggone!"

DENNY DOODLENUT The character created by Barney for his bimonthly traffic seminars for the school children. His routine went like this:

Kids: "Denny, Denny, Come out Denny! Denny, Denny, we'll give you a candy!"
Barney: "I can't! I've got a stomach-ache!"
Kids: "What did you have for lunch?"
Barney: "I had a hundred ginger snaps and a gallon of chocolate milk. I'm Denny Doodlenut and I'm gonna cross the street. What do I do first?"
Kids: "Look both ways!"
Barney: "Not me. I'm gonna cross this here street and the first thing I'm gonna do is step right off the curb."
Kids: "No! No! No!"
Barney: "Oh, that's right. Before taking a step I'm supposed to look up."
Kids: "No! No! No!"
Barney: "I'm supposed to look down?"
Kids: "No! No! No!"
Barney: "Well, I'm Denny Doodlenut so I'm not gonna bother looking at all!"

Barney then faked being hit by a car and the kids would clap.

"DOOLEY" Song Andy performed with the Darlings.

DUTCH CHOCOLATE BUBBLEGUM One of Otis Campbell's "flavors of the week."

THE ELBERT BOY The boy Barney wanted to use in his attempt to snare the Mayberry Monster, but couldn't. The boy had "that fungus on his back."

UNCLE EPHRAM Thelma Lou's uncle. He was buried in the same cemetery as Aunt Bee. Thelma Lou was back in Mayberry to put a new stone on Uncle Ephram's grave. Andy said the stone (which we didn't see) was "modern." "Well, you know Uncle Ephram," responded Thelma Lou. "He was the first one in town to have a convertible."

ERNEST T. BASS'S POEM When he first saw Sheriff Taylor, he recited the following:

"Sheriff Andy's back in town
The sun goes up
The pants fall down
Your hair was brown
Now it's gray
Make that monster go away."

This poem later clued Andy as to who was behind the "Mayberry Monster."

ERNIE'S OASIS Mayberry nightspot. Barney wanted to go there after dinner and "hoist a couple of cold Riunites."

ESKIMO CHEESE WHIP One of Otis Campbell's products.

"EVERYBODY KNOWS EVERYTHING!" The remark Thelma Lou made when Andy told her he knew that her differential was greased.

FLAMENCO BROWN The second hair color Howard used to dye his hair in an attempt to win Rose, the librarian.

FOUR CHICKENS Juanita's sister had four chickens stolen by Ernest T. Bass. She lived up by Myer's Lake.

LLOYD FOX The reporter who interviewed Barney about the monster. He worked for Channel 10 out of Siler City. At one point during the interview, Barney mistakenly called him "Floyd."

"THE FREESEBORO DAILY RECORD" Newspaper Barney spoke to regarding the "Mayberry Monster."

"THE FRENCH RIVIAREA" Barney said that if somebody got a hold of the carbons to his charge slips, they could be skinny-dipping on the "French Riviarea" while he was sleeping. By tearing up (and burning) the carbons, he was "nipping white collar crime in the bud."

A FROZEN CHICKEN The bait Barney used to snare the "Mayberry Monster."

G & G GARAGE The filling station that had formerly been Goober's Service, and before that, Wally's

Service, and before that probably George Safferly's Service. When Gomer returned to Mayberry from the Marines, he bought into Goober's Service and became partners with his cousin. Opie and Eunice Taylor's son was born in their lot in the back seat of Andy's Buick.

GAS SIGN At the G & G Service Station: "Gas Wars Low Prices." On the back of this sign, Goober and Gomer had hung Barney's election poster.

"GRAND-DAD, GRAND-DAD, GRAND-DAD" Goober's teasing way of kidding Andy about becoming a grandfather.

HUBACHER'S HARDWARE Main Street business located three doors down from the courthouse. It appears to have taken over the location of the Mayberry Hotel. Apparently the Hubacher brothers went straight when they got out of prison. Andy and Barney always did like Elmer ("he's the baby") and his two brothers.

"IDLE TALK ABOUT SOME LONG-AGO SONGBIRDS" When Opie was undecided about whether or not to take the job at the "Binghampton Post," he and Andy had the following conversation:

> Opie: "Well, what shall I do? Shall I leave Mayberry? You know, I like this job a lot. It's running smooth. I can take off fishing when I want. And I've got all my friends here. Real good friends, too. We have a nice house. And I can't imagine a better place to raise a family.
> Andy: "Mayberry's special."
> Opie: "Well, even you wanna come back, Paw."
> Andy: "Well, remember I also left."
> Opie: "Eunice says do whatever'll make me happy, but I don't know. What do you think, Paw? Am I better off just stayin' put?"
> Andy: "Something like that nobody else can tell you, son. A big thing like that . . . you have to call it. You know sometimes I think about things. You remember those baby songbirds you raised?"
> Opie: "Oh yeah. You got me that big old white cage. Yeah, I remember that."
> Andy: "You remember when they were no longer babies, it was a great temptation to keep 'em. Remember?"
> Opie: "Yeah."
> Andy: "Remember what you did?"
> Opie: "I turned 'em loose."
> Andy: "Yeah. You decided the time had come that they were no longer babies. Time to let 'em spread their wings, see how high and how far they could fly."
> Opie: "So, then you're telling me . . ."
> Andy: "No, no, no, no. Just some idle talk about some long-ago songbirds. As for your problem . . . sleep on it, son."

"INTENTIONAL LOCAL RESIDENCY" One of the forms Andy had to file in order to run for sheriff in Mayberry. Another was his original birth certificate. Howard had them all ready when Andy came back to town, but when the former sheriff heard that Barney was running, he cancelled his candidacy.

"IS IT OR ISN'T IT?" The headline of the article Opie ran in the "Courier" with Goober's "Monster picture."

ITALIAN SLUDGE One of Otis Campbell's products.

"A JAZZED-UP TWO-TONE" Thelma Lou's car, according to Goober. It had the "driest differential" Goober'd ever laid his eyes on.

JUANITA Barney's old flame. When Andy returned to Mayberry, Barney was on the phone with Juanita. He was singing "Juanita" to her.

JUANITA'S SISTER Four of her chickens were stolen. She lived up by Myer's Lake.

"JUST GAS AND GO" Thelma Lou, according to Goober.

RICHARD KELLY The painter of the following sign:

> WARNING
> UNIDENTIFIED LARGE PREDATOR
> NO: SWIMMING
> BOATING
> FISHING
> B. FIFE, SHERIFF (ACTING)

The sign was painted by Richard Kelly, "who painted our warning sign despite painful arthritis in two knuckles." (Note: Richard Kelly is also the name of the author of the very first book about "The Andy Griffith Show" entitled, appropriately, *The Andy Griffith Show*.)

"THE LACS, THE PETS" Barney's exercise routine at the Y in Raleigh built up his "lacs" and his "pets."

"LURCHING" How Andy described his bad carburetor problem to Gomer and Goober.

"LURKING" All first babies like to lurk, according to Sheriff Taylor. He gave Opie this info to calm his worries about Eunice and the baby.

THE MACHINERY ROOM The room where Ernest T. hoisted the "Mayberry Monster" in and out of the lake.

THE MACON BUS The bus that brought Helen Taylor to Mayberry.

MAIN STREET The center of Mayberry almost completely changed in the past twenty years. There was now a flagpole diagonally across from the courthouse, and the street was at least twice as wide as it had originally been. Directly across from the jail was the new town newspaper, "The County Courier Express." Three doors down from the courthouse was Hubacher Hardware. The Mayberry Feed and Grain had expanded and moved when the streets were widened. Most importantly, though, the bench in front of the courthouse had not been moved.

MAYBERRY MANOR The new convalescent home that was being built in Mayberry across the street from the G & G Garage.

"THE MAYBERRY MONSTER" Also called "The Monster of the Lake." The "Mayberry Monster" was actually just a pink dragon that had once graced the sign of the old Shanghai Garden Restaurant. When Wally Butler bought the place, he changed the name to Butler's Pantry & Inn and came up with the scheme of using Ernest T. Bass to raise and lower the old dragon in and out of Myer's Lake. He figured this would attract tourists who would then patronize his restaurant and new sixteen-unit motel. Andy figured it out when he saw an old picture of the Shanghai Garden. The monster—as described by Otis—had "a great big head, horns like that, tongue hanging out. It was horrible!"

THE MAYBERRY SIGN As Andy drove into Mayberry he saw a sign that said "Mayberry 5" with an arrow, and "Mt. Pilot 10" with an arrow pointing the other way.

"THE MONSTER PICTURE" The snapshot Gomer took of Goober that showed Goober holding a fish, as well as the monster in the background coming up out of the lake.

MYER'S LAKE The first thing Andy saw as he drove back into Mayberry after being away for twenty years. He got out of his car and, as he stood there looking at the lake, he remembered walking down there with Opie. Myer's was also where "The Mayberry Monster" first reared its ugly head, thanks to Wally Butler and Ernest T. Bass. We found out in "Return to Mayberry" that Myer's Lake was nothing more than "a flooded out old stone quarry."

MYER'S STONE QUARRY Sign on the shore of the lake.

"THE OLD DAYS" After Thelma Lou saw Barney for the first time, she asked him, "Do you ever think about the old days?" Barney answered, "A lot." Enough said.

"OLD HOME WEEK" Gomer described the week Andy returned to Mayberry as "like Old Home Week" when he heard that Helen would soon be arriving. Thelma Lou was already in town. She had come to change the headstone on her Uncle Ephram's grave.

OPIE'S GRAHAM CRACKERS Gomer remembered that Opie used to have to stand on a phone book to eat his graham crackers over the sink.

OTIS CAMPBELL'S ICE CREAM Otis's business after he quit drinking. He drove his own truck and usually sang over the loudspeaker, "I scream, you scream, we all scream for ice cream." He usually sold a "flavor of the week." Two of them were "White Chocolate Bubblegum" and "Dutch Chocolate Bubblegum." Other items he carried were "Peanutty Pops," "Sidewalk Gobble-Ups," "Italian Sludge," and "Eskimo Cheese Whips."

SHERIFF PATTERSON The sheriff of Mayberry after Andy Taylor. Barney had been acting sheriff since Patterson's death, which occurred sometime before Andy got to town.

PEANUTTY POPS One of Otis Campbell's products.

EDDIE PETERSON He was dropping depth charges in the lake in an attempt at locating the monster.

"PIG ON A PIANO" Song Ernest T. danced to as entertainment for Charlene.

THE PREACHER The man who married Barney and Thelma Lou. (He was played by Rance Howard, Ron and Clint's father.)

VIRGIL PRODDY Mayberry man who called Barney to tell him some of his animals were missing, and that there were huge claw prints in his yard. Barney immediately went back on the air with Lloyd Fox and said, "We do have a menace and he's on a feeding frenzy!"

RAG-4 The first four digits of Ben Woods' license plate number. (These were the only digits visible.)

"THE RALEIGH OBSERVER" Newspaper sold out of a box that sat next to one for the "County Courier Express."

RALPH Either the cameraman or soundman for Channel 10 out of Siler City.

ROSE Mt. Pilot librarian. Howard was sweet on her and died his hair three times to make himself look younger for her. We never got to see Rose.

S-9437 The license number of the squad car. It wasn't said why it was changed from JL-327.

SALT-AND-PEPPER SUIT Barney still had his original salt-and-pepper suit twenty years later. He said that if you took care of them they lasted forever.

790-VTQ The license plate number of Andy Taylor's Buick.

SHANGHAI GARDEN RESTAURANT Mayberry restaurant. During the twenty-year span Andy was away, Wally Butler bought the place, changed the menu to Continental, and changed the name to "Butler's Pantry & Inn." When it was the Shanghai Garden, it had a pink dragon on its sign. That dragon became the "Mayberry Monster." Andy and Barney reminisced about taking Skippy and Daphne—the "fun girls"—to the Garden a long time ago. Barney said that Skippy once danced with him so close that she bent his badge. (This "bending of the badge" seems to have taken place sometime prior to the episode "Suppose Andy Gets Sick" (232F/233B). In that episode, Andy comes down with the flu and (very) reluctantly agrees to reactivate Goober's auxiliary deputy status for the brief time in which he was to be out sick. After Goober insists on being sworn in, which Andy does by raising his hand and saying "You're a deputy," the gas jockey asks for a badge. Andy tells him to take the one in the desk at the courthouse. Goober—very disappointedly—reminds Andy that that one was bent. Apparently, this is the renowned "bent badge" of Mayberry lore. In fact, since we now know that Skippy did the bending while Barney was doing the wearing, we can conclude that this badge belonged to none other than the legendary Barney Fife!)

SIDEWALK GOBBLE-UPS One of Otis Campbell's products.

SOLID WASTE PUMP STATION Mayberry finally had one. Howard covered the ribbon-cutting for the paper. The ribbon was cut by a registered nurse, and the construction of the plant convinced Andy that "Mayberry's moving right along."

"SUGARHEART" The affectionate nickname Ernest T. called Charlene Darling.

EUNICE TAYLOR Opie's wife. It wasn't said if she was a born-and-bred Mayberrian, but it's likely. (Although he could have met her at college and brought her back to live in Mayberry.) Eunice gave birth to Opie's unnamed son during "Return to Mayberry."

PAPA TAYLOR The name Opie's wife, Eunice, called Andy.

TEN PERCENT The tip Barney always left: "Easy arithmetic."

THELMA LOU'S SISTER Thelma Lou had an unnamed sister who lived in Mayberry. Thelma Lou stayed with her when she was in town.

DAVIS TICKS Barney camouflaged Davis's rowboat the day he attempted to capture the monster.

TRAFFIC SEMINAR Barney gave one for the school-kids every other week. He played Denny Doodlenut to instruct the kids about traffic safety.

TROLLEY CARS What women are like, according to Barney. "You miss one, so what! There's another along any minute!"

THE TWO CAMPERS Two old men who Barney was afraid would panic when they heard Gomer ranting about the sea monster. Quite the contrary, they looked at Barney as though he were nuts.

UNITED STATES POSTAL INSPECTOR Andy's job after he moved away from Mayberry. He was based in Cleveland, Ohio.

"AN UPWARDLY MOBILE YUPPIE" Barney's self-description.

VISA The card Barney used to pay the tab at Butler's the night the four of them went out. Barney planned on writing it off as a business expense. He said, "I'm entertaining three vice cops from Miami."

THE WARNING SIGN Barney had the following sign painted and put up at Myer's Lake:

WARNING
UNIDENTIFIED LARGE PREDATOR
NO: SWIMMING
BOATING
FISHING
B. FIFE, SHERIFF (ACTING)

The sign was painted by Richard Kelly, "who painted our warning sign despite painful arthritis in two knuckles." (Note: Richard Kelly is also the name of the author of the very first book about "The Andy Griffith Show" entitled *The Andy Griffith Show*.)

"WELCOME SWEET SPRINGTIME" "Good old 14-A." The choral piece Andy and Barney heard the choir rehearsing from Opie's front porch.

WHITE CHOCOLATE BUBBLEGUM One of Otis Campbell's "flavors of the week."

GERALD WHITFIELD Thelma Lou's first husband. Their marriage lasted sixteen months. He made "less than $14,500 per annum take home" according to Barney. They had lived in Jacksonville, and Thelma Lou probably stayed there after their divorce.

BEN WOODS Barney's only opponent for the sheriff's office. Ben was a heavyset guy who, as we heard three times, finished twelfth in his class. He often stooped to insults and smear tactics during his campaign. He said the following over his car loudspeaker during the campaign:

- "Clean up the city government. Get rid of the dead wood in the sheriff's office. Get the job done right. Vote for me. Vote for Ben Woods for sheriff."
- "Citizens of Mayberry. You want a real sheriff in office or some clown chasin' Godzilla 'round Myer's Lake? Vote for me. Vote for Ben Woods for sheriff."
- "A vote for Fife is a vote for foolishness. Elect no-nonsense Ben Woods. Vote for me. Vote for Ben Woods."
- "You had senile Patterson. You got incompetent Fife. Time to vote for dependable Ben Woods. Vote for me. Vote for Ben Woods for sheriff."

"YOU'RE A FED" The way Barney described Andy—the postal inspector—Taylor.

ZENO Mayberry man. Ben Woods handed him some campaign literature.

ZOOLOGY PROFESSOR The man Opie called to find out if it were possible for a prehistoric monster to be living in Myer's Lake. The professor had been teaching for fifteen years.

RETURN
TO MAYBERRY
OPENING CREDITS

RETURN
TO
MAYBERRY

STARRING
ANDY GRIFFITH

RON HOWARD

DON KNOTTS

JIM NABORS

ALSO STARRING
(IN ALPHABETICAL ORDER)

ANETA CORSAUT

JACK DODSON

GEORGE LINDSEY

BETTY LYNN

HOWARD MORRIS

MAGGIE
PETERSON-MANCUSO

DENVER PYLE

HAL SMITH

RODNEY DILLARD
DOUG DILLARD
MITCH JAYNE
DEAN WEBB
AS
THE DARLINGS

MUSIC BY
EARLE HAGEN

EDITED BY
DAVID SOLOMON

PRODUCTION DESIGNER
RAYMOND G. STOREY

DIRECTOR OF PHOTOGRAPHY
RICHARD C. GLOUNER, A.S.C.

PRODUCED BY
ROBIN S. CLARK

WRITTEN BY
HARVEY BULLOCK
&
EVERETT
GREENBAUM

DIRECTED BY
BOB SWEENEY

RETURN TO MAYBERRY

CLOSING CREDITS

EXECUTIVE PRODUCERS
ANDY GRIFFITH
DEAN HARGROVE
RICHARD O. LINKE

ASSOCIATE PRODUCER
DONNA COLABELLA

GUEST STARRING
RICHARD LINEBACK

KARLENE CROCKETT

ALLEN WILLIAMS

PAUL WILLSON

FEATURING
RANCE HOWARD
ROBERT BROYLES
KAREN KNOTTS

CASTING BY
EILEEN KNIGHT, C.S.A.

Production Manager
ROBIN S. CLARK
First Assistant Director
RAY MARSH
Second Assistant Director
NILO OTERO

Art Director
DALE ALLAN PELTON
Costume Designer
PAT WELCH
Make-Up
BOB MILLS
Hair Stylist
ADELE TAYLOR
Property Master
DOMINIC BELMONTE
Set Decorator
GARY J. MORENO

Production Sound Mixer
ROBERT. J. MILLER
Camera Operator
JAMES HOOVER
Gaffer
TOM LINDNER
Key Grip
KENNETH A. ADAMS
Script Supervisor
BARBARA ATKINSON

Special Effects
TECHNIPROPS

Location Manager
KARLENE GALLEGLY
Transportation Coordinator
JAMES ANTUNEZ
Extra Casting
RICK MONTGOMERY
Assistant Art Director
SANDY GETZLER
Women's Costumer
AUDREY TANNENBAUM
Men's Costumer
JESSE J. FIELDS

Production Coordinator
MIRIAM HOLDER JACOBS
Production Controller
AVI LEVY
Production Auditor
DONNA CIPRIANI
Assistant Editor
CARTER DEHAVEN IV
Negative Cutter
DENNIS BROOKINS
Titles and Opticals
HOWARD A. ANDERSON CO.

*SOME HOTEL ACCOMMODATIONS
FURNISHED BY*
THE LOS OLIVOS
GRAND HOTEL
LOCATION SITE FURNISHED BY
THE DANISH COUNTRY INN
Special Thanks to the Town of
LOS OLIVOS, CALIFORNIA

*Re-Recording
And Sound Effects Editorial By*
GLEN GLENN SOUND
Re-Recording Mixers
GARY BOURGEOIS, C.A.S.
NEIL BRODY, C.A.S.
CHRIS CARPENTER
Supervising Sound Editor
JON JOHNSON
Music Editing
KEN JOHNSON
COLOR BY DE LUXE
© Copyright MCMLXXXVI Viacom Productions Inc.
All Rights Reserved

**EXECUTIVE IN CHARGE OF
PRODUCTION**
RICHARD BIRNIE

STRATHMORE
PRODUCTIONS
IN ASSOCIATION WITH

VIACOM

Mayberry
My Hometown

Part IV
Mayberry Confidential:
Some of Our Favorite Mayberryites
Speak Their Minds

THE MAYBERRY SONG

Mayberry'll shine tonight
Mayberry'll shine
When the moon comes up
And the sun goes down
Mayberry'll shine

AN INTERVIEW WITH JIM NABORS

A little over a year is not a long time in TV Land, but it was long enough for Jim Nabors to create one of the most loved characters ever to fade-in on America's televisions. Gomer Pyle was funny—often hilarious—and the viewers of "The Andy Griffith Show" took to him immediately. Gomer was sensitive, giving, and unbelievably naive. And his popularity grew so rapidly that after a season or so on "The Andy Griffith Show" he was given his own show, "Gomer Pyle, USMC." I talked to Jim Nabors about his role on "The Andy Griffith Show" and I found him to be an affable, completely charming man. He was scheduled to call me from his balmy home state of Hawaii at 3:00 P.M. on what was for me a cool autumn afternoon. The phone rang at 2:45. It was Jim asking me if he could call me back in an hour. He did call back an hour later, and the following is an edited version of our conversation. Jim Nabors possesses a childlike genuineness that is quite captivating. He remembers the enthusiasm and delight he felt when creating a perfectly lovable character, who, as he says, "was all good." But above all, Jim Nabors is a down-to-earth guy who feels it's important to periodically revisit Mayberry, our hometown.

Steve Spignesi: Can you tell me about the time Andy Griffith saw you at The Horn in Santa Monica and gave you the job as Gomer Pyle?

Jim Nabors: He came to see me with some friends of mine from my hometown. They had told him about me. So, Andy and his wife and the other couple came down to see me—it was Bill Cannon and his wife—and I had an act where I "talk like this" [Gomer Pyle's high hayseed voice] and "sing like this" [Jim Nabors' deep baritone voice]. And Andy afterwards came up to me outside and he said "I really don't know what you do," he says, "but you do it very well." [Laughs.] And he said if a part ever came up on his show, he would have me read for it. Of course, I had had that happen to me many times before, but Andy's very much a man of his word, and three weeks later he called me. There was a part in an episode called "Man In A Hurry." It was the filling station kid, and his name was Gomer Pyle. Andy asked me to read for it, and so I read the part as the same character I was doing in the nightclub.

Steve Spignesi: What did they think?

Jim Nabors: They thought I was a bit too exaggerated, because in nightclubs you have a tendency to do that. So, they asked me if I could tone it down a bit. But they were very, very helpful to me. I was totally inexperienced, and I'd never been in front of a camera—I mean acting-wise—and everybody was really very helpful. It worked out real well for me.

Steve Spignesi: Don Knotts, on the recent WTBS Anniversary Special, said that your favorite episode—with Gomer in it—was "Citizen's Arrest." What was special about that for you?

Jim Nabors: There was a bunch of reasons. First of all, I like the episode. And because as much as anything it sort of firmed up my character in the series. "Man In A Hurry" sort

of introduced me, and so as a result of that they decided to use me as sort of a regular person on the series, as one of the town people. So, I appeared in a couple of more kind of brief ones, and I didn't do too much—I was just sort of in 'em. And, then "Citizen's Arrest" came along, and after this number of times, it sort of solidified me in the series. And besides that, it was just *very funny*. I remember I laughed so hard at Don's takes. It was the first time we had really ever confronted each other, as it were. And it just worked out so beautifully for me.

Steve Spignesi: Don Knotts remembers breaking up while filming with Howard McNear. Do you remember anything similar happening with you with actors you worked with?

Jim Nabors: Well, I used to break up with Don because his takes were so funny. They were just hysterical. To be doing a close-up scene with him—where we were face to face—and he started telling me his philosophy of life, and things like that, he would just kill me. He would just break me up. And the other one? Well, Carol Burnett. I used to break up with her quite a bit. When we first worked together we used to laugh a lot. But not many, really. With Frank, only a couple of times. He was a very rigid actor, Frank Sutton. But occasionally he would go.

Steve Spignesi: How did Gomer change your life, and how has Jim Nabors changed since his Mayberry days?

Jim Nabors: Oh, that would take us four or five hours to get into. It's changed my life totally. Completely, as far as my life style. Also my life, my career, my ambitions—everything! It was a complete switch from anonymity to having everyone know you. It's quite a change. You can't really put it into words.

Steve Spignesi: "Shazam" came from Captain Marvel. Whose idea was it to use it? Was it conceived by a writer or did you have anything to do with it?

Jim Nabors: No, that was mine.

Steve Spignesi: Completely?

Jim Nabors: Yeah, right.

Steve Spignesi: That became your trademark.

Jim Nabors: "Surprise, surprise, surprise" came from Aaron Ruben, the producer and writer.

Steve Spignesi: How about "Golly"?

Jim Nabors: "Golly" was mine.

Steve Spignesi: Do you watch "The Andy Griffith Show" in syndication?

Jim Nabors: I used to. I haven't seen it in quite a while. When it comes back on, or I happen to be someplace it is, sure, yeah.

Steve Spignesi: How about "Gomer Pyle, USMC"?

Jim Nabors: No. Because it's like it's been done. It has some wonderful, wonderful memories, but it's almost like watching someone that I know very, very well—or intimately—rather than to be watching myself. And also, Frank passed away. You know, that sort of thing. Occasionally I will watch it, but not very often.

Steve Spignesi: On "The Andy Griffith Show," you worked with six directors. They were Dick Crenna, Bob Sweeney, Coby Ruskin, Earl Bellamy, Jeffrey Hayden, and Aaron Ruben. Did you have a favorite?

Jim Nabors: Hmmm. Gee whiz. Of course, Sweeney was the first one that I worked with, and he was absolutely marvelous to me. He helped me tremendously getting used

to the . . . he's a very supportive director. He gets with you and he'll talk and he'll work with you on it, he really will. You can kind of . . . you feel secure with Sweeney. And then, of course, Aaron Ruben created "Gomer Pyle," and so naturally he knew what he wanted in the way of the character. And so, I was very secure with Aaron when he was directing because I knew he would have the ultimate say-so anyway. He was very creative as a director. And of course Dick Crenna was just a real joy to work with—so were all the others, really—but Dick was a friend. And then Coby, of course, did a tremendous amount of "Gomer" and was wonderful. They all were. They all were very good in their own way.

Steve Spignesi: In "A Date for Gomer," you danced with your blind date, Mary Grace Gossage, and in "The Song Festers" you sang "Santa Lucia." Were these musical scenes written for your talents? Whose idea were they?

Jim Nabors: I think they were just pretty much part of the episode. I don't really know. Aaron might have written them that way. I don't know who wrote those episodes. I don't remember to be honest with you. I don't think they were written for me, though. I think they were just part of the episode and I did it. They knew I sang because most of the writers and everybody else had seen me work in the nightclubs. They didn't know that I danced.

Steve Spignesi: They were both written by Jim Fritzell and Everett Greenbaum.

Jim Nabors: Right. So, I don't think they knew that I danced. They did know that I sang.

Steve Spignesi: Speaking of Everett Greenbaum . . .

Jim Nabors: I just talked to him the other day.

Steve Spignesi: He's quoted as saying the following about you: "He left all of us behind, and to this day has never looked back." Do you agree with that? Do you have any comment on that?

Jim Nabors: I don't know what that means.

Steve Spignesi: He said that to Richard Kelly in Richard Kelly's book, *The Andy Griffith Show.* They were talking about your career and how from "Andy Griffith" you went on to "Gomer," and then to movies and music, and so on.

Jim Nabors: No, what happened was I changed straight from Gomer. He and Jim had written some of those episodes, and yet they were doing other things at the time. They weren't doing so many "Gomer Pyle" scripts. They were trying to do movies and plays and things like that. And then I changed totally when I moved from "Gomer Pyle"—after five years—into my variety hour.

Steve Spignesi: It was a complete switch.

Jim Nabors: Yeah, really. So, I guess that's what he meant. I don't think I left him behind personally.

Steve Spignesi: What do you think of the incredible resurgence of interest in the show?

Jim Nabors: It was always just very solid. I think it was always totally underestimated. It never received an award, or anything like that, from the Emmys or anything, and yet, twenty years later, it's still as solid as anything that's on today. "Gomer" was never, ever nominated for anything,

ever. And "Andy" wasn't, or "Gilligan's Island," or any of those things. Or "Lucy," for that matter. She went years and years and years and years. But it seems that with your peers, comedy doesn't seem to register. They can't quite see the quality in it. I don't know, maybe I'm wrong. If a show won an Emmy, it was soon to be off the air, because the public would turn against it. They didn't like it.

Steve Spignesi: What do you know about "Return to Mayberry"?

Jim Nabors: Well, nothing, except that I talked to Andy the other day, and he said that Everett Greenbaum and Harvey Bullock are writing the script and he asked me if I could clear some time to shoot it, so I said sure.

Steve Spignesi: That's great. Why did everybody love Gomer?

Jim Nabors: Oh, gee, you got me. I loved him, too. If your gonna play a character, he's probably the nicest character you could ever play. He was all good.

Steve Spignesi: Whatever happened to Gomer Pyle anyway?

Jim Nabors: I really won't know until I "Return to Mayberry"! Then I'll find out the answers to all these questions.

Steve Spignesi: What do you remember about working with Ronny Howard?

Jim Nabors: Well, actually, I was always closer to his father.

Steve Spignesi: Rance.

Jim Nabors: Rance was a good friend of mine. I considered him a real good friend on the set. We were real good friends. Ron was just always a good kid. He was terribly professional, and he was so good—as a kid—that you just sort of expected it of him. It was just sort of natural that he was great. You didn't just stand back and say, "Oh my God, is he wonderful!" It was just sort of natural with him. He was so natural with it that you never did that. You just sort of accepted him at face value, he was just always a terrific kid.

Steve Spignesi: Have you seen his movies?

Jim Nabors: Oh, yeah! He's absolutely wonderful. But he's had a lot of good experience. He's never been without a job since he was six, has he?

Steve Spignesi: No, he's been working since then. What do you recall about Howard McNear?

Jim Nabors: Oh, he was a wonderful man. Just wonderful. He was personally one of the kindest, sweetest people you'd ever want to meet. And he was just a marvelous character. I was watching him in a movie the other day, and he was absolutely wonderful. I forget what movie it was, but I just couldn't take my eyes off of him in a scene.

Steve Spignesi: OK, lastly, if you had to describe Mayberry in a couple of sentences, how would you do it?

Jim Nabors: I could do it with one word: Caring.

Steve Spignesi: Jim, thanks for all your help.

Jim Nabors: OK buddy, lotsa luck to you and yours!

ANETA CORSAUT
INTERVIEW

Aneta Corsaut is great! She is a talented, lovely lady who refuses to take either herself or show business too seriously. She is lively, animated, honest and funny, and I greatly enjoyed our conversation. She was extremely generous with her time and, thanks to her, I was also able to interview Betty "Thelma Lou Fife" Lynn for *Mayberry, My Hometown*. The following is an edited version of our conversation.

Steve Spignesi: You were the first successful romantic interest for Andy on the show. Why do you think Helen and Andy's relationship worked while the others failed?

Aneta Corsaut: Andy was very shy with women. There were two or three girls on the show before I came on and they were all wonderful actresses and Andy liked them all, but it was very hard for a lot of women to become friends with Andy. I think just the fact that he was comfortable with me personally made it possible for the characters to develop. Also, I think it was because we got into a huge argument about women's rights the first day on the set. We were out in the middle of the street on location screaming at each other and it ended up being very funny to both of us and we became friends . . . almost by accident. Since then, we have been good friends for a great many years.

Steve Spignesi: Your remark about women's rights brings up another question. In "Opie's Girlfriend," Helen beats Andy at bowling and then Helen's niece, Cynthia, beats Opie at sports and gives him a black eye. Helen tells Cynthia that women should sometimes let men feel as though they can do things better than women. Did that speech stick in your throat?

Aneta Corsaut: Dreadfully. Just dreadfully. Towards the end of the series they started checking with me a little bit on how I thought Helen might feel about things. But the show was done in another time. It was very hard to get any kind of point across. And I guess the very fact that on the show they allowed us to beat the guys at a couple of things in itself was something. Yes, that scene was very hard for me. And I think all the acting in the world couldn't have given those lines a sincere ring from me. I don't feel Helen would have accepted that. I really never felt that Helen would have said that.

Steve Spignesi: "Opie's Girlfriend" was written by Budd Grossman and since it was the only episode he ever wrote, he might not have been as familiar with the characters as, for instance, Jim Fritzell and Everett Greenbaum were.

Aneta Corsaut: Jim was my fella, and that was kind of special. But it was a little strange working with him even though we'd been dating quite a while when I started doing the show. He was wonderful. But he never knew quite how to write for women. He and Ev both admitted that they could write for little girls and older women but anything in between always came out sort of sweet and bland. In fact, we had a lot of trouble on the show writing for women at all. Andy himself admits that they really just didn't know what to do. And actually, they were not predisposed to listen to us. It sounds like I'm fussing about it but I'm not

at all. It was such a wonderfully written show and it was so much fun, that these were very small quibbles on my part.

Steve Spignesi: Where did you personally find the spirit of Mayberry? What was the essence of the Mayberry experience for you?

Aneta Corsaut: It was a job! (Laughs)

Steve Spignesi: (Laughs) Elinor Donahue said the same thing to me. I asked her about being a feminist on the show and particularly about the episode "Ellie for Council"—in which she ran for council and stood up for women's rights—and I said, "You know, that episode was almost revolutionary for that time. What did you think of it?" She said, "I learned my lines, was on time on the set, and just did it."

Aneta Corsaut: (Laughs) Elinor's a darling woman, I just love her. It really was our home over there on the set. We all came to work days we weren't working and we would come early and stay late. We were a wonderful family. It was the best I had ever seen that way. I've been told by people who guested on the show that it was the most comfortable show to come onto from the outside. It's always very difficult for actors to do a guest spot on a show that's already running because either the company is getting along and they're sort of closed in on themselves or they're not getting along and they don't like anybody! But I think we were a nice, friendly group. And we liked each other and I think we were good for people who came in.

Steve Spignesi: What are your personal favorite "Andy" episodes?

Aneta Corsaut: Well, the one I think is the very very best was one Jim and Everett Greenbaum wrote called "Man in a Hurry." I think that's just a brilliant piece of work. Of the ones Helen was in, I guess the one I enjoyed most was when she wrote the kid's book.

Steve Spignesi: "Helen the Authoress."

Aneta Corsaut: Yes. Because I got to do a little bit in that one. Mostly Helen was just around asking if somebody packed the salt and pepper.

Steve Spignesi: I enjoyed that episode very much but I was very disappointed in Helen for allowing them to change her name.

Aneta Corsaut: Yes! Well, think what *I've* gone through in this business not changing *my* name. Unspellable, unpronounceable.

Steve Spignesi: Yes. I've seen your name spelled dozens of ways.

Aneta Corsaut: I once did a movie years and years ago out of New York and I hated it so much I thought it would never be released. I guess I saw a preview of it and noticed that they misspelled my name. I never had them correct the spelling. I assumed it wouldn't be released and once it was I thought that if I'd had any sense I would've changed my name to "Sally Jones" or something. At least for that one film.

Steve Spignesi: What do you hear from Frances Bavier?

Aneta Corsaut: I haven't heard from her for awhile. I loved Frances. We were very good friends on the show. I guess she is not well. Andy told me he had gone to see her one day and she wouldn't let him in.

Steve Spignesi: That happened to Ron Howard, too. Ron told me he went down to North Carolina to see her and he couldn't make contact.

Aneta Corsaut: That's too bad. She's a brilliant actress. The funny thing about Frances was that she was a complete and total ingenue—and the only one I ever knew. Here she was a sixty-year-old woman who was the ideal, perfect ingenue. I never was an ingenue. It was fascinating to watch her work.

Steve Spignesi: Let's talk about Don Knotts.

Aneta Corsaut: Oh, darling Don.

Steve Spignesi: What was it like working with Don? Was he Barney when the cameras weren't rolling?

Aneta Corsaut: No. Not at all. He was quite the lady's man, and he was funny! He was a very funny man—but he was kind of introspective. He was more fun when we did "Return to Mayberry" than I ever personally found him on the set during the series. I always liked Don very much but I never felt totally comfortable with him. But when we went back up to do this "Return" thing, he was just darling. Maybe we've both changed a little bit somehow. Perhaps I didn't understand something before. But Don and Ronny were two of my favorite people on the set. I adore Ronny Howard.

Steve Spignesi: What do you think of Ron's movies? And how do you think he's developed?

Aneta Corsaut: He's just wonderful. He was an incredibly nice kid. His parents did everything right as far as having a showbiz kid. Rance or Jean were always on the set. He was never left to social workers as most child actors are. And they didn't hound him to become an actor. It was entirely up to him and he couldn't do it any time he wanted to. If he did it he had to be completely professional about it. In all the years we did the show I saw him only once say something sort of snappish. Rance marched him behind a set, and Ronny came out about three minutes later, apologized to everybody and that was the end of that. He was just great fun, a sweet, sweet kid. And he wasn't allowed to play "little kid star" or anything. He went to public school all the time that he wasn't actually on the set. He played baseball. He had as normal a life as a kid actor can have. And I remember saying to his mom once, "Boy, Ronny's smart." She said, "Well, not extremely smart. He's smart, but he's not unusual. He's just an awfully good boy." You know, most mother's rave "I've got the smartest kid in the world." They kept him very sane. And his work now—I think he does lovely things. His work is within the acceptance of his age group and yet there's something for older people. There's a gentleness about his work that isn't in most people's work these days, I think. He's just such a nice guy. Doesn't he do wonderful work?

Steve Spignesi: He really does. The direction is so sure. He seems to have been confident of who he was and what he was capable of from a very early age. I envy him that.

Aneta Corsaut: This is one of the very earliest memories I have of Ronny and it just breaks me up now. I told him about this the other day and he fell down. He couldn't have been more than seven or eight. He was standing at the desk in the schoolhouse and they were setting up a shot. I was just getting acquainted with him and I said, "Ronny, what do you want to do when you grow up? Do you want to be an actor or is there something else you have in mind?" He thought about it for a long, long time and finally he said, "Well, I guess I'm gonna have to be an actor. It's all I know

how to do." But it wasn't long until it wasn't all he knew how to do!

Steve Spignesi: No, he learned quickly.

Aneta Corsaut: Very quickly. But I just loved that! For a seven-year-old to have something he could do.

Steve Spignesi: He had a career when most kids were just starting first grade.

Aneta Corsaut: He was a real trooper.

Steve Spignesi: I found him charming. He was such a gentleman. He was concerned about fitting our interview into *my* schedule. And of course it was the complete opposite. I was willing to do anything to make it convenient for him. But that's just an indication of the kind of guy he is.

Aneta Corsaut: He's a thoroughly considerate, nice man. And he really is. I mean he's not being that way so the people will like him. He just is nice. He lives near my sister in Connecticut. And he was so funny about moving to the East Coast. He said that he wanted the kids to have as a normal an upbringing as they could. He didn't want them to grow up in Hollywood. And then he sort of laughed and said, "I guess it's probably Bryce who is probably a very good little actress already." Bryce is so beautiful! But Ron didn't want to come home and find his kids hitting him up for a job.

Steve Spignesi: Tell me about Howard McNear.

Aneta Corsaut: I'm sure you've heard from everybody that we—to a one—adored Howard McNear. Howard McNear was the funniest, the most naturally funny man just to sit in a room with I have ever met in my life. And sweet! Oh, I just can't say enough good things about him. And what a talented man! And he came from mostly doing drama. It wasn't till later in his life when he did comedy. He was just brilliant. After he was ill, he handled that beautifully. Howard really couldn't walk and a lot of the scenes where he was standing up he was literally propped up. Andy particularly just adored Howard.

Steve Spignesi: They were close?

Aneta Corsaut: Yes. And the jokes on the set! We would have running gags that would last all day because of Howard. When he came back after he had been ill, his wife was with him all the time and she was a darling lady. A wonderful, wonderful man.

Steve Spignesi: What do you remember about working with Jim Nabors?

Aneta Corsaut: I never knew Jim all that well. He wasn't on the show all that long. He's a lovely man. And he's the only one of the whole crowd that I had not seen since we were off the air. I guess I saw him once or twice at parties, but the rest of us had remained friends. It was particularly nice to see Jim. But I don't really know Jim very well.

Steve Spignesi: Jack Dodson sent me a photo for the book.

Aneta Corsaut: Jack is a funny, funny man. The first day we worked together on the set he told me an outrageous story which I didn't know whether to believe or not but I believed it because I didn't know him. He's got an insane sense of humor. After about six months of knowing each other I said one day, "Jack I don't care what you tell me. I will not believe it. Nothing you ever tell me again will I ever believe." And I don't. He could tell me that my dress

had fallen off, and that I was standing there naked. If I looked down and saw that it was true I still wouldn't believe it. An outrageous man. And a good actor. A good, good actor.

Steve Spignesi: I loved him in Ray Bradbury's "Something Wicked This Way Comes." He was sort of like Howard Sprague with an edge.

Aneta Corsaut: Yes. That's a wonderful way of putting it! I had a couple of friends in that film. Jake Dengel played the Indian. He's a very old, old friend of mine from college. So, that was a particularly nice movie for me.

Steve Spignesi: Tell me about your writing. What do you have in print and what are you working on?

Aneta Corsaut: The book we have in print is a quiz book on mysteries. I did that with my friends Bob Wagner and Muff Singer—who are both brighter than I am! I'm a mystery collector and an absolute fiend on reading mysteries. I love 'em. I've gotten to be sort of a minor authority on mysteries. People call and ask who wrote what and how to get a hold of it. I always have it, so I loan it to 'em. And now we're writing a second quiz book. And I'm also writing a mystery myself. A mystery novel. I don't know whether I can slug through it, though. It's very hard work. And I've never been a word person. I've been a picture person. So, it's hard going for me but I'm enjoying it very much. The reason that I even tried to write a novel was that Jim and I wrote some "Anna & the King of Siams" together because Ev didn't want to work up a show. Jim asked me if I'd work with him and I ended up actually doing some of the writing. And then we did a pilot together right before he died. And I found that I could do it. I don't know if I can do it alone yet, but I can with other people.

Steve Spignesi: Have you titled it?

Aneta Corsaut: No. I titled it eight times but none of them work yet. So, it'll tell me when it's time. The way my pets named themselves, the book's gonna have to do the same thing.

Steve Spignesi: What was it like returning to Mayberry? Was there anything there that brought back memories? Did the nostalgia hit you the way it did the 56 million people who watched it?

Aneta Corsaut: Yes, I think so. But in a funny way I think we were all a little nervous about trying to be the same people again. We weren't nervous about the show itself because we all work and everything. But we've all done so many other things in between, I think the first day or two was sort of awkward. From there after it just fell absolutely into place—the same old jokes, even the same attitudes toward each other for the most part. And thank goodness we got the script that we got from Ev and Harvey, who are both wonderful guys. They hadn't written together before. They had both written with other partners. From what I understand the network originally had a script which was about a lot of car chases and nobody in Mayberry.

Steve Spignesi: Yes, they turned it down.

Aneta Corsaut: Yes, Andy would have never done that one. And he fought very hard to get Ev and Harvey, both of whom I adore! I guess he had to fight to get them. And they're both such good writers. So, thank goodness we got the script we did. Even though I still think that it's a rather delicate show to stretch to two hours. But, at least everything within it was consistent and all. It was a good

experience for the most part. But the weather was very difficult.

Steve Spignesi: The weather looked fine on the screen.

Aneta Corsaut: We had rain and wind and heat and everything you could imagine. Remember the stuff we shot inside the barn at the reception? We shot it inside because it was raining and we couldn't do it outside where it was supposed to be shot. And it was freezing, freezing cold in there. The scene was shot very late at night and physically it was sort of uncomfortable. And, of course, we weren't familiar with the crew either. We had worked with the same crew for so many years on the show and they were so much a part of the company that I had not even realized how important they were to us. We were all a family unit. It wasn't just the cast, it was the entire outfit.

Steve Spignesi: It must have been nice seeing Bob Sweeney again.

Aneta Corsaut: Yes, it was. But I've seen Bob and Bev on and off over the years. It was nice to work for him again, though.

Steve Spignesi: Do you have any plans to work on the "Christmas in Mayberry" special that's being talked about?

Aneta Corsaut: Well, maybe, if they do it. But it doesn't seem likely, with Andy's show being picked up. And if "Matlock" stays on the air for awhile he really won't have time to do another "Mayberry" movie for awhile. And I'm not sure that Andy is wild to do another one right away. I hope that, ultimately, we will do another one, but I don't think that it'll be this year.

Steve Spignesi: Well, of course, the network is trying to reap what they can from it.

Aneta Corsaut: Well, I just hope they rerun it again soon because I'd like some money, please! (Laughs) Actors are not known for being very clever with money!

Steve Spignesi: What do you think about this current fascination with the old show?

Aneta Corsaut: I love it because I hadn't seen the show for so many years and somebody recently sent me some prints of some episodes and they were just so good. I'm just tickled to death that it's still around to see. I don't know why it's become so popular again. It's a nice show. It's a good show. And I don't really mean on any great sociological basis, just that it's a well-done show.

Steve Spignesi: Where do you see Helen Crump in a few years and what was she doing for twenty years?

Aneta Corsaut: I don't really know. I really wasn't sure the movie was going to get done so I didn't really have a chance to give her past much thought.

Steve Spignesi: It was great to see Betty Lynn acting again.

Aneta Corsaut: Oh, it was fun to work with Betty again. She's such a doll. By the way, I think she's probably going to be working on "Matlock."

Steve Spignesi: I didn't know that.

Aneta Corsaut: I had heard that rumor and recently Betty finally said, yes, she thought that that was going to work out.

Steve Spignesi: What movies have you seen recently that struck you as particularly well done?

Aneta Corsaut: I saw "Agnes of God" recently. I thought the actress who played Agnes was brilliant.

Steve Spignesi: Meg Tilly.

Aneta Corsaut: Yes. And the story was one of the few intelligent movies I've seen in a long time. But my favorite movie of the last year or two was "Ladyhawke." I thought that was beautiful. It's just so pretty! I rented it one night. It's just beautiful. It's not intelligent or deep or anything—it's just a little fantasy thing but I loved it.

Steve Spignesi: Miss Corsaut, this has been a real thrill. I appreciate your time and I really want to thank you for your visit to Mayberry, my hometown.

Aneta Corsaut: Good, good, good luck with the book.

Steve Spignesi: Thanks very much.

A TALK WITH THELMA LOU

Betty "Thelma Lou Fife" Lynn is a quiet, serious person who gives very well-considered answers and isn't afraid to admit when she doesn't know something. She is as down-to-earth as one can be and I found her to be pleasant, open, and extremely charming. She is a doll! The following is an edited version of our talk.

Steve Spignesi: I guess my first question is obvious. How did it feel—after twenty years of waiting—to finally be Mrs. Barney Fife?

Betty Lynn: (Laughs) Well, it was terrific. I think Thelma Lou was real happy. And it was nice to finally get a last name! It's something that I—that *she'd* — been looking forward to. You realize I have to speak of it from her point of view.

Steve Spignesi: Of course!

Betty Lynn: All of the time she'd known Barney she'd really been crazy about him—had her eyes on him all the time. And that this should finally happen was just the greatest thing in her life. And it made me feel very good, too. Thelma Lou got to be a pretty good friend to me, too. I enjoyed every minute of doing the show—the anticipation of the wedding and having the dress—the whole thing, the excitement of it. And—at long last—Barney by my side. Yes, it was really nice.

Steve Spignesi: It sounds like "Returning to Mayberry" was wonderful for you personally.

Betty Lynn: Oh, it was. It was like some sort of dream in a way, when I think back. I mean, who would dream that that would happen? And then when it did it was almost like a little time and space that was given to us—it was just absolutely wonderful—seeing everyone again. And everything went so well! And we all enjoyed each other. It really was a marvelous, marvelous time.

Steve Spignesi: What did Mayberry personally mean to you? What was the essence of Mayberry to you?

Betty Lynn: I think the gentleness and a capturing—in a sense—of a place and a time and era we don't see much anymore. Mayberry had people that were warm and funny and yet had depth and cared about each other. It kind of became home for a lot of people, I think. And it *was* home. When we worked it was like a family. You loved to be there and you looked forward to going. It was like another home.

Steve Spignesi: What are your first memories of "The Andy Griffith Show"?

Betty Lynn: I was seated alone in my living room and I happened to turn on the show, and sitting there all of a sudden I heard this laughter, and I was shocked—it was me! I was laughing out loud for the first time in a long time at a show on television in my living room by myself. It made me feel good, you know? And I thought, "My goodness! This is really a marvelous show." My reaction was so spontaneous and so startling to me. You see so many shows and for something to hit me like that—I thought that was great. And then about three or four weeks later I got a call to come in and see about a part in the show. At the

time I was on a series at Disney, so it was a big surprise and they said, "Well, this is a new show. It's only been on..." —and I interrupted them and said, "Oh, I've seen it. I saw it and I liked it very much." My reaction has always kind of stuck in my mind because it was something that hit me so strong. I was really surprised at my reaction because it was unusual for me. I mean, I might be amused or smile at something but to be sitting there and laugh out loud—it startled me.

Steve Spignesi: That only happens to me with two shows. "The Andy Griffith Show" and "Late Night with David Letterman."

Betty Lynn: (Laughs) He's great!

Steve Spignesi: I laugh out loud at what goes on on either of those shows. Watching anything else I may smile—but nothing much more. Those two shows, however, always set me off!

Betty Lynn: I know. That's true. And there's something else, too. We had great writers and producers on that show. And we had fine directors—particularly Bob Sweeney—who did "Return to Mayberry." All of that meant a great deal to the show.

Steve Spignesi: What's it like working with Don Knotts?

Betty Lynn: Well, that is a fantastic experience. Don is a great actor. And he can do so many things. Just watching him when he starts working with something is a great privilege. And it's a pleasure watching him as he develops it and how quickly things will come to his mind. He's very quiet but then things happen. There were a few times when we were shooting that he would make me laugh so hard I could hardly control myself. And I was trying to play the scene sincerely when really I wanted to laugh. I think Don is one of the top actors in the business. There isn't any emotion he can't do—and well. Something once happened I thought was interesting. At the time my aunt was living here with my mother and me. Before that she had lived in Cleveland. And she had watched Don years ago on "Search for Tomorrow." In that soap, he played Wilbur Peabody, the mute brother of Rose Peabody—who was the main character. And Wilbur was a very serious, sad character. But I had personally not seen the show myself. But my aunt—even though she loved "The Andy Griffith Show" and loved everybody in it and especially loved Don, she one day said to me—after she'd told me about the part he'd played in the soap and how wonderful he was in it—she said, "I'm so concerned about Don. I still see him that way (like Wilbur) even though he's funny and he's doing all this." He had convinced her so completely in that character that—even though she enjoyed him—she still saw him as that sad, pitiful character. It was funny—he was that convincing all the time. I remember once that "Three's Company" gave Don a huge party for—I think—his thirty-fifth year in show business. It was about two years ago. And they had excerpts from everything Don's done running all the time on a huge screen. And one of them was "Search for Tomorrow."

Steve Spignesi: I know that you and Aneta Corsaut are very good friends. What was it like working with her?

Betty Lynn: Oh, she was delightful. She added a great deal to the show and was just a darling person. She really was. I didn't really get to know Aneta real well, but we

207

certainly got along beautifully. But we don't see each other a lot. I hadn't seen her until just before "Return to Mayberry" started, except at that party for Don. But I always am happy to see her, and whenever we speak on the phone or anything it's always very up. She's a very cheerful and a very up and positive person—which is a lovely way to be.

Steve Spignesi: What do you hear from Frances Bavier, if anything?

Betty Lynn: Nothing. And I feel that I have really been the wrong one here. I feel like I should have made every effort to contact Frances, because I truly love her. I ask about her. I've talked to people from that area that have contacted her and I always inquire. I finally got an address once from someone but now I can't find it. My intentions are good but I have to admit I have not really done all that I could have. I've had her on my mind many times. I loved working with her and I admire her so much. I wish I could be the kind of actress Frances was. I felt very bad that she was not able to do "Return to Mayberry." I know everyone would have loved that.

Steve Spignesi: Ron Howard told me that at one point he actually went down to see her but couldn't make contact.

Betty Lynn: Well, I hear it's difficult. You know, as we all get older it's not always easy to manage to do things or see people—even if we want to. And I have heard that it's not an easy thing. But at least whether I heard from her or not, I wish that I had tried. I've written her in my mind many times. Maybe someday someone'll give me her number and I'll try calling her. I've been determined that I would do this. I have not. So, it's my fault in that sense and even if I didn't get a return or I didn't hear from her—that isn't important. I would like to let her know. I wish she did know that I was thinking of her and I have not seen to it that she does. But I have her in my prayers.

Steve Spignesi: Well, I'll try to send her a copy of *Mayberry, My Hometown* so she can read what you just said. Then she'll know.

Betty Lynn: Oh, I hope so.

Steve Spignesi: What was she like on the set?

Betty Lynn: I enjoyed her. I really love Frances and we enjoyed visiting and being together. I really had fun with her. As you know, that face of hers just lights up and those eyes dance. And she's very pretty. A very pretty woman. And she's fun and cute and I enjoyed her always.

Steve Spignesi: Tell me about working with Andy.

Betty Lynn: I love Andy. I really do. He's a marvelous actor. Did you ever see "Face in the Crowd?"

Steve Spignesi: No.

Betty Lynn: Oh, you must see it. You must see it. It's a marvelous movie and Andy is fantastic in it. And that was long before he did the "Griffith Show." Elia Kazan directed it. Andy's always been a terrific actor. And as a person he's fun. And he's a tease, and he's very lovable. He's serious about his work. He's serious about everything he's involved with. And he's considerate, he's loyal—well, it's difficult to think of all the adjectives.

Steve Spignesi: He seems to be a consummate gentleman, from what I know of him.

Betty Lynn: Yes, he is. And a gentle man.

Steve Spignesi: Tell me about Howard McNear?

Betty Lynn: Howard was darling. Howard had a great humor, a tremendous humor. Almost a pixie-like quality. He had a lovely wife who was with him quite often—especially after he had his stroke. He was so thrilled to be working after his illness. He was marvelous in everything he did. And he was limited only in his movements. Otherwise, he was terrific. And Andy saw to it that everything possible could be done to make him comfortable. We all missed him terribly. I often think of Howard and his lovely wife. As I say, we were like a family in a way. You don't forget your family, do you?

Steve Spignesi: No, not at all. This is a three-part question which involves the same family. What was it like working with Ron and Rance Howard and what do you think of Ron's movies?

Betty Lynn: Oh, golly! Well, we all called him Ronny until we did "Return to Mayberry." That was when I began to call him Ron. I still call him Ronny part of the time, though. He was so special. There are some child actors that are particularly attuned to everything and just do everything right. They just have a natural talent. And it's not that they're grown up as children, but that they have an insight that is particularly marvelous. And yet they can still have a childhood. Natalie Wood was one, I think. I worked with Natalie when she was young and she was a wonderful little actress. Very professional. But she was still a child. But a darling one. And Ron was the same way. He was active in many things—his baseball, his schooling—he was very good in everything. And his parents were wonderful. Absolutely wonderful with him. And Rance was great. He'd be there on the set. And Jeannie, too, sometimes. It was always a great pleasure to work with Ronny. And I love his movies! I think they're great. I can remember sitting around the table on the days we would read the script and block it out and rehearse. And one day—I do forget whether it was Aaron or Bob Sweeney (I think it might have been Aaron... Aaron Ruben)—in any case, one of them said, "I found out this morning what Ronny wants to be when he grows up." So, we all looked at Ronny, who was seated there, and he kind of smiled and we said, "What?" And Aaron said, "A director." And we all said, "Well, that's terrific Ronny, my gosh!" And I said, "Well, I think you will be if you want to be Ronny, and you'll be a good one and I hope you'll remember me when you are!" (Laughs) But that hasn't happened as of yet. But anyway, something was in his mind then and he was tiny! He had really thought about it. So, this has been coming for a long time. Then he did some films when he was a teen-ager with his brother, Clint, and his mother and father. So, this is not a surprise at all. I think he was bound to be such a tremendous success. And working with him on "Return to Mayberry"—he's still the same. If anything I think Ronny is even much more outgoing now. He was outgoing as a child, too. He was terrific. He's so warm. And his mother and father haven't changed a bit. They're so happy and so thrilled for him. And rightly so. We all are.

Steve Spignesi: Let's talk about episodes.

Betty Lynn: Oh, my goodness. That may not be too easy for me. They kind of all meld together. It's been a long time you know!

Steve Spignesi: Well, do you have a favorite episode in general? One that really sticks out in your mind as being your ultimate favorite, whether or not it was a Thelma Lou episode?

Betty Lynn: That's a hard one. Golly. It's hard for me to pick out one favorite, I'll have to be honest. I've got a lot of favorites. And I'm not good at remembering the names of the episodes. I have difficulty with that.

Steve Spignesi: My favorite is "Opie the Birdman."

Betty Lynn: Oh, I loved that!

Steve Spignesi: And Aneta Corsaut's favorite was one written by Jim Fritzell and Everett Greenbaum called "Man in a Hurry."

Betty Lynn: Yes, I remember that one!

Steve Spignesi: Ron Howard's favorite is "The Ball Game"—which was written by his father.

Betty Lynn: How wonderful!

Steve Spignesi: Do you have a Thelma Lou episode that you remember as being important to you?

Betty Lynn: Well—I can't remember the name of the episode—but it was the one where Don was getting his place fixed up—getting furniture for the new place he'd moved into. But I can't think of the name of it.

Steve Spignesi: Could it be the episode "Up in Barney's Room?" In that episode, Barney gets evicted from Mrs. Mendlebright's boarding house and moves into the backroom of the courthouse . . .

Betty Lynn: Oh, yes!

Steve Spignesi: . . . and then "Mr. Independent" takes Thelma Lou on a tour of his new "pad." He shows her his orange crate bookcase . . .

Betty Lynn: Yes!

Steve Spignesi: . . . and his hot plate—his kitchen area—he was so very proud. And Thelma Lou was so impressed with. . .

Betty Lynn: With what he's done. (Laughs) Yes, that one was very funny.

Steve Spignesi: What was it like working with Jim Nabors?

Betty Lynn: Oh, he was delightful. I loved him. He came into the series after Andy heard him sing at a place called The Horn in Santa Monica. Andy was very impressed with him. And they wrote the Gomer character—I presume—with Jim in mind. I really don't know how it all came about but it seems to me that it might have happened that way. I mean, I was never privy to how everything exactly happened, you know. But anyway, Jim was wonderful as Gomer and I think he really loved playing him, too. And it shows that he did. He gave everything he had to it. And there was great fun on the set. In fact, Andy, Don and Jim made a great threesome!

Steve Spignesi: You didn't work with Jack Dodson, but Aneta Corsaut says that he was a real cutup.

Betty Lynn: Yes. He came in after I left the show. But I had met him and of course watched his work. I enjoyed him tremendously. But I really got to know him better on "Return to Mayberry." I found him wonderful. I think he's such a fine, wonderful actor. And a very handsome man. Very nice. But I was just leaving as they were all coming in.

Steve Spignesi: What do you think about the current fascination with "The Andy Griffith Show?" *Mayberry, My Hometown* will be the third book out about the show, and the "Return to Mayberry" movie garnered incredible ratings.

Betty Lynn: Yes, I know!

Steve Spignesi: Why are people so fascinated with Mayberry?

Betty Lynn: I can't really give you a lot of fast answers on that. But I think it's wonderful that they are. When we did it, I thought it was a terrific show. And I loved being connected with it. And people loved it then, too. So, that kind of humor is lasting in that sense. It's a combination of many, many things on the show. It's some slapstick and some gentle comedy and some craziness that somehow is all made believeable.

Steve Spignesi: And drama.

Betty Lynn: And drama. It's quite a mixture. And stirred together rather well. And I think Andy—as the mainstay of the show—had a quality that people cared about. His philosophy, the way he handled his life, his child, his relationships in general—they were exemplary. Something to look up to. And then we had Don. Don's character was someone who is confident on one hand and completely vulnerable on the other. He encapsulates what is in all of us—maybe in extremes but there's that something in all of us that kind of shows up here and there. And the combination of the two—of Barney's struggles and then the love between the two men—made the show what it was. There's a lot of love there. And then there is sacrifice in the show, which I think is a very integral part of love that a lot of people don't think about or don't want to think about. But it's a very crucial element. And there are times in the script where one gives up for the other—through love—that is very touching. And finally, I think today's fans like the people of Mayberry. But I don't know. Those might not be any of the answers. When we were up in Los Olivos, California, filming "Return to Mayberry," there were young people around who had grown up with the show and were thrilled that it was being done. They would talk to me about the show and there was a young man who was a friend of one of the cameramen. And he said that when he was little he sometimes felt kind of isolated. Like maybe he didn't have a lot of friends or maybe nobody liked him. And he'd go to his room and shut the door and he'd turn on our show and he always felt that if he could be in Mayberry or if he could talk to Andy, they'd understand him. And I later said to Andy, "I wonder if you know how many people you've fathered in this country," because in a sense they felt that kind of a relationship with him. And he said, "You know, I guess that's true in a lot of ways." I guess he hears it, too, you know.

Steve Spignesi: What can you tell me about "Matlock?"

Betty Lynn: Well, I can't give you a lot about it, because I was just there one day so far. But it seems to me that it's going to be terrific. Andy is just wonderful in the part. I think you'll be fascinated with him. He's a brilliant lawyer in it and yet there's moments of his "hominess" in some of what he brings to the character. He has a lovely daughter in it who's also an attorney. Linda Purl. ["Matlock" premiered on NBC on Saturday, September 20, 1986, at 10:00 P.M. —sjs]

Steve Spignesi: Oh, sure.

Betty Lynn: She's beautiful and extremely talented and they work very well together, and they really look well together—the coloring and everything—you really feel she could be his daughter. We're working on the first episode and I think it's terrific. There's a young girl in the show named Kari, who I think will be a tremendous hit. I don't know her background or what she's done, but she's so good in it and Andy's so pleased with her work. And Andy's enjoying it. It's hard work doing that type of thing, an hour show with trials and all kinds of things in it, but at the same time I know that Andy's so enthused. He's very happy. He's so happily married—he has the most beautiful wife. Cindi is a beautiful person. So, his life is so happy at this time. It means everything to him. He's doing so well. And he looks wonderful.

Steve Spignesi: Does this mean a return to the acting field for Betty Lynn?

Betty Lynn: Well, I hope so. I really love it. I had continued to act after I left the show, but the last few years or so, I haven't really done anything. I'll tell you, it's funny to get back to it because there's so many things you forget—it's amazing. A lot of things about the actual shooting and business come natural to you when you're working. It seems so easy when you're doing it and you've been continuing to do it—it's just always there. But when you suddenly come back into it! There have been changes made. There are a lot of different things that are new to me. So, I have to kind of adjust to it, get used to it. But it's fun. Andy is really the one who suggested me for this part—playing his secretary. So, I really have him to thank for working in "Matlock." It's a great opportunity for me and especially to work with Andy again. I'm very grateful for that. I don't know how it'll all work out as far my part is concerned. I'm just thrilled to be a part of it.

Steve Spignesi: Miss Lynn, thank you so much for visiting Mayberry, my hometown. You are an absolute delight!

Betty Lynn: Well, I think it's wonderful that you're doing this and I wish you all the best with the book.

Steve Spignesi: Thank you. It was a pleasure talking to you.

AN INTERVIEW WITH ELINOR DONAHUE

Elinor Donahue was much loved as Betty "Princess" Anderson, the oldest daughter and America's big sister on "Father Knows Best" from 1954 until its last season in 1960. From the small hometown of Springfield, she then moved to the small hometown of Mayberry as Ellie Walker, the "lady druggist." I talked with Miss Donahue about the episodes of "The Andy Griffith Show" in which she participated and her memories of living in Mayberry, my hometown.

Steve Spignesi: "Ellie Comes To Town" was the very first episode you ever appeared in and the first words you spoke in Mayberry were "Officer! Quick! Burglars!" Your character here was a classic cold professional who very quickly allowed the ways and warmth of Mayberry to change her. Two questions: 1) Andy's character was rather sexist towards Ellie. He called her "Pharmacy Gal" and didn't take her seriously. He did, however, eventually change his attitude. What do you remember about playing this first episode as what was then a rare bird on television: an independent professional woman? 2) How did you feel as the new person on the set and how did the others treat you?

Elinor Donahue: No thought of sexism entered my mind, as to playing the character. What I remember most was the feeling that I'd "left the nest too soon," the protection of "Father Knows Best," where I'd only during the last two years of that show begun to learn my craft and I felt like a little girl having to play grown-up all of a sudden. As to how I was treated, I came to the show very early on and knew some of the cast and most of the crew already, having been in movies and TV since age five. It was a warm and professional group and they wanted me to be good in the part. The pressure I felt was totally self-inflicted.

Steve Spignesi: "Irresistible Andy" was the first episode involving Ellie Walker and Andy in any semblance of a romance. After Andy heard that Ellie wasn't going to the dance he said she's "pretty as a peach" and boys should be buzzing around her "like flies around a spoonful of honey." But then his male ego stepped in and made a fiasco of what should have been a simple date. Ellie put him in his place, however, and everything worked out. What can you remember about your first romantic scene with Andy that took place in the drugstore and culminated in your fixing him a mustard, milk of magnesia, and castor oil milkshake?

Elinor Donahue: I remember it as being very difficult for me as a performer. I've since learned, through experience, that in a series situation it takes a few hours for my character to settle in. In those days, if I didn't have "it" *right now* I'd panic. Of course, that only gets in the way of the work and slows the actor's whole natural process down. That episode went by in a haze of panic and fear of failure.

Steve Spignesi: "Ellie for Council" was a very important episode for the character of Ellie Walker. Even though Otis thought that "all [women] understand's a leg 'a lamb," and Andy sang that "Everybody knows she's just a filly/Runnin' for council's just plain silly," Ellie got enough names to run for—and win—the council seat. You played

this episode with strength and conviction. Did you object to the sexist attitudes so prevalent in male-dominated Mayberry and what were your feelings upon reading what was then an almost revolutionary script?

Elinor Donahue: I learned my lines, was on time on the set, and just did it. As for it being revolutionary, I saw it as a well-written sitcom and enjoyed playing it because it was one of the few times I felt in control of the situation.

Steve Spignesi: "Christmas Story" was a classic Scrooge story, sort of "A Christmas Carol" comes to Mayberry. Ellie played her part in "converting" old Ben Weaver by paying his two dollar fine (even though he wanted to get locked up). My question: Was that really you singing "Away In A Manger" to Andy's guitar accompaniment?

Elinor Donahue: As far as I know. However, after a *long* excrutiating evening of taping (I hated to hear my own voice in those days) I felt I'd dissapointed everyone and it is possible they went later with someone else and to save my feelings, didn't tell me. It sounds much better than I'd have thought it would. You'll have to ask someone else for the truth on that.

Steve Spignesi: In "The Horse Trader," Andy was uncharacteristically unethical in his handling of the sale of the old cannon. Ellie played a part in bringing him to his senses. I never really believed Andy would lie the way he did. What were your thoughts upon reading a script that had the fairest, most honest man on earth lying and cheating a total stranger, even though it was for the good of the town?

Elinor Donahue: Please forgive me. I don't remember this episode at all.

Steve Spignesi: In "The Beauty Contest," Ellie Walker nominated Andy as judge of the Founder's Day beauty pageant. Of course, he misread her nomination and thought she did it so he'd pick her as the winner. Aunt Bee quietly entered Ellie after she refused to participate and Andy had a problem from which he gallantly extricated himself by choosing the pageant seamstress. What is your personal opinion of beauty pageants?

Elinor Donahue: I have no personal problem with beauty pageants. At least in this day and age the main thrust seems to be on personality and achievements and future goals, rather than just measurements. From what I've read, it is hard work: one has to be mentally and physically prepared for hours and hours of close scrutiny by the judges. My hat's off to anyone with the stamina to get in one of the major pageants.

Steve Spignesi: In "Mayberry on Record," Ellie introduced Mr. Maxwell, the record promoter, to the townfolk and immediately Andy was skeptical. His worries were unfounded, though, and the investors began to collect royalties from their record, "Music from Mayberry." Do you enjoy folk music? What are your personal tastes in music? Also, was the music played on the show performed live or dubbed in later?

Elinor Donahue: At first I couldn't remember anything about this one and still don't know the whole answer regarding live or dubbed music. However, most music for film or TV is prerecorded and, if so, was recorded by those you saw. I remember the day the fellows came to the set to play for Andy. I was enchanted and quite tickled by their antics. Country-western is not my most favorite music,

although I enjoy it in measured doses. I like classical (light and otherwise), Broadway show scores, popular music from the thirties to the fifties, things like that.

Steve Spignesi: In "Cyrano Andy" we are faced, as Andy puts it, with the "eternal quadrangle." When Barney got the idea that Andy was after Thelma Lou, Ellie's the one who came up with the idea of calling their bluff, of her and Andy playing up to Barney and Thelma Lou in order to force them to be honest with each other. Andy was right when he told Ellie that "behind that pretty face" there's an "awful handsome brain." How were you able to keep a straight face when Don Knotts played his "suave loverboy" scene with you in the backroom of the pharmacy?

Elinor Donahue: I didn't. Seriously, though, Don and I had the nicest working relationship possible. We really liked each other, and so the work was easy.

Steve Spignesi: In "The New Doctor," Andy Taylor proposed to Ellie Walker, thanks—once again—to Barney's meddling and misinterpretation of circumstances. What I remember most about this episode is the tag of the show. Ellie put a bandage on Opie's knee and comforted him, telling him she loved him. Was your relationship with the very young Ronny Howard as warm and caring offstage as came through in this—and other—episodes?

Elinor Donahue: I've since worked with many child actors and most all have been delightful, but I've not yet worked with any child as talented as Ronny. We weren't "acting" in our scenes. Something lovely happened that can't be thought out or intellectualized, we just "were," he and I, Ellie and Opie. I'm so proud of the man he's become, just as talented as ever and every bit as nice a person. His father—Rance Howard (an actor and good, too)—and his mother, also an actress, raised him beautifully. He is a real credit to them.

Steve Spignesi: In "Ellie Saves A Female," you were very convincing as a caring, concerned friend of the daughter of the obstinate farmer. I know Ellie Walker would, but would Elinor Donahue ever step in when faced with a similar plight and attempt to change what she considered an unacceptable situation?

Elinor Donahue: Absolutely. I'm a real "busy-body" when I see a wrong that needs correcting.

Steve Spignesi: In "The Guitar Player Returns," your part was rather small, the main story centering around the return of Jim Lindsey and his subsequent redemption. But one thing I do remember: you had cut your hair short and you looked great! Whose idea was it to cut it and did you prefer the shorter style over the longer pageboy you had been wearing?

Elinor Donahue: I'd forgotten about that! Apparently, I used to cut my hair as a symbol of something—liberation, defiance, who knows. I cut my hair short once before, while on a "Father Knows Best" hiatus. The producer, Gene Rodney, was furious at me for having married and

then having given birth to a son (though I only missed shooting one show. I worked up to six weeks before the birth and was back five weeks after—our whole spring hiatus). He planned to send Betty to college and get rid of her. So, I thought, "Well, phooey on you" and cut my hair. This "ritual haircutting" while on "The Andy Griffith Show" was probably due to the fact that I suspected I'd not be back for the next season. My agent asked for my release, at my request, before they had a chance to ax me.

Steve Spignesi: What is your favorite episode of the ones you were in?

Elinor Donahue: I think the Christmas show.

Steve Spignesi: What are your thoughts on a reunion movie, or is Mayberry a place to which you can never return?

Elinor Donahue: I think taking part in such a reunion would be a delight. Not only would I work with old friends again, but as I'm a stronger actress and person now than I was then, I could make up for some past mistakes. [This interview was conducted when "Return To Mayberry" was still only a rumor. As we now know, the movie aired on NBC on April 13, 1986, and Elinor Donahue's character, Ellie Walker, was not part of the script.—sjs]

Steve Spignesi: What is your overall opinion of TV today?

Elinor Donahue: Overall the scope is so broad, and much of it is excellent, I would have to say that it is quite good considering the changes that have occurred in life in general in the past twenty-two years.

Steve Spignesi: Do you ever watch the reruns of "The Andy Griffith Show" when they're on?

Elinor Donahue: No, I seldom watch any old shows, not even "Father Knows Best!" Not consciously. I just don't think to turn them on.

Steve Spignesi: What do you believe was the biggest factor contributing to the tremendous popularity of the show both when it was originally on and now in syndication?

Elinor Donahue: In the first place, Andy had quite a following at the time; the show was an excellent vehicle for him. It had warmth, humor, and a genuineness about it. I believe such a show would fare well today.

Steve Spignesi: What ever happened to Ellie Walker anyway?

Elinor Donahue: Last I heard she was a V.P. in a major pharmaceutical firm *up north*. She's married to a successful corporation lawyer, and has two teen-age children (a boy and a girl). In her quiet moments, she sometimes daydreams of her early days in Mayberry, and thinks of Andy fondly, wondering what turns his life has taken, if he's happy, married, etc. Though her business has not sent her south as yet, who knows if one day they might not accidentally meet again.

Steve Spignesi: Miss Donahue, thank you for your visit to Mayberry, my hometown.

213

A TALK WITH THE REAL FATHER OF OPIE AND LEON

Rance Howard, the real-life father of Ron (Opie) and Clint (Leon) Howard, has had a long and varied career in show business from his early days in the Air Force, up through his role as a preacher in "Return to Mayberry." The Howard clan, even though it is first and foremost a show biz family, are more a quiet family unit than a fast-paced group of "party people." When I initially wrote to Rance, he responded immediately with photos and the offer of an interview. I called him one Sunday afternoon, and the following is an edited version of our talk.

Steve Spignesi: Thanks very much for agreeing to visit Mayberry, my hometown.
Rance Howard: I don't mind helping at all. I am very, very close to "The Andy Griffith Show" and the Mayberry people and, as a matter of fact, I feel like I am one of them myself.
Steve Spignesi: I'd say you definitely are a Mayberry person.
Rance Howard: Well, I'm glad to do anything I can to help further that cause. There's a lot of entertainment—and interest—there, and I'm very happy to help you.
Steve Spignesi: Great. How did you get involved on a creative level with "The Andy Griffith Show" and how did your script, "The Ball Game," become an "Andy Griffith" episode?
Rance Howard: Well, I've been interested in writing almost from the time I was in grade school. And I had toyed with writing in college and then later on the road with different plays when I was touring. Also, I had written a couple of plays when I was in the Air Force, and some sketches and things like that. So, when "The Andy Griffith Show" came along, and Ronny became Opie, I was afforded an opportunity to be close to the creative end of it. (From here on I'll call my son Ron because that's what I call him now. That's what he prefers. When he was a little fellow, we called him Ronny. But when he became a big fellow, he decided that he would be Ron and so that's what's natural for me to call him.) Here's the way "The Andy Griffith Show" was approached creatively. The way they worked, they would read—at the beginning of a season for example—two scripts. Now on a Thursday, one script would be the one they were going to put into rehearsal on Friday. They would rehearse it and do some work on the script itself and then they would start shooting it on Monday. And they would shoot this script Monday, Tuesday, and Wednesday. And then they would read the second script plus another script on Thursday, putting the original second script into rehearsal. The second script would now become the priority—the one that they would be working on. They'd put that into rehearsal on Friday, and then they would start shooting it on Monday and shoot Monday, Tuesday, and Wednesday. So, scripts were always in the process of evolution, of being worked on, of being polished, and of being honed. Now, when Ron when started on the show, he was unable to read.

So, I went to the studio with him, and I would read for him. This put me in very close contact with the producer Aaron Ruben and with Andy and Don and Sheldon Leonard (the executive producer) and also the writers. I became very familiar with the format and how the show worked. So, I began to say to myself, "Hey I can write for this show." And I said that for quite a while. In the meantime, I had written a comedy—a play that I produced and directed. Bob Sweeney, the director of the series at that time, came to see it and he was very complimentary about it and he helped give me a boost up the creative ladder as far as getting an "Andy Griffith Show" to write. I was always pitching ideas to Aaron Ruben, who was the producer and story editor at the time. Now, somewhere down the line "The Ball Game" actually happened. That story actually happened to me. We had a birthday party for Ron. I forget which birthday it was, but it was a birthday party, and we took a group of his friends out to the ball park to play softball and I was the umpire. And that incident actually happened to me. I was faced with the call and I called Ron out at the plate. He swore up and down he was safe and many of his friends thought he was safe and we had a big family argument. We still discuss it to this day and Ron still thinks he was safe. But suddenly I said, "My Gosh! this'd be a terrific episode for 'TAGS'!" So, I went in and I told the story to Andy and he thought it was wonderful. I then went down to the story editor's office. By this time the story editor was a guy named Bob Ross. I told the story to Bob and he thought it was very good, and so I ended up writing the script. After it was written, they felt that the script needed "jazzing up" a little bit so they brought in another writer—Sid Morse—to do some work on it. In all due respect to Sid and everybody else, "The Ball Game" was about eighty-five percent my script. But I was happy to get my foot in the door.
Steve Spignesi: In the real-life incident that prompted the script, were there pictures taken that proved you wrong the way pictures proved Andy wrong in the episode?
Rance Howard: No, there weren't. There weren't any pictures to back up the call one way or the other. That was a device that I needed to use to end the story. I think I came up with that device, but I'll tell you—my way was to originally prove Andy right. And then the twist was to prove that—actually—Andy was wrong. I think Andy himself may have come up with that idea. Aunt Bee and Helen Crump saw the pictures and they thought, no, they weren't going to reveal Andy's error. They were going to be gracious and let the call stand. They had the proof that he was wrong but they didn't make a big deal out of it.
Steve Spignesi: Especially after Howard "reminded" the town that they had asked Andy to do a job and then chastised him for doing it the way he felt was right. The thrust of the episode to me was the town's realization that they should have stood by Andy—and his call.
Rance Howard: That's right.
Steve Spignesi: I'm very interested in your answer to this next question. What does it feel like for you to be directed by your son, as in "Splash," "Cocoon," and "Gung Ho"?
Rance Howard: Well, I feel very comfortable. I have a lot of confidence in his direction. Ron has a way of communicating with all actors, but he communicates with me very well. I can tune in to him and know exactly what

he wants. But it's largely him. He has a real great way of communicating with actors. I always enjoy working with Ron in the position of my being an actor and him as director because I feel comfortable and confident that I can give him what he wants. That's sometimes a problem for me. I always wonder if I'm really giving the director what he wants in a scene. But with Ron I just enjoy it. It's just a real, real pleasure to work with him. I discovered that the first time I worked with him. I've been in just about all of his movies. From the time he first started directing little experimental films, I found that he was really capable of telling me what he wanted. And it's so great to look at the director and the director says, "Now this is what I want to get out of this scene. This is what I want you to do." And to be able to then—as an actor—run that through my mind and say, "Yeah, I can do that, I know what you mean," and then be able to do it.

Steve Spignesi: How often do you see Ron and Clint?

Rance Howard: Well, since Ron is in Connecticut I don't see him quite so often. Probably on an average of every couple of weeks I suppose. It seems like he gets out here every couple of weeks for something. And now when he comes out here on business, he always stays at our place, which is very nice. So, actually, since he's moved to Connecticut, in a way we see more of him because he comes here and he has breakfast or he has dinner and we chat a little bit. We see Clint two or three times a week. Clint lives over in Malibu, but he drops by here a lot.

Steve Spignesi: Does Ron ever come to you for advice on the business or is he such a seasoned pro now that he's confident that he's making the right moves? Does he ever come to you as a son and say, "Dad, you know, I'm a little bit muddled about this or that?"

Rance Howard: Well, we do all of that. We talk on all levels. Sometimes I talk as his father, sometimes I talk as a writer. Sometimes he'll have me read something and he'll say, "What do you think about this? What is wrong with this? What's wrong with this character? How could we help this character?" And sometimes he'll want input and sometimes he'll just read it to get a general reaction from it. And so I'd say he "consults" me. I'm not his big official advisor or anything. But we talk. And sometimes if he's doing something and there's something I don't agree with—I think he might be missing a bit or something—I'll say, "Hey Ron, did you ever consider this?" And sometimes he'll say, "Yeah, I considered it, but it's not what I'm looking for." And sometimes he'll say, "No I didn't, that's a good idea!" and use it. So, Ron and I have a very, very open line of communication. We can talk show business or personal things, we can talk about kids and bringing up children or we can talk about business and business deals. We have a real nice relationship.

Steve Spignesi: Jim Nabors told me that he considers you a real, valued friend. What do you remember about Jim when he first started working for Andy?

Rance Howard: Well, Jim is a real, real open, warm, pleasant guy.

Steve Spignesi: I got the same feeling talking to him.

Rance Howard: Jim came onto the show with a lot of talent, but his talent was all in music. He had a talent for acting, but as an actor he was totally inexperienced. When Jim first came on the set, the show was in its third year.

And he was the kind of guy who was easy to be friends with. We just fell into a nice, nice friendship. I could give him a little help on acting and working and even just the technique of working in front of a camera. But mainly here was a nice guy who wanted to be friends. Jim is totally open and I don't think he's ever seen anybody that he didn't like. And it's like this: Jim walks in a room and all over his face is "Love, Friend, Love, Friend." And you say, "Well, hey, how you doing, Jim!" and he beams back, "Oh, pretty good buddy, how you doing?" He's really an easy guy to be friends with.

Steve Spignesi: What do you remember about Howard McNear?

Rance Howard: Oh, Howard was a real nice guy, a real nice guy. And funny, with a great, droll, subtle sense of humor. A very, very nice guy. I don't have a lot of good Howard McNear stories, though. There was one thing that kind of bothered Howard a little. He and I talked about it some, too. Howard played "Doc" on the radio production of "Gunsmoke," and when the show went to television, he didn't get the part. That kind of always bothered him. Well, it didn't *bother* him—I mean it wasn't a great cross he had to bear—but he felt it was something that he was "that close" to being "Doc" in "Gunsmoke." After all, he was "Doc" on the radio. But he didn't get the part. But it really didn't bother him a lot. It was just one of those things. Sometimes as actors we have little sensitive spots. Like maybe we didn't get a part that we thought we should have gotten. Or we didn't get the part that might have been a real career maker. But he was such a sweet guy, and he was always so nice to Ron. Of course, everybody was. And his wife, Helen, was also a very nice person. I just have real fond memories of Howard McNear.

Steve Spignesi: How about a favorite "Andy" episode? Is there a #1 episode in your heart?

Rance Howard: Gosh! There are so many good ones. One that I recall is "Opie the Birdman."

Steve Spignesi: That's my favorite.

Rance Howard: Is it really?

Steve Spignesi: Yes.

Rance Howard: I just think that episode says so much. It's so full and rich. I just love that episode.

Steve Spignesi: What do you think about the current incredible popularity of the show? It seems that more and more people are visiting Mayberry and wanting to live there. What are your thoughts on this "exodus to Mayberry"?

Rance Howard: Well, I'm pleased by it. But I don't know if it's that incredible or not. Because with "The Andy Griffith Show," something happened. There was a chemistry the way the show came together and the characters worked together. And the writing! The writing was so wonderful. I keep getting back to that because they really had good writers. And they also had Sheldon Leonard—the executive producer—who is really a brilliant man. And then Aaron Ruben was the story editor and producer for the first five years. And Aaron is great with comedy and just very, very, very talented. Aaron understands story structure and character. And then there was Andy . . . Andy brought the truth and the honesty and the reality of Mayberry to the series. And if any one person should have credit for making that series stand up today, it would be Andy. Andy was always very sensitive and aware of never going for the big

216

cheap laugh that—while it might be a funny moment—would lessen the overall episode. He felt it would somehow be cheating. It wouldn't quite be honest. He really had such integrity about the characters and what the characters would do and how far they would go. The series was always a top-rated show. It was always in the Top Ten, I believe.

Steve Spignesi: Every season.

Rance Howard: And it ended . . .

Steve Spignesi: In its eighth season as #1.

Rance Howard: Yeah. So people never grew tired of it. It never wore out its welcome. So, now anytime that you get a chance to watch an episode, you go back and it's like, it's like *going home*. If you could go back to where you went to high school or where you went to grade school and spend thirty minutes, wouldn't it be wonderful? "The Andy Griffith Show" kind of gives you an opportunity to go back in time, I think. And I think that's part of it, part of the show's popularity.

Steve Spignesi: Have you got any good Andy or Don anecdotes? Any specific memories that really stick out about working with either of them?

Rance Howard: You know. I really don't know that I do. Neither one of them are great outgoing, demonstrative guys around the stage, around the set. They have a tendency to be quiet. Andy loves music. We had a makeup man named Lee Greenway and Lee is a good banjo player, so Andy and Lee would get together for a few minutes during lunch hour and Andy would play the guitar and Lee would play the banjo, and Don would come in and listen. Don is great listener. But I don't really have any great funny stories.

Steve Spignesi: About your writing. You wrote "Grand Theft Auto" with Ron. Are you still writing and, if so, what are you working on?

Rance Howard: I've got two projects right now. One of them is a treatment for a feature film called "The Crystal Skull." It's based on a true artifact or "art object." You may have read about it. There's a crystal skull of mysterious origin and it was found by a guy named Michael Mitchell Hedges down in British Honduras in the 1920s. It is thought that perhaps the ancient Mayan priests somehow used it in some of their ceremonies to make pronouncements and things. But nobody is sure. It has been examined by biocrystalographers. It's made out of quartz crystal and it is so perfectly sculpted or made, but there are no signs that modern-day gemcutting tools were used on it. And so its origin is a mystery. And we don't know how old it is. Nobody can figure it out. Some say it could be 12,000 years old, some say maybe 500 years old, other people say it might be from the Atlantis civilization. So, anyway, there are two of these skulls in existence. One belongs to a lady named Anna Mitchell Hedges, who is still living. Michael Mitchell Hedges was her foster father, and she lives up in Canada, and she's in her eighties, and she has it. There's another similar skull—with not quite as good detail as the one she has—in the British Museum over in London. The skull has sometime been referred to as the "Skull of Doom." There's been quite a lot written about it. It's been on several TV shows like "Believe It or Not," "That's Incredible," things like that. And it supposedly has legendary power of healing or power of destruction. So, anyway, I have—with

another guy—concocted a story about it which answers—without conjecture—the mystery of its origin.

Steve Spignesi: That sounds like fun.

Rance Howard: The treatment is kind of an interesting science fiction, action adventure thing. And then I'm working on something dealing with the Pony Express which I hope may be a miniseries.

Steve Spignesi: That sounds interesting.

Rance Howard: It is. As a student of American history, I read a little about the Pony Express. But lately I've been doing a lot of research on the Pony Express. Just a fascinating, fascinating subject. And I'm getting into dealing more with the guys behind the Pony Express, the guys who saw the need for it and backed it. I think it would make an excellent six or eight hour miniseries.

Steve Spignesi: Have you got a favorite of Ron's movies?

Rance Howard: You mean movies that he has directed?

Steve Spignesi: Yes.

Rance Howard: Well, that's pretty tough. I like all of his movies. Of course, I love "Grand Theft Auto." Of course, I'm probably prejudiced and you'll have to forgive me for that. But that was an enormous job, a huge job to do that—especially for a first-time director. But I thought the results were just excellent, almost even without considering the fact that it had to be jammed through in twenty-two days. But I thought he did a great job. But beyond that, I think that "Cocoon" is very good. It shows tremendous strides in direction. Another thing he did here some time ago that I thought was a very good project was a movie called "Skyward." That was on television and starred Bette Davis. But it's hard. In making these selections, we're talking just by degrees, and no big measurements.

Steve Spignesi: How does TV today compare to the era in which "The Andy Griffith Show" was so popular, and how is it different?

Rance Howard: That's a good question. And I don't know that it's that much different. There are some really good series around today, and there are some really good "Movies of the Week" and good miniseries which we didn't have when "TAGS" was originally on the air. But, I don't know. We seem to be missing something. At the time "The Andy Griffith Show" was on, you had "The Danny Thomas Show," you had "The Dick Van Dyke Show," you had "Gunsmoke," you had "Bonanza." And it seems to me that maybe we don't have the shows that run parallel in popularity and quality right now quite as much as we may have had at that time. Like you have "Hill Street Blues," which is definitely a quality show, but it's never really been able to quite achieve the popularity of a "Gunsmoke" or a "Bonanza" or one of those shows. An "Ironside," an "Ellery Queen." They were good shows, and they were good quality and they had enormous popularity. Right now we have one really good sitcom that's a hit and that's "The Cosby Show." OK, Bob Newhart has a good show, but it's never quite been able to make the grade as far as the ratings are concerned, as, for instance, the first Bob Newhart show did. So, maybe there's not quite that crop of fresh talent that's on the horizon right now. Maybe the shows aren't quite in tune with the audience, with what the audience wants to see. But we definitely have good writers and I get back to the "Movies of the Week" and the miniseries. Some of them are just better than movies, better than feature films.

Steve Spignesi: Andy Griffith—on a recent "Donahue" show—said that Frances Bavier was too ill to make "Return to Mayberry." What do you hear from her?

Rance Howard: I haven't talked with her recently, but she is ill. I'm very sorry about that. She's such a nice person. Ron went down to North Carolina one time kind of hoping to see her, but he was never able to. He found where she lived but either she was not home or wouldn't answer the door. And he left notes and tried to call her but he never was able to make contact with her. And she's such a sweet lady.

Steve Spignesi: What do you remember about the actual physical set of the town of Mayberry?

Rance Howard: I'll tell you a little bit of history about that. At Desilu 40 Acres, where they had Mayberry Main Street, the courthouse, the church, and Andy's house, they did a lot of "Gone With the Wind" back there originally.

Steve Spignesi: So, they went from Tara to Mayberry.

Rance Howard: Right!

Steve Spignesi: Mr. Howard, thank you very much for visiting Mayberry, my hometown. You helped make Mayberry what it was—and is!

Rance Howard: Glad to help!

TALKING TO LEON

Clint Howard—like his brother Ron—has been acting since he was two years old. First as the silent Leon (the cowboy) in "The Andy Griffith Show," and then on to the starring role (after the bear) in "Gentle Ben," Clint has been working steadily for the past twenty-five years. I thought it mandatory to speak with him and complete the Howard trilogy. He called me from Ron's house, where he was visiting. Clint is much less serious than his brother and is a genuine "wild and crazy guy." He knocked Ron's phone off the desk twice while we were speaking, and I could easily picture him as the fast-talking Eaglebauer from "Rock & Roll High School," feet up on the desk, kicking the phone into oblivion. I found him to be a charming, intelligent guy who is not afraid to speak his mind. Ron's success has not soured Clint or affected their relationship. He is genuinely happy and proud for his big brother and "best friend." The following is an edited version of our talk.

Steve Spignesi: As a citizen of Mayberry, can you describe for me what it was like living there and why the town is special to you?

Clint Howard: Well, the town is special to me because it was my first recollection as a human being. My first recollections were being around my brother and being around Don and Andy. And the whole crew was so warm and friendly and it wasn't just because I was a Howard—that's the way they were. Bob Sweeney, Aaron Ruben. I really don't remember when I first started in Mayberry, but I remember later on just how incredibly well-run the whole operation was. And that's something that I really enjoy. I really enjoy a good old-fashioned team effort where there's not a lot of egos. I enjoy a good team effort, and "The Andy Griffith Show" really was. Show business and just life in general is filled with a lot of prima donnas. That's the way life is. And if someone is the least bit insecure, the easiest thing for them to do is to throw up a front and try to be tougher, either try to be the bully or try to be the know-it-all. I never sensed that from anybody on that show. It was always a good old-fashioned team effort. We do the best we can and then step away from it. The thing is . . . acting and show business are not brain surgery. They're not the most important things in the world. Being a celebrity is not very important at all. I really do believe that. I think the important people in the world are schoolteachers and surgeons. And to me politicians and actors are kind of in the same boat, because it really doesn't matter. The world is gonna go on without either one of them. And nobody that I can remember on "The Andy Griffith Show" or anybody that lived in that town had that attitude. Now, you also have to remember that I first started working on "The Andy Griffith Show" when I was two. I can't actually remember when I started show business. But until I went down to Florida and worked on "Gentle Ben," I was constantly down on the set of "The Andy Griffith Show" hanging out, going there and having lunch so my parents could be together. Because when I wasn't working, my dad would usually go with Ron. And my mom would stay home and take care of me. But then my mom and I would go down to the set to visit so our whole family could be together for more than just that couple of hours at nighttime.

Steve Spignesi: As you know, Leon did not "Return to Mayberry."

Clint Howard: No, the reason why Leon didn't "Return to Mayberry" was because Leon got another part in another movie and so there was a conflict. As a matter of fact, I felt really honored because they did ask me to come back—not necessarily as Leon—but to play the young heavy, the guy who tried to start the rumor that there was a monster in the lake.

Steve Spignesi: Sure. The Wally Butler character, played by Richard Lineback.

Clint Howard: But I was down working in Tucson on a movie called "The Wraith" with Randy Quaid and Charlie Sheen. I knew the "Andy Griffith" movie was coming up but with me being Leon, I knew I was not going to have a huge part. So, I went ahead and I took this movie, "The Wraith," and then they offered me what ended up being a very nice part. So,I felt a little bad. I'm not sure what Ron's future plans are with the Mayberry operation, but if they go ahead and do another one, I'm gonna be in there pitching to try to play Leon because I think Leon is still walking around in his cowboy hat and his boots, and I even imagine Leon might have a gun or two on him.

Steve Spignesi: That was my next question. Whatever happened to Leon and what do you think he's doing now?

Clint Howard: Well, I definitely don't think he's in San Francisco living in that community. I don't know. Leon is alive and well somewhere. And in all humor I believe he probably owns a gun shop. Either that or he's got a peanut farm somewhere down there.

Steve Spignesi: Speaking of your brother's views on the future of the Mayberry thing . . . I asked him about that and he said that he really wanted to be involved in the first but he wouldn't feel so compelled to be involved in any of the later ones, if there were going to be more.

Clint Howard: Yes. Well, I think Andy knew that. Ron has talked about this a lot with the family. He has a real fondness and a real respect for Andy. And I mean a real serious one. He knows now what that show and what Andy and his leadership did for Ron as a human being and for his career. So, it wasn't that Ron felt obligated to do it, but he wanted to. But Ron is first and foremost now a director. And he thinks it would be giving the public and the movie business the wrong sign if he started doing these "Andy Griffith" shows because it would give people the signal that he wants to be an actor and he really has his mind set on spending the next forty-five years directing. So, I hope they wouldn't cop an attitude and become bitter because Ron wouldn't want to do another one. But old Leon and the gun shop—that's the first time I had ever thought of that.

Steve Spignesi: That is funny.

Clint Howard: I really think he might own a gun shop somewhere.

Steve Spignesi: Maybe in Mayberry?

Clint Howard: Yeah! Or he might have had to move to Mt. Pilot because Andy might have had to send him on down the road.

Steve Spignesi: What's it like working with and *for* Ron?

Clint Howard: Well, it's tremendous. He is the best director I've ever worked for. And it makes it a lot easier when you're best friends with your director. There's a trust that Ron and I have. There's a trust and a straightforward honest kind of a thing that we have going. We'll tell each other when we think that we're blowing it on the set or in life. If Ron thinks that I'm not doing this scene properly or I'm not taking the right attitude with a certain character, he'll have no hesitation but to come up and tell me straightforward, which is the way I like to work. When you're working, it's a business. And you have to put all the personal things aside. It's great that we get along so well, but then there's this business thing where we can tell each other what we don't like. And that makes for very healthy filmmaking. Because a lot of times—getting back to the ego thing—a lot of times with "big stars" or "big directors" people get intimidated about approaching them about a different way to play a scene. It's just that there is not that ego thing involved working with Ron. And then besides that, he's a terrific director because he's an actor's director. He's been there. He knows the feeling. He sympathizes with actors and if there's distractions on the set, he'll make sure that the distractions get eliminated so the actors can do their work. So, I've worked with a lot of good directors and I would not want to rate them. But I will say that Ron is my favorite director.

Steve Spignesi: Would you like to hear what he says about you in my interview with him?

Clint Howard: Sure!

Steve Spignesi: OK. I had asked him about working with your father—which I also want you to address—and then I said, "How about Clint?" Ron responded, "Clint is so inventive and brings so much to every scene that he's an absolute joy to work with." So, then I say, "He was hilarious on 'Letterman' last week." And Ron answers, "Yeah, he was good and that was only a short segment. It was too bad he didn't get a little bit more time. But he's great. And he just has a lot to offer any director and, again, we have a shorthand and I love being able to spend time with him. He's a no-nonsense guy. He'll tell you exactly what he thinks. Whether it's good or bad. But I appreciate that in him, and I just find him a very creative, very helpful person."

Clint Howard: Well, ditto that to Ron. He puts it a lot better than I put it! But there is something about that "shorthand." We don't need to spell it out for each other only because we're brothers. Do you have any brothers?

Steve Spignesi: Yes, two.

Clint Howard: It's as though you can just look at him and he know what you're thinking and because of what you're thinking you know what he's thinking about what you're thinking, you know? That's the shorthand I'm talking about. Another thing: I think it's very helpful for Ron having me around if it's at all possible for him to hire me . . . And the thing is, I always have to earn my parts. I have to go in on the interviews the same as anybody else because we both think that the nepotism—if it's forced—it can hurt. But I bring quite a bit of levity to any set that I work. And Ron is a real hard worker. A lot of times I'll see Ron not having fun on the set. And I'll start joking around, shadowboxing with him, telling jokes at his cost, you know, ragging on him . . . little things to lighten things up.

And this helps the crew because the crew then realizes that Ron is someone that they can approach. You see, it's important that the director has communication with the cast and crew. But because the director is *the* boss on the set, a lot of times people will get intimidated by the director. And when they see me fartin' around with the guy, it's like "Oh, wow! If he can do it, anybody can do it!" So, I'll bring baseball gloves to the set. And if Ron's not busy in between a shot, I'll run to the dressing room, grab the baseball gloves, and we'll play catch for a minute. And that kind of stuff helps him because there's a lot of pressure directing. And eventually, I'm gonna attempt to direct. Not attempt, I'm *going* to direct. But there needs to be that lightening of the load every day when you're on the set because it is *not* brain surgery. It's a business and it's a profession, but then again if you can't have fun doing it . . . I would not want my doctor having fun operating on me, but it's OK to have fun on a movie set.

Steve Spignesi: That was one of my questions. Do you have any desire to write and/or direct?

Clint Howard: Well, Ron and I wrote a movie called "Cotton Candy." He was working on "Happy Days" at the time, so I was the pusher of the pen. We would get together and go over the scenes and then Ron would send me off and I would write 'em, and then we'd get back together and edit them. And I also write. As a matter of fact I'm working on a script right now. It's on spec, but it's the first thing that I've written in two years on my own. I have two writing partners that I've worked with in the past. And I've been lucky enough to sell a couple of pilots. Four or five years ago, I did a pilot called "Thrills & Chills " with The Osmonds, in association with Ron. We produced it and it did not sell, but it gave me the experience of going through that whole thing.

Steve Spignesi: So, then one of your long term goals is to direct?

Clint Howard: Yes. At this point in my life, I don't have the discipline that I think a director really needs. You know, Ron settled right down with Cheryl right out of high school and he knew what he wanted to do and he did it. He busted his bones for ten years directing. Every day he would think about it and he'd do the footwork, he'd make the phone calls. And now it's paid off for him because he's directing hit movies. But with me, I kind of took the bachelor road. I mean, I'm a fun-loving guy. I love to have fun, play golf, screw around with my buddies, go to baseball games, play wiffle ball in the backyard. I enjoy having fun and only now do I realize that "Hey, I'm now twenty-seven years old and directing is something that I could do." And I wanna do it. First of all, I picture myself as a character actor. I'm not a young leading man. I'm not a member of the "Brat Pack." What I am is an interesting character actor—kind of an inventive kind of a guy. And when I was twenty-two, twenty-three years old, I was just not getting the chance to go up on these character parts because I was too young. So, I realize now that at the age of twenty-seven, people are starting to discover me as one of these young character actors, like a young Brian Dennehy, a young Strother Martin, a young Slim Pickens. And this last year has been terrific for me. I worked in two good films, and the year before I was in "Cocoon" and now this "Gung Ho"—the TV series—looks like it might sell. And I'm involved with that. So, I think now more than any time since I was in "Gentle Ben," that the road is really looking bright and positive for me to work a lot. And another thing, it's a lot easier to get someone to hire you as a director if you're hot as an actor. That's the way Ron did it. Ron broke in at a very early age directing because he had the leverage of working on a hit TV show. You know, it's "if you wanna hire me as an actor, you better hire me as a director, too." And that's what he did. So, I see myself within the next five or six years directing at least one feature. And I'm not dead set that I would want to do that as a career. I just know that this is my twenty-fifth year in the entertainment business and I know that I've been around long enough. I see how things work and I think I can do it. And I wanna give myself that opportunity when the time comes.

Steve Spignesi: Do you watch "Andy Griffith" reruns and do you have any favorite episodes?

Clint Howard: You know, as a matter of fact I have not really watched them consistently in the last five years because back in L.A. I do not get Ted Turner and Ted Turner is the main outlet for "Andy Griffith" now. But I remember and enjoy the early ones. I enjoy the first two or three seasons, when the show was really backwoods. When it went color and Ron became sort of a young teen-ager, I felt that the show changed. And then, of course, when Don left, things still worked well...what is the gentleman's name who replaced Don? Burns?

Steve Spignesi: Jack Burns.

Clint Howard: Jack Burns. I think Jack Burns is hilarious, but in my mind it was impossible to replace Don. I was listening to a Jack Burns comedy album. I live out in Malibu and there's a radio station out in that direction that's "Comedy Radio." They play just twenty-four hours a day comedy radio cuts. And I hadn't really thought of Mr. Burns in a long time and he was just hilarious. He was very funny. But as far as favorite episodes, I really couldn't give you any. I would have to say the ones that Leon was in, right?

Steve Spignesi: Your father's favorite episode is "Opie the Birdman." And yet Ron's favorite episode is the one your father wrote, "The Ball Game."

Clint Howard: I can see why Ron would say that because Ron is just a sports nut. Now, my three favorite "Gentle Ben" episodes were all sports-oriented. "Ben the Wrestling Bear," the Bob Gibson episode, and the Bart Starr episode. So, Ron and I, we're both sports nuts. Ron and I—even me—I would rather watch a ball game than a movie. To me, an athletic event—as long as it's not fixed—is the ultimate drama because you don't know what's gonna happen. Most of the time I can watch a movie and in twenty minutes tell you who's gonna die, who's gonna get the girl, and what's gonna happen. And I would just as soon not know what's gonna happen. I was watching a baseball game last night. Guidry struck out the first nine outs! I couldn't believe it. I was sitting here going, "God, look at this! This is amazing!" Then he went ahead and only struck out thirteen or fourteen for the whole game, but to me that's drama. "Is he gonna get that guy? Is he gonna strike him out?"

Steve Spignesi: I asked Ron about his reading habits. I said, "What do you read other than scripts? First thing out of his mouth. . .

Clint Howard: The sports page.

Steve Spignesi: Right! Exactly. The sports section. And then he mentioned a book by Frank Capra—called *Name Above The Title*—and magazines. He said he doesn't have time for much more reading than that and he's not a great reader anyway. How about you?

Clint Howard: Well, I love to read and I go further than just the sports page. I usually wake up in the morning and stare at the box scores, still kind of half asleep. Two or three hours later I'll read the sports section and then go ahead and read the majority of the paper. And sometimes when I really don't have anything to do I'll buy the other local paper. In L.A., it's the *Times* and the *Herald* and I read them both to get both angles. A lot of times—when you can get two different slants on a story—I think you can get closer to the truth. But I'm not a big magazine man. Mostly I look at the pictures in magazines. When I'm working on a film and I'm really trying to concentrate and keep my mind sharp, I will usually try and pick up a book—either a sports book or a book about a piece of history—and I will read just chapters out of it. I won't sit down to read it for entertainment—but just to keep my mind working and just to keep me from going and doing things that would be negative towards my work.

Steve Spignesi: Other than the Wally Butler role in "Return to Mayberry," is there a role in a recent film that you would have done anything to get—one that you feel you could have really hit a home run with?

Clint Howard: Yes. Now, the guy who worked on this film did a terrific job but Tom Cruise had a buddy in "Risky Business" that I could have really knocked on the head and done real well with. ["Miles," played by Curtis Armstrong—sjs] But you only get what you're supposed to get. I'm a firm believer that God gives you what you can handle. An actor goes on ten interviews to get a part. So, nine out of ten times, even me—as long as I've been in the business and as well-known as I am—I still only get one out of eight parts. So, seven times I will not get the part. So, I take that deep breath and I usually quit show business for ten or fifteen minutes and then I come back and I say, "Well, you know, if I didn't get the part there's a reason for it." And then you just try to go ahead and keep a positive attitude and go on to the next deal.

Steve Spignesi: Do you have a favorite of the movies you've been in?

Clint Howard: Well, I'm a fan of "Rock & Roll High School." I don't think it's the greatest picture ever made, but I like it. I'm also proud of this part that I just finished in "The Wraith." First of all, I got to work with one of my idols—Randy Quaid. There's three people that I've always wanted to work with as actors. One is David Bowie, one is Jack Nicholson, and one is Randy Quaid. I think Randy Quaid is probably one of the best American actors going today. Because he's not a cartoon, he's not a leading man, yet everything he does he's believable. And I got to do a couple of scenes with him in this movie and it was just a delight to do. And I feel that this was my first opportunity in quite a while to really do a character. I played this character with a kind of an "Eraserhead" hairdo and I had real thick Coke bottle glasses. The character's name was Rughead. I'm anxious to see it come out. In fact, I saw the looping. When you loop a film you get to see most of the things you've done and this was one of the first times in my life I did not cringe and say, "Oh, God, that was terrible." Usually most actors will see themselves and think that they just were terrible. But in this instance I saw myself and I go, "Yeah, Clint! That's pretty good!" A little smile came to my face. So, I'm anxious to see this come out. I also did a part in a film called "The Red Pony," with Henry Fonda and Maureen O'Hara. It was a pretty big "high prestige" show. Ben Johnson was in it, Jack Elam was in it, and it was directed by another really great director, a guy named Robert Totten. I played Jody, which was the lead in the movie. And I hit that on the head. But I was also thirteen years old and I've improved a lot as an actor since I was thirteen.

Steve Spignesi: Which do you think are the best—or your favorites—of Ron's movies?

Clint Howard: As an actor or as a director?

Steve Spignesi: Both.

Clint Howard: Well, I think "Cocoon"—by far—is my favorite picture with him as director. I thought "Cocoon" was just magical and he just hit it right on the head. And Ron was very good in "The Shootist." Ron's a good actor. He was good in a thing called "Bitter Harvest." It was a TV-movie. The one trouble with doing TV-movies is they kind of come and go. You know, they'll be on and if they're lucky they might play cable for a little while, but people don't get a chance to see it because it's a one night deal and if you're bowling that night or whatever, you're gonna miss it. But I thought "Bitter Harvest" was his best role as an actor. But I'm learning very quickly that I can't judge other people and other actors because I'm an actor, I'm not a critic. First of all, if I start being critical I'll just tear up the world. But as far as a director, I would watch "Cocoon" all day long. It was shot beautifully. Don Peterman did an excellent job photographing it, the casting was great, Ron's direction was good. I have great memories working on it, but more than that I had great memories watching it.

Steve Spignesi: Why do you think the spell "The Andy Griffith Show" cast over its audience twenty-five years ago still holds?

Clint Howard: Oh, I would say that it was just real honest.

Steve Spignesi: Honesty?

Clint Howard: Honesty, and you got humor out of the whole series, yet it was honest humor. It wasn't people slipping on banana peels, it wasn't people falling over women and landing in their boobs, it was a real honest kind of natural humor. First of all, even in city people there's a lot of country in 'em. Because our nation was founded by country folk, and everybody—it might be two or three generations ago—has country in 'em. People that grew up on farms or whatever. And I think people love that kind of lifestyle, they envy that lifestyle and that's the kind of lifestyle that Andy had, and Opie had, and Aunt Bee. And there were very likeable characters, too. When you really look at it, even the goofballs were likeable. Even George Lindsey and Jim Nabors. They were the real comic relief. And Don. But they were likeable, you enjoyed them. They became part of your family.

Steve Spignesi: Do you stay in touch with any of the cast members?

Clint Howard: I see George Lindsey probably more than anyone else, and every once in awhile I'll see Jack Dodson around on an interview for some show or something, 'cause he's out hitting the pavement like all the actors are. And Andy Griffith has always lived kind of around the neighborhood that I grew up in. I have a house in Burbank now, and every once in awhile I would see Andy down at the Altadena Dairy, which is a little milk and soda store. I'd see him and we'd wave and say hi and talk for a minute. But through most of the time when "The Andy Griffith Show" was really in its prime, I was down in Florida working on "Gentle Ben." In fact, one week—I believe it was in 1968—"The Andy Griffith Show" was #1 and "Gentle Ben" was #2 in the Nielsen's. And this was kind of an honor for the Howards. And so there was a period of time where both of us were in the Top Ten together all the time. So, I was off in Florida with my dad while Ron was really in the prime time of the show and I can't really remember much. You know, I really don't remember much about my life much before four or five years old. I don't know whether that's unusual or not but like I said, I don't remember when I started acting. But it had to have gotten a lot easier when I learned how to read. Because I would not have had to have been spoon-fed the lines. Once I learned how to read I was able to go off on my own and study.

Steve Spignesi: Your father told me he did that with Ron also. He had to go to the set every day and teach him his lines.

Clint Howard: My dad is just so terrific. He came out of the farms in Oklahoma and Kansas and went to New York to become an actor. Then he met my mom and they got married, and he set aside his career to raise us. And it had to have been real tough for him because here's this young actor and all of a sudden he's got these kids that are working more than him. But it's paid off for him now because now he's working more than anybody. He's working more than me and I'm working a lot as an actor. So, I really have to take my hat off to Dad. Not only did he teach us well, but he gave us the fundamentals of acting: "The most important things in the world are just your basic fundamentals of listening and being natural. Try not to be caught acting." He taught us that and he was just there with us all the time. He was down working on "Gentle Ben" with me and I learned so much in that two or three year period being around my dad. My dad is such a mild-mannered, easygoing guy. I feel that a human being's strongest asset is not blowing up and not copping attitudes and Dad is just not one of those guys. So, I think both Ron and I got our easygoing natures from my dad. And, of course, my mom. My mom usually let dad work with us professionally. Mom was just Mom . . . She would do the PTA shows, and Dad would take care of the acting business.

Steve Spignesi: Isn't your mom an actress also?

Clint Howard: Well, my mom has done some acting, but I don't think she really considers herself an actress. She's done some student films for friends of hers and she's been in a couple of Ron's movies. She started out being an actress. That's how my mom and dad met. But then once they started having a family, she said well, three actors in a family are enough.

Steve Spignesi: So, you enjoy working with your father?

Clint Howard: Yes, I do. I find it a little difficult to write with him, though, because he's so meticulous and such a detailed person . . . I kind of like to write and fly. I like to write something and move on to the next thing. Dad will sit there and study things, each individual line, which is the right way to do it, but it's just something I don't have the patience for. My dad has incredible patience.

Steve Spignesi: Did you enjoy "Return to Mayberry?"

Clint Howard: To be honest . . . I didn't see it.

Steve Spignesi: Oh, really?

Clint Howard: No, I was still working; it was one of those things where it was just on at the wrong time. I *want* to see it, and I've been bugging people to let me see a tape of it, but I have not seen it. As a matter of fact, I saw about ten minutes of it, and it looked neat. It looked good. You know, to be perfectly honest, I'm not a big one for sequels and reunions. But the "Andy Griffith" reunion was a remarkable success. I mean it's like the seventh highest rated TV-movie of all time.

Steve Spignesi: Yes. The ratings were phenomenal.

Clint Howard: I would just as soon work on something and then let it go and move on to something else. But again, it was proven that old Clint's wrong. I think they'll do a Christmas one.

Steve Spignesi: Well, I heard that "Christmas in Mayberry" has already been booked.

Clint Howard: Well, good. I'll have to get on Dick Linke's case and see if they want Leon. You know, I really feel that people who think that Andy had a downtime were wrong. I think, first of all, that a guy who's that recognizable has to really be careful not to get totally oversaturated. And I think they waited just the right time. They waited long enough and they scored big on their reunion show.

Steve Spignesi: I've heard that there's even talk about a live Maybery theater production. I asked your brother about it but he hadn't heard anything.

Clint Howard: Oh, I don't know. Yeah, I would think that their medium is film.

Steve Spignesi: That was my first reaction also.

Clint Howard: No, they need to be able to do those camera jokes and stuff.

Steve Spignesi: I asked Ron about the "Christmas" movie just to verify what I had heard and he said it's on, but he's not involved.

Clint Howard: No, I think he's gonna have to pass. I think if they end up doing six or seven and he's available to do one down the road, I think he might. But he just doesn't want to commit to becoming part of that troupe.

Steve Spignesi: Bullock and Greenbaum did write him out at the end of the movie. Opie took a job in upstate New York and was moving out of Mayberry.

Clint Howard: So, if worse comes to worse, they can always have a phone conversation.

Steve Spignesi: Exactly. At Barney and Thelma Lou's wedding reception, Andy is toasting everyone and he says, "Not everybody's moving in. Opie and his little family will be leaving for a big new job out of state. But I wouldn't be surprised at all if someday they'll be coming back."

Clint Howard: Well, that's leaving the door open! That's smart writing. This has got me excited. I'll have to watch it now!

Steve Spignesi: A lot happened. It really did write the final chapter on the history of Mayberry. It tied up a lot of loose ends and it finally married Barney and Thelma Lou. It also gave Opie a son, and it gave Andy his job back. And Barney is now his deputy again. It really was a lot of fun—a very warm, touching film. I enjoyed it a lot. Clint, I want to sincerely thank you for your visit to Mayberry, our hometown.

Clint Howard: Well, I appreciate your remembering me. I really enjoyed our talk.

Steve Spignesi: Thank you. I hope you'll be pleased with *Mayberry, My Hometown.*

A TALK WITH
RON "OPIE"
HOWARD

Ron Howard is an American success story and a Hollywood movie come to life. Starting at the age of four in "The Journey," and continuing all the way through his thirty-two year life up to "Return to Mayberry," Ron Howard has been before the cameras, growing up. Now he's all grown up and behind the camera, a "hotshot hitmaker" as "Life" magazine called him.

We—as "Andy Griffith Show" fanatics—of course know and love him as Opie Taylor, the fresh-faced young son of Sheriff Andy Taylor of Mayberry, North Carolina, a role he literally "grew up" with, and one from which he can never be separated.

But there's more to Ron Howard than Opie Taylor.

He has appeared in a "Who's Who" of American television. His credits include episodes of "Dobie Gillis," "Dennis the Menace," "Pete & Gladys," "Make Room for Daddy," "The Great Adventure," "The Smith Family," "M*A*S*H," and "Love, American Style."

He starred in "The Andy Griffith Show," for eight years, and in "Happy Days," as Richie Cunningham, for six years.

But he always wanted to direct, and boy does he now direct!

His movie director credits include "Grand Theft Auto" (which he also starred in and co-wrote with his father, Rance), "Skyward," and four hits in a row: "Night Shift," "Splash," "Cocoon," and "Gung Ho."

Since he now lives in my home state of Connecticut, it was a lot easier than you would think to arrange an interview with this incredibly busy director/producer. But there were still hitches. When talking to Ron about when and where to have our talk, I made it clear that I would work with him whenever *he* had any free time. His schedule was paramount, I told him. I could do it evenings, weekends, whatever. "No," he told me to the nights or weekends. "I prefer to do it on a weekday." Why? Because he also has another major project in his life: his family. It consists of his lovely wife, Cheryl, and his three daughters—five-year-old Bryce, and one-year-old twins, Jocelyn and Paige. We set it up for me to call him one Thursday morning. "If I'm not there," he said, "I'll get back to you as soon as I get in. I might not be back from taking Bryce to school."

Here is obviously a man who has his priorities straight, wouldn't you say?

During our interview, I was continually impressed with Ron. He was modest, unassuming, and went out of his way to be accommodating. In fact, at one point he apologized to me for putting me "through the ringer on this thing." What I just assumed was to be expected—considering his schedule—he saw as something he should apologize for. Ron Howard is a considerate gentleman, and speaking with him for *Mayberry, My Hometown* was a joy and an honor.

Steve Spignesi: First of all, I really appreciate your visit to Mayberry, my hometown. This is a big thrill for me.

Ron Howard: Well, thank you. Let's get started.

Steve Spignesi: OK. First question. Can you describe the Mayberry magic for me, and what has kept it alive for you for the past twenty-five years?

Ron Howard: Well, I think that the Mayberry magic is probably not magic at all but a very simple ideal. A notion that if people live together and basically try to do the right thing and try to look out for each other—then life might not be too spectacular, but it can be rich and very rewarding. And, of course, the show has always offered a very idealistic perspective on small town life. But I think that's what's been nice about it over the years.

Steve Spignesi: I agree. Opie Taylor has become a symbol of the ultimate American boy next door. How much of Opie was Ronny Howard and how much was the writers' creation?

Ron Howard: I think that the two were very close. Oh, there were some things that the writers would have Opie doing that I would have never done, of course. But I think—particularly as the show developed—that they wrote with my own personality in mind. And I know I was always encouraged to try and make the material as believable as I could. And, I was also given an opportunity to say, "Gee, I don't think this is the way a kid would say this."

Steve Spignesi: In the April 7, 1986, "Us" magazine you were quoted as saying that Andy Griffith taught you how to put humor and truth in a story, and that this has helped your storytelling abilities. If you had to pick one real-life Andy Griffith story that has stayed in your memories, what would it be?

Ron Howard: Well, specifically in terms of the show, there was a kind of a lesson that I may have learned from Andy. A lesson not so much about life, but about working on stories and shows. I remember we would always gather around on Thursdays and read a couple of the scripts that we'd be doing in the future. All the actors would read all their parts and the writers would be there and the director would be there. And everyone would be able to evaluate the script. Afterwards, there was always a lot of discussion. All the actors were invited—including *me*—to participate in that discussion. Well, I remember reading this one script that got a lot of laughs. It was very funny, and it was pretty outrageous. It had Andy and Barney being pretty goofy. And when it was over, people were smiling, and they were happy, and then Andy said, "I think we're gonna have to rewrite this script." And there was kind of a silence because everyone had thought it was a very funny script, and one of the producers said so. But Andy said, "Yeah, I think it's funny, too." He said, "We're not doing 'Beverly Hillbillies.' It's important for this show that the humor not be derived from viewers laughing *at* our characters because they're hillbillies. And dumb. But it's all gotta always be because they're laughing *with* the characters. The situation needs to be funny. Maybe the way they react needs to be funny. But these are not stupid people."

Steve Spignesi: Was that episode filmed?

Ron Howard: Oh, yeah. I don't remember which episode it was, but it was filmed. And I think that the difference between laughing *at* something or somebody and laughing *with* them is really a line that the show continued to walk very successfully. And it's something that I've always kept in the back of my mind.

Steve Spignesi: I noticed that in "Cocoon" I did laugh *with* the senior citizens, so you've achieved that balance in that film.

Ron Howard: Well, it was because as human beings they always maintained their integrity and their believability. And that was very much something that Andy was always striving for. And you could maintain that integrity and still get very funny. I mean, Barney could make honest mistakes. After all, he was kind of a kooky guy. And Goober could be a little dumb. But they were always left with their integrity intact.

Steve Spignesi: What are your memories of working with Howard McNear?

Ron Howard: He was very much the same guy off camera as he was on—his speech patterns and everything . . . they were just Howard. He suffered a stroke—two strokes actually—during the course of the show, but he always came back. Each time he would have lost a little bit of his mobility, but not that wonderful sense of timing and that comedic delivery that made him such a great character.

Steve Spignesi: How about Jim Nabors?

Ron Howard: You know, Jim was really only on the show a couple of years before he spun off it, so I remember Jim very fondly—and liked him—but I really got to know him a lot better, I think, on this "Andy" reunion show where we were able to spend a couple of afternoons really talking. He's a wonderful guy.

Steve Spignesi: I interviewed Elinor Donahue for *Mayberry, My Hometown* and she remembers you fondly and speaks very highly of you. What are your memories of her?

Ron Howard: Well, she also was only on the show one season. I remembered her from "Father Knows Best," and so I was kind of a fan of hers. I used to love to watch that show—and still do sometimes in reruns. She was probably one of the first actors that I was ever "aware" of . . . one of the first actors I ever worked with where I was aware of their past. Otherwise, I just always took everybody completely at face value.

Steve Spignesi: Your father told me about how you once went down to North Carolina in an attempt to see Frances Bavier, but couldn't make contact.

Ron Howard: This was very recent. This was just two years ago.

Steve Spignesi: What do you remember about that trip and what do you hear from her?

Ron Howard: I haven't heard anything. She was always kind of a reclusive lady. Wonderful and charming to be around, but when she went home—that was her own world. She didn't socialize a lot or anything. And when she retired, she took that to the next step and now very few people talk to her. Andy talks to her every once in awhile. And Lee Greenway—who was our makeup man on the show—he talks to her occasionally. But I have been unable to make contact with her.

Steve Spignesi: Andy mentioned on "Phil Donahue" that she was ill and that was the reason why she couldn't do "Return to Mayberry."

Ron Howard: That's right. She's not real well, no.

Steve Spignesi: Speaking of "Return to Mayberry"...

Ron Howard: Let me just say one other thing about North Carolina.

Steve Spignesi: Go right ahead.

Ron Howard: I had never been there. And first of all, I was pleasantly surprised to see how accurate our locations had been when we were doing the show. North Carolina looked just the way I thought it was gonna look, based on my experience with the show. And the people were just wonderful, and it was not a letdown at all. It was strangely nostalgic even though it was the first time I'd set foot in the state.

Steve Spignesi: That's wonderful. So, you've returned to North Carolina. What was it like "Returning to Mayberry?"

Ron Howard: That was a great experience . . . one that I actually went into with some trepidation. I just didn't want anything to "color" my memory of the show. And I think in a lot of ways it was just the opposite. I got to know Jim Nabors, I got to know a lot of these people more as adults. Of course, they were always adults, but now I knew them with myself as an adult, and from an adult perspective. And they didn't let me down at all. They're a terrific bunch of people. Hard workers, very talented, and a pleasure to be with. I really enjoyed the experience.

Steve Spignesi: Well, as you know, the movie went through the roof in the ratings, and NBC has already booked it for at least two reruns. I've heard that now there's talk about a live Mayberry theater production. What are your thoughts on that and would you participate or maybe even direct?

Ron Howard: Well, I haven't heard anything at all about it and my participation would always be based on my schedule as a director. I *really* wanted to be involved in the very first reunion show. I probably would feel a little less "compelled" to be in all the rest—if there were going to be more. But it would be something that I would always be open to depending on what was going on.

Steve Spignesi: Aside from the repeats of "Return to Mayberry," I've heard that NBC has already scheduled "Christmas in Mayberry."

Ron Howard: Right.

Steve Spignesi: Are you involved?

Ron Howard: I'm not. So far, I'm not involved in that. I haven't heard anything about it, and it may be that they just know that the schedules would conflict and so haven't asked. But so far I haven't heard anything about it.

Steve Spignesi: Do you have any idea why Barney called Andy "Ange?"

Ron Howard: That's something that Don just started doing on the set. And then they worked it into the script. Don was the first one to do it in between filming.

Steve Spignesi: For *Mayberry, My Hometown*, we really wanted to come up with some kind of an answer for that and so I just kept watching the episodes and thinking about it and it struck me that since Andy Taylor's middle name was "Jackson," Barney—as his cousin—would have known his middle name, and that his middle initial was "J" and he might have called him "Andy J," "Andy J," and it might have just . . .

Ron Howard: Become "Ange."

Steve Spignesi: . . . just become "Ange." It made sense, but I thought I'd ask you about it.

Ron Howard: You know, I don't know about that. But I do remember Don calling him "Ange," on the set before they started using it in the scripts.

Steve Spignesi: Do you have a favorite "Andy" episode?

Ron Howard: My favorite probably was the baseball episode.

Steve Spignesi: "The Ball Game."

Ron Howard: Yeah. Because I had so much fun doing it. My dad actually wrote the story for that.

Steve Spignesi: He told me about it.

Ron Howard: I just loved baseball at that time and it was so great to get to do a film—to get to work on a show that dealt with baseball.

Steve Spignesi: He told me that the incidents in that episode happened in real life?

Ron Howard: Yes, they did. So, I could really relate to it and I got a big kick out of it. I also, though, really remember the show about the little birds.

Steve Spignesi: "Opie the Birdman."

Ron Howard: Yeah.

Steve Spignesi: "The long-ago songbirds."

Ron Howard: Yes. I loved that show.

Steve Spignesi: That's your father's favorite.

Ron Howard: Is it?

Steve Spignesi: Yes. Speaking of Rance, what's it like directing your father?

Ron Howard: It's really easy. He's so professional and I think he bends over backwards just to kind of help me out and not cause any problems. I'm able to work very well with him, and very easily. And we get a lot of good work done.

Steve Spignesi: How about Clint?

Ron Howard: Clint is so inventive and brings so much to every scene that he's an absolute joy to work with.

Steve Spignesi: He was hilarious on "Letterman" last week.

Ron Howard: Yeah, he was good and that was only a short segment. It was too bad he didn't get a little bit more time. But he's great. And he just has a lot to offer any director, and again, we have a shorthand and I love being able to spend time with him. He's a no-nonsense guy. He'll tell you exactly what he thinks. Whether it's good or bad. But I appreciate that in him, and I just find him a very creative, very helpful person.

Steve Spignesi: I know your daughter Bryce watches "Andy Griffith" reruns.

Ron Howard: Once in awhile, yeah.

Steve Spignesi: What does she think of seeing her father at her age?

Ron Howard: Well, she's five years old, and she's just now beginning to really be able to understand that those are like home movies. So, she'll see an episode of "The Andy Griffith Show," and then I'll take a videotape of her when she was six or seven months old and show her that. She's beginning to see that images can be preserved and shown later. And so, beyond that I don't know how much she understands except she knows that I was an actor.

Steve Spignesi: Let's talk about "Splash." Specifically, the "Up yours, Gomer" line.

Ron Howard: (Laughs) Right.

Steve Spignesi: Was that originally part of the script or was that your contribution?

Ron Howard: No, it was part of the script and I actually thought about taking it out because I was afraid that Jim might see it and be upset about it. But it was so funny that I left it in. Jim mentioned to me the other day when we were working that he got a big kick out of that. He came right out and said that he saw it and enjoyed it. So, I was a little bit relieved, although I didn't tell him that.

Steve Spignesi: OK, about your movies, "Splash" and "Cocoon." They both end begging for a sequel. Are either destined "to be continued"?

Ron Howard: Well, we are working on a "Splash" sequel right now, on the script.

Steve Spignesi: With Daryl Hannah?

Ron Howard: Everybody would be involved if we get a good script. But if we don't get a good script, it won't be done. And there has been some discussion of a "Cocoon" sequel, but I'm not involved in that. [Interestingly, in the June 5, 1986, "Rolling Stone"—the issue released immediately after I spoke with Ron—there was the following blurb about Daryl Hannah: "Hannah's now developing scripts based on her own stories—the 'Splash' writers have adapted one—but she has no intention of jumping back into the water for 'Splash II'."—sjs]

Steve Spignesi: Do you have a favorite of your own movies?

Ron Howard: It's pretty hard to say. There are things that I like about all of them and then there are little problems that I have with all of them, too. So, I guess what I'm most pleased with on each of them are the individual moments or scenes that I really loved the most. I think I've kind of stopped looking at them as a whole because I'm proud of all of them, but then there are these individual moments that I really appreciate.

Steve Spignesi: What kind of stuff—other than scripts—do you read?

Ron Howard: The sports section. And I read magazines.

Steve Spignesi: Do you have time for books, novels?

Ron Howard: I'm not a great reader, unfortunately. I read Frank Capra's book a couple of times, though. *Name Above The Title*. It's a great book, and it really was kind of inspirational to me.

Steve Spignesi: Where do you see yourself in twenty years?

Ron Howard: Directing movies and television. Pretty much where I am now. Hopefully better. More autonomy and more control. And I hope to be a lot smarter in twenty years than I am now.

Steve Spignesi: I've noticed that a predominant theme that seems to running through some of your recent movies is that of the "stranger in a strange land." Is this a conscious choice on your part and, if so, why do you think you're attracted to the symbol of "the alien"?

Ron Howard: Well, it really isn't a conscious choice, as a matter of fact, but it's something—particularly when I did "Gung Ho"—that I began to realize that that line could clearly be drawn. And I suppose that it interests me because it gives you such a choice . . . when you have a character who is looking at our world and our culture from a different point of view, it allows us to make interesting observations about ourselves which are very touching and humorous and strike a chord in all of us. And it's easier for someone else to be complimentary or critical and it's also easier for us to accept that and be entertained by it.

Steve Spignesi: Howard Morris directed you in some "Andy" episodes. What was it like directing him in "Splash"?

Ron Howard: Well, I was nervous. I just hoped that the scenes would go well and that Howard would respond and feel good about the work. And he did make a few jokes about it in the beginning, but then he was very complimentary and, of course, he did a terrific job. And we had a lot of fun that day. But also, there's another interesting facet involving the cast of "Splash" and Howard Morris. Eugene Levy is from "Second City," and "SCTV" is really kind of the eighties version of "Your Show of Shows," which Howard Morris began.

Steve Spignesi: You've appeared on everything from "Dobie Gillis" and "Dennis the Menace" to "M*A*S*H" and "Happy Days." You've been on everything.

Ron Howard: (Laughs)

Steve Spignesi: But . . . is Opie Taylor your all-time favorite role and, if so, why. And if not, why not?

Ron Howard: Well, it's probably not my all-time favorite role. But it's very hard for anything to compare with Opie because I don't think any character that I ever do will be quite as close as Opie was to me. It just didn't really feel like I was creating a character.

Steve Spignesi: You were just being you.

Ron Howard: Yes, I was really just being me most of the time. And for that reason it's *not* my favorite character because an actor likes to do something different and be able to pull it off. Something a little bit more challenging. So, Opie has a special place in my life and probably no other acting experience will ever be able to live up to what it was like working on that show and playing Opie. But, there's a character in a TV-movie that I did called "Act of Love" that's my favorite character.

Steve Spignesi: One last question. Do you keep in touch with any "Andy Griffith" cast members regularly and, if so, who?

Ron Howard: Andy is the closest, and I also hear a lot about what he's got going on because he stops by and visits my parents every once in awhile. They live near each other. But usually it's just a matter of bumping into people. I worked with Jack Dodson several times on "Happy Days." I see George Lindsey around from time to time. John Ritter was working with Don Knotts, so I bumped into Don a couple of times. John's a friend of mine. So, consciously, no, I don't. But I've seen just about everybody periodically since the show ended. And the reunion was wonderful on that level because it'll probably stimulate a little bit closer contact.

Steve Spignesi: Ron "Opie Taylor" Howard, it has been a great and sincere pleasure talking to you and I want to thank you again for your visit to Mayberry, our hometown.

Ron Howard: Well, thank you. It's been nice talking to you, and I'm looking forward to seeing your book.

Steve Spignesi: Thanks again.

Mayberry
My Hometown

Part V
Mayberry Fandom:
"A Rendezvous With Destiny"

**THE BALLAD OF
ANDY AND BARNEY**

Andy and Barney were lawmen
Bravest you ever did see
Warned every crook in the record book
To stay out of Mayberry
They were the law
And they didn't know fear

THE MAYBERRY TOP TEN

These are my ten favorite episodes, and in the accompanying essays I attempt to tell you why they're my favorites. It was very difficult deciding on the Top Ten, and some fans may lament the omission of their own personal favorites. Take solace in knowing that I went through some strenuous mental gymnastics choosing one episode over another, and I actually considered assigning some episodes to a "tie" rank. The final judgement is always, however, in the hands of the "Andy Griffith Show" fan, and I welcome your comments on your own personal favorites.

AUTHOR'S CHOICE—"TEN BEST EPISODES"

1. "Opie the Birdman" (101F/96B)
2. "Class Reunion" (82F/B)
3. "Convicts-at-Large" (74F/B)
4. "Barney's Sidecar" (112F/111B)
5. "Man in a Hurry" (77F/79B)
6. "Citizen's Arrest" (106F/B)
7. "Dogs, Dogs, Dogs" (93F/B)
8. "My Fair Ernest T. Bass" (113F/112B)
9. "Fun Girls" (123F/122B)
10. "The New Housekeeper" (1F/B)

1. *OPIE THE BIRDMAN*: This is the single best "Andy Griffith" episode, and the funny thing is, it's not even that funny. It's a dramatic piece of work—fully developed and meticulously written and acted—that stands as a supreme example of what twenty-two or so minutes of television air time can become in the hands of the right people. We have Harvey Bullock and Dick Crenna to thank for this masterpiece, and the accolades are well deserved. I go into detail on the specifics of "Birdman" in the Introduction to *Mayberry, My Hometown*, so I won't rehash the same material here. But the next time you see "Opie the Birdman," pay attention to the performance of Ron Howard, and while you're watching, keep in mind that he did "Birdman" when he was *nine* years old. His performance is just one part of a super "Andy Griffith" experience. I, for one, can never get enough of this episode.

2. *CLASS REUNION*: This episode—written by Jim Fritzell and Everett Greenbaum—is a terrific one because it shows more of not only Andy and Barney's past, but also that of Mayberry's. We find out that Barney's landlady, Mrs. Mendlebright, had the rather bizarre hobby of growing mushrooms in her basement. And we also learn that Barney was part of the tin foil drive and the volleyball court maintenance crew while in Mayberry Union High. Once again we are told that the people in Mayberry had pasts and that they cherished their memories. Barney remembered what Ramona Wiley wrote in his yearbook ("The tears on my pillow bespeak the pain that is in my heart."), and Andy fondly recalled being voted "Couple of the Year" (with Sharon Duspaine) in his junior and senior year. Here is character comedy at its finest. The humor comes from

watching Barney and the rest of the alumni become totally caught up in the thrill of seeing old friends and reliving what was a very important time in their lives. In fact, Barney so looks forward to seeing Ramona Wiley that he fantasizes that the sparks will fly again and that they'll take up exactly where they left off. For his part, Andy has forgotten the personality/career conflicts that caused him and Sharon to sever their relationship while still in high school. The strength of this episode comes in the turn of events as the reunion progresses: Ramona doesn't even remember Barney, and Andy and Sharon—after a romantic rekindling of their former relationship—have the exact same fight that broke them up almost twenty years before. At the end of the reunion, Andy and Barney have learned a lot: they realize that memories are not always accurate, and everything happens for a reason. "Class Reunion" is a sentimental, beautifully written, well-drawn portrait of a few important events in the life of a few people in Mayberry.

3. *CONVICTS-AT-LARGE*: "Convicts-at-Large" is a real comic masterpiece—almost surreal—from the minds of Jim Fritzell and Everett Greenbaum. The funny lines come fast and furious: we learn that one of Big Maude Tyler's aliases is "Ralph Henderson," and we find out that Barney feels that "in civvies, I'm a little hard looking." The cons start calling Barney "Al" because he reminds them of an old boyfriend from the Cascade Club, and Floyd goes right along, entering their little world, calling Barney "Al," and becoming totally possessed by the situation. The lady cons are tough and professional: they hold the pistol right to Barney's head as he makes his call to Andy, and yet when the music is put on, they start dancing and enjoying themselves. Floyd sits serenely on the sofa, eating a banana, and watching the dancing as though he himself were ringside at the Cascade Club. The writing is brilliant. From the beginning, the lines are sharp, the characters defined and funny, and the situations hilarious. One of my favorite scenes occurs at the beginning of the episode when Barney and Floyd come upon Charlie O'Malley's cabin in the woods. The cons are holed up inside and Naomi and Sally start to worry when Barney calls out. Maude's a brilliant woman, though, they assure themselves, and she'll definitely come up with something. She does: she yells out, "There's nobody here!" The first time I saw this episode and Reta Shaw screamed "There's nobody here!" through the window, I knew that this was one of the best. When Andy comes up to the cabin with O'Malley, they decide on a ploy to lure Big Maude outside: Barney will dance with her. Barney asks her to tango because (as he tells her, looking into her eyes) "You're beginning to get to me." He offers to take her to the "land of rhythm and pleasure" and he ends up getting her out on the porch, where Andy handcuffs her. And, throughout all this, Floyd sits calmly, watching the dancing, talking to Al and, at the end of the episode, our barber gets the credit for capturing the convicts-at-large. All in all, an impeccably written, hilarious episode.

4. *BARNEY'S SIDECAR*: This is another Barney Fife episode (and another Jim Fritzell-Everett Greenbaum masterpiece), and it is without a doubt one of the most hilarious episodes of "The Andy Griffith Show" ever produced. Seeing Barney Fife in helmet, gauntlets, and goggles was one of the high points in my study of the show. The hilarity is almost endless: Barney driving off with the

sidecar still parked (with Andy sitting in it), Barney driving his "motorsickle" camouflaged by an entire bush strapped on the front, Barney's oft-repeated lecture on speeding ("You give 'em forty, they'll take forty-five, you give 'em forty-five, they'll take fifty," etc.), and Barney's exhortation to Andy not to wear his hat. Barney couldn't stand to wear a hat after it had been on somebody else's head. His mother was like that. Andy remembered that about Barney's mother. Barney Fife was in rare form in this episode. He had a mission to nip speeding in the bud, and he required full combat gear in which to do it. He also started issuing tickets to anyone and everyone, including one to Aunt Bee for jaywalking. In fact, he got everyone so upset that Aunt Bee suggested stringing a wire across the road like they used to do in the Nazi movies. Andy scolded her, telling her they didn't want to kill Barney. Hurt him a little, maybe, but not kill him. They didn't have to resort to such extreme tactics, though. Andy convinced Barney that the "sickle" was used by Blackjack Pershing and the deputy donated it to the National Guard Armory. A riotous, belly-laugh episode.

5. *MAN IN A HURRY*: This episode—once again by Jim Fritzell and Everett Greenbaum—is important because rather than being a "Barney Fife," a "Gomer," or an "Aunt Bee" episode, this is a "Mayberry" episode. The transformation that takes place in Malcolm Tucker—the "man in a hurry"—is mesmerizing to watch. The magic of Mayberry is slow-working, perhaps, but by the end of the episode, Tucker is calmer, more relaxed, and has learned an important object lesson: slow down. This is a beautifully written portrait of a beautiful town and also a fully realized study of just why the magic of Mayberry works. One of the most touching scenes in the episode is when Tucker is preparing to leave. Gomer has fixed his car free, Opie's handed him a lucky penny "to protect him in his travels," and Aunt Bee has given him two chicken legs and a piece of pie. Tucker's thoughts are visible on his face: he realizes at this moment just what he'll soon be driving away from, and that's when he accuses Gomer of not doing a good job on the car, thereby giving himself an excuse to stay overnight and bask in the warmth of Mayberry for just a little bit longer. But who can blame him? Malcolm Tucker—in "Man in a Hurry"—became another honorary resident of Mayberry, our hometown.

6. *CITIZEN'S ARREST*: In addition to this being one of my personal favorites, "Citizen's Arrest" (once more written by Fritzell and Greenbaum) is also Jim Nabors's all-time favorite episode. And even though Gomer Pyle was the catalyst in this episode (beginning with his citizen's arrest of Barney), "Citizen's Arrest" is actually a Barney Fife episode. The funny stuff is everywhere in this episode, beginning with Gomer running across Main Street, yelling "Citizen's arrest!" "Citizen's arrest!" to the scene that takes place—after Barney decides to take the five days in jail as a protest rather than pay the five dollar fine—with Barney and Otis in adjoining cells. Otis knew how to get Barney going, chanting "Barney's in jail!" "Barney's in jail!" This elicited a machine-gun fast "Nip it! Nip it! Nip it!" from Barney. Also, the way Don Knotts played "Barney the Jailbird"—with a cigarette dangling out of his mouth (and making him cough), along with his crossing off days on the calendar—is classic, a really great performance. Later, when Gomer learns from Opie that Barney had decided to quit the

force, he turns in a false alarm to let Barney know how much he's needed. It works, and Barney gives Gomer three tickets for the phony holdup. Funny show with on-the-money performances by the whole cast.

7. *DOGS, DOGS, DOGS*: Yet another classic Jim Fritzell and Everett Greenbaum episode. The old adage about kids and animals stealing scenes didn't prevent the writers or producers from writing an entire episode about these lovable "dogs, dogs, dogs." All the standard "Andy Griffith" devices are here: Barney and Otis's continual bickering, Otis's reluctant downing of Andy's hangover cure (Warren and Otis had a similar scene in "Otis the Artist" (175F/B)), and the exploration of Barney's sometimes peculiar eating habits. But the drama—as evidenced by the growing affection for the dogs—is here, too. The best scene in the show—where Barney gives his "giraffe" speech—is excerpted and analyzed in Richard Kelly's *The Andy Griffith Show* (pp. 84-86) and I heartily recommend it. After the dogs are returned to the courthouse, one of the nicest touches in the episode is the transformation of the hard-edged Inspector Somerset after he's introduced to the dogs. Turns out he's a dog lover, and he ends up willingly giving Barney and Andy the funds they had requested. The writing is superb, and Fritzell and Greenbaum even give Barney a little poetry to recite. He quotes "The quality of mercy is not strained, etc."—to Andy's amazement—and Barney comes back with a classic line: "You're not talking to a jerk, you know!" Yup. "Dogs, Dogs, Dogs" is good Andy. In fact, it's extry good!!

8. *MY FAIR ERNEST T. BASS*: Do you know why Ernest T. talks through his nose? As Ernest T. explained it: "So's I can talk whilst I eat." From Ernest T.'s manic giggle after breaking Mrs. Wiley's window, through Barney's lecture on police procedures (he talks about the "boys at the lab" and the Mayberry "staff artist"), to Ernest T.'s clobbering of one of the dancers with a vase, this episode—again written by Jim Fritzell and Everett Greenbaum —stands as almost too good to be true. The characterization is perfect and some of the little conversational bits are so good, you almost can't believe what you just heard. The following scene in the courthouse—where Andy and Barney try to find out why Ernest T. is back in Mayberry (and back to breaking windows)—is just one example of the superb writing:

Andy: Last time you was in town, we gave you Barney's uniform to help you get a girl.
Ernest T.: Uh, Uh, that was the plan alright, but it didn't take a-hold none. That's why I brung it back. You see, when I went home wearing that uniform, I just 'spected all the girls just to go plunk, flop right down at my feet, but—same as always—just gazed right on through me.
Andy: Well, I'm sorry to hear that Ernest. T. I know how important it is to you to get a girl.
Ernest T.: I tried courtin' Old Hog Winslow's daughter Hoggette.
Barney: (To Andy) Pretty name.
Ernest T.: Hoggette? Yeah, it's French. French name. Well, I courted her just as proper as proper can be. First off, I wrote her a love note, you know, askin' her to go on out with me? And then I tied that love note onto the prettiest rock you ever did see. And then I give it the

prettiest toss you ever did see, right through her front window.

Andy: Well, did Hoggette come out with you?

Ernest T.: Couldn't. Caught her rightcheer. (Points to left top of head) Seven stitches. All my charms, good looks, and lovable traits didn't mean a peckity thing.

Andy: Ernest T., you don't throw rocks through windows! Now maybe if you gave it another chance with Hoggette, with a more proper courtship?

Ernest T.: She's accounted for now. She gonna marry the taxidermist what sewed up her head. Yeah, I reckon the bestest thing for me to do is find myself a cave and just hermitize myself.

"My Fair Ernest T. Bass"—an adaptation of "Pygmalion"—is brilliantly constructed and executed. (The writers give Barney a great aside: After Andy "makes over" Ernest T., Barney is so impressed he exclaims, "You know, if you wrote this into a play, nobody'd believe it!"). And a great part of the credit must go to Howard Morris's explosive portrayal of the maniacal Ernest T. Bass. All in all, an "Andy Griffith Show" classic.

9. *FUN GIRLS*: Aaron Ruben didn't write many episodes, but when he did, he always hit a home run. "Fun Girls" is just that: great fun. It's the only episode in which we're treated to both Gomer Pyle and Goober Pyle together in the same show. And we also get to see all of Goober's impersonations at once: Cary Grant, Edward G. Robinson, and Chester. And then there's the "fun girls" themselves. Daphne's "Hello, Doll" to Andy and Skippy's "Bernie" to Barney are perfect. Granted, the "fun girls" are drawn with a broad stroke and we don't really get beyond their "trademarks," but the two girls work as the centerpiece of the whole episode, playing off the trouble they start between Andy, Barney, Helen, and Thelma Lou. There are a lot of funny scenes here: Barney's continual references to Andy's jaw muscles working (even after Andy assures Barney he ain't sore anymore), Goober's performances for the "fun girls" at the dance, and Skippy and Barney's "tango-ish" dance are just three favorites that round out this episode. Funny stuff, done funny.

10. *THE NEW HOUSEKEEPER*: This was the very first "Andy Griffith" episode, and it still stands as one of the best. It was written by Jack Elinson and Charles Stewart and was directed by Sheldon Leonard. "The New Housekeeper" doesn't have the broad laughs found in some of the other episodes in the Top Ten, but there is a subtler humor that has a thread of tenderness running through it, as shown in the growing relationship and increasing affection between Aunt Bee and Opie. Opie's "forty-five-minute eggs" is a cute bit, as is Aunt Bee's attempting to become "one of the boys." Also, this episode introduced us to "Reliable Barney Fife," the hyper deputy who knocks his own cap off when saluting his "cousin" Andy. And how can we keep a straight face when Barney arrests that chronic jaywalker, Emma Brand, asserting that Mayberry is becoming "a regular sin town"? Emma's scolding of Barney as a "naughty deputy" is perfect. The episode winds up with Opie realizing that he did love and want Aunt Bee, and his running out in his pajamas to call her back is a real tear-jerking scene. "The New Housekeeper" was a great way to start a great series!

THE MAYBERRY QUIZ

QUESTIONS

This quiz will make you a Mayberry expert.

The following 228 questions were specifically chosen to force you to delve into the history of Mayberry, either by using this book, or by watching the episodes.

Try the quiz without using *Mayberry, My Hometown*, but if you can't get very far, feel free to look up the answers in this book.

This quiz was designed to be fun, and to show the broad beauty of the town of Mayberry and its good people.

If you have trouble finding an answer even using *Mayberry, My Hometown*, the answer section follows this one. There you'll find the correct answers and, of course, the episode reference number from which the question came.

Good luck, and long live Mayberry!

1. Who was Andy's first boss?
2. What was Andy's first job?
3. What was Howard Sprague's first job?
4. Who played the character of Mario Vincente?
5. What was the elevation above sea level of Mayberry?
6. What did Mayberry's only Indian call the Battle of Mayberry?
7. What was the supposed value of the legendary Ross Treasure?
8. Name Opie's dog.
9. Name the three orphaned songbirds Opie adopted after he accidentally killed their mother.
10. Who played the character of Reverend Leighton?
11. What company did Roy Swanson say he worked for?
12. What was Andy's home phone number?
13. What did it say inside the fortune cookie Andy got at Aunt Bee's Canton Palace?
14. Who played sax with Carl Benson's Wildcats, except on Friday nights when the library was open?
15. Who played the character of Gentleman Dan Caldwell?
16. What were the three karate moves Barney learned from the book, *The Art of Karate*?
17. What were Aunt Bee's two license plate numbers?
18. What was the name of the book Helen Crump wrote?
19. What was Andy's favorite dish?
20. Who played the character of Colonel Harvey?
21. Who played the character of Congressman John Canfield?
22. What was the name of Charlene Darling Wash's daughter?
23. Who wrote the "Mayberry After Midnight" column in the "Mayberry Gazette"?
24. What did the Morrison sisters call their moonshine?
25. What was the price of Colonel Harvey's Indian Elixir?
26. What was Juanita's last name?

27. Who was the "woman speeder"?
28. For whom did Jean Boswell work?
29. What was the name of Bee's cousin Edgar's wife?
30. Who was Malcolm Merriweather's boss in England?
31. Who was "Andy's Old Girlfriend"?
32. Who played "Andy's Old Girlfriend"?
33. What Mayberry business held the "Lucky Peppermints" contest?
34. Who was "Andy's Rich Girlfriend"?
35. Who played "Andy's Rich Girlfriend"?
36. What was described as an "embryonic megalopolis" and who used that term?"
37. What was the name of Attorney Lee Drake's maid?
38. Name the "fun girls."
39. Name their hometown.
40. What was the name of Mr. Frisby's rooster?
41. Who was the judge at Marvin Jenkins' trial?
42. Who was the original owner of Aunt Bee's car?
43. What did he weigh?
44. What was the name of Professor St. John's book?
45. What was the first color episode of "The Andy Griffith Show"?
46. What was Clara Cartwright's birthday?
47. On what TV show was Aunt Bee the sweepstakes winner?
48. Who was "Aunt Bee's Cousin"?
49. Who played "Aunt Bee's Cousin"?
50. Who talked Bee into buying a wig?
51. What was the name of Orville Hendricks' son?
52. Who was Aunt Bee's partner in her "Canton Palace"?
53. Name Evie Joy's father.
54. What was the name of Opie's softball team?
55. Who was the "Banjo-Playing Deputy"?
56. Who played the "Banjo-Playing Deputy"?
57. What was the name of the bargain meat market where Aunt Bee bought a side of beef?
58. As you face the Mayberry jail cells, on which side was cell #1, and which was #2?
59. What was Teena Andrews real name?
60. What was the Russian ambassador's name at Barney's "Summit Meeting"?
61. Name Lydia Crosswaithe's hometown.
62. On what radio station did Leonard Blush sing?
63. What was the license plate number of "Barney's First Car?"
64. What year did Barney first meet Thelma Lou?
65. Where did Barney first meet Thelma Lou?
66. Who was "The Beaver"?
67. Why was "The Beaver" called "The Beaver"?
68. Who was Barney's judo instructor?
69. Name Mayberry's only Indian.
70. Who won "The Beauty Contest"?
71. Who wrote the song "My Hometown"?
72. Who sang "My Hometown"?
73. What was the name of Andy's fishing pole?
74. Where did Tommy Parker's sister, Betty, work?
75. Who was Old Sam?
76. Who was "The Bookie Barber"?
77. Who played "The Bookie Barber"?
78. Who wrote "A Fading Flower of Forgotten Love"?

79. Who was the head of the Mayberry Department of Water and Power?
80. Who did Robert Gribbel marry?
81. When was Otis's first arrest for intoxication?
82. Who was the "baby" of the Hubacher brothers?
83. Who willed $500 to All Souls Church?
84. What was Harlan Robinson's address?
85. Who arrested Purcell Branch in 1931?
86. What was the name of Andy's and Barney's high school yearbook?
87. Who signed the following in Barney's yearbook: "The tears on my pillow bespeak the pain that is in my heart?"
88. What club did Roger Courtney want Andy to join?
89. Opie was in two clubs. Name them.
90. What crook used the alias "Ralph Henderson"?
91. What mountain man refused a tetanus shot from Mary Simpson?
92. Name Barney's cousin Virgil's home state.
93. To whose memory was the Memorial Horse Trough in the center of Mayberry dedicated?
94. Who wrote *Fun In The Garage On A Rainy Day*?
95. Which was the "fun-loving" Darling boy?
96. What flavor ice cream did Barney bring Thelma Lou from Murphy's House of the 9 Flavors?
97. How much did the ice cream cost?
98. What was the cost per jar of Miracle Salve?
99. What was the name of Otis Campbell's brother?
100. What was the secret ingredient of Goober's tomato sauce?
101. With whom did Dud Wash hunt foxes?
102. The license plate number of the squad car was JL-327. In only one episode however, another plate number was used. What was that number?
103. What was the name of Opie's imaginary horse?
104. Who was Bee's first blind date?
105. Who was Clint Biggers?
106. Who claimed possession of a map showing the location of the Ross Treasure?
107. Flora the waitress. What was her last name?
108. How much did it cost Ernest T. Bass to put gold leaf on his front tooth?
109. Who was Old Man Flint's next-door neighbor?
110. Name the furrier to whom Flora introduced Emmett.
111. Who was Emmett's brother-in-law?
112. What did Cecil Gurney have but wouldn't admit?
113. Why was Plain Claude Beeman called "Plain"?
114. Who was Jeff Pruitt's "little buddy"?
115. Name Jedediah Wakefield's mule.
116. Who originally owned the building in which Floyd's Barbershop was located?
117. Name the play in which Aunt Bee played the queen.
118. What was Willard Foster's address?
119. Name Edith Gibson's dating service.
120. Name Gomer's dog.
121. What was the Marine camp to which Gomer reported?
122. What was Lydia Crosswaithe's house number?
123. Name Early Gilly's gasoline promotion.
124. How much did Goober need for a down payment on Wally's Service Station?
125. Who was "Goober's replacement"?
126. Where was "Bread, Love, and Beans" playing?
127. Who took over Walt Simpson's route when he went on vacation?
128. Who offered Andy a job with Hogarth Detectives?
129. Who was the real crook in the "great filling station robbery"?
130. Name Sheldon Davis' girlfriend.
131. Who was supposed to marry Horace Frisey?
132. What was Jim Lindsey's big hit record?
133. What was "the haunted house"?
134. With what known hoodlum was Helen Crump arrested?
135. What gift did Luke Comstock bring Andy?
136. What was Lonnie Lattimer's travel column called?
137. Who donated the town cannon back to Mayberry?
138. What was the license plate number of Otis Campbell's car?
139. Against what team did Howard Sprague bowl a perfect 300 game?
140. On what amateur show did Howard Sprague do his comedy routine?
141. At what bakery did Millie Hutchins work?
142. Where was the King Arthur pageant?
143. Where did Howard Sprague start his "new life"?
144. Who was "The Inspector"?
145. Name Floyd's dog.
146. Who were the two farmers who refused to stop selling from their truck?
147. Who was "the loaded goat"?
148. What was Mayberry's men's lodge?
149. What was the name of the men's magazine with Barney's name on it that Andy found in the dump?
150. What ring did Newton Monroe try to sell to Barney?
151. What was the name of Andy's rowboat?
152. Who was "the manicurist"?
153. Name Goober's dog.
154. Who was lifting a few fryers from Al's Poultry Headquarters?
155. Who was the "man in a hurry"?
156. What was the name of Barney's cymbals?
157. What was the name of Aunt Bee's cooking show?
158. Who owned Channel 12 in Siler City?
159. How much was Frank Myers bond worth in 1961?
160. Name Mayberry's TV repairman/funeral director.
161. What was the name of the album of folk songs recorded in Mayberry by Mr. Maxwell?
162. What was Juanita's phone number at the Diner?
163. Who was "the merchant of Mayberry"?
164. Who was Goober's doctor when Goober thought he had whiplash?
165. What were Mr. McBeevee's "twelve extra hands?"
166. Who did Charlene Darling marry?
167. Who did Andy try to pass Ernest T. Bass off as at Mrs. Wiley's party?
168. Who was "the youngest doctor ever" in Mayberry?
169. Who was Dr. Peterson's surgical assistant?
170. Who did Andy's former housekeeper, Rose, marry?
171. What studio made the movie "Sheriff Without A Gun"?
172. What did Steve Quincy's father sell?
173. What was the name of Bee's almost-prizewinning rose?

174. What two rose varieties did she cross-pollinate to create the rose?
175. What was Barney's best trick shot using a slingshot?
176. What did Sheldon the Bully take from Opie every day?
177. What was the name of the essay Opie wrote, in which he hinted for a tool chest?
178. Where did Opie and his "merry men" meet Wary Willy the Hobo?
179. What was the name of Sam Jones' son?
180. What was the name of the "spoiled kid"?
181. What did Arnold Bailey say he'd carry when he became sheriff?
182. What was Barney's school nickname because of his bullet football passes?
183. Who was "The Beast of the 4th Floor"?
184. What was the only summer camp Opie ever attended?
185. Who was in charge of the Underprivileged Children's Charity Drive?
186. What will happen if you "give 'em forty"?
187. What girl had Opie been stuck on since first grade?
188. Who played drums in Opie's band, "The Sound Committee"?
189. What was the magic word Dave the Hobo used to steal gumballs?
190. What was Opie's favorite pie?
191. Who was Mr. Bristol?
192. What was the name of "Opie's newspaper?"
193. When Andy was young, who was the most popular kid in town?
194. Who was "Opie's Rival"?
195. What was the name of Otis Campbell's imaginary dog?
196. Who was Otis's lawyer when Otis tripped and fell in the courthouse?
197. Who was Barney's singing coach?
198. Who was the woman's skeetshooting champion of Arkansas?
199. What were "kerosene cucumbers"?
200. Otis was a descendant of what Revolutionary War hero?
201. Who was Mabel J. Mosley?
202. What did Sam Becker name his son?
203. Who was in charge of the Ladies League musicale?
204. What was the name of the monthly magazine Barney subscribed to that on one occasion had an issue called "Odd Facts Known By Few."
205. What year did Andy and Barney graduate high school?
206. Who made dreadful meatballs?
207. Who was the "Runaway Kid"?
208. Why did Herb Bradshaw resign as head of Mayberry city council?
209. Who was the principal who objected to Helen's "Senior Play"?
210. Where was Dr. Harrison Everett Breen from?
211. What was Barney's address?
212. Who was Ben Weaver's night watchman?
213. Who could only sing high after a fight with his mother?
214. Who carved the statue of Seth Taylor?
215. Name Mrs. Buntley's twins.
216. What contest won Bee "A Trip to Mexico"?
217. Who was Eddie Blake's lawyer?
218. Where did the Taylors stay in Hollywood?
219. Who went to Raleigh to buy a new set of teeth?
220. Name Barney's favorite pizza.
221. Who did Barney claim to contact in the netherworld with his gypsy lamp?
222. Goober's last name was Pyle. However, he was called by a different last name only once in the series. What was that last name?
223. Barney had bound issues—dating back to 1959—of what magazine?
224. Who was Barney's boss in the Raleigh police department?
225. Who predicted an avalanche in Warsaw in 1928?
226. Where did George propose to Mrs. Sprague?
227. Who was the drycleaner who became an item with Aunt Bee?
228. Why was Harvey Kester the "last famous person in Mayberry"?

THE
MAYBERRY QUIZ

ANSWERS

1. Old Man MacKnight (239F/238B)
2. Running the popcorn machine at the theater (239F/238B)
3. He was a truck driver for the Mayberry Transfer Company (239F/238B)
4. Gabrielle Tinti (241F/249B)
5. 671 feet (241F/249B)
6. The Victory of Tucahoosee Creek (188F/B)
7. $100,000 in gold (205F/B)
8. Gulliver (1F/B)
9. Wynken, Blynken, and Nod (101F/96B)
10. Ian Wolfe (194F/B)
11. Amalgamated Motors (242F/241B)
12. 426 (239F/238B)
13. "Try to avoid temptation in the coming week." (209F/210B)
14. Mrs. Atzell (176F/B)
15. Dan Tobin (21F/B)
16. The Hawk, The Bull Elk, and The Rattlesnake (56F/B)
17. In 199F/196B, AY-321. In 219F/B, GP-780.
18. *Amusing Tales of Tiny Tots* (213F/B)
19. Leg of lamb (92F/B)
20. John Dehner (87F/B)
21. Charles Ruggles (160F/163B)
22. Andelina (139F/B)
23. Sixteen-year-old Red Akins (136F/B)
24. "Special Elixir." (17F/B)
25. $1 per bottle (87F/B)
26. Beazley (28F/B)
27. Elizabeth Crowley (35F/B)
28. J. Howard Jackson (61F/B)
29. Maude (23F/B)
30. Colonel Chumley (89F/B)
31. Alice Harper (207F/209B)
32. Joanna McNeil (207F/209B)
33. Pierson's Sweet Shop (110F/109B)
34. Peggy McMillan (67F/65B)
35. Joanna Moore (67F/65B)
36. Raleigh, described by Frank Smith (163F/161B)
37. Marie (226F/223B)
38. Skippy and Daphne (155F/B)
39. Mt. Pilot (155F/B)
40. Bo, short for Beauregard (111F/110B)
41. Judge Cranston (223F/226B)
42. Jed Koontz (180F/B)
43. "Over 290 pounds" (180F/B)
44. *I Know South America* (230F/229B)
45. "Aunt Bee, The Swinger" (160F/163B)
46. August 21 (171F/172B)
47. "Win or Lose" (165F/169B)
48. Bradford J. Taylor (234F/232B)
49. Jack Albertson (234F/232B)
50. Bernice (194F/B)
51. Evan (154F/B)
52. Charlie Lee (209F/210B)
53. Darryl (184F/B)
54. The Mayberry Giants (195F/193B)
55. Jerry Miller (159F/B)
56. Jerry Van Dyke (159F/B)
57. Diamond Jim's (120F/119B)
58. #1 was on the right, #2 on the left (109F/108B)
59. Irene Flogg (212F/208B)
60. Mr. Vasilievich (240F/B)
61. Greensboro, North Carolina (68F/69B)
62. WMPD, the "Voice of Mt. Pilot" (128F/133B)
63. MP-3791 (90F/B)
64. 1960 (131F/129B)
65. Wilton Blair's funeral (131F/129B)
66. Mrs. Beggs' sister, Tilly (112F/111B)
67. She had long teeth from a gum condition (112F/111B)
68. Mr. Izamoto (135F/B)
69. Tom Strongbow (188F/B)
70. Erma Bishop, the seamstress (20F/16B)
71. Clara Edwards and Bee Taylor (189F/B)
72. Keevy Hazleton (189F/B)
73. Eagle-Eye Annie (75F/B)
74. The Embassy Dance Hall (217F/B)
75. The only silver carp in Tucker's Lake (198F/200B)
76. Bill Medwin (60F/B)
77. Herb Vigran (60F/B)
78. Alice Ellicott Strong (96F/100B)
79. Harry Bosworth (172F/170B)
80. Emma Larch (152F/B)
81. September 23, 1941, 2:00 P.M. at the Mayberry Garden Club flower show (152F/B)
82. Elmer (11F/B)
83. Jarrod Hooper (238F/239B)
84. Oakmont Road, Mt. Pilot (174F/173B)
85. Sheriff Pinckley (106F/B)
86. "The Cutlass" (82F/B)
87. Ramona Wiley (82F/B)
88. The Esquire Club (42F/B)
89. The Tomahawks (42F/B), and The Wildcats (46F/B)
90. Big Maude Tyler (74F/B)
91. Rafe Hollister (56F/B)
92. New Jersey (62F/B)
93. David Mendlebright (88F/B)
94. Seymour Schreck (139F/B)
95. Rodney (193F/195B)
96. West Indian Licorice Mocha Delight (105F/104B)
97. 40¢ (105F/104B)
98. 35¢ (122F/121B)
99. Ralph Campbell (63F/B)
100. Oregano (206F/B)
101. Hasty Buford (121F/120B)
102. DC-269 (6F/4B)
103. Blackie (66F/64B)
104. Orville Buck (173F/174B)
105. The real owner of the "Dogs, Dogs, Dogs" (93F/B)
106. George Jones (205F/B)
107. Mallerby (182F/183B)
108. $1 (133F/131B)
109. Jenkins (27F/B)
110. Bernie (245F/244B)
111. Ben Beecham (236F/237B)

112. Two sets of false teeth (99F/98B)
113. Because he wasn't a "Jr." or a "Sr." (129F/130B)
114. Barney (45F/B)
115. Emmie (8F/9B)
116. The Robinson family (210F/211B)
117. "Six Who Pass While The Lentils Boil" (71F/72B)
118. 403 Elm St., Raleigh, North Carolina (187F/186B)
119. Scientific Introductions, Inc. (249F/248B)
120. Sport (97F/101B)
121. Camp Wilson (107F/127B)
122. 598 (147F/B)
123. "Line Up For Loot" (219F/B)
124. $2,000 (221F/235B)
125. Flora Mallerby (186F/187B)
126. Raleigh (144F/B)
127. Ben Curtis (214F/B)
128. Herb Mason (137F/B)
129. Pothrow Henson (85F/B)
130. Madge (53F/B)
131. Alice Drumhiller (151F/B)
132. "Rock 'N Roll Rosie From Raleigh" (31F/B)
133. The Rimshaw House (98F/97B)
134. Harry Brown (244F/243B)
135. A shotgun (80F/B)
136. "Longtitudes & Latitudes" (168F/B)
137. Milford Phillips (14F/B)
138. AY-321 (115F/114B)
139. The Trucker's Cafe of Mt. Pilot (224F/221B)
140. "Colonel Tim's Talent Time" (216F/B)
141. Boysinger's Bakery (222F/225B)
142. Morgantown (233F/231B)
143. St. Benedict's Island in the Caribbean (235F/234B)
144. Ralph Case (26F/B)
145. Sam (49F/B)
146. Neil and Matt (73F/70B)
147. Jimmy (81F/B)
148. The Regal Order of the Golden Door to Good Fellowship (192F/191B)
149. "Love" (146F/B)
150. "The Star of Peoria" (156F/B)
151. Gertrude (2F/B)
152. Ellen Brown (48F/B)
153. Spot (170F/171B)
154. Buzz Jenkins (77F/79B)
155. Malcolm Tucker (77F/79B)
156. Andre Kostalanez Marchers (72F/71B)
157. "The Mayberry Chef" (237F/236B)
158. Carl Phillips (237F/236B)
159. $349,119.27 (39F/36B)
160. Orville Monroe (13F/B)
161. "Music from Mayberry" (19F/B)
162. 242 (51F/B)
163. Bert Miller (54F/B)
164. Dr. Bennett (199F/196B)
165. His tools (66F/64B)
166. Dudley J. (or A.) Wash (94F/B)
167. His cousin from Raleigh, Oliver Gossage
168. Dr. Robert Benson (24F/B)
169. Nurse Oakley (201F/204B)
170. Wilbur Pine (1F/B)
171. Belmont Picture Studio (166F/B)
172. Farm implements (79F/77B)

173. Deep Pink Ecstasy (203F/201B)
174. A Mrs. Pinckney Variegated Red with an Alma Swarthouse Sunset Pink (203F/201B)
175. "Tail-Gunner" (101F/96B)
176. His nickel for milk (34F/33B)
177. "What I Would Do If I Had A Tool Chest" (158F/B)
178. Crouch's Woods (108F/107B)
179. Mike (248F/247B)
180. Arnold Winkler (84F/B)
181. An Australian bullwhip (202F/199B)
182. "Rifle Fife" (157F/B)
183. Mrs. VonRoder, Andy and Barney's teacher (132F/128B)
184. Camp Winoke (225F/224B)
185. Annabelle Silby (5F/8B)
186. "They'll take forty-five." (112F/111B)
187. Mary Alice Carter (220F/B)
188. Jessie Clayton (229F/228B)
189. "Tuscorora" (40F/38B)
190. Butterscotch pecan (103F/B)
191. One of Aunt Bee's eggmen (218F/B)
192. "The Mayberry Sun" (153F/B)
193. Harvey Belfast (215F/B)
194. Peggy McMillan (64F/73B)
195. Spot (175F/B)
196. Neil Bentley (141F/142B)
197. Eleanora Poultice (138F/B)
198. Thelma Lou's cousin, Karen Moore (37F/40B)
199. Aunt Bee's homemade pickles (43F/B)
200. Nathan Tibbs (25F/B)
201. The author of *Roses Are the Backbone of Your Garden* (200F/197B)
202. Andy Becker, in honor of Andy (29F/B)
203. John Masters (83F/B)
204. "Learn-A-Month" (145F/B)
205. 1945 (82F/B) or 1948 (176F/B)
206. Lillian (125F/124B)
207. George Foley from Eastmont (4F/6B)
208. To become head teller at the Raleigh Security Bank (247F/246B)
209. Mr. Hampton (197F/198B)
210. New York City (100F/99B)
211. 411 Elm St. (44F/B)
212. Asa Breeny (117F/116B)
213. Bruce Flowers (116F/115B)
214. Brian Jackson (208F/212B)
215. Robert and William (10F/12B)
216. The Tampico Tamale Contest (227F/222B)
217. Myles Bentley (228F/227B)
218. The Piedmont Hotel, room 403 (167F/B)
219. Rose Blake (15F/B)
220. Mozzarella (59F/B)
221. Count Iz Van Talecki (142F/141B)
222. Beazley (150F/B)
223. "True Blue Detective Magazine" (104F/105B)
224. Captain of detectives, M. L. Dewhurst (211F/207B)
225. Sonya Walachaka (169F/165B)
226. Morelli's (246F/245B)
227. Fred Goss (58F/B)
228. He used to repair Gloria Swanson's radio set (179F/B)

JIM CLARK INTERVIEW

Jim Clark is the Presiding Goober of "The Andy Griffith Show" Rerun Watchers Club, an organization that unites "Andy Griffith Show" fans everywhere, and allows them to speak with one voice when necessary, such as when stations drop reruns of our favorite show. With over 12,000 members, TAGSRWC (we'll use some acronyms during this fan confabulation, folks) is the largest TAGS ("The Andy Griffith Show") fan club in existence. Jim, (with Ken Beck) recently authored *The Andy Griffith Show Book* (St. Martin's Press $11.95) and when he's not watching the show, he answers the massive amounts of correspondence the club receives from Mayberry residents all over the world. We talked about the club, the show, everything in between, and the following is an edited version of our conversation.

Steve Spignesi: Tell us how and why the "The Andy Griffith Show" Rerun Watchers Club was formed.
Jim Clark: "The Andy Griffith Show" Rerun Watchers Club was founded in the fall of 1979 at the Phi Kappa Sigma fraternity house at Vanderbilt University in Nashville. The club started with four devoted TAGS fans who were looking for a way to assure their control of the fraternity's sole TV set during the times that TAGS was on the air. We felt the need to organize because M*A*S*H also aired at the same time, and there were some unenlightened fraternity members who preferred watching the 4077th gang. The club began to grow as other TAGS fans became aware of our activity. Following an article by Ken Beck in *The Tennessean*, Nashville's morning daily newspaper, the club began to snowball and has continued to the point that we now have over 12,000 members in the forty-eight continental states and in six foreign countries. In addition, the club now has over 300 organized chapters, all following the original Nashville group, which took the name "Andy Chapter." [In fact, one chapter of TAGSRWC is the "Mayberry, My Hometown Chapter," headed by yours truly. Write for info on joining!—sjs]
Steve Spignesi: Describe the day-to-day operations of the club. How much time do you put into it? How many new members do you average each month? How often do you watch the show, etc.? What's on the agenda for the near and distant future?
Jim Clark: The purpose of TAGSRWC is the promotion and enjoyment of watching "The Andy Griffith Show." So, mostly what we do is simply watch reruns of our favorite show and do whatever we can to make sure it stays on the air in order that we can continue watching. TAGSRWC has voluntary membership dues. We don't want dues to be a barrier to anyone's membership. We feel it's the Mayberry way to let anyone join who wants to be a member. (We do suggest an amount of two or three dollars per member in annual dues, but payment is up to each member.) Our chapters around the country operate however they want to. We try to run the club much as Andy handles Mayberry—without a gun. Chapters frequently host cookouts and that kind of thing in order to get together with others who enjoy watching the show. Andy Chapter serves

as the club's administrative center and helps coordinate the founding and operation of the club's other chapters. All new members join through Andy Chapter and are placed in the chapter nearest them. An average of between one and two thousand hear about and join the club each year (though we're not really counting.) Andy Chapter takes care of most of the day-to-day business of the club, which consists primarily of answering correspondence that the club receives. Andy Chapter is also responsible for publishing *The Bullet*, the club's newsletter, which comes out two or three times a year. Chapters and individual members also write to their local TV stations and encourage them to air TAGS, or thank the stations if they are already airing the show. Again, though, we mostly just watch the show. That's what the club is all about. For my part, I watch the show whenever I can. Because I still don't have a VCR, I have to catch the show when it is broadcast, which currently is four times per weekday in Nashville. The club really has no long-range plans to speak of . . . except to continue watching the show and sharing that fun with others.
Steve Spignesi: In Richard Kelly's book, *The Andy Griffith Show*, the top ten favorite episodes (as supplied by TAGSRWC) were slightly different from the ranking in your book *The Andy Griffith Show Book*. [The two lists are compared below.] Why the change? Describe the additional data you obtained since the original survey was taken in 1983.

Original 1983 Rankings	New 1985 Rankings
1. "Barney's Sidecar"	1. "Man in a Hurry"
2. "My Fair Ernest T. Bass"	2. "Barney's Sidecar"
3. "The Pickle Story"	3. "The Sermon for Today"
4. "Man in a Hurry"	4. "Goober and the Art of Love"
5. "Mountain Wedding"	5. "Dogs, Dogs, Dogs"
6. "Goober and the Art of Love"	6. "Opie the Birdman"
7. "The Education of Ernest T. Bass"	7. "The Education of Ernest T. Bass"
8. "Ernest T. Bass Joins the Army"	8. "The Pickle Story"
9. "The Sermon for Today"	9. "The Christmas Story"
10. "Dogs, Dogs, Dogs"	10. "Fun Girls"

Jim Clark: The reason for the difference in the two TAGSRWC polls is that we heard from more fans after the first poll. In addition, Ken Beck and I sought the opinions of particular fans and cast members. We also contributed our own opinions to the judging. The results of the second poll were just enough different from the first one to merit their own listing. Overall, though, the results of the two polls are remarkably close, especially when considering the full top twenty. Whenever discussing any poll of favorite TAGS episodes, I like to qualify the results by saying how difficult it is to pick the ten or twenty best episodes of a series that has such consistently high quality. The poll results are just what *might* be the top episodes.
Steve Spignesi: The majority of favorite episodes seem to come from the middle seasons. In fact, the latest "favorite" episode—"Big Fish in a Small Town"—is from the seventh season. Why do you think the earlier episodes were so popular? Were there particular characters or story lines that you feel contributed to the attraction of the earlier episodes? Was it the writing? Or was it just the romance of American black-and-white sitcom television?

Jim Clark: I think the middle years of TAGS are perhaps the most popular among fans for a variety of reasons. First, the cast members had had time to settle into their roles and shape their characters into a comfortable harmony. The writers, directors, and other members of the production crew had also honed their feel for the show. In particular, I think the relationship between Andy and Barney became established during the middle years. They were no longer simply sheriff and deputy, and cousins, but best friends. By the second season, most of the major characters were dropping their exaggerated country accents. This was particularly important for allowing Andy to become more believable and less of a clown. Andy could then become more of a straight man to Barney's antics and more the problem-solving leader of Mayberry. Also, lovable Floyd really came into his prime during those years, prior to Howard McNear's stroke. Gomer and then Goober were also introduced during those years. Andy finally got a steady girl, Helen, during that time, too. And we first meet recurring characters like the Darlings, Ernest T. Bass, and Malcolm Merriweather during the middle seasons. In other words, the entire production crew gelled during those middle years. It was also still early enough in the show's run that there were plenty of truly fresh script ideas. And I do feel that filming in black and white contributed a lot to making Mayberry dreamlike and stirring up feelings of nostalgia. Toward the end of the show's glory middle years, several factors affected the show's direction. Gomer Pyle left to join the Marines (and start his own show), and with him went Aaron Ruben, one of the primary creative forces behind TAGS. Then, Don Knotts left the show after the fifth season. That loss was important. But I don't think we should underestimate the tremendous importance that characters like Goober and later Howard Sprague and Emmett Clark had in preserving the charm of Mayberry and the quality of the show. Those characters are a vital part of Mayberry and were played exquisitely. Still, Opie was getting older and becoming more the young man than the cute little boy. Warren Ferguson didn't quite fill Barney's 7 1/2B shoes, and Howard McNear's deteriorating health was reflected in Floyd. Otis Campbell also figured less prominently in the later years, as the production crew became more concerned about the portrayal of an alcoholic on television. Fresh script ideas also became harder to come up with. Yet, Mayberry was still magical, and the show remained superb throughout its eight seasons. The extraordinary excellence of the show's middle seasons should not be a detraction from the other outstanding seasons and individual performances.

Steve Spignesi: Do you have an overall favorite episode? If so, what is it and why is it so special for you?

Jim Clark: I don't have one favorite episode, but I'll try and narrow it down a little. I love them all so much that it's almost cruel to ask me to pick just one. I will say that for me "Man in a Hurry" epitomizes what Mayberry stands for as much as any episode. I think "Opie's Charity," "Opie the Birdman," and "Mr. McBeevee" demonstrate the relationship between Andy and Opie as well as any. I think "The Pickle Story," "Barney's Sidecar," and "Goober and the Art of Love" are three of the funniest episodes to me. But I can't leave out episodes with the Darlings and Ernest T. They're classics. And I particularly enjoy any episode that features Goober, Howard, or Floyd.

Steve Spignesi: Without question, the excellence of the writing on TAGS played a giant role in the tremendous popularity of the show, both when it was originally on, and now that it's in syndication. Take the opening of "Back to Nature," for instance. Floyd is telling Andy and Barney why he'd never get an automatic lather machine. Floyd was "anti-automatic" because he loved the "klep, klep" sound the brush made when making lather by hand. And to add insult to injury, with those machines, the lather came out cold!! This is one of my favorite scenes. Describe your favorite scene, if you can pin it down to just one (I know I can't), or your favorite scenes and why they're special to you.

Jim Clark: Asking me to pick a favorite moment or scene is even worse than trying to pick a favorite episode. I love scenes on the Taylors' front porch. They're my favorite recurring scenes. I am also still touched every time I see Andy tell Opie that he believes him about Mr. McBeevee. And every time I watch the birds fly away in "Opie the Birdman" (a porch scene!), I get a lump in my throat. Barney's testimony on behalf of Andy in "Andy on Trial" is another touching dramatic moment. Perhaps my single favorite funny scene is Barney's "Boy, giraffes are selfish" speech in "Dogs, Dogs, Dogs." But Goober doing his imitations and sewing his fingers up is hilarious. And almost any scene with Floyd is automatically funny. And the thrill of anticipating that Barney is about to lock himself in a jail cell or that his gun is about to go off grows with each viewing. There are just too many funny and dramatic moments in TAGS to pick just one.

Steve Spignesi: Do you have a favorite character on TAGS?

Jim Clark: Selecting a favorite character on TAGS is like trying to select a favorite relative. Just as any person might have different kinds of affection for his parents than his spouse or children or friends, so do I like characters in Mayberry in different ways . . . not necesssarily more or less than other characters, just differently. I have a special affection for all the characters. But I will say that I identify the most with Goober and Howard. And I laugh the most about Barney and Floyd. And without a doubt I think Andy is the most important character on the show.

Steve Spignesi: Many fans of the show have expressed concern to me regarding the reunion movie, "Return to Mayberry," currently in production. Andy Griffith himself is on record in Kelly's *The Andy Griffith Show* that one of the reasons he never wanted to do a reunion was because he didn't want such a project to become a "sad caricature of the eight years of Mayberry that he crafted through hard labor into a work of art." What are your views on the upcoming NBC-TV movie? The fact that the first script was rejected didn't help calm the fears of fans. But of course, with Harvey Bullock and Everett Greenbaum writing the final script, and Bob Sweeney directing, fans shouldn't worry. Nonetheless, there is concern that such a reunion will tamper with the magic. What do you think? Also, what can you tell us about possible story lines?

Jim Clark: I have mixed feelings about the "Return to Mayberry" movie. As a fan of the original series, I don't have a *need* for a return movie. I am content to watch reruns of the old series whenever I want to visit Mayberry. The episodes get better every time I watch them. I also think it is extremely difficult to recreate the magic of

Mayberry—especially after being out of production for eighteen years. One of the attractive qualities about Mayberry is that most things never change much there. But major change (in ages of the characters, if nothing else) after so many years will be unavoidable. In addition, the high quality of the original series is difficult to match. Andy Griffith is keenly aware of that difficulty and of the danger of disappointing fans with an inferior return visit. For that reason, he has for years refused to do a follow-up movie. However, I am comforted to know of Andy Griffith's insistence on not tarnishing the wonderful work of the original series. I think that his wanting to preserve the integrity of Mayberry, combined with the same attitude and unsurpassed talents among the other returning cast and crew members, will make "Return to Mayberry" a delight for TAGS fans. At the very least, the cast and crew are getting a chance to reunite and reminisce. And TAGS fans will be able to share that experience through the film—and see that when Mayberry does change, it changes for the better. I'm happy that the movie is giving us this chance. That's neat. Regarding the plot of the movie, most of what I know I've been told under threat of the "Curse of the Claw," so I can't go on record about it. But I think that what I do know will probably be moot by the time *Mayberry, My Hometown* comes out anyway. [Jim was right! See Part III of this book.—sjs]

Steve Spignesi: OK. Let's do a little free association —Mayberry style! I'll give you the name of a character and you say the first thing that comes into your mind.

Jim Clark: OK.

Steve Spignesi: Andy Taylor.

Jim Clark: The foundation of Mayberry.

Steve Spignesi: Barney Fife.

Jim Clark: One of a kind.

Steve Spignesi: Opie Taylor.

Jim Clark: A good feller.

Steve Spignesi: Aunt Bee.

Jim Clark: Loving and kind. She has all the qualities an aunt should. And boy, can she cook. (But just stay away from her homemade pickles and marmalade!)

Steve Spignesi: Floyd Lawson.

Jim Clark: Sa-a-y . . . He's as refreshing as a Nectarine Crush.

Steve Spignesi: Gomer Pyle.

Jim Clark: Aw, shucks!

Steve Spignesi: Goober Pyle.

Jim Clark: He's really got talent . . . and a big heart, too.

Steve Spignesi: Otis Campbell.

Jim Clark: He has a thirst for the good stuff.

Steve Spignesi: Helen Crump.

Jim Clark: Mrs. Andy Taylor.

Steve Spignesi: Thelma Lou.

Jim Clark: The cat's!

Steve Spignesi: Skippy and Daphne.

Jim Clark: Just fun girls.

Steve Spignesi: Clara Edwards.

Jim Clark: A busybody, but well-meaning and kind.

Steve Spignesi: Ellie Walker.

Jim Clark: She's got the right prescription.

Steve Spignesi: Ernest T.

Jim Clark: He's a nut!

Steve Spignesi: Briscoe Darling.

Jim Clark: As long as he's breathing, he's got time for music.

Steve Spignesi: The Darling boys.

Jim Clark: Warm. fun-loving, and amusing.

Steve Spignesi: Howard Sprague.

Jim Clark: A good citizen, a good friend, and a *very good* son.

Steve Spignesi: Emmett Clark.

Jim Clark: Mr. Fix-It.

Steve Spignesi: Roger Hanover.

Jim Clark: Best when thought of as carbolic acid—"that's goodbye in any language." He ought to "hang it on the wall."

Steve Spignesi: Warren Ferguson.

Jim Clark: A likeable fellow, but no one can replace Barney Fife, huh . . . huh . . . huh??

Steve Spignesi: Regis.

Jim Clark: Belongs in the hills, away from the "barbarians . . . worshippers of Hammon."

Steve Spignesi: One last question: Try and put into words your affection for "The Andy Griffith Show."

Jim Clark: The main reason I like TAGS is that the show is very entertaining. First and foremost for me, TAGS is a situation comedy of the highest quality. The entire production of the show—from the casting and writing to the directing and acting—is simply superb. I don't think that an ensemble like that has ever been equalled in television. But TAGS is more than just comedy. It also has some of the most sensitive dramatic moments and episodes ever filmed. I think one of the secrets to TAGS being able to balance its comedy and drama is that the show really developed believeable characters who are true to life and exhibit the full range of human emotions. Mayberry literally takes on a life of its own. We can all picture ourselves on the streets of Mayberry. We can almost taste Aunt Bee's gooseberry pie. When the show was in its original run back in the sixties, it provided a way to take our minds off the turmoil of the war in Vietnam and the race riots in our own streets. Today, the show provides the same relief from the hurried life of the eighties. Mayberry reminds us of how things used to be or how we wish things used to be, even if they never were. And the messages of TAGS are timeless. The show is as relevant and poignant today as it was a generation ago. Excellence has a way of surviving, and I think TAGS therefore will be around for us to see for a long, long time.

Steve Spignesi: Jim Clark, thank you very much for your visit to Mayberry, my hometown.

The Mayberry Gazette ™©

THE WORLD AUTHORITY ON MAYBERRY, NORTH CAROLINA

SPRING/SUMMER 1986

NO. 1

The Ultimate Reunion: *Return to Mayberry*

WELCOME

Welcome to **The Mayberry Gazette!** In case you've been away at Myers Lake and haven't heard, this newsletter marks the first ___ new format and layout **(Volume** ___ ___ of this new layout, ___ our "official ___

On April 13, 1986, television viewers ___ the country witnessed television his ___ the making. NBC aired a two-hour m ___ TV movie, **"Return to Mayberry,"** a ___ reunited many of the original cast ___ members from **"The Andy Griffi** ___ (CBS, 1960–1968).

"Return to Mayberry," which s ___ over a year in pre-production, h ___ ultimate reunion. Not only did it ___ members of the original cas' ___ brought back director **Bob S** ___ directed the first three years ___ show), writers **Everett Greenb** ___ **Bullock** (who wrote many ___ show's episodes) and ___ **Hagen** (who scored the ___ original).

The reunion, which w ___ Andy Griffith (who also ___ producer), was filmed ___ Olivos, California, just o' ___ Using photographs an ___ show, the set decorat ___ resemble the origin ___ possible.

The storyline four ___ returning to Maybe ___

THE BULLET

Volume 3, Issue 3

OFFICIAL NEWSLETTER OF
The Andy Griffith Sho ___
RERUN WATCHERS CLUB

September 14, 198 ___

Oh, It Was Really Big!

It was a movie made for Otis and Sarah. It smashed the ratings and lit up the switchboards!

Return to Mayberry was the made-for-TV hit of 1985-86. It was the highest rated TV event in its category for the season (and the seventh highest rated one of all time), finishing with 34.6 rating and 53 share in the Nielsen ratings.

What that means is that almost 30 million households (representing about 55 million people and over half of all the households watching TV at the time) watched *Return to Mayberry*. And that was against what was considered strong competition from the other networks.

It was wonderful to see the old familiar faces back together again. It's true that, for **TAGS** fans, nothing will likely ever replace the original series. It represented eight years of excellence that will probably never be surpassed.

But *Return to Mayberry* was an important renewal of what Mayberry stands for —a remind- er of all that Mayberry mean ___ The movie delighted man ___ fans—new and old. But most o ___ all, it let us know not so much ___ that we can go home again, but ___ that we should always be glad ___ when we get to see old friends.

(NBC-TV is talking about a second Mayberry movie—one with a Thanksgiving or Christmas theme—for the 1987-88 season. Andy Griffith and others from **TAGS** aren't doing the talking, but they do have ears. Nevertheless, Andy Griffith has indicated that a second movie is just as unlikely to happen as he thought the first one would be.

However, NBC does have the broadcast rights for two more airings of *Return to Mayberry*. Fall '86 seems like a good bet for the first *Return* rerun.)

We've Moved. Have You?

The Andy chapter of **TAGSRWC** and *The Bullet* have a fancy new address in the heart of Nashville's Music Row. (No, we haven't run into the Darlings yet, but we're keeping an eye out for their truck.)

Correspondence for Andy chapter and *The Bullet* should now be sent to:

TAGSRWC
27 Music Square East
Suite 146
Nashville, TN 37203.

This new address should also be used when ordering club bumper stickers and T-shirts, or back issues of *The Bullet.*

In addition, please let us know (at our new address) if *you* have a new address. The nice people at the Post Office will forward your *Bullets* to you from your old address for a while.

Then all of a sudden they'll nip it, nip it, nip it in the bud! When they start their budnipping, we start getting your *Bullets* returned to us.

IN APPRECIATION OF MAYBERRY, OUR HOMETOWN

"The Andy Griffith Show" Appreciation Society (AGSAS) is yet another organization devoted to the continued airing of our favorite show. (See their address in the Preface.) Even though it has fewer members than "The Andy Griffith Show" Rerun Watchers Club, the AGSAS nonetheless maintains a blur of activity surrounding the show and the cast members. The AGSAS puts out a bulletin called, appropriately, "The Mayberry Gazette," and any fans out there who are interested in joining the Society can write for information on becoming a member. (All real "Andy" fans should be members of both "The Andy Griffith Show" Rerun Watchers Club and "The Andy Griffith Show" Appreciation Society. Joining is the best way to stay in touch with those who share the love we have for the show, the people, and the town.) I asked John Meroney (founder of the Society) to write something that expressed his appreciation for the show and, yes, the town of Mayberry itself. — **Steve Spignesi**

Since I founded "The Andy Griffith Show" Appreciation Society in 1983, if I've been asked one question more than any other it would have to be, "Why, after twenty-five years, is 'The Andy Griffith Show' so popular?"

Each time I answer that question, I say three things: the chemistry between the cast was truly remarkable; the writing was of superb quality; and the viewers seemed to forget that they were actually watching a television show—they felt that they were paying a visit to their hometown, which happened to be Mayberry.

"The Andy Griffith Show" stands far above all the other situation comedy contenders because the characters on the show had a richness about them that was simple and, at the same time, very realistic.

The show disproved the quotation from Thomas Wolfe that you can't go home again; millions of Americans did—and still do—go to Mayberry, North Carolina, each and every week for the past twenty-five years.

The humor wasn't contrived, nor did it depend on the rat-a-tat jokes and one-liners so commonplace on today's television. Rather, it came from within the characters, from the love and closeness that these people had for one another, both on stage and off. That's why the show is so very appealing today, and that's what's called *real* talent.

Luckily for us, "The Andy Griffith Show" had some of the best writers and performers in the entertainment business. Without them Andy, Aunt Bee, Opie, Barney and all the others would not have been as real to us as they became. The show was pure Americana in every sense of the word. It was as good as apple pie and just about as popular. It wasn't complicated, it was just simple and fun, and when you tuned in, you felt as if you were a citizen of Mayberry, a part of the gang.

Those are just some of the reasons "The Andy Griffith Show" remains popular today. Every viewer and admirer has their own reason to like the show but, for most, it's just that special feeling you get when you visit Mayberry, one that really can't be defined—that "special something" that made Mayberry what it is: everyone's favorite hometown.

John Meroney
Clemmons, North Carolina
1986

Mayberry
My Hometown

Part VI
The Subconscious Prober Primer:
A Topical Index to the Encyclopedia

THE
MAYBERRY UNION HIGH
THEME SONG

Mayberry Union High
Victory is yours well nigh
We'll hit the line for points everytime
The orange and blue will try, try, try, try
And when the victory's won
You'll be our favorite son
Proud waves your banner in the sky
Mayberry Union High

INDEX

This index attempts to group by categories those encyclopedia entries that fall into the same general topical area. This will allow the reader to search by topic, thereby eliminating the need to know a specific entry in order to find it in *Mayberry, My Hometown*. I have not been strict with limiting the inclusion of entries to the exact topic. The entry "Clint Biggers" has been included under the heading "The Animals of Mayberry," for example, because he was the original owner of the "dogs, dogs, dogs" and such information is mentioned in his entry. I hope this section will facilitate the rapid location of most entries, over 4,000 of which have been indexed and cross-indexed under thirty-nine topical headings. Happy hunting, and long live Mayberry!!

BUSINESSES & BUSINESS RELATED MATTERS (CONT.)

BOWLING ALLEY
"BOY WANTED AFTER SCHOOL AND SAT. APPLY INSIDE"
BOYSINGER'S BAKERY
"BRADFORD INTERNATIONAL ICE CREAM"
MARTIN BRECKINRIDGE
ASA BREENY
"BRIAN JACKSON STONE MASON HEADSTONES + ART OBJECTS"
BRICE'S DEPARTMENT STORE
MR. BRISTOL
MR. BRONSON
BROWN
BURFORD'S
BUNNY CALDWELL
CARROLL'S OF MAYBERRY
CB & Q RAILROAD
CINEMASCOPE CAFE
MR. COEFIELD
FLOYD COLBY
CORNWALL'S GAS STATION
MR. CRAWFORD
BILLY CRENSHAW
CROWLEY'S MARKET
BEN CURTIS
CYMBAL CITY
DARCY FURS
DAVIS' STORE
DIAMOND JIM'S
DOAKES MARKET
ELROY DOCKING
DOGWOOD DAIRY FARMS
DOLLY
DOWNEY'S
ED'S REFRIGERATION
MR. EDINGER'S CARPENTER SHOP
8¢
1890
80¢
87¢
ELM CITY DELIVERY SERVICE
ELMO
EMMETT'S FIX-IT SHOP
ESSEX BANK BUILDING
"EVERYTHING IN TIME OF NEED"
F. WAKEFIELD BEAUTY SALON
FEED AND GRAIN STORE
HARLAN FERGUS
RICHIE FERRARO
"FIFE REALTY"
FIFTY BOXES
ARNOLD FINCH
WILBUR FINCH
FLEUR DE LIS BEAUTY SALON
"FLOYD LAWSON ENTERPRISES"
FLOYD'S TONSORIAL PARLOR
CHARLIE FOLEY
MR. FOLEY
"FOR SALE HARRY WALKER REAL ESTATE CO. DON'T DISTURB TENANT"
WILLARD FOSTER
FOSTER FURNITURE POLISH
MR. FRANKLIN
FRANKLYN PHARMACY
FRASER'S
FRED
MR. FRISBY
FURNITURE FACTORY

"FURNITURE NEW AND USED"
FURNITURE STORE
GEM HOTEL - ROOMS
GENERAL STORE
GEORGE
GEORGE SAFFERLY'S SERVICE STATION
DR. EDITH GIBSON
MR. GIDDINGS
EARLY GILLY
FRANK GLENDON
"GLUE-DIPPER"
"GOOBER'S GUSHER OF GOLD"
GOOBER'S SERVICE
FRED GOSS
H. GOSS
"GRAB BAG FOR CASH"
THE GRAND
GREEN
HAROLD GRIGSBY
HALF MOON ROADHOUSE
HALF MOON TRAILER PARK
HANSEN'S PRINT SHOP
HARDWARE AND APPLIANCES
HARDWARE STORE
MR. HARKINSON
HARRIET
HARVEY WILLICK'S SHOE STORE
HILLSIDE UNIVERSITY
HI-TEST
HOGARTH DETECTIVES
GEORGE HOLLANDER
HOLLYWOOD FUNERALS
IDEAL CONSTRUCTION COMPANY
BRIAN JACKSON
J. HOWARD JACKSON
MR. JASON
JENSEN ORTHOPEDIC LOAFERS
JOE
CHARLIE JOHNSON
JOHNSON'S SPORTING GOODS
KIEGELHEIMER'S
MYRA KOONTZ
LAMPS AND SHADES
LAUNDERCOIN, INC.
LEMONADE STAND
LIFFER'S
"LINE UP FOR LOOT"
THE LINGERIE SHOP
LIVING ROOM GROUP
LONAS HILL AND DAVISON ATTORNEYS
"LUCKY PEPPERMINTS"
LUCY BERNETT'S DRY GOODS STORE
LUKEN'S STYLE SHOP
MACDONALD'S FLYING SCHOOL
MADAME OLGA'S
MANHATTAN SHOE COMPANY
MARTIN PHILLIPS COMPANY
MR. MARTINELLI
MRS. MASON
RALPH MASON
MASON'S DRUGSTORE
MAX
MAYBERRY HOTEL
MAYBERRY ICE HOUSE
MAYBERRY MOTOR LODGE
MAYBERRY SECURITY BANK
MAYBERRY THEATER
MAYBERRY TRANSFER COMPANY
MR. MELDRIM
FRED MICHAELS
MID-MOUNTAIN FINANCE COMPANY
THE MILL
BERT MILLER
MIRACLE SALVE COMPANY

MIRACLE-SWEEP
MME. PHOEBE'S BEAUTY SALON
NEWTON MONROE
ORVILLE MONROE
MONROE NURSERY
MORT'S CLOTHING
MURPHY'S HOUSE OF THE NINE FLAVORS
MYER'S REAL ESTATE COMPANY
NELSON'S FUNERAL PARLOR
NORMA'S BEAUTY SHOPPE
NORMAN'S GROCETERIA
$1.00
177 MAIN STREET
ORVILLE MONROE'S FUNERAL PARLOR
OTTO
"A PAPERMILL IN CANADA"
PATTERSON'S
PEGGY'S BEAUTY SALON
DOYLE PERKINS
PERKINS REALTY
RAFE PETERSON
PICKLE BOTTLING PLANT
THE PICKLE FACTORY
JESSE PIERSON
PIERSON'S SWEET SHOP
PILOT PINES FUNERAL PARLOR
PINK LADY COSMETICS
PIZZA PLACE
R & M GRAIN ELEVATORS
RAZOR BLADES
CHARLIE ROSS
ROY'S LAUNDRY SERVICE
RUDY
GEORGE SAFFERLY
SAM
MR. SCHLUMMER
SCIENTIFIC INTRODUCTIONS, INC.
SILO RENTALS
MR. SIMMONS
WALT SIMPSON
OSCAR SKINNER
JIM SLATER
SNEADLEY'S
SOCKS
SPENCER'S PIPES AND TOBACCOS
"THE STAR OF PEORIA"
FRED STERLING
JIM STEVENS
JIM SUMMERS
SUPER BARGAIN MARKET
TATE WARREN'S STORE
TED'S PET SHOP
"THREE HOUR SERVICE"
"TOYS GAMES HOBBIES MODELS"
TUCKER ENTERPRISES
MALCOLM TUCKER
TWENTY-FIVE YEARS
$299.00
$200.00 A MONTH
$2,000.00
TYLER BAKERY
VACUUM CLEANERS
ELLIE WALKER
HARRY WALKER
WALLY
WALLY'S SERVICE STATION
RAY WASHING
SHORTY WATSON
BEN WEAVER
WEAVER'S DEPARTMENT STORE
MISS WELLINGTON
MISS WELLINGTON'S SCHOOL FOR GIRLS

WILLIAMS INTERIORS AND
    FURNITURES
YE OLDE BOOK SHOP

OTIS CAMPBELL

"ACCIDENTAL INJURY OCCURRING
    ON COUNTY PROPERTY"
"AN ALLIGATOR FARM IN FLORIDA"
BIG JACK ANDERSON
*THE BARNEY FIFE SUBCONSCIOUS
    PROBER PRIMER*
MRS. BIXBY
"BLOODY MARY"
BREAKFAST FOR OTIS
"BRINGING IN THE SHEAVES"
OTIS CAMPBELL
RALPH CAMPBELL
VERLAINE CAMPBELL
COUNTY LINE CAFE
OLD MAN DAVIS
"DIPSY-DOODLE"
8:00 A.M.
411
GIN RUMMY
GLUE-DIPPER
THE HARPERS
JIMMY JACKSON
MRS. JACKSON
OTIS'S BEGINNINGS
OTIS'S CAR
OTIS'S DIRECTIONS TO RAFE
    HOLLISTER'S STILL
OTIS'S EULOGY
PINK ELEPHANT
"THE ROCK"
SEPTEMBER 23, 1941, 2:00 P.M.
SPOT
THUNDER
NATHAN TIBB
TWENTY-SEVEN YEARS
"THE TWILIGHT ZONE"
UNCLE NAT
CHARLIE VARNEY
WARREN'S HANGOVER CURE FOR
    OTIS
MRS. WICKS
WOMEN'S HISTORICAL SOCIETY

EMMETT CLARK

AKRON, OHIO
BEN BEECHAM
BEN BEECHAM AGENCY
BERNIE THE FURRIER
MARTHA CLARK
$8.00
$850.00
$1800.00
$1100.00
$1150.00
FLETCHER EMERSON
$15,000.00
FLORA
FORTY PERCENT OFF
FOX STOLE
"FULLY LET OUT RANCH MINK"
HARRY
HEATING PAD
LIQUOR CONTROL BOARD OF
    NEBRASKA
"A NEGLIGEE WITH A BLACK
    NIGHTGOWN"
NINE DOLLARS PER MONTH
NYLON TIRES

PERFUME
PURPLE
PURSE
SHORT-HAIRED MINK COAT
6:00 P.M.
$3.95
361 POUNDS
$3000.00
TWENTY-ONE
WOOLEN BATHROBE

CLERGY AND MATTERS
RELATED TO RELIGION

REVEREND AIKEN
ALL SOUL'S CHURCH
"BE YOURSELF"
BLUE ROBES
DR. HARRISON EVERETT BREEN
REVEREND DARGOOD
"DICE ARE LOADED AGAINST THE
    EVIL-DOER"
11:00 A.M.
$500.00
FIVE INCHES
GENESIS 6:10
"HAPPINESS"
HAZEL
FRED HENRY
JARROD HOOPER
REVEREND LEIGHTON
REVEREND MARTIN
THE MINISTER
MORAVIAN CHURCH BASEMENT
NINETY-THREE
CISSY NOONAN
PREACHER RAYMOND OPEL
THE PASTOR
MAGGIE PETERS
"SEEK AND YE SHALL FIND"
"THE SEVEN DEADLY SINS"
"THE STORY OF NOAH"
SUNDAY SCHOOL
ROSE TEMPLE
#10
$37.50
REVEREND HOBART M. TUCKER
TWELVE
$1200.00
"WHAT'S YOUR HURRY?"
PREACHER WINSLOW

HELEN CRUMP

AMUSING TALES OF TINY TOTS
ANDY AND HELEN'S BEDROOM
AUGUST 3 AND 4, 1959
"BELLE OF THE BALL"
"BEST BETS"
"BEST COOK IN MAYBERRY"
MISS BLANCHARD
HARRY BROWN
ROGER BRYANT
BRYANT PUBLISHING COMPANY
MR. CALVIN
"A CARY GRANT MOVIE"
"CHILDISH"
"CONCEALING A .38 REVOLVER"
CYNTHIA
"DEALING CARDS AT AN ILLEGAL
    GAMING HOUSE"
895
EIGHT YEARS
EIGHTH GRADE
"EMBRYONIC MEGALOPOLIS"

ETHEL
ROBLING FLASK
FLOYD'S ENGAGEMENT CARD TO
    ANDY AND HELEN
MISS FOSTER
FRIED CHICKENS
GEORGE
"GRACE"
H141Q5
MR. HAMPTON
HELEN CRUMP'S HOUSE NUMBER
HELEN CRUMP'S PHONE NUMBER
HELEN'S FORTUNE
"HELENE ALEXIAN DUBOIS"
MR. JUDSON
LEMON PIE
JANE MARCUS
"MILLIE"
"MILLIE GRACE"
"MISS HELEN CRUMP BEING
    BROUGHT IN FOR ARRAIGN-
    MENT IN CONNECTION..."
MAYNARD MYERS
"OLD LADY CRUMP"
OPIE'S LETTER TO HELEN
DALE ROBERTSON
74¢
SIX CHILDREN
FRANK SMITH
STATE SPELLING BEE CHAMPION
STOCKINGS
JOHN TRACY
2389
UNCLE EDWARD
MISS VOGEL
MISS WARNER
WATKINS GRADING MANUAL

THE DARLINGS

ANDELINA
"BOIL THAT CABBAGE DOWN"
HASTY BUFORD
IDELE BUSHY
"DAN TUCKER"
"DANCE TILL YOUR STOCKINGS ARE
    HOT AND RAVELIN"
BRISCOE DARLING
CARL DARLING
CHARLENE DARLING
DEAN DARLING
DOUG DARLING
JED DARLING
MITCH DARLING
RODNEY DARLING
THE DARLINGS
DIVORCE INCANTATION, "MOUNTAIN
    STYLE"
MRS. JONES
"NEVER HIT YOUR GRANDMA WITH A
    GREAT BIG STICK"
907
PREACHER RAYMOND OPEL
ROBERT E. LEE NATURAL BRIDGE
SEVENTEEN
"SHADY GROVE"
"THERE IS A TIME"
THIRTY
317
"TILLER OF SOIL, FELLER OF TREES"
"TOW SACK FULL OF LOVE"
DUDLEY J. WASH
"WET SHOES IN THE SUNSET"

CLARA EDWARDS

ALLSPICE
ALMA
MRS. ARBESTER
"A BARBECUE FIESTA"
BETH
BOOSTER'S CLUB
EMMA BRAND
BROWNIES AND HOT CHOCOLATE
CHICKEN CASSEROLE
CHIPPED BEEF PUFFS
CLARK COOPER
A CURRENCY CONVERTER
BERTHA EDWARDS
CLARA EDWARDS
COLONEL EDWARDS
GAYLE EDWARDS
ELEVEN YEARS
EMMETT'S FIX-IT SHOP
4
HIPPIE HARRISON
HEATING PAD
CLARA JOHNSON
"MISS GADABOUT"
NEURALGIA
HARLAN ROBINSON
SAYBERTOWN
SEVEN YEARS
SNOW VALLEY WHITE
"SOME ENCHANTED EVENING"
SWEET BRIAR NORMAL SCHOOL
THIRTY PERCENT OFF

BARNEY FIFE

AFGHAN
"AG"
AGNES JEAN
"AIR FRESHENER AND ANTACID
    TABLETS"
NETTIE ALBRIGHT
JEREMY AMBROSE
MRS. AMBROSE
ANDRE KOSTALANEZ MARCHERS
TEENA ANDREWS
ANDY AND HELEN'S BEDROOM
"ANDY GUMP"
"ANIMAL CRACKERS"
"APPLE PIE ORDER"
THE ARCADE
ARMY STORY #17
THE ART OF JUDO
THE ART OF KARATE
AUGUST 1953
BACKROOM OF THE COURTHOUSE
BAKED ALASKA
JIM BAKER
KEVIN BAKER
"BANK HOLD-UP FOILED HERE"
"THE BANK POEM"
"BARN"
BARNEY AND THELMA LOU'S FIRST
    MEETING
BARNEY AND THELMA LOU'S
    ROUTINE
"BARNEY FIFE FOR SHERIFF, THE
    MAN FOR THE JOB, WIN WITH
    FIFE"
BARNEY FIFE, M.D.
*THE BARNEY FIFE SUBCONSCIOUS
    PROBER PRIMER*
"BARNEY FIFE THE BULKHEAD"
"BARNEY THE BEAST"
BARNEY'S ADDRESS

BARNEY'S BEGINNINGS
BARNEY'S BREAKFAST
BARNEY'S CAR
BARNEY'S COFFEE
BARNEY'S CRIME WAVE
BARNEY'S DEN
BARNEY'S FIRST CAR
BARNEY'S FRIENDSHIP QUOTE
BARNEY'S GEAR
BARNEY'S GIFTS TO THE TAYLORS
BARNEY'S HELMET
BARNEY'S LETTER TO ANDY
BARNEY'S MIDDLE NAME AND/OR
    INITIAL
BARNEY'S MOTHER'S STOMACH
BARNEY'S #1 JOB
BARNEY'S PHONE MANNERS
BARNEY'S PHONE NUMBER
BARNEY'S RIDDLE
BARNEY'S "SON"
BARNEY'S TRICK SLINGSHOT SHOTS
BARNEY'S TWO WAYS (TO TELL A
    GIRL YOU LIKE HER)
BARNEY'S VACATION
BARNEY'S WEIGHT
"BARON VON RICHTOFEN"
"THE BEAST OF THE FOURTH
    FLOOR"
"BEASTO MARISTO"
JUANITA BEAZLEY
SAMUEL W. BECKER
HENRY BENNETT
"BERNARD P. FIFE, ATTORNEY AT
    LAW"
"BERNIE"
"BERT AND SQUIRT"
BEST MAN
BETTY ANN
"THE BIG BOMB"
"THE BIG FREEZE"
"BIG HOUSE"
BILL
"A BIRD IN THE HOUSE MEANS A
    DEATH IN THE FAMILY"
WILTON BLAIR
BLANCHE
"BLOOD WILL TELL"
"BLOODHOUND OF THE LAW"
BLUE
BLUE BOY
BLUE CONVERTIBLE
"BLUE STEEL BABY"
"BLUEPRINT STAGE"
JEAN BOSWELL
"BOYS AT THE LAB"
"BREAD, LOVE, AND BEANS"
"BREAKFAST FOR OTIS"
BRINGING IN THE SHEAVES"
CLIFF BRITTEN
GEORGE BRONSON
"BUDDY"
"BUSTER"
"BUT BARNEY, I'M YOUR MOTHER"
MR. BUTLER
CAL
THE CAPONE GANG
HAROLD CARSON
THE CASCADE CLUB
CASSINO
CENTRAL HIGH
CHARLIE
CHARLOTTSVILLE
"CHECKPOINT CHICKIE"
"THE CHICKEN"
"CHICKIE-BABY"
"CHIEF"

"CHILDISH"
"CHIRIBIRIBIN"
CHONEY
"CHOPPER"
CLARENCE
MISS CLARK
THE CLARKS
MR. CLIFFORD
"COMPELSHION"
"CONCERT TONIGHT—RELAX TO
    MUSIC UNDER THE STARS"
"A COTTON MILL IN SAVANNAH"
"COUNT OF MONTE CRISTO"
COUNTY PENMANSHIP CONTEST
"COUSIN" ANDY
TRACY CRAWFORD
"CRAZY GUN BARNEY"
"CRIMINAL LOOKS"
GLENN CRIPES
OLD MAN CROWLEY
"CUFF SLAPPING"
CUSTOM SEDAN
"THE CUTLASS"
CYMBAL CITY
"DAME"
JOHN DANBY
DAPHNE
"DARN CUTE"
"THE DEADLY GAME"
"DEPUTY FIFE HERO"
"DEPUTY FIFE HERO IN CAVE
    RESCUE"
THE DEPUTY OATH
"DEPUTY PHYSICAL
    REQUIREMENTS"
DETECTIVE BUREAU
M.L. DEWHURST
DIAMONDS
DILLINGER
CLARIE DORSETT
MORGAN DOWNEY
D-QUEEN JUNCTION
PURLIMAE DUBOIS
"EAGLE-EYE BARNEY"
"EARLY, EARLY, URCHIN FREE"
EDDIE
JACK EGBERT
8:00 A.M.
$18.50
"ELECTRONILLY"
ELEVEN BOYS
11:00 P.M.
ELEVEN SPEED WARNINGS
JARVIS ELRIDGE
THE EMANCIPATION
    PROCLAMATION
"AN ENGLISH OTIS"
ERECTOR SET
ESCARGOT AND BRAINS
THE ESQUIRE CLUB
"EXTRA-SENSITIVE PERCEPTION"
"FACE ON THE BARROOM FLOOR"
"FACITIOUS"
FAMILY DINNER FOR ONE
"FAST GUN FIFE"
FBI
"FEARLESS FIFE"
FEBRUARY 7
HOWARD FELCHER
LORRAINE FELCHER
"FELIX THE CAT"
MRS. FENTON
"BARNEY FICE"
MISS FICKETT
FIFE REALTY
"FIFE THE FIERCE"

BARNEY FIFE (CONT.)

"A STUDENT OF HUMANITY"
"SUBTLE BARNEY FIFE"
PHIL SUNKEL
SUNNY JIM BARS
JACK SWEET
SWEET CIDER
THE "SYMBOL" SPEECH
"TAIL-GUNNER"
TAILSPIN TONY
"TATTLETALE"
"A TED WEEMS RECORD"
$10.00
$10.00 IN THREE DAYS
TEN YEARS
"THERAPETIC"
"THE THIRD DEGREE"
"THOSE ENDEARING YOUNG
    CHARMS"
$3.95
3,000 BOOKS
"TICO TICO"
"TIGER"
"TIGHTLIPS BARNEY"
TIN INKBLOT
TUESDAY NIGHT
"TWEAKY"
"A 21 JEWEL WATCH WITH A PURE
    GOLD BAND"
20/20
"TWINKLETOES TIME"
$2.75
TWO SUGARS
"U.T. PENDYKE, D.V.M."
"THE UMBRELLA MAN"
"US FIFE'S IS WIRY"
US/USSR SUMMIT MEETING
VACUUM CLEANERS
MR. VASILIEVICH
TYLA LEE VERNON
VIRGIL
MRS. VONRODER
"A WAITRESS AND A REGISTERED
    NURSE"
WAR SURPLUS AUCTION
"A WEB-FOOTED RED-CRESTED LAKE
    LOON"
DR. WEBSTER
"WELCOME BACK CLASS OF '48"
"WILD BILL FIFE"
RAMONA WILEY
"WILL YOU HELP US?"
MR. WILLIAMS
HALCYON LORETTA WINSLOW
"WORDS THAT START WITH 'S'"
"THE WORKS"
WRISTWATCH
"WYATT EARP"
YEARBOOK ENTRY: BARNEY FIFE
"YOU'RE THE CATS"

THE FOODS OF MAYBERRY

ALLSPICE
AMMONIA
ANDY'S FAVORITE DISH
ANDY'S SHOPPING LIST
APPLE CRUMB PIE
APPLE PIE
AVOCADO SALAD AND HOT ROAST
    BEEF SANDWICHES
BAKED ALASKA
BARNEY'S BREAKFAST
BARNEY'S COFFEE

BEEF CASSEROLE
BEEF STEW
"BEST COOK IN MAYBERRY"
BLACK JELLYBEANS
BLUEBERRY PIE
BOILED BEEF
BREAD PUDDING
BREAKFAST FOR OTIS
BROWNIE RECIPE
BROWNIES AND HOT CHOCOLATE
BUSINESSMAN'S SPECIAL
BUTTERSCOTCH PECAN
CASHEW FUDGE
CATFISH CASSEROLE
CHICKEN
CHICKEN A LA KING
CHICKEN AND DUMPLINGS
CHICKEN AND DUMPLINGS AND
    SWEET TATER PIE
CHICKEN CASSEROLE
CHICKEN FRICASEE
CHICKEN IN A POT
CHICKEN OR POT ROAST
CHICKEN PAPRIKASH
CHICKEN WITH CRUST
CHILI
CHIPPED BEEF PUFFS
CHOCOLATE LAYER CAKE
COLD CHICKEN AND POTATO SALAD
CORN ON THE COB
CORNED BEEF HASH
CORNISH PASTRY
CREAM BUN
"CROW"
THE DELUXE SPECIAL
THE DINER LUNCH
THE DINER LUNCH SPECIAL
EGGNOG
11
ESCARGOT BOURGINOIN
MRS. FELDON
MRS. FLETCHER
40¢
FORTY-FIVE-MINUTE EGGS
MRS. FOSTER
FRIED CHICKEN AND CORNBREAD
FRIED CHICKENS
FRUITCAKE
GOOBER'S FAVORITE VEGETABLE
GOOSEBERRY PIE
GRAPEFRUIT JUICE
GUMBALLS
HAM LOAF AND GREEN BEANS
    CHINESE STYLE
HOT BULLION
HOT FUDGE SUNDAES
HUCKLEBERRY SMASH
ICE CREAM SODAS
"KEROSENE CUCUMBERS"
KETCHUP AND MUSTARD
LADYFINGER
A LEG OF LAMB
LEMON PIE
LILLIAN
LUNCH FOR ANDY
LUNCHES FOR THE TAYLORS
MACARONI SURPRISE
MARTHA
MARY
JAMES MASEFIELD
"MAYBERRY PRIDE ICE CREAM"
MEATLOAF
MEATLOAF PLATE
ABIGAIL MILLIKEN
MR. COOKIE BAR
MOZZARELLA

MULBERRY SQUEEZINGS
MULLIGAN'S STEW
MURPHY'S HOUSE OF THE NINE
    FLAVORS
MUSHROOMS
NECTARINE CRUSH
NEW YORK CUT STEAK
$133.50
OPIE'S FAVORITE PIE
ORANGE SODA
OREGANO
MRS. PARKINS
PEANUT BUTTER
"PEANUT BUTTER AND BOLOGNA,
    PEANUT BUTTER AND LIVER-
    WURST, PEANUT BUTTER AND
    PEANUT BUTTER"
MRS. PETERS
PORK CHOPS AND FRIED APPLE
    RINGS
PORK ROAST
POTATO SALAD
PUMPKIN PIE A LA MODE
PUNCH SUPREME
RHUBARB PIE
RIB ROAST
RICE PUDDING
ROAST BEEF DINNER
ROAST BEEF ON RYE
RUM CAKE
SALAD AND ROAST BEEF
7:00 A.M.
SHRIMP AND DUCK
600 SANDWICHES
SMOKED HAM
STRAWBERRY
STRAWBERRY ICE CREAM
SUNNY JIM BARS
SUPPER
SWEET CIDER
SWISS CHEESE SANDWICHES
TAILS
MRS. TILMAN
TUNA SALAD
TURKEY WITH ORANGE DRESSING
TWELVE OR FIFTEEN
TWO ROWS
"TWO SLICES OF APPLE PIE
    BETWEEN TWO PIECES OF APPLE
    PIE AND A SLAB OF APPLE PIE
    FOR DESSERT"
TWO SUGARS
VITAMINS
WALLPAPER
WARREN'S HANGOVER CURE FOR
    OTIS
WEENIES AND BEANS
WEENIES AND ROOT BEER
WEST INDIAN LICORICE MOCHA
    DELIGHT
WINTERGREEN MINTS

GROCERIES: THE MAYBERRY MARKET BASKET

APPLES
BACON
BANANAS
BEANS
BELL PEPPERS
BOLOGNA
CABBAGE
CARROTS
CAULIFLOWER

CELERY
COFFEE
COLLARD GREENS
CORN
CRANBERRY SAUCE
CUCUMBERS
DRESSING
EGGS
FATBACK
FOLEY'S MARKET
FRANKS
FRESH FARM PRODUCE
FRUITS AND VEGETABLES
FRYERS
HAM
HAMS
HENS
HOGBACK
HOMINY GRITS
JAMS
LETTUCE
OKRA
ONIONS
ORANGES
PEACHES
PEARS
PEAS
PICNICS
PIGS
PLUMS
POTATOES
SAUSAGE
SIRLOIN STEAK
SOREGHUM MOLASSES
SPINACH
STEAK
SUGAR
SYRUP
TOMATOES
WAXPAPER
YELLOW WAX BEANS

KIN AND FAMILY CONNECTIONS IN MAYBERRY

HAROLD ALBRIGHT
BEULAH ALBRIGHT
THE ALBRIGHTS
JEREMY AMBROSE
MRS. AMBROSE
AUSTRALIA
MRS. BAILEY
CINDY BARTON
MRS. BARTON
ANDREW BEAZLEY
ANDY BECKER
LILY BECKER
THE BEEMANS
BERTHA
TYLER BRANCH
BRUCE
MRS. BUNTLEY
ROBERT BUNTLEY
WILLIAM BUNTLEY
NATE BUSHY
ELMER CARSON
"COUSIN" ANDY
LYDIA CROSSWAITHE
DARRYL
ELLEN
EVIE JOY
$54.20
FLOY
41,000 ACRES

FRIDAY EVENING AT 8:00 O'CLOCK
GILBERT
MARY GRACE GOSSAGE
OLIVER GOSSAGE
GRACE
AUNT HANNAH
EVAN HENDRICKS
MR. AND MRS. HUTCHINS
WENDELL JOHNSON
MAROON TWO-DOOR
AUNT MARTHA
CORA MENDLEBRIGHT
MINNIE
EVAN MOORE
MRS. MORGAN
BILLY MUGGINS
BESS MUGGINS
EFFIE MUGGINS
OLLIE
MAJOR GENERAL LUCIUS PYLE
ROGER
"RUSTLE CATTLE"
ETHEL MONTGOMERY ST. JOHN
JONATHAN ST. JOHN
SICK LEAVE
HANNAH SMITH
WILLIS SPOONER
MABEL STONER
BRADFORD J. TAYLOR
TOD
LAMAR TUTTLE
VERDY
VIRGIL
VIRGINIA LEE
WARREN
HOWIE WILLIAMS
SIMON WINKLER
EMMIE WINTERS
"A WOODEN COWBOY AND A WOODEN DOG"

THE LAW IN MAYBERRY: MANPOWER, JURISPRUDENCE & THE CODES

"ACCIDENTAL INJURY OCCURRING ON COUNTY PROPERTY"
AL
SAM ALLEN
"AMBER ALERT"
CAPTAIN ARDELL
BADGE #2
RALPH BAKER
CAPTAIN BARKER
BARNEY'S GEAR
BARNEY'S #1 JOB
CHIEF BENSON
"BLOCKHOUSE LOOKOUT"
AGENT BOUTON
MR. BRADY
SHERIFF DALE BUCKLEY
INSPECTOR RALPH CASE
CELL #1
CELL #2
"CHECKPOINT CHICKIE"
CITY STATUTE 249A, V
CODE 404B
CODE 421
CODE 721-8
CONTEMPT
THE CRIME PATTERN IN MAYBERRY
"THE DEPUTY OATH"
"DISTURBING THE PEACE"
EDDIE

11:00 P.M.
ELEVEN SPEED WARNINGS
"EMPTYING TRASHCANS ON THE CITY STREETS"
JUD FLETCHER
FORTY-FIVE MILES PER HOUR
OFFICER DEAN FRIENDLY
"THE GREEN RIVER ORDINANCE"
WARDEN HIX
HORTON
SGT. JACOBS
OFFICER JOHNSON
LAKE PATROL
LAW OFFICER'S MANUAL
LES
LIEUTENANT
"LOITERING"
"LOITERING, ILLEGAL ASSEMBLY, AND TAMPERING WITH OFFICIAL EQUIPMENT"
BEN LUCAS
"MARRIAGE LICENSES, BUILDING PERMITS, DOG LICENSES, SALES TAX PERMITS"
"MAXIMUM SECURITY"
MAYOR'S COURT
LEROY MILLER
OFFICER MILLER
MR. MILTON
MONROE
SERGEANT NELSON
907
911
912
923
115
"ONLY LAW WEST OF MT. PILOT"
ORDINANCE 502
SHERIFF FRED PALEY
JUDGE PARKER
SHERIFF PINCKLEY
SHERIFF POINDEXTER
POLICE EMERGENCY COMMITTEE
TROOPER PORTER
PRETTY BOY FLOYD
JEFF PRITCHETT
"ROBE-DIGNITY OFFENDING"
"ROBE OFFENDING"
MR. ROBERTS
"THE ROCK"
RODNEY
BOB ROGERS
INSPECTOR ROGERS
RULE 8, SECTION B
SECTION 17B ARTICLE 4
785
7-10
$70.00
"THE SHERIFF RULES"
SHERIFF'S DUTIES
THE SHERIFFS OF MAYBERRY
603
6-12
$60.00
63
STANDARD OUTFIT
"TAMPERING UNLAWFULLY WITH A MOTOR VEHICLE"
"A 10-12"
302
317
"$20.00 OR TWENTY-FOUR HOURS IN JAIL"
$25.00
$2.00 OR TWENTY-FOUR HOURS
$2.00 OR TWO DAYS IN JAIL

204
215
UNIT ONE
WILLIAM UPCHURCH
TROOPER WALKER
DEPUTY JOE WATSON
SHERIFF WILLIAMS
"WILLOUGHBY VS. PERKINS"
TROOPER WILSON

LAWBREAKERS, CRIMINALS, CON ARTISTS, BULLIES & VILLAINS

ABLE, BAKER AND CHARLIE
AL
AL'S POULTRY HEADQUARTERS
BIG JACK ANDERSON
"ANNABELLE TYLER"
APPLE DUMPLING
GEORGE ARKIS
ARTHUR
AUGUST 3 AND 4, 1959
AUGUST 9, 1946: 11:25 A.M.
RONALD BAILEY
BARNEY'S "CRIME WAVE"
BASTILLE DAY
BEE'S PURSE
MRS. BEGGS
MILES BENTLEY
NEIL BENTLEY
EDDIE BLAKE
THE BLAKE BOY
FRED BOONE
JENNIE BOONE
PURCELL BRANCH
EDDIE BROOKS
HARRY BROWN
DAVID BROWNE
BROWNEYED MARY
GENTLEMAN DAN CALDWELL
THE CANNON
THE CAPONE GANG
CARSON SHACK
MR. CARTER
THE CASCADE CLUB
CB & Q RAILROAD
CHARLIE
"CHARLIE CHASE"
CHICKEN
CHICKEN WIRE FENCE
MRS. CLAREBURN
"CLARISSE TYLER"
MR. CLARK
LUKE COMSTOCK
NAOMI CONNORS
CORN MASH MOONSHINE
"THE COUNT OF MONTE CRISTO"
COWSILL FLAT
JES CRAWFORD
TRACY CRAWFORD
THE CRIME PATTERN IN MAYBERRY
ELIZABETH CROWLEY
DAVE THE HOBO
SHELDON DAVIS
"DEALING CARDS AT AN ILLEGAL
    GAMING HOUSE"
DEXTER STREET
FLETCH DILLBECK
DIRKSEN
DOC
DOC MOLLOY
DRY WELL
8216
80¢

81
FANCY GAP
MR. FIELDS
$15.00
$50.00
FIFTY PERCENT
ARNOLD FINCH
THE FINNEYS
"FIREBUG"
FIVE DAYS IN JAIL
$5.00
5831
FIVE FEET FOUR INCHES TALL, 115
    POUNDS, SLENDER, BLONDE
FIVE FEET SIX INCHES TALL, DARK
    HAIR 175 LBS.
FIVE FOOT NINE INCHES
FIVE HOURS
JUD FLETCHER
TATE FLETCHER
CLARENCE FOLK
JUBELL FOSTER
411
"FOUR EYES"
"FOUR YEARS LAST OCTOBER"
FRANKLIN HOLLOW
FRED
"GOLDBRICK WHEELER"
"THE GOLLYWOBBLER"
BILLY GORDON
IKE GORDON
JUNIOR GORDON
SHERMAN GORDON
THE GORDON BOYS
GRANGER
THE GREAT FILLING STATION
    ROBBERY
"GREETINGS FROM STATE PRISON"
GUMBALLS
THE GYPSIES
LARS HANSEN
"HARBORING A RUNAWAY"
HARRY
HARVEY
COLONEL HARVEY
C.J. HASLER
JED HENSON
POTHROW HENSON
C.J. HOFFMAN
RAFE HOLLISTER
JUNIOR HUBACHER
ELMER HUBACHER
THE HUBACHER BROTHERS
"HUBCAPS LESH"
WEDDY HUFF
INTERCONTINENTAL NEWS
JA-4128
JACK
JAKE
"JAYLENE NAOMI CONNORS"
BUZZ JENKINS
FRED JENKINS
MARVIN JENKINS
LUKE JENSEN
JIM
GEORGE JONES
KELLY
RALPH KINGSLEY
L73218
LADYBUG
LARRY
JOE LAYTON
LENNY
HENRY LEONETTI
BERNARD LESH
MYRT LESH

LIGHTER
JIM LINDSEY
LINDY LOU
LUKE
LUMBAGO
MADGE
"MARSHALL DILLON"
EDGAR J. MASTERS
MATT
"MAUDE CLARISSE TYLER"
MAUDIE
BILL MEDWIN
"MERRY CHRISTMAS FROM STATE
    PRISON"
MIRACLE SALVE
"MR. BIG"
THOMAS A. MOODY
JESS MORGAN
JIM MORGAN
CLARABELE MORRISON
JENNIFER MORRISON
MORT
SAM MUGGINS
MR. MUNDT
"MY LITTLE GRAY HOME IN THE
    WEST"
NAIL POLISH AND EAU DE COLOGNE
NATIONAL POTATO WEEK
NAYLOR
RALPH NEAL
NEIL
JEFF NELSON
NELVIN
NICOTINE
9:00 A.M.
AVERY NOONAN
NORBERT
"NORMAN FELDSPAR"
CHARLIE O'MALLEY
$1.50
$1.60
163 POUNDS
177 MAIN STREET
ONION
"OSCAR FIELDS"
OSGOOD
"OTTO BELL"
PANAMA CANAL DAY
AGNES JEAN PARKER
HENNY PARKER
LEROY PARKER
MA PARKER
THE PARKERS
PASSKEY
"PETULLA ABONDOLA"
"PETULLA OBLONGATA"
PINK TOWELS
PLANTING MARIJUANA
CLYDE PLAUNT
FRED PLUMMER
THE PRISONER OF LOVE
QUAIL
STEVE QUINCY
LUKE RAINER
"RALPH HENDERSON"
MAX RASMUSIN
RD-757
REO FLYING CLOUD
THE RIMSHAW HOUSE
MRS. RODENBACH
MRS. ROSENBACH
ROSS'S RAIDERS
SALLY
BENJAMIN SCHUSTER
7458
SEVENTY MILES PER HOUR

BEN SEWELL
SHELDON
ED SIMKINS
GRACE SIMKINS
SIR WALTER RALEIGH LANDING DAY
RUBE SLOAN
"SMALL TOWN ADMINISTRATION"
HODIE SNITCH
"SPECIAL ELIXIR"
STATE MOBILE MUSEUM
STELLA
GEORGE STEVENS
GLADYS STEVENS
MELISSA STEVENS
LUKE TAFT
10:31 A.M.
"A THIRTEEN-INCH, ONE BLUE-EYED,
    PART-OF-HIS-TAIL-FIN-MISSING
    FISH"
THIRTY PERCENT
$3,600.43
"THREE TIME LOSER DOING TWENTY
    YEARS"
THUNDERBIRD CONVERTIBLE
"TIGER LIL"
MRS. TILMAN
TINY
TURKEY
"TUSCORORA"
$200.00
26043
"BIG MAUDE" TYLER
VND-323
WARY WILLY THE HOBO
JOE WATERS
EDGAR WATSON
EMMA WATSON
HUEY WELCH
HENRY WHEELER
CYRUS WHITLEY
WILLY JACK
ARNOLD WINKLER

FLOYD LAWSON

ALVIN
"ANDREW PAUL LAWSON"
AUGUST 9, 1946: 11:25 A.M.
BILLY
"BLOODHOUND OF THE LAW"
"CHARLIE CHASE"
CHIROPRACTOR
CLAUSE 6
MR. COEFIELD
FLOYD COLBY
COWLICK
"DEAD EYE ANDY"
DELI-TIME SNACK BAR
A DOCTOR
DOWNTOWN BUSINESSMAN'S CLUB
"THE DRINKING FOUNTAIN
    SCANDAL"
ED
THE FERGUSON GIRL
$15.00
$1500.00 DOWN
$50.00
FLOYD LAWSON AND CALVIN
    COOLIDGE
"FLOYD LAWSON ENTERPRISES"
FLOYD LAWSON'S CAREER
FLOYD'S ENGAGEMENT CARD TO
    ANDY AND HELEN
FLOYD'S TONSORIAL PARLOR
CHARLIE FOLEY

"FOR RENT BY OWNER HOWARD
    SPRAGUE CALL MAYBERRY
    397"
"FOR SALE HARRY WALKER REAL-
    ESTATE CO. DON'T DISTURB
    TENANT"
"FOUR EYES"
FREE RADIATOR FLUSH
"FRICK AND FRACK"
GOOBER'S BEST FRIEND
GORDON
MADELINE GRAYSON
NED GRESHAM
ROBERT GRIBBEL
"HAIL TO THEE MISS MAYBERRY"
"A J.C. PENNEY WINDOW"
"KLEP, KLEP"
EMMA LARCH,
"LAWSON PICTURES, INC."
COLONEL CALEB "STONEWALL"
    LAWSON
DANIEL LAWSON
MELBA LAWSON
NORMAN LAWSON
"THE MACHINE"
MAYBERRY'S FIRST INDIAN AGENT
"MUSIC TO SNIP BY"
"PRICE-SPIRALING"
"A PRINCE"
RED AND PURPLE
RHEUMATISM
THE ROBINSON FAMILY
SAM
"SAXIMINIA"
$7.50
$70.00
$75.00
SHAMPOOER
$65.00
$3.75
LAMAR TUTTLE
TWENTY-EIGHT YEARS
"TWENTY OR THIRTY YEARS"
TWO BITS
"TWO CHAIRS NO WAITING"
VIRGINIA LEE
WALKING STICK
WARREN
"THE WHIPLASH TEST"
"THE WORKS"

LICENSE AND OTHER IMPORTANT REGISTRATION NUMBERS

A1A
AUNT BEE'S LICENSE NUMBER
AY-321
BADGE #3
DC-254
DC-269
DF-153
GP-780
H141Q5
INH-851
IR51957
J86-449
JA-4128
JL-327
KS-321
L73218
MBB624
MP-3791
N59558
NC-206

R24-871
RD-757
RJ300
SD-561
"78"
"75"
VEB-368
VND-323
VT-772
WP754

MAYBERRY

AFGHAN
AIR CONDITIONER, NEW STOVE,
COLOR TV, STEREO PHONO-
GRAPH
AL
AMERICAN HISTORY
ANCHRAM CHARCOAL COMPANY
APRICOT FESTIVAL
BAND FESTIVAL
ELLA BATKINS
THE BATTLE OF MAYBERRY
THE BEEMANS
GORDON BELLFIELD
"BEST COOK IN MAYBERRY"
"BEST SALESMAN IN MAYBERRY"
ERMA BISHOP
MRS. BIXBY
BLUEBERRY
BOND
BOY'S DAY
EMMA BRAND
MR. BURTON
CANNON
THE CANNON
CANTEEN
HAROLD CARSON
HANNAH CARTER
MR. CARTER
CENTENNIAL SIGN
CHAMBER OF COMMERCE DANCE
CHARITY DANCE
CHOIR MEETING
CHURCH BASEMENT
CHURCH SOCIAL
CLASS VALEDICTORIAN
CONFEDERATE MONEY
A.J. CONSIDINE
COUNTY EMPLOYMENT OFFICE
COUNTY FAIR
COUNTY INSECTICIDE CONVENTION
THE CRISIS OF 1874
THE DEPOT
OLD MAN DOBBINS
SHARON DOBBINS
DOWNTOWN BUSINESSMAN'S CLUB
THE DRINKING FOUNTAIN
    SCANDAL
ALICE DRUMHILLER
SAM EFFLEY
8 AND 1/2 PERCENT, COMPOUNDED
    ANNUALLY
EIGHT QUARTERS
1864
1861
1870
EMMIE
THE FERGUSON GIRL
$54.20
$50,000.00
THE FIREHOUSE
FIVE SECTIONS
CRAIG FOLGER

261

MILLIE FOLGER
FOUNDER'S DAY
FOUNDER'S DAY PICNIC
400
CARTER FRENCH
"THE FRIENDLY CITY"
"GARDEN CITY OF THE STATE"
"GARDEN SPOT OF MAYBERRY"
"GARDEN SPOT OF THE STATE"
THE GAS WORKS
"GATEWAY TO MONTE CARLO"
"GERONIMO"
GRAND MARSHAL
GRANITE
THE GREATER MAYBERRY
HISTORICAL SOCIETY AND TOURIST
    BUREAU, LTD.
HAROLD GRIGSBY
SUE GRIGSBY
"HAPPY VALLEY"
MR. HARMON
HARVEST BALL
KATHY HAWKINS
WILBUR HENNESSEY
HIP
"HOW TO MAKE FRIED CHICKEN
    AND JOHNNYCAKE"
"HOW TO MAKE POSSUM PIE"
"HOW TO MAKE TURNIP JAM"
CHARLES HUMBONE
INDIANS
INVENTORY
JENKINS
JUD
TILLY KINCAID
ALFRED KITTERLY
KIWANIS CLUB MEETING HALL
LADIES AUXILIARY
LADIES AUXILIARY BAZAAR
LADY MAYBERRY
LADY'S CLUB
"LAW-ABIDING GOD-FEARING
    CITIZENS"
COLONEL CALEB "STONEWALL"
    LAWSON
THE LODGE
"THE LOOP"
LOU
HAROLD LOVITT
LOWELL
"LOWEST CRIME RATE IN THE U.S."
MR. MACGRUDER
MASON'S PICNIC
MAY 1762
JOHN MAYBERRY
MAYBERRY GARDEN CLUB
MAYBERRY GOOD GOVERNMENT
    LEAGUE
MAYBERRY ROLLERS
"MAYBERRY RULES FOR A LONG
    HAPPY LIFE"
MAYBERRY TOWN COUNCIL
MAYBERRY UNION HIGH
MAYBERRY'S BIGGEST INDUSTRY
MAYBERRY'S TOWN CENTER
MAYBERRY'S BEGINNINGS
MAYBERRY'S ELEVATION
MAYBERRY'S FIRST INDIAN AGENT
MAYBERRY'S POPULATION
MAYBERRY'S SECRET
"MAYBERRY'S SHAME"
MEMORIAL HORSE TROUGH
THE MILO BOYS
FRANK MYERS
THE NAYLENS
9:00 P.M.

1931
NORTH SIDE OF TOWN
OLD OAK TREE
OLD SAM
ONE-AND-A-HALF BOYS PER SQUARE
    MILE
$100.00
103 YEARS OLD
ORANGE AND BLUE
PANSY DIVISION
PEACE OFFICER'S BOWLING
    TOURNAMENT
MRS. ETHEL PENDLETON
MILFORD PHILLIPS
MAYOR PIKE
MABEL POLLACK
PTA FUND
PTA MEETING
"R.I.P. THOMAS SILBY 'A FINE \MAN
    AND A DEAR HUSBAND' 1908-
    1958"
THE REGAL ORDER OF THE
    GOLDEN DOOR TO GOOD
    FELLOWSHIP
REGIS
OLD MAN RIMSHAW
ROOM 209
ROOM 216
THE ROSS TREASURE
TRACY RUPERT
SARAH
SATURDAY NIGHT SOCIAL
"THE "SAVE THE SCOBY HOUSE"
    FUND
ED SAWYER
SEPTEMBER 14, 1908
SETH TAYLOR DAY
1762
MR. SIMMONS
SIXTEEN YEARS
VIOLA SLATT
SNUFF
BERT STEVENS
MAYOR ROY STONER
CHIEF STRONGBOW
TOM STRONGBOW
STUFFED WHALE
COLONEL CARLTON TAYLOR
SETH TAYLOR
"TAYLORTOWN"
$10,000.00
3:45 P.M.
$349,119.27
THE TORNADO OF '55
TOWN PICNIC
267 SQUARE MILES
200 YEARS
UNDERPRIVILEGED CHILDREN'S
    CHARITY DRIVE
MRS. VICKERS
THE VICTORY OF TUCAHOOSEE
    CREEK
JEDEDIAH WAKEFIELD
JOSH WAKEFIELD
MR. WAKEFIELD
WALNUT HILLS
WALNUT HILLS GOLF COURSE
THE WALRAVENS
"WELCOME TO MAYBERRY, THE
    FRIENDLY TOWN"
MRS. WICKS
MARY WIGGINS
WOMEN'S BRIDGE CLUB
WORLD WAR I VETS IN MAYBERRY
"THE WORST HOUSE IN TOWN"

MAYBERRY GOVERNMENT AND ADMINISTRATION

ARTISTIC COMMITTEE
MRS. BLAIR
BOOSTER'S CLUB
HARRY BOSWORTH
CHARLIE BRADSHAW
HERB BRADSHAW
GEORGE BRICKER
MR. BRONSON
BUILDING AND SAFETY
    COMMITTEE
MR. CALVIN
FRANK CHASE
CIVIC IMPROVEMENT COMMITTEE
CIVIC IMPROVEMENT LEAGUE
CLAUDE
COUNTY LEGAL DEPARTMENT
DEPARTMENT OF PUBLIC WORKS
COUNCILMAN DOBBS
"FAIR AND SQUARE SAM"
FARLEY
FINANCE COMMITTEE
FREEBERGER
FUND SOLICITING COMMITTEE
THE GOVERNOR
HARVEY
HEAD OF CITY COUNCIL
MAYOR JENKINS
JOHN
SAM PEABODY
RALPH
"SAM'S THE BEST, THE HECK WITH
    THE REST"
MR. SOMERSET
TALBOTT
CYRUS TANKERSLEY
TOWN COUNCIL
TOWN HALL
$1200.00
VT-772
WELFARE DEPARTMENT

MAYBERRY IN PRINT, INCLUDING NEWSPAPERS AND SIGNS

RED AKINS
"ANDY GUMP"
RHODA APFEL
"BANK HOLD-UP FOILED HERE"
"THE BANK POEM"
THE BATTLE OF MAYBERRY
"BEAUTY AND THE BEAST"
"BEST BETS"
ROGER BRYANT
BRYANT PUBLISHING COMPANY
MR. BUTLER
"THE CASE OF THE PIGHEADED
    DEPUTY WHO WAS KILLED BY A
    BERSERK SHERIFF"
CENTENNIAL SIGN
"CONCERT TONIGHT—RELAX TO
    MUSIC UNDER THE STARS"
"COUNTY HAS NO HEART"
"THE CUTLASS"
"D'S & E'S"
"DARN CUTE"
"DEPUTY FIFE HERO"
"DEPUTY FIFE HERO IN CAVE
    RESCUE"

"DOES THE SHERIFF RUN THE TOWN
    OR DOES THE TOWN RUN THE
    SHERIFF?"
DUANE
EDGAR
ENCYCLOPEDIA EUROPA
"A FADING FLOWER OF
    FORGOTTEN LOVE"
"BARNEY FICE"
FIFTH GRADE
"FIKE"
BLANTON FULLER
"HOLLYWOOD COMES TO
    MAYBERRY"
HONG KONG SUITS
"HOW IT FEELS TO PULL THE
    SWITCH"
"I MARRIED A FINK"
"I PICKED A POCKET AND PAID"
"IF YOU CAN FILL THE
    UNFORGIVING MINUTES"
"INTERNATIONAL DATELINE"
"IS THERE NO MERCY?"
"IS THIS DARLENE MASON'S NEXT
    CONQUEST?"
"JACK AND THE BEANSTALK"
"KANSAS CITY CHRONICLE"
"KING ARTHUR"
LONNIE LATTIMER
"THE LEGEND OF SLEEPY HOLLOW"
"LITTLE ORPHAN ANNIE"
"LONGTITUDES & LATITUDES"
"MAYBERRY AFTER MIDNIGHT"
"MAYBERRY CONFIDENTIAL"
"THE MAYBERRY GAZETTE"
"MAYBERRY MERRY-GO-ROUND"
"MAYBERRY SHERIFF RATED BEST
    IN STATE"
"THE MAYBERRY SUN"
"MEANDERING WITH MARGARET"
"MISS HELEN CRUMP BEING
    BROUGHT IN FOR ARRAIGN-
    MENT IN CONNECTION WITH..."
"MOON MULLINS"
"NEWS FROM THE ALTAR"
1¢
OPIE'S WANT AD
"PICKUPS AND SPLASHES FROM
    FLOOR AND POOL"
"SAFETY PROCEDURES ON
    COUNTY ROADS"
"SHERIFF TAYLOR TAKES
    HOLLYWOOD BY STORM"
"SHERIFF WITHOUT A GUN"
"SOCIAL SECURITY IN ACTION"
HECTOR STILES
SUGAR NOTES
HERBERT SWINDELL
$10.00
TWO PAGES
FARLEY UPCHURCH
WANT ADS
"WASHINGTON ROUNDUP"
"WHAT I WOULD DO IF I HAD A
    TOOL CHEST"
"WHAT IT'S LIKE TO BE THE SON OF
    A SHERIFF"
MARGARET WILLIAMSON
WOMEN'S CLUB SIGN

MAYBERRY IN SONG, INCLUDING ALL MUSICAL MATTERS

ALTOONA

ANDRE KOSTALANEZ MARCHERS
"ANIMAL CRACKERS"
THE ARISTOCRATS
MRS. ATZELL
"AWAY IN A MANGER"
KEVIN BAKER
"THE BALLAD OF ANDY AND
    BARNEY"
BAND FESTIVAL
"THE BEAGLES"
TOM BEDLOW
LEONARD BLUSH
BOBBY FLEET AND HIS BAND WITH A
    BEAT
"BOIL THAT CABBAGE DOWN"
"BRINGING IN THE SHEAVES"
"BRINGING NELLIE HOME"
WILSON BROWN
BUGLE
BURT
"CALIFORNIA, HERE WE COME"
FRED CALLAHAN
CARL
CARL BENSON'S WILDCATS
CASPER TICE AND HIS LATIN
    RHYTHMS
CHARLIE
"CHINATOWN"
"CHIRIBIRIBIN"
"CONCERT TONIGHT-RELAX TO
    MUSIC UNDER THE STARS"
COUNTY INSECTICIDE CONVENTION
GLENN CRIPES
"LA CUCARACHA"
CYMBAL CITY
"DAN TUCKER"
"DANCE TILL YOUR STOCKINGS ARE
    HOT AND RAVELIN"
"DECK THE HALLS"
"MRS. DENNIS"
"DIPSY-DOODLE"
"DOWN AT THE DOUBLE EAGLE"
"DOWN IN THE VALLEY"
MORGAN DOWNEY
EIGHT
ESTELLE
THE ETHEL PAGE ORGAN RECITAL
"FACE ON THE BARROOM FLOOR"
WILBUR FINCH
"FINICULI FINICULA"
"THE FISHIN' HOLE"
$5.00 PER MAN
$5000.00
FLEET AND LINDSEY
FLOSSIE
BRUCE FLOWERS
"THE FOSTER JINGLE"
14-A
$14.50
"FRANKIE AND JOHNNY"
FREDDY FLEET AND HIS BAND WITH
    A BEAT
"THE GANGSTER'S MISTAKE"
JESSE EARL HAGEN
"HAIL TO THEE MISS MAYBERRY"
HIPPIE HARRISON
LILLIAN HARTZELL
HAZEL
KEEVY HAZELTON
"HERE COMES THE BRIDE"
MR. HIGBY
"I'M JUST A VAGABOND LOVER"
THE "ITALIAN NATIONAL ANTHEM"
RICK JACKSON
MRS. JEFFREYS
"JINGLE BELLS"

"JOHN HENRY"
"JOHN JACOB JINGLEHEIMER
    SCHMITT"
CLIFFORD JOHNSON
ROSAMAE JOHNSON
MR. JOHNSTON
JUGHEAD PETERS AND HIS
    ARISTOCRATS
KESTER
"KITTEN ON THE KEYS"
LADIES LEAGUE MUSICALE
"THE LAND OF RHYTHM AND
    PLEASURE"
"LEANIN' ON THE EVERLASTING
    ARMS"
JIM LINDSEY
"LOVE LIFTED ME"
LUTHER
"MAIRZY DOATS"
"THE MARINE'S HYMN"
"THE MASKED SINGER"
"FRED MASON"
JOHN MASTERS
MR. MAXWELL
MAYBERRY DRUM AND BUGLE CORP
"MAYBERRY, MY MAYBERRY"
"THE MAYBERRY SONG"
"THE MAYBERRY UNION HIGH
    THEME SONG"
MERLE
"MIDNIGHT SPECIAL"
JERRY MILLER
"THE MOON OF MANICURA"
"MUSIC FROM MAYBERRY"
"MY HOMETOWN"
"MY LITTLE GRAY HOME IN THE
    WEST"
NATIONAL RECORDS
THE NEW MAYBERRY MINSTRELS
"NEW RIVER TRAIN"
"NOW IS THE MONTH OF MAY"
"O SOLO MIO"
"OFF WE GO INTO THE WILD BLUE
    YONDER"
"OH, MY BARNEY"
"OH MY DARLING"
CLIFF PAMALEE
BURLEY PETERS
PICK
PERRY PLUMMER
"POMP AND CIRCUMSTANCE"
ELEANORA POULTICE
RALPH PRITCHARD
RALPH
BRENDA RHODES
RHYTHM GUITAR
HARLAN ROBINSON
"ROCK AND ROLL ROSIE FROM
    RALEIGH"
"ROLL OUT THE BARREL"
ROSEMARIE
"ROSES OF PICCARDY"
"ROW, ROW, ROW YOUR BOAT"
"SANTA LUCIA"
"SAXIMINIA"
SECOND TENOR
THE SENIOR PLAY
"SHADY GROVE"
SHARON
"SHE'LL BE COMIN' ROUND THE
    MOUNTAIN"
"THE SILVER HERRINGBONES"
"SIX WHO PASS WHILE THE LENTILS
    BOIL"
"THE SKATER'S WALTZ"
OZZIE SNAKE

"SOME ENCHANTED EVENING"
THE SOUND COMMITTEE
"SOURWOOD MOUNTAIN"
"THE STAR-SPANGLED BANNER"
"STARS AND STRIPES FOREVER"
THE SULTAN'S FAVORITE
PHIL SUNKEL
"SWEET BRIAR NORMAL SCHOOL
    THEME SONG"
"SYLVIA"
"A TED WEEMS RECORD"
"THAT LONESOME ROAD"
"THEME TO 'THE ANDY GRIFFITH
    SHOW'"
"THERE IS A TIME"
THIRD TUESDAY EVERY MONTH
THIRTY HOURS
NEVIN THORPE
"THOSE ENDEARING YOUNG
    CHARMS"
THE THREE BELLS
"TICO TICO"
"TIPTOE THROUGH THE TULIPS"
"TOOT TOOT TOOTSIE"
"TOW SACK FULL OF LOVE"
"TREES"
TROMBONE
MABEL TROTTA
#12
"THE UMBRELLA MAN"
MISS VOGEL
"THE VOICE OF MT. PILOT"
BILL WATKINS
"WE SHALL MEET"
"WE'RE BROTHERS TOGETHER"
"WELCOME SWEET SPRINGTIME"
"WET SHOES IN THE SUNSET"
"WHEN THE SAINTS GO MARCHING
    IN"
THE YOUNG SWINGERS

MOVIES, TELEVISION, RADIO & THE ARTS IN MAYBERRY

TEENA ANDREWS
"THE ANTEATERS FROM OUTER
    SPACE"
"THE BEAST THAT ATE MINNESOTA"
BELMONT PICTURE STUDIO
BRYAN BENDER
PAT BLAKE
"A CARY GRANT MOVIE"
"COLONEL TIM'S TALENT TIME"
"AN EDDIE BRACKEN MOVIE"
IRENE FLOGG
"A GEORGE RAFT MOVIE"
"GOODBYE MR. CHIPS"
THE GRAND
"A GREER GARSON MOVIE"
"GREGORY PECK MOVIES"
MR. HARMON
MR. HARVEY
SID HICKOX
"THE HOUSE OF BLOOD"
GILBERT JAMEL
"THE JEROME SANGER SHOW"
"JIM APACHE, INDIAN SPY"
HARVEY KESTER
EVA KRYGER
"LATE SHOW SAT. NIGHT"
"THE LIVES OF SHEP AND RALPH"
LOU
"MANHATTAN SHOWTIME"
JIM MARTIN

"THE MAYBERRY CHEF"
MAYBERRY THEATER
"THE MERRY MADCAP OF
    MAYBERRY"
PAT MICHAELS
"THE MONSTER FROM MARS"
"THE MONSTER FROM OUT-OF-
    TOWN"
"THE MONSTER FROM THE MOON"
"THE MONSTER THAT ATE
    MINNESOTA"
CARL PHILLIPS
"PICNIC"
"ROCK HUDSON MOVIES"
"RUDOLPH RABBIT"
MR. SABLE
AL SAUNDERS
BOB SAUNDERS
"SECRET AGENT F-45"
"SHERIFF WITHOUT A GUN"
6:30 P.M.
JACK SMITH
"SOMETHING ABOUT BLONDES"
ART SPIEGEL
STAGE 40
STATION KNC
"THE THEATER OF MAYBERRY"
COLONEL TIM
"TWO IN LOVE"
"LA VIE DU FEMME"
"THE VOICE OF MT. PILOT"
WASG
"WIN OR LOSE"
WMPD
WZAZ
YLRB

NICKNAMES, ALIASES & TERMS OF ENDEARMENT

"ACE"
"AG"
"ANDREW PAUL LAWSON"
"BABY DOLL"
"BARN"
"BARNEY FIFE, M.D."
"BARNEY FIFE THE BULKHEAD"
"BARNEY THE BEAST"
"BARON VON RICHTOFEN"
"THE BEAST OF THE FOURTH FLOOR"
"BEASTO MARISTO"
"THE BEAVER"
"BENJY"
"BERNIE"
"BERT AND SQUIRT"
"BLOODHOUND OF THE LAW"
"BLUE STEEL BABY"
TREY BOWDEN
"BUDDY"
"BUSTER"
"CANNONBALL"
"CANNONBALL EXPRESS"
"CHARLIE"
"CHARLIE CHASE"
"CHARLIE MONEYBAGS"
"THE CHICKEN"
"CHICKIE-BABY"
"CHIEF"
"CHOPPER"
"CLARISSE TYLER"
"CONSTABLE"
"COWBOY"
"CRAZY GUN BARNEY"
"DAME"
"DEAD EYE ANDY"

"DEFENDER OF THE UNDERDOG"
"DIAMOND JIM"
"DOPEY"
"DOPEY THE DWARF"
"EAGLE-EYE ANNIE"
"EAGLE-EYE BARNEY"
"AN ENGLISH OTIS"
"FAST GUN FIFE"
"FEARLESS FIFE"
"FELIX THE CAT"
"FIFE THE FIERCE"
"FINGERS"
"FOUR EYES"
"FOXY FIFE"
"FRICK AND FRACK"
"HEATER"
"HIRAM"
"HONEY"
"JOE ORDINARY"
"THE JUG"
"KEROSENE CUCUMBERS"
"LAUGH-A-MINUTE TAYLOR"
"LIFESAVER MAN"
"LITTLE BUDDY"
"LITTLE PERSUADER"
"THE LONE RANGER"
"THE LONE RANGER'S HORSE
    SILVER"
"THE MACHINE"
"MAD DOG"
"MARSHALL DILLON"
"MAUDE CLARISSE TYLER"
"THE MERRY MADCAP OF
    MAYBERRY"
"MILLIE"
"MILLIE GRACE"
"MISS CITY SLICKER"
"MISS FRIED CHICKEN OF
    MAYBERRY"
"MISS GADABOUT"
"MISS GOTROCKS"
"MISS LUNCHEON TRAY"
"MISSY"
"MR. BIG"
"MR. FIXIT"
"MR. INDEPENDENT WHEELS"
"MR. INDEPENDENT"
"MR. ROCKEFELLER"
"THE MONSTER"
"NEAT"
"OLD MR. TRANSPARENT"
"OLD PERSUADER"
"OLD ROSCOE"
"OLD TIGER FIFE"
"PETE THE TRAMP"
"PHANTOM FIFE"
"A PRINCE"
"PUDDINTANE"
"PUSSYCAT"
"THE RABBIT"
"RELIABLE BARNEY FIFE"
"RIFLE FIFE"
"RIP VAN WINKLE"
"ROD"
"ROSCOE"
"SANDY"
"THE SCAMP"
"SCOOP FIFE"
"SHERIFF MATT DILLON"
"SHERIFF TRAILER"
"SLIM"
"SPORT"
"SQUIRT"
"SUBTLE BARNEY FIFE"
"SUGARPLUM"
"TATTLETALE"

"TAYLOR SANDERS"
"TEX"
"TIGER"
"TIGHTLIPS BARNEY"
"TILLY"
"TWEAKY"
"WILD BILL FIFE"
"WYATT EARP"

OUT-OF-TOWN

JOHNNY ADAMS
VIDA AKINS
AKRON, OHIO
AL
ALASKA
"AN ALLIGATOR FARM IN FLORIDA"
ALTOONA
THE ARCADE
ARKANSAS
ASHEVILLE, NORTH CAROLINA
ATLANTA
AUBURN COUNTY
AUSTRALIA
AUTO TRADE SCHOOL
JOHN JUDSON BAILEY
RONALD BAILEY
BAKED ALASKA
JIM BAKER
BALTIMORE
BANGKOK
DETECTIVE BARDOLLI
BARNEY'S LETTER TO ANDY
BARNEY'S LETTER TO THE GANG
BARNEY'S VACATION
ALVIN BARROWS
BERNIE THE FURRIER
PAT BLAKE
BLUE ROCK CAVERNS
BLUE THUNDERBIRD
"BLUEBERRY"
BOB
JEAN BOSWELL
NATE BRACEY
BRADBURY BUSINESS COLLEGE
HERB BRADSHAW
BILL BRADY
MARY BRADY
JUDGE BRANSON
BRAZIL
DR. HARRISON EVERETT BREEN
BRICE'S DEPARTMENT STORE
CLIFF BRITTEN
GEORGE BRONSON
GEORGE BROOKFIELD
ROGER BRYANT
BURSITIS
CALIFORNIA
CAPITOL CITY
MARTHA CARRUTHERS
THE CASCADE CLUB
INSPECTOR RALPH CASE
CENTERVILLE
CHANNEL 12
CHARLOTTSVILLE
CHICAGO
COLONEL CHUMLEY
CIVIL SERVICE BUILDING
    DIRECTORY
MISS CLARK
HARRIET CLEAVER
CLEVELAND
MR. CLIFFORD
COLD STREAM GUARDS
COMMODORE HOTEL

LUKE COMSTOCK
JUDGE CONNOLLY
ROGER COURTNEY
JUDGE CRANSTON
JOHN DANBY
DARCY FURS
DAVIS COUNTY
MRS. DEACON
DELI-TIME SNACK BAR
DENVER MINT
DETECTIVE AGENCY
DETECTIVE BUREAU
DETROIT
M.L. DEWHURST
DICK
DRAFT BEER
ATTORNEY LEE DRAKE
EASTMONT, NORTH CAROLINA
ED
EDGAR
DIXIE BELL EDWARDS
8:00 A.M. - 5:30 P.M.
8:28 A.M.
EKMONDWIGHT
EL CARP
ELLEN
ELM CITY
ELM CITY DELIVERY SERVICE
EMBASSY DANCE CLUB
ERIE, PENNSYLVANIA
THE ESQUIRE CLUB
MISS FAIN
FAR EAST
MISS FENWICK
FIFTY-FIVE MILES
FILLMORE
FIVE CHAIRS
5:00 P.M. - 8:00P.M.
FLAMENCO DANCER
FLIGHT 17
FLORIDA
FOOT POWDER
FOOTLORE TOUR
MR. FORSYTH
FORT LAUDERDALE
41,000 ACRES
FOSTER FURNITURE POLISH
WILLARD FOSTER
4
403
439-7123
OFFICER DEAN FRIENDLY
GATE 12
GETTYSBURG
FRED GIBSON
GIBSON'S WILD WEST SHOW
THE GIGOLO CLUB
MR. GILBERT
GINGER ROGERS
FRANK GLENDON
THE GOLDEN PALACE
GOVERNMENT
GRANGER
MADELINE GRAYSON
THE GREAT DISMAL SWAMP
THE GREAT MANDRAKE
GREEN
GREENDALE CITY HALL
GREENSBORO, NORTH CAROLINA
MISS GRETHAM
HANSON
HARNET
ALICE HARPER
ARTHUR HARRINGTON
BILLY HOLLANDER
GEORGE HOLLANDER

LAURA HOLLANDER
THE HOLLYWOOD MARQUEE
EILEEN HOPKINS
MR. IZAMOTO
JACKSONVILLE
JEFFERSON COUNTY SEAT
AL JENKINS
KANSAS
CHARLES KEYES
KIT KAT CLUB
KL-5-7486
KOREA
ED KRUMPACHER
KURRITUCK
LADIES HISTORICAL SOCIETY OF
    SUMMITVILLE
LAKE CHARLES
EDNA LARCH
LARCHMONT COUNTY
JOE LARSON
LONAS HILL AND DAVISON
    ATTORNEYS
THE MACON BUS
SHERIFF MALONEY
MARIE
MARSHALL COUNTY
HERB MASON
MEXICAN FARMACIA
MEXICO
MIAMI
SHERIFF MITCHELL
MOLINE, CALIFORNIA
EVAN MOORE
KAREN MOORE
MOREHEAD CITY
MORGANTOWN
DETECTIVE MORLEY
MT. PILOT
"MT. PILOT BUGLE AND SUN"
MT. PILOT CIVIL SERVICE OFFICE
MT. PILOT COMETS
MT. PILOT 4872
MT. PILOT HOSPITAL
MT. PILOT JUDO SOCIETY
MT. PILOT HIGH SCHOOL
MT. PILOT MUNICIPAL COURT
"MT. PILOT TIMES"
NASHVILLE
NASHVILLE BUS
NATURAL BRIDGE, VIRGINIA
NEW JERSEY
NEW ORLEANS
NEW YORK
NINE PESOS
NORMAN
NORTH CAROLINA STATE PRISON
NORTHERN PART OF MOZAMBIQUE
OAKMONT ROAD, MT. PILOT
"THE OLD COUNTRY"
162 YARDS
OREGON TO NOVA SCOTIA
OUTER MONGOLIA
PALM BEACH
PARIS
PARKINSON'S FALLS
PAUL REVERE HIGH SCHOOL
"PEANUT BUTTER AND BOLOGNA,
    PEANUT BUTTER AND LIVER-
    WURST, PEANUT BUTTER AND
    PEANUT BUTTER"
PEORIA
CARL PHILLIPS
PIEDMONT HOTEL
PIERCE COUNTY
PIERRE
PILOT PINES FUNERAL PARLOR

PIZZA PLACE
MARY PLEASANCE
PORK CHOPS AND FRIED APPLE
    RINGS
PORTLAND, OREGON
MAYOR PURDY
"A RACETRACK IN AFRICA"
RALEIGH AQUARIUM
RALEIGH BANK ROBBERY
RALEIGH PHILARMONIC
RALEIGH SECURITY BANK
RALEIGH YMCA
RAPI
RED FORD CONVERTIBLE
RENEE
ROANOKE, NORTH CAROLINA
HARLAN ROBINSON
ROBINSON FAMILY
CEASAR ROMERO
RUBY CREEK, NORTH CAROLINA
MR. SABLE
ST. BENEDICT'S ISLAND
ST. LOUIS WORLD'S FAIR 1906
ST. PETERSBURG
AL SAUNDERS
SAVANNAH
SAYBERTOWN
DAVE SCHNEIDER
SEBASTIAN
SENIOR CITIZEN LODGE
$7.00
SHERIFF'S SAFETY CONFERENCE
SILER CITY
MR. SIMMONS
STEWART SIMMONS
SIX HOURS
SKIBALL
SOMBREROS
SOUTHERN BUS LINES
LOUISE SPOONER
SPRINGVILLE
STAGE 40
STARBRIGHT MOTEL
STATE POLICE BUILDING
STATE PRISON
STATEN ISLAND
STOKES COUNTY
SUPER BARGAIN MARKET
$10.00 IN THREE DAYS
TEXAS
THELMA LOU'S DENTIST
30,000
THURSDAY NIGHTS AT 8:00
TOD
TOLEDO
TOWER OF PISA
TRIPLETT
CHARLOTTE TUCKER
TWELVE MILES EACH WAY
TWENTY-FIVE MINUTES
$25,000.00
MR. TWYFORD
RACINE TYLER
TYLER BAKERY
UNIVERSITY OF NORTH CAROLINA
    AT CHAPEL HILL
MR. VASILIEVICH
MARIO VINCENTE
PAPA VINCENTE
SOPHIA VINCENTE
SONYA WALACHAKA
WASHINGTON, D.C.
"WELCOME HOME MAYBERRY JET
    SET"
MISS WELLINGTON

MISS WELLINGTON'S SCHOOL FOR
    GIRLS
WES
WEST VIRGINIA
WESTWOOD FEDERAL PRISON
WHEELING
WILMINGTON
SHERIFF WILSON
TOM WILSON
WINSTON-SALEM, NORTH CAROLINA
WOMAN'S SKEETSHOOTING
    CHAMPION OF ARKANSAS
WOMEN'S HISTORICAL SOCIETY
WYOMING
YANCEY
THE YMCA
ZONE DETECTION SYSTEM

GOMER PYLE

BERTIE BLUSH
"BUCKET ISSUE"
BUNNY CALDWELL
CAMP WILSON
GUNNERY SERGEANT VINCE CARTER
CORSAGE
"CUFF SLAPPING"
MERLE DEAN
PETE DOOLEY
DRESS BLUES
MRS. DRUMM
EAGLE
ELEVEN BOYS
"THE FIRST BORN CHILD OF THE
    MAN THAT SAVED MY LIFE"
FIVE DAYS IN JAIL
FIVE HOURS
MISS FLETCHER
GAS HEATER
GOLFBALL
GOMER'S OUTFIT
MARY GRACE GOSSAGE
"HE'S UGLY, BUT HE AIN'T STUPID"
LORILEE HOBBS
HOOT OWL
"LIFESAVER MAN"
"LUCKY PEPPERMINTS"
LUTHER
VIOLA MACARTHUR
"THE MARINE'S HYMN"
NELSON'S FUNERAL PARLOR
OIL RAGS
"OPIE TAYLOR, SR."
PHEASANT
PIERSON'S SWEET SHOP "LUCKY
    PEPPERMINT" PROMOTION
MAJOR GENERAL LUCIUS PYLE
"RALPH BELLAMY"
"SANTA LUCIA"
SUE SAWLEY
SEVEN WINTERS
SKINNY GRIFFIN
"SPORT"
363
COLONEL WATSON

GOOBER PYLE

ACME GASOLINE
ALASKA
ALVIN
AUTO SHOW
AUTO TRADE SCHOOL
MRS. BARTON
"THE BEAGLES"

JAMES ARTHUR BEASLOW
GOOBER BEAZLEY
JUANITA BEAZLEY
SPOOKY BENSON
BILLY
BUSTER
CARBURETOR RECORD
CHAMPION HAND WRESTLER
COUNTY FAIR
"CRABMONSTER"
FIFTY-SEVEN PANCAKES
HORACE FLOOD
FLOY
"FOR SALE $295"
EARL FOSTER
FOX STOLE
FREE RADIATOR FLUSH
GEORGE
DR. EDITH GIBSON
GINNY
GLORIA
GOLDEN PALACE
GOOBER'S BEGINNINGS
GOOBER'S BEST FRIEND
GOOBER'S FAVORITE VEGETABLE
GOOBER'S FORTUNE
"GOOBER'S GUSHER OF GOLD"
GOOBER'S HOME PHONE NUMBER
GOOBER'S IMPERSONATIONS
GOOBER'S SERVICE
"GRAB BAG FOR CASH"
HARRY
HARVEY
"HE'S UGLY, BUT HE AIN'T STUPID"
HOLLIS
"HOW TO TELL IF A WATERMELON'S
    RIPE"
IRENE
KEEPER OF THE DOOR
WILLIS KUNDIFF
MRS. LARCH
ERNIE LEWIS
"LINE UP FOR LOOT"
LOUISE
MAIN AND GARDEN ROAD
FLORA MALLERBY
SALLY MARSH
RUTHIE MATTHEWS
MAYBERRY GIANTS VS. MT. PILOT
    COMETS
ALICE NATHAM
NORRIS
NYLON TIRES
$1.25 AN HOUR
PANCAKE EATING CONTEST
"THE PURPLE AVENGER"
COLONEL GOOBER PYLE
"RUDOLPH RABBIT"
SCIENTIFIC INTRODUCTIONS, INC.
SD-561
THE SOFTBALL TEAM
"THE SPACE PHANTOM"
"THE SPACE RACE"
"THE SPIDERMAN"
SPOT
ROY SWANSON
SWEDISH
"THE THINKER"
371-J
363
THREE WEEKS
TOMMY
TRUCK TIRE CUFFLINKS
"TWELVE OF FIFTEEN"
$2.40
$2,000.00

"LA VIE DU FEMME"
GILLY WALKER
WALLY
AB WINTERS
YOUNG PEOPLE'S MEETING

QUOTES TO NOTE

"THE AGE OF MIRACLES"
ANDY'S LAST LINE
"APPLE PIE ORDER"
BARNEY'S "FRIENDSHIP" QUOTE
BARNEY'S RIDDLE
"BE YOURSELF"
"A BIRD IN THE HOUSE MEANS A
    DEATH IN THE FAMILY"
"BLOOD WILL TELL"
"BREADWINNER"
"BUGS AND WORMS AND THINGS"
"BUT BARNEY, I'M YOUR MOTHER"
"THE CASE OF THE PIGHEADED
    DEPUTY WHO WAS KILLED BY A
    BERSERK SHERIFF"
"CHRISTMAS, HA!"
"CODE OF THE WEST"
COLD STREAM GUARDS
"COMPELSHION"
"THE DEADLY GAME"
"EAST TO WEST, GIBSON'S THE
    BEST"
"EBUM SHUBUM SHUBUM SHUBUM"
"ELECTRONICALLY-CONTROLLED"
"ELECTRONILLY"
"AN EMBRYONIC MEGALOPOLIS"
FLETCHER EMERSON
ERNEST T. BASS' "SENTENCE"
"EXTRA-SENSITIVE PERCEPTION"
"FACITIOUS"
"A FAIR DEAL FOR THE FAIR SEX"
"FIRE BY CONSTRICTION"
"THE FIRST BORN CHILD OF THE
    MAN THAT SAVED MY LIFE"
FLOYD LAWSON AND CALVIN
    COOLIDGE
"GARDEN CITY OF THE STATE"
"GARDEN SPOT OF STATE"
"GOOD EVENING"
"HAND-TO-HAND"
"HE'S UGLY, BUT HE AIN'T STUPID"
"THE HEATHEN CANNIBALS"
"HELLO DOLL"
"HOLY JUMPING CATFISH!"
"HOMELY AT THE CRADLE, PRETTY
    AT THE TABLE"
"HORATIO WHO?"
"HOW DO YOU DO, MRS. WILEY?"
"KLEP, KLEP"
"KLEPTOMINERAC"
"LAW-ABIDING GOD-FEARING
    CITIZENS"
"LET NO HORSE GO THIRSTY"
"MACHO" IN MAYBERRY
JED MCINTYRE
"A MACKEREL SWIMMING
    DOWNSTREAM"
"A MAN IN PRISON" SPEECH
"MAY I HAVE THE NEXT DANCE?"
"MAY I HAVE THIS DANCE?"
"MAYBERRY: GATEWAY TO DANGER"
"MAYBERRY RULES FOR A LONG
    HAPPY LIFE"
"MEANER THAN A BEAR BACKED
    INTO A BEEHIVE"
THE "MILLIONS FOR..." QUOTE
""A NAKED SAVAGE"

"NEKOO YUTA AY CHOCHOONAY"
"NICE"
"NICE EVENIN' AIN'T IT?'"
"NIP IT (IN THE BUD)"
"NO COFFEE, TEA, OR PUNCH, THANK
    YOU"
"NOBODY LEAVES A WASH BASIN
    THE WAY YOU DO"
"ONCE BIT, BEST FORGIT"
"ONCE BURNT IS A LESSON LEARNT"
"ONE MISTAKE A BETTER CAKE"
CHARLES COATSWORTH PAYNTON
"PEETON PLACE"
"A PENNY EARNED IS A PENNY
    TAXED"
CHARLES COATSWORTH PINCKNEY
"PLAY CHECKERS, TALK, GRUNT"
"PLEASE TAKE CARE OF MY BABY"
"POW, POW, POW"
ELVIS PRESLEY
"A REGULAR BOBBYDAZZLER"
"A RENDEZVOUS WITH DESTINY"
"RIGHT IN HIS HIP POCKET"
SAM
"SAME OLD COURTHOUSE, SAME
    OLD DESK, SAME CHAIR"
"SAY HELLO TO TONTO"
"SIGMUND FROOD"
"SPIT ON MY FINGER AND HOPE TO
    CROW"
"SUCH A LOVELY CAMPUS"
THE "SYMBOL" SPEECH
"THANK YOU FOR THE DANCE"
"TILLER OF SOIL, FELLER OF TREES"
"US FIFE'S IS WIRY"
"WATCH OUT FOR THE RED BARON"
"WE DEFY THE MAFIA!"
"THE WEATHER"
"WELCOME TO MAYBERRY, THE
    FRIENDLY TOWN"
"WHAT A TOWN IS DEPENDS ON THE
    PEOPLE"
"WILL YOU HELP US?"
"WORDS THAT START WITH 'S'"
"YOU'RE THE CATS"
"YOUNG LADY MOST LIKELY TO
    BECOME CHARMING"

RESTAURANTS AND MATTERS RELATED TO DINING OUT

ANDY'S FORTUNE
AUNT BEE'S CANTON PALACE
THE BAMBOO PODS
BANQUET ROOM
JUANITA BEAZLEY
BEE'S FORTUNE
BLUE VIEW MOTEL
THE BLUEBIRD DINER
BUSINESSMAN'S SPECIAL
THE CAFE
CHARLIE
CHICKEN FRICASEE
CHING LEE'S
CINEMASCOPE CAFE
COFFEE SHOP
THE COUNTY LINE CAFE
DAVE'S HONG KONG
DELI-TIME SNACK BAR
THE DELUXE SPECIAL
THE DINER LUNCH
THE DINER LUNCH SPECIAL
DINER PHONE NUMBER
DRAFT BEER

ELLA
FAMILY DINNER FOR ONE
FLORA
THE GIGOLO CLUB
GOLDEN PALACE
GOOBER'S FORTUNE
HALF MOON ROADHOUSE
HELEN'S FORTUNE
THE HOFBRAU
HOWARD'S FORTUNE
JUNCTION CAFE
KIT KAT CLUB
KLEIN'S COFFEE SHOP
CHARLIE LEE
MALCOLM'S RESTAURANT BILL
THE MARCIER
MOM'S DINER
MORELLI'S RESTAURANT
OLIVE
142 R
PALMERTON CAFE
PATTY'S PLACE
POT 'O HONEY RESTAURANT
POUNDED STEAK A LA MORELLI
THE REEF AT NAGTIN
THE ROADSIDE RESTAURANT
SHABOB'S
SNACK BAR
THE SNAPPY LUNCH
SPARERIBS TAVERN
TIP-TOP CAFE
TRUCKER'S CAFE
$2.75
242
THE WEENIE-BURGER
WONG SOO'S CANTON PALACE

HOWARD SPRAGUE

"ACE"
BEARSKIN RUG
TOM BEDLOW
"BELLE OF THE BALL"
BESS
"BEST DANCER IN MAYBERRY"
THE BIG BROTHER MOVEMENT
HARRY BLAKE
BLUE ROCK CAVERNS
BRADBURY BUSINESS COLLEGE
FRED CALLAHAN
CARL
CLAUSE 6
"COLONEL TIM'S TALENT TIME"
CREAM BUN
EMBASSY DANCE CLUB
IRENE FAIRCHILD
FIDO
$15.00
"FIFTEEN MINUTES, MORNING AND
    NIGHT"
FIVE PERCENT
"FOR RENT BY OWNER HOWARD
    SPRAGUE CALL MAYBERRY
    397"
$40.00 TO $10.00
4-10 SPLIT
BLANTON FULLER
GEORGE
GINNY
GP-780
DENIECE GRABER
GRAPEFRUIT JUICE
GROVER
HARD STUFF
HARRY

HOWARD'S COMEDY ROUTINE
HOWARD'S FORTUNE
HOWARD'S PHONE NUMBER
HOWARD'S SHOPPING LIST
CHARLES HUMBONE
MILLIE HUTCHINS
IMPRESSIONISTIC PAINTINGS
INDIAN
THE KING ARTHUR PAGEANT
LADYFINGER
LEMON AND LIME SODA
MARION
SALLY MARSH
MAYBERRY 397
MAYBERRY TRANSFER COMPANY
"MERRY MADCAP OF MAYBERRY"
"OLD HOMESTEAD"
OLD SAM
"ON HIS STOMACH"
BETTY PARKER
UNCLE PHIL
"PRICE-SPIRALING"
THE PROPRIETOR
RALEIGH AQUARIUM
ST. BENEDICT'S ISLAND
$7.50
$70.00
$75.00
DR. AMIEL SHARLOCK
SHIRLEY
"THE SILVER HERRINGBONES"
SIX MONTHS
$65.00
MRS. SPRAGUE
SWISS CHEESE SANDWICHES
$10.00 A MONTH
34,000 TO 1
THREE INCHES
397
$3,628.00
COLONEL TIM
BILL WATKINS
WENDELL
WES
"WHAT A TOWN IS DEPENDS ON THE
    PEOPLE"
CYRUS WHITLEY

STREETS, ROADS AND LOCALES IN AND ABOUT MAYBERRY

BAKER STREET
BANNER STREET
THE BIRCH PLACE
CARSON SHACK
"CHECKPOINT CHICKIE"
CHIMNEY ROCK
COWSILL FLAT
CROUCH'S WOODS
CRYSTAL CREEK ROAD
"DANGEROUS CONDEMNED MINE"
DEXTER STREET
D-QUEEN JUNCTION
DRY WELL
EAGLE ROCK
ELM STREET
ELM STREET PLAYGROUND
FANCY GAP
FERGUSON'S FARM
FIFTH AND ELM
FINNEGAN FLATS
FIRST AND THIRD STREETS
FISHER'S POND
FORTY-FIVE MILES PER HOUR

FOUR BEDROOMS AND ONE-AND-
    A-HALF BATHROOMS
FOURTH AND MAIN
FRANKLIN HOLLOW
FRANKLIN WOODS
FURNACE CREEK
GROVE STREET
GROVER'S PLACE
HANSON'S HILL
HARRY'S POND
HASH ROAD
HAWKINS CREEK
HIGHWAY 43
HIGHWAY 6
HIGHWAY 214
HOPKIN'S CREEK
JOHNSON MINE
THE JOHNSON PLACE
JUNIPER ROAD
LOST LOVER'S CAVE
LOVER'S LEAP ROCK
MAIN AND GARDEN ROAD
MAPLE STREET
THE MARSH
MARTIN'S COTTAGES
MILES ROAD
MILLER'S POND
THE MILLSTONE FARM
MYER'S LAKE
NORTH AVENUE
OLD MINE CAVES
OLD PLANK BRIDGE
ONE MILE
ORCHARD ROAD
PARKER CREEK
PAYMORE AND ROCKFORD STREETS
THE PIERSON PLACE
PINE AND MAIN
POST ROAD
POTTER'S CAVE
THE POWELL PLACE
RANCH ROAD
RIMSHAW HOUSE
RIVER ROAD
THE ROBERT E. LEE NATURAL
    BRIDGE
ROUTE 88
ROUTE 43
ROUTE 31
SOUTH SIDE
SPRING STREET
THATCHER'S WOODS
TROUBLESOME CREEK
TUCKER'S LAKE
TURNER'S GRADE
TWO MILE HILL
WAWYER RIVER
WHITE WATER CREEK
WILLOW AVENUE
WILLOW CREEK ROAD
WILLOW LANE
WILLOW STREET
WOODS WAY

ANDY TAYLOR

AFGHAN
"THE AGE OF MIRACLES"
AL
ALASKA
SAM ALLEN
ALTOONA
ALVIN
AMANDA
AMERICAN HISTORY

ANDELINA
"ANDREW PAUL LAWSON"
"ANDREW TAYLOR—SHERIFF OF
    MAYBERRY"
ANDY AND HELEN'S BEDROOM
ANDY'S ADDRESS
ANDY'S "BAD DAY"
ANDY'S BEGINNINGS
ANDY'S FAVORITE DISH
ANDY'S FORTUNE
ANDY'S LAST LINE
ANDY'S PHONE NUMBER
ANDY'S SHOPPING LIST
"ANGE" OR "ANJ"
ARKANSAS
ARMY STORY #17
AUSTRALIAN BULLWHIP
"AWAY IN A MANGER"
JIM BAKER
RALPH BAKER
THE BARNEY FIFE SUBCONSCIOUS
    PROBER PRIMER
BARNEY'S LETTER TO ANDY
BASS
"THE BATTLE OF THE SEXES"
"THE BEAST OF THE FOURTH
    FLOOR"
"BEASTO MARISTO"
BEAVER DAM
EDGAR BEAZLEY
ANDY BECKER
SAMUEL W. BECKER
BEGONIAS
HARVEY BELFAST
BELMONT PICTURE STUDIO
BRYAN BENDER
SAM BENSON
"BERT AND SQUIRT"
"BEST BETS"
"BEST DANCER IN MAYBERRY"
BEST MAN
"BEST SALESMAN IN MAYBERRY""
BETTY ANN
"BIG HOUSE"
TOM BIGGERS
BIOLOGY CLASS
BLACK JELLYBEANS
MRS. BLAIR
MISS BLANCHARD
BLANCHE
JEAN BOSWELL
MERLIN BRACEY
"THE BREADWINNER"
CLIFF BRITTEN
GEORGE BRONSON
BUNNY CALDWELL
"CANNONBALL"
CARP
MR. CARP
"A CARY GRANT MOVIE"
"THE CASE OF THE PIGHEADED
    DEPUTY WHO WAS KILLED BY A
    BERSERK SHERIFF"
"CATCHING THE WINNING
    TOUCHDOWN PASS"
"CHARLIE"
CHARLIE
"CHARLIE MONEYBAGS"
CHICKEN OR POT ROAST
CHICKEN WIRE FENCE
CHICKEN WITH CRUST
"CHILDISH"
CHIROPRACTOR
MRS. CLAREBURN
COLD CHICKEN AND POTATO SALAD
MRS. COLITA

LUKE COMSTOCK
JUDGE CONNOLLY
A.J. CONSIDINE
"CONSTABLE"
CONTEMPT
MRS. COREY
CORLIS
CORNED BEEF HASH
COUNTY PENMANSHIP CONTEST
"COUPLE OF THE YEAR"
"COUSIN ANDY"
"COWBOY"
COWLICK
LYDIA CROSSWAITHE
MRS. CROUTE
CROW
HERB CROWLEY
"THE CUTLASS"
"DAME"
JOHN DANBY
DAPHNE
"DEAD-EYE ANDY"
MERLE DEAN
"DIAMOND JIM"
DICK
"A DOLLAR-AND-A-QUARTER"
DON
"DOPEY"
"DOPEY THE DWARF"
"DOWN IN THE VALLEY"
D-QUEEN JUNCTION
DRAFT BEER
ATTORNEY LEE DRAKE
PURLIMAE DUBOIS
SHARON DUSPAINE
"EAGLE-EYE ANNIE"
"EBUM SHUBUM SHUBUM SHUBUM"
ED
EDGAR
8:00 A.M.
ELDERBERRY WINE
ELEVEN BOYS
ELI
JARVIS ELRIDGE
FLETCHER EMERSON
ENCYCLOPEDIA EUROPA
ERECTOR SET
THE ESQUIRE CLUB
"THE FACTS OF LIFE"
FAT KNEES
MR. FERRIS
MISS FICKETT
"FIFI THE UPSTAIRS MAID"
FIFTEEEN
$15.00
FINISH LINE JUDGE
"THE FIRST BORN CHILD OF THE
    MAN THAT SAVED MY LIFE"
FISHING POLE
FIVE HOURS
IRENE FLOGG
FLOWER SEEDS
FLOYD'S ENGAGEMENT CARD TO
    ANDY AND HELEN
4-A
FOUR BEDROOMS AND ONE-AND-A-
    HALF BATHROOMS
"FOUR OR FIVE"
14 MAPLE STREET
4:30 A.M.
439-7123
426
"FOURTH QUARTER, FOUR SECONDS
    TO GO, FOURTH DOWN"
FRANK
"FRICK AND FRACK"

"A GARDENIA BLOSSOM"
GAS HEATER
THE GAS WORKS
GERTRUDE
MR. GIDDINGS
GIN RUMMY
GLORIA
GOOSEBERRY PIE
OLIVER GOSSAGE
"GRACE"
GRANITE
"GREGORY PECK MOVIES"
GUIDED MISSILES
H141Q5
KATHRYN HARNEY
ALICE HARPER
FRED HARTLEY
HAT
HEADS
"HIRAM"
MAJOR HOBART
HOGARTH DETECTIVES
HONG KONG SUITS
"THE HONOR SYSTEM"
"HOW TO MAKE FRIED CHICKEN
    AND JOHNNYCAKE"
"HOW TO MAKE POSSUM PIE"
"HOW TO MAKE TURNIP JAM"
"IF LOST PLEASE RETURN TO WYATT
    EARP"
INTERSTATE PEST CONTROL
JACKSON
"JOE ORDINARY"
MRS. JOHNSON
JUSTICE OF THE PEACE
MELINDA KEEFER
KING OF ENGLAND
LAUNDERCOIN, INC.
LAVINIA
MRS. LEGRANDE
LIGHTER
PEGGY MCMILLAN
"THE MAN WITH THE GOLDEN ARM"
DARLENE MASON
HERB MASON
"MISSY"
MISS MORAN
"NATIONAL GEOGRAPHIC"
NATIONAL STILL-SMASHING DAY
"A NEGLIGEE WITH A BLACK
    NIGHTGOWN"
1952
1948
1945
"OLD MR. TRANSPARENT"
"OPERATION PICKLE SWITCH"
ESTELLE PARSONS
PHILOMATHIAN LITERARY SOCIETY
POCKETWATCH
PRESERVING JARS
THE PRESIDENT
ELVIS PRESLEY
"A PRINCE"
PRISONER OF LOVE
PUMPKIN PIE A LA MODE
PUNCH SUPREME
QUAIL
QUEEN OF ENGLAND
QUEEN OF THE STATE APRICOT
    FESTIVAL
"THE ROCK"
"ROCK HUDSON MOVIES"
ROSEMARY
RUNAWAY NOTE
"SANDY"
SECOND CLASS SCOUT

SETH TAYLOR DAY
SHAVING CREAM
"SHERIFF TRAILER"
SHOOTING GALLERY PRIZES
MARY SIMPSON
SKIPPY
HODIE SNITCH
MR. SNYDER
MRS. SNYDER
"THE SPRING OF 1938"
ALICE STAPLETON
STUDENT SPECIAL
SUNDAY SCHOOL
JACK SWEET
"TAILOR TAYLOR"
"TAYLOR SANDERS"
3:00 P.M.
332 MAPLE ROAD
LAMAR TRUNDLE
$12.00
25 - 23
24 ELM STREET
TWENTY-ONE
TWO DOZEN
$200.00 A MONTH
"THE 2 STEP"
"UNCLE" HENRY
MRS. VONRODER
VOTING PROCTOR
CISSY WAINWRIGHT
ELLIE WALKER
"A WANDERING SPIDER"
"A WEB-FOOTED RED-CRESTED LAKE
    LOON"
MISS WEBSTER
"WELCOME BACK CLASS OF '48"
RAMONA WILEY
WOMAN'S SKEETSHOOTING
    CHAMPION OF ARKANSAS
YEARBOOK ENTRY: ANDY TAYLOR

AUNT BEE TAYLOR

"AIR FRESHENER AND ANTACID
    TABLETS"
VIDA AKINS
ALICE
ALMA
ALMA SWARTHOUSE SUNSET PINK
AMMONIA
DR. ANDERSON
"APPLE PIE ORDER"
APRON
AUNT BEE'S CANTON PALACE
AUNT BEE'S LICENSE NUMBER
AUNT MARTHA
AUSTRALIA
"AVIATION JOURNAL"
AY-321
THE BAMBOO PODS
"BEE TAYLOR FOR CITY COUNCIL"
BEE TAYLOR'S BIRTHDAY
BEE'S BEGINNINGS
BEE'S BIRTHDAY
BEE'S FORTUNE
BEE'S HOMEMADE ICE CREAM
BEE'S PURSE
BEEF STEW
BERNICE
"BEST COOK IN MAYBERRY"
ROSE BLAKE
"BLOODY MARY"
BLUE ROBES
BLUE SUIT, PEARLS, HAT, AND
    WHITE GLOVES

269

BOOSTER'S CLUB
BRADFORD INTERNATIONAL ICE
  CREAM
EMMA BRAND
MR. BRISTOL
BRUCE
ORVILLE BUCK
BURSITIS
BURT
MR. CALVIN
CONGESSMAN JOHN CANFIELD
MARTHA CARRUTHERS
CLARA CARTWRIGHT
CHANNEL 12
CHARLIE
CHICKEN
CHICKEN AND DUMPLINGS
CHICKEN IN A POT
"CHINATOWN"
CHIPPED BEEF PUFFS
CHOCOLATE STAIN
CLAUDE
HARRIET CLEAVER
COLLEGIATE DICTIONARY
COUNTY FAIR
"COUNTY HAS NO HEART"
CREAM BUN
CROWN PRINCE OF DENMARK
CURRENCY CONVERTER
DARCY FURS
DARRYL
DECEMBER 19
DEEP PINK ECSTASY
"DEFENDER OF THE UNDERDOG"
DIAMOND JIM'S
DICK
"DON'T PATRONIZE THIS JAIL"
ED'S REFRIGERATION
EDGAR
EIGHT
EIGHTEEN
87¢
11
ELLA
ELLEN
EMILY
EVIE JOY
"A FADING FLOWER OF FORGOTTEN
  LOVE"
FARLEY
MRS. FARLEY
MRS. FELDON
"FIFI THE UPSTAIRS MAID"
ARNOLD FINCH
AUGUSTA FINCH
"FIRST BASH OF THE MAYBERRY
  SOCIAL SEASON"
$5.00
5:00 P.M. - 8:00P.M.
FLETCH
FLIGHT 17
"4 SALE $295"
"THE FOSTER JINGLE"
FREEZER
FRIDAY EVENING AT 8:00O'CLOCK
MR. FRISBY
FROM THE CRADLE TO JUNIOR
  COLLEGE
GATE 12
GOLFBALL
GP-780
GRACE
GRANITE
THE GREATER MAYBERRY
  HISTORICAL SOCIETY AND
  TOURIST BUREAU, LTD.

ROGER HANOVER
COLONEL HARVEY
HAT
AGENT HEATHCOTE
MR. HENDRICKS
ORVILLE HENDRICKS
"HIGHWAYS ARE KILLERS"
INDIAN ELIXIR
ITALIAN NATIONAL ANTHEM
"KEROSENE CUCUMBERS"
JED KOONTZ
DORIS LACY
LITERARY GUILD
"THE LITTLE PRINCESS"
LOUISE
MARCH 17
MARCH 3, 1951
"MISS BEE TAYLOR FOR
  PROGRESSIVE GOVERNMENT"
"MISS FRIED CHICKEN OF
  MAYBERRY"
"MISS GADABOUT"
"MISS LUNCHEON TRAY"
"MRS. PINKNEY VARIEGATED RED"
MOUSETRAP
MOUSTACHE CUP WITH ROSES ON IT
N59558
"NEARLY TWENTY CENTS MORE"
"NEWS FROM THE ALTAR"
NORA
OLD PEOPLE'S HOME
150 POUNDS
145,000
"OVER 8,000 FEET"
PATTY'S PLACE
PEABODY ROSE
JENNIE PETERS
PIN
WILBUR PINE
ORVILLE PORTNOY
PRESERVING JARS
RHINESTONE BUTTONS
"A RIOT OF COLOR"
MRS. RITTER
MRS. ROBERTSON
ROSE
RUSTLE CASTLE
PROFESSOR HUBERT ST. JOHN
VIOLET ROSE SCHUMAKER
SETH TAYLOR DAY
"SHERIFF MATT DILLON"
THE SHRINER CLUB
MR. SIMMONS
6:30 P.M.
"SIX WHO PASS WHILE THE LENTILS
  BOIL"
THE SMEDLEY SISTERS
LOUISE SPOONER
SUE
SUPER FREEZE
SWEET BRIAR NORMAL SCHOOL
TAMPICO TAMALE CONTEST
FARLEY THURSTON
"TOOT TOOT TOOTSIE"
MYRA TUCKER
TWENTY-THREE
TWO DOZEN
"WE SHALL NOT BE MOVED"
"WELCOME HOME MAYBERRY JET
  SET"
HENRY WHEELER
"WIN OR LOSE"

OPIE TAYLOR

"ADVENTURE SLEEPING"
"THE AGE OF MIRACLES"
CINDY AMES
AUGUST
AUNT MARTHA
B AVERAGE
B+
ARNOLD BAILEY
BARN PAINT
BARNEY'S TWO WAYS (TO TELL A
  GIRL YOU LIKE HER)
BASEBALL
"BEAUTY AND THE BEAST"
EDGAR BEAZLEY
THE BELFASTS
BERNICE
"BERT AND SQUIRT"
BIKE
BILLY
BILLY THE KID
BLACKIE
THE BLAKE BOY
BLUE MOONLIGHT
BLUEBERRY PIE
BLYNKEN
FREDERICK BOWDEN III
BOY'S DETECTIVE DISGUISE KIT
MRS. BRIGGS
WILSON BROWN
DAVID BROWNE
BUGLE
"BUGS AND WORMS AND THINGS"
KAREN BURGESS
BUTTERSCOTCH PECAN
C+ AVERAGE
CLAUDIA CAMPBELL
HEATHER CAMPBELL
"CANNONBALL"
CARTER
MARY ALICE CARTER
CASH REGISTER BANK
CATCHER'S MITT
"CHARLIE MONEYBAGS"
CHARLOTTE
CHICKEN FRICASEE
CHICKEN OR POT ROAST
CHICKEN WITH CRUST
BILLY CINCIPAUL
CLASS PRESIDENT
JESSIE CLAYTON
THE CLUBHOUSE
COMMERCIAL ART COURSE
FLIP CONROY
COURTHOUSE STEPS
MRS. COX
BILLY CRENSHAW
MRS. CRIPPS
CROW
"CURSE OF THE CLAW"
CYNTHIA
"D'S & E'S"
"DAN TUCKER"
"DANGEROUS CONDEMNED MINE"
"DARN CUTE"
"DEFENDER OF THE UNDERDOG"
"DIAMOND JIM"
DIANA
DICKIE
DOCTOR
MR. DODSON
MR. EDINGER'S CARPENTER SHOP
EIGHT PLACES
"ELECTRONICALLY-CONTROLLED"
ELM STREET PLAYGROUND
ERECTOR SET
"F"

"A CARY GRANT MOVIE"
"CHILDISH"
EDGAR COLEMAN
LYDIA CROSSWAITHE
596
40¢
FRIED CHICKENS
MARY GRACE GOSSAGE
"A HEN PARTY"
"HONEYPIE"
MARY
KAREN MOORE
1960
PINEAPPLE SKINNER
JEFF PRUITT
"PUSSYCAT"
"QUE SERA SERA"
"RIGHT IN HIS HIP POCKET"
"THE STAR OF PEORIA"
"STEAK SANDWICH TIME"
"SUGARPLUM"
SWEET CIDER
THELMA LOU'S DENTIST
THELMA LOU'S PHONE NUMBER
THREE MILES
TUESDAY NIGHT
247
WEST INDIAN LICORICE MOCHA
    DELIGHT
GERALD WHITFIELD
WOMAN'S SKEETSHOOTING
    CHAMPION OF ARKANSAS
"YOU'RE THE CATS"

ELLIE WALKER

"AWAY IN A MANGER"
"A FAIR DEAL FOR THE FAIR SEX"
FRANKIE FLINT
OLD MAN FLINT
FOURTEEN TIMES IN TWO DAYS
FROSTED CHERRY BERRY BON BON
MIDNIGHT MADNESS
"MISSY"
PERFUME

FRANKLIN POMEROY
JEFF PRITCHETT
"SALINE SOLUTION: 2 CC IN THE
    GLUTEUS MAXIMUS"
SHIMMERING ROSE
TEMPTING TOUCH
TWILIGHT BLUSH
$2.16
ELLIE WALKER
FRED WALKER
HARVEY WILLICK
WILSON VS. THORPE'S PHARMACY
WOMAN'S STUFF

THE WOMEN IN ANDY'S & BARNEY'S LIVES

AG
AGNES JEAN
AL
NETTIE ALBRIGHT
AMANDA
TEENA ANDREWS
"BARN"
BARNEY'S DEN
BARNEY'S RIDDLE
BEAVER DAM
"BIG HOUSE"
BLANCHE
CHICAGO
"CHILDISH"
"COUPLE OF THE YEAR"
ELIZABETH CROWLEY
HELEN CRUMP
DAPHNE
CHARLENE DARLING
ATTORNEY LEE DRAKE
PURLIMAE DUBOIS
SHARON DUSPAINE
FAT KNEES
IRENE FLOGG
4:30 A.M.
THE GIGOLO CLUB
GLORIA
GRACE

VICKI HARMES
KATHRYN HARNEY
ALICE HARPER
"HELLO DOLL"
HILDA MAE
JUANITA
"JUANITA'S POEM"
JUNE 23, 1952
MELINDA KEEFER
LAVINIA
PEGGY MCMILLAN
FLORA MALLERBY
DARLENE MASON
MAVIS NEFF
1960
PALMERTON CAFE
ESTELLE PARSONS
"PERSONAL"
"PRISONER OF LOVE"
QUEEN OF THE STATE APRICOT
    FESTIVAL
RED FORD CONVERTIBLE
ROSEMARY
MISS ROSEMARY
SALLY
MARY SIMPSON
SKIPPY
"A SLIGHT OVERBITE"
ALICE STAPLETON
MELISSA STEVENS
THELMA LOU
3:00 P.M.
TUESDAY NIGHT
25 - 23
CISSY WAINWRIGHT
"A WAITRESS AND A REGISTERED
    NURSE"
ELLIE WALKER
"A WANDERING SPIDER"
RAMONA WILEY
HALCYON LORETTA WINSLOW
WOMAN'S SKEETSHOOTING
    CHAMPION OF ARKANSAS
"YOU'RE THE CATS"